MUNICIPAL REFUSE DISPOSAL

The Prince George's County, Maryland, Brown Station Road Sanitary Landfill is part of the county's plan to the year 2000. The scale house and maintenance buildings are set back from the road behind landscaping. Trees screen the operational area (upper right). Note the four containers located near the entrance for the convenience of the county's rural residents who are not served by the organized collection system.

MUNICIPAL REFUSE DISPOSAL

prepared by the
INSTITUTE FOR SOLID WASTES OF
AMERICAN PUBLIC WORKS ASSOCIATION

assistance provided by the
BUREAU OF SOLID WASTE MANAGEMENT
U.S. DEPARTMENT OF HEALTH, EDUCATION, AND WELFARE

American Public Works Association, Institute for Solid Wastes.

PUBLIC ADMINISTRATION SERVICE
1313 EAST 60TH STREET, CHICAGO, ILLINOIS 60637

TD 795
.A45
1970

628.4
A512m

Printed by

Interstate Printers and Publishers, Inc.

Danville, Illinois

The following are acknowledged for their cooperative assistance in supplying illus-
trative material for this edition: *Caterpillar Tractor Co., Peoria, Illinois; Chicago
Tribune; City of Richmond, Virginia; Dempster Brothers, Inc., Knoxville, Tennessee;
Department of Streets and Sanitation, Bureau of Sanitation, Chicago, Illinois; Frigi-
daire, Division of General Motors, Chicago, Illinois; Hercules Galion Products, Inc.,
Galion, Ohio; Hotpoint, Melrose Park, Illinois; General Electric, R. Cooper Jr., Inc.,
Chicago, Illinois; Government of the District of Columbia, Department of Sanitary
Engineering, Washington, D. C.; National Association of Counties, Washington, D. C.;
New York District Corps of Engineers, New York; Prince George's County, Mary-
land; Public Works, Ridgewood, New Jersey; United Management Corporation,
Chicago, Illinois; Westinghouse Appliance Sales and Service Co., Chicago, Illinois;
Williams Patent and Pulverizer Co., Inc., St. Louis, Missouri.*

FOREWORD

The 1968 National Survey of Community Solid Waste Practices, conducted by the U.S. Public Health Service, estimates that some 360 million tons of solid household, commercial, and industrial wastes are produced each year in the United States and that about 190 million tons are actually collected and disposed of by public and private collectors. Perhaps 75 per cent of this comes from areas designated "urban" under census definitions and represents a generation of about 10 pounds per capita per day. To this might be added a huge 550 million tons of agricultural and crop residue wastes, about 1.5 billion tons of animal wastes, and another 1.1 billion tons of mineral wastes, for a total of *3.5 billion tons* of solid wastes generated each year—a staggering 17.5 tons per capita per year, or about 96 pounds per capita per day of all classes of waste materials.

This survey shows additionally that despite the public expenditures by communities of about $1.5 billion annually for collection and disposal of the municipal component of this load (over $6.80 per capita per year), private expenditures of some $1.8 billion for industrial and other wastes management costs, and self-disposal costs to individuals, businesses, and industries of another $1.0 billion annually (for an accumulated sum of $4.3 billion expended on solid wastes each year), the total picture is not only unsatisfactory, it is even alarmingly deficient.

Although the costs of final disposal are normally 20 per cent of the total cost of collection and disposal service, the survey indicates that the overall disposal operation falls far short of acceptable standards. Ninety-four per cent of existing land disposal systems do not meet sanitary land-fill criteria, and 75 per cent of incinerator facilities have inadequate air pollution control provisions. With the increasing public awareness and concern about the basic pollution of our land, air, and water resources, this is a situation that *must* be improved. Open, burning dumps which pollute the air and water and offend the aesthetic senses and sophisticated yet inadequate and inefficient incinerators and other disposal facilities can no longer be accepted in the disposal of urban solid wastes.

Mishandling is costlier than the use of good refuse disposal methods. The economic losses—in medical bills; fire and rodent damage; air and water pollution; use of makeshift insect sprays, traps, and poisons; exterminators' fees; and depreciated property values—can be staggering. Prompt and efficient collection and disposal of refuse are essential to environmental sanitation and the establishment of preventive health measures.

The objective in this manual, therefore, is to review past and present disposal practices, principally in the United States; gather pertinent data, bearing in mind geographic and seasonal differences; describe and analyze the best current practices; broadly indicate the costs; and discuss administrative and management problems. In short, to provide authoritative information for officials responsible for refuse disposal in local, state, and federal governments.

PREFACE TO THE THIRD EDITION

The first edition of *Municipal Refuse Disposal* was published in 1961. It was updated in 1966 following the enactment of the Solid Wastes Act of 1965. The original edition was the result of five years of effort by the APWA Committee on Refuse Disposal, the members of which are listed on pages xii and xiii. It was financed by a grant from the APWA Research Foundation.

The second edition, as well as the first edition, was prepared with the cooperation and valuable assistance of the U.S. Public Health Service. William A. Xanten, former superintendent of sanitation for Washington, D. C., and past president of the American Public Works Association, served as editorial consultant for the second edition.

The APWA Institute for Solid Wastes, organized in January of 1966, was responsible for preparing the current edition of this important publication. It was produced with the cooperation of the Bureau of Solid Waste Management of the U. S. Department of Health, Education, and Welfare. The task was specifically entrusted to the ISW Committee listed on page xi. Special acknowledgement is due Leo Weaver, General Manager of the Institute, and John Kerstetter, Norman Crampton, and other members of the APWA staff, and particularly Robert L. Anderson, former superintendent of public works of Winnetka, Illinois, and past president of the Association, who served as staff consultant and technical editor.

This new publication is the companion text to *Refuse Collection Practice*, which was also prepared by the APWA. Both books are available from the publisher—Public Administration Service, 1313 E. 60th Street, Chicago, Illinois 60637. Members may purchase each publication at a discount through the Association's headquarters, which is located at the same address.

Robert D. Bugher
Executive Director
American Public Works Association

PREFACE TO THE SECOND EDITION

Although only five years have elapsed since its original publication, *Municipal Refuse Disposal* has been updated in this the second edition to include, where possible, 1966 statistics. Publication of the second edition is particularly appropriate at this time in light of the recent enactment of the Solid Wastes Act of 1965, provisions of which are included in this volume, as are the attendant guidelines. The original edition was the result of five years of effort by the APWA's Committee on Refuse Disposal. It was financed by the APWA Research Foundation, which is supported, in part, by a portion of the annual service fees of Public Agency Members of the Association. This revised edition, as with the first, also was made possible by the continued cooperation and valuable assistance of the United States Public Health Service.

The Institute for Solid Wastes was formally organized within the APWA framework in January of 1966. It is now responsible for activities in this field that were formerly conducted by the Committee on Refuse Disposal, and for the work of the Committee on Solid Wastes. The latter committee was responsible for publication of *Refuse Collection Practice*, the companion text to *Municipal Refuse Disposal*.

The purpose of the Institute for Solid Wastes is to: "promote the development and adoption of safe, sanitary and efficient methods of storing, collecting, utilizing or otherwise disposing of solid wastes discarded in urban communities by establishing and encouraging the adherence to sound technical requirements and regulatory measures and high professional standards for employees of public agencies who are responsible for street cleaning and refuse collection and disposal programs conducted by employees under their direct supervision or by private contractors and to represent such officials of the United States and Canada in the International Association of Public Cleansing."

We wish to thank the many public agencies and individuals who contributed to the publication of *Municipal Refuse Disposal*, particularly William A. Xanten, who served as editorial consultant for the second edition of this important publication.

Robert D. Bugher
Executive Director
American Public Works Association

ABOUT THE APWA/ISW

Public works facilities and services are of growing importance to virtually every individual and particularly to those living in urban areas. Many persons are responsible for the development and maintenance of these facilities and services. The American Public Works Association aims to provide a common meeting ground for administrators, engineers, and other responsible officials whose work pertains to this important field of human endeavor, and to promote the advancement of improved practices which best serve the interests of the general public.

The American Public Works Association has for many years been recognized as the leading organization in the United States and Canada serving street sanitation and refuse collection and disposal officials. It has also played a leading role in stimulating increased research efforts in this field, as evidenced by the fact that it conducted for the U. S. Public Health Service the First National Conference on Solid Wastes Research, which was held in Chicago in December of 1963. An Institute for Solid Wastes was established by the APWA in 1966 to further advance the aims and objectives of the Association in this important field of activity.

The purpose of the Institute for Solid Wastes is to promote the development and adoption of safe, sanitary, and efficient methods of storing, collecting, utilizing, or otherwise disposing of solid wastes discarded in urban, rural, and agricultural communities by establishing and encouraging adherence to sound technical requirements and regulatory measures and high professional standards for employees of public agencies who are responsible for street cleaning and refuse collection and disposal programs conducted by employees under their direct supervision or by private contractors, and to represent such officials of the United States and Canada in the International Solid Wastes and Public Cleansing Association. The work of this international organization is coordinated with that of the World Health Organization and its International Solid Wastes Reference Center in Zurich, Switzerland.

The American Public Works Association was organized in 1937 through the merger of the American Society of Municipal Engineers—founded in 1894—and the International Association of Public Works Officials—organized in 1919. It is a non-profit organization which devotes its efforts to the fulfillment of these specific objectives: collect and disseminate information pertaining to public works activities; promote cooperation among all persons and organizations concerned with public works problems; sponsor research projects and committee work so that members may pool their resources and unite their efforts in the study and solution of common problems; stimulate and encourage the advancement of knowledge and the attainment of proficiency in the field of public works engineering and administration; provide opportunities for consultation and the exchange of ideas and experiences; inform members of opportunities for advancement; and encourage the adherence by all members to high business and professional standards.

INSTITUTE FOR SOLID WASTES

EXECUTIVE COUNCIL

President: JEAN V. ARPIN, Director, Department of Roads, Montreal, Canada

Vice President: CHARLES E. FARLEY, Chief, Bureau of Sanitation, Baltimore County Department of Public Works, Towson, Maryland

Immediate Past President: THEODORE C. EPPIG, Deputy Commissioner, Department of Streets and Sanitation, Chicago, Illinois

Secretary-Treasurer: ROBERT D. BUGHER, Executive Director, APWA, Chicago, Illinois

ALFRED H. BECK, Operations Engineer, Department of Public Works, Kansas City, Missouri

RALPH H. BLACK, Director of Information, Bureau of Solid Waste Management, Environmental Control Administration, Rockville, Maryland

ROSS L. CLARK, Commissioner of Works, Municipality of Metropolitan Toronto, Canada

DONALD S. FRADY, Director, Department of Public Works, Falls Church, Virginia

LESTER A. HAUG, Deputy Assistant Chief Engineer, Sanitation District of Los Angeles

NORMAN B. HUME, Member, State Water Resources Control Board, Sacramento, California

H. N. MYRICK, Associate Professor, Cullen College, University of Houston, Houston, Texas

FREDERICK R. RUNDLE, Superintendent and Village Engineer, Department of Public Works, Hempstead, New York

CARL D. SMITH, Administrative Officer, Linn County Health Department, Cedar Rapids, Iowa

General Manager: LEO WEAVER, Director, Washington Office, APWA, Washington, D. C.

1969-70 COMMITTEE ON REFUSE DISPOSAL

J. GRADY PHELPS, Solid Wastes Consultant, Miami, Florida

DALE N. GARST, Sanitation Director, Wichita, Kansas

O. N. COCHRAN, Sanitary Engineer, Trumbull County Engineering Department, Warren, Ohio

LESTER A. HAUG, Deputy Assistant Chief Engineer, Los Angeles County Sanitation Districts, Los Angeles, California

ELMER R. KAISER, Senior Research Scientist, New York University, Scarsdale, New York

IAN McKAERRACHER, Director of Refuse Disposal, Department of Works, Municipality of Metropolitan Toronto, Canada

MELBOURNE A. NOEL, Chief Engineer, Department of Streets and Sanitation, Chicago, Illinois

ROBERT L. ANDERSON, Staff Consultant—Technical Editor

AMERICAN PUBLIC WORKS ASSOCIATION

1961 COMMITTEE ON REFUSE DISPOSAL
(at time of publication of First Edition)

CASIMIR A. ROGUS, *Chairman;* Director of Engineering, Department of Sanitation, New York, New York

ABRAHAM MICHAELS, *Vice Chairman;* Deputy Commissioner, Department of Streets and Sanitation, Philadelphia, Pennsylvania

EDWARD R. WILLIAMS, *Secretary;* Chief, Solid Wastes Engineering Unit, United States Public Health Service, Washington, D. C.

BERNARD J. GEISHEKER, Superintendent, Bureau of Garbage Collection and Disposal, Milwaukee, Wisconsin

CARL SCHNEIDER, Consulting Engineer, New Orleans, Louisiana

JOHN R. SNELL, President, John R. Snell Corporation, Consulting Engineers, Lansing, Michigan

JEAN L. VINCENZ, Director of Public Works, San Diego County, California

LEO WEAVER, Chief, Water Quality Section, Robert A. Taft Sanitary Engineering Center, United States Public Health Service, Cincinnati, Ohio; formerly Director of Research, American Public Works Association, Chicago, Illinois

THEODORE E. WINKLER, Engineer of Waste Disposal, Department of Public Works, Detroit, Michigan

WILLIAM A. XANTEN, Superintendent, Division of Sanitation, District of Columbia

TASK GROUP MEMBERS

D. A. ANDERSON, Director of Operations, City Engineering Department, Seattle, Washington

RALPH J. BLACK, Bureau of Vector Control, Division of Environmental Sanitation, California State Department of Health, Berkeley, California

EDWARD BOOTH, City Engineer, Bismarck, North Dakota

F. R. BOWERMAN, Assistant General Manager, Los Angeles County Sanitation Districts, Los Angeles, California

H. D. BRADLEY, Commissioner, Department of Public Works, Toronto, Ontario, Canada

SAMUEL M. CLARKE, Greeley and Hansen, Consulting Engineers, Chicago, Illinois

RICHARD FENTON, Assistant to Director of Operations, Department of Sanitation, New York, New York

WILLIAM S. FOSTER, Editor, *The American City,* New York, New York

LAWRENCE HEGER, Assistant Superintendent, Bureau of Bridges and Public Buildings, Department of Public Works, Milwaukee, Wisconsin

PAUL JAMES, Mechanical Engineer, United States Department of Agriculture, Beltsville, Maryland

BENJAMIN LINSKY, Air Pollution Control Officer, Bay Area Air Pollution Control District, San Francisco, California

PAUL MAIER, Senior Sanitary Engineer, United States Public Health Service, Phoenix, Arizona

CONTENTS

1   INTRODUCTION

The community that protects the health and safety of its residents and is clean and attractive must have an efficient, well-organized refuse collection and disposal system. Without one, disease-carrying rats, flies, and insects abound; water and air become polluted; fire hazards increase; unpleasant odors are common; and streets, parkways, lots, and alleys are littered and unattractive.

As the population of the United States increases and more and more people are concentrated in urban areas, the problem grows more acute. Furthermore, as standards of living go up, the public demands better refuse disposal service. At the same time, the higher standards of living complicate the problem by increasing the amount of refuse produced and the cost of properly disposing of it.

GOVERNMENTAL RESPONSIBILITY

In large metropolitan areas particularly, the disposal problem has reached serious proportions in recent years due to the steady exhaustion of available spoil (landfill) areas, the impact of more rigid air, water, and land pollution controls, and the decline of markets for major salvage items such as ferrous metal and paper products. Recognition of the overall problem is clearly stated in the Solid Waste Disposal Act (Pub. Law 89-272), passed by Congress on October 20, 1965, under Sec. 202 which states that Congress finds:

1. that the continuing technological progress and improvement in methods of manufacture, packaging, and marketing of consumer products has resulted in an ever-mounting increase, and in a change in the characteristics, of the mass of material discarded by the purchaser of such products;
2. that the economic and population growth of our Nation, and the improvements in the standard of living enjoyed by our population, have required increased industrial production to meet our needs, and have made necessary the demolition of old buildings, the construction of new buildings, and the provision of highways and other avenues of transportation, which, together with related industrial, commercial, and agricultural operations, have resulted in a rising tide of scrap, discarded, and waste materials;
3. that the continuing concentration of our population in expanding metropolitan and other urban areas has presented these communities with serious financial management, intergovernmental, and techni-

1

cal problems in the disposal of solid wastes resulting from the industrial, commercial, domestic, and other activities carried on in such areas;

4. that inefficient and improper methods of disposal of solid wastes result in scenic blights, create serious hazards to the public health, including pollution of air and water resources, accident hazards, and increase in rodent and insect vectors of disease, have an adverse effect on land values, create public nuisances, and otherwise interfere with community life and development;

5. that the failure or inability to salvage and reuse such materials economically results in the unnecessary waste and depletion of our natural resources; and

6. that while the collection and disposal of solid wastes should continue to be primarily the function of State, regional, and local agencies, the problems of waste disposal as set forth above, have become a matter national in scope and in concern and necessitate Federal action through financial and technical assistance and leadership in the development, demonstration, and application of new and improved methods and processes to reduce the amount of waste and unsalvageable materials and to provide for proper and economical solid-waste disposal practices.

The purposes of the Act therefore are:

1. to initiate and accelerate a national research and development program for new and improved methods of proper and economic solid-waste disposal, including studies directed toward the conservation of natural resources by reducing the amount of waste and unsalvageable materials and by recovery and utilization of potential resources in solid wastes; and

2. to provide technical and financial assistance to State and local governments and interstate agencies in the planning, development, and conduct of solid-waste disposal programs.

Responsibility for disposal services can be carried out in various ways. The municipality may (1) have its own crews dispose of refuse at municipally owned facilities; (2) contract with or license private collectors to dispose of refuse in municipally owned or private facilities, but with municipal control over practices; (3) pass ordinances specifying the ways in which refuse must be disposed of by householders, businesses, and industry (household or commercial garbage grinders, for instance, are required by law in some places, and the municipality collects and disposes of only nonputrescible refuse); and (4) use any combination of direct municipal and private disposal.

Regardless of whether the city takes direct responsibility for disposal, licenses or contracts with private collectors to do the work, or requires the producer to dispose of at least some refuse, the city must coordinate its disposal program with the collection service. The collection methods used may have a great deal of influence on the type of disposal service provided. Separate or combined collections of various kinds of refuse, frequency of collections, and other factors must all be considered in relation to the city's responsibility for disposal.

Most of the duties of municipal refuse handling agencies consist of collection and disposal of garbage, rubbish, and ashes. The collection of street refuse is usually a street cleaning function, with the refuse disposed of at facilities operated by the municipal sanitation or public works department. While the removal and disposal of dead animals is frequently one of the duties of a municipal refuse collection and disposal agency, it is often handled as a special problem rather than routinely. The responsibility for the removal of abandoned vehicles from the streets is frequently assigned to the street cleaning agency or to the police department. The vehicles are usually sold or given to junk dealers, who sell them for the spare parts or as scrap metal.

Fig. 1. The open dump is a crude means of refuse disposal and is particularly undesirable in a residential neighborhood. It is unsightly and creates odor and smoke nuisances as well as fire and health hazards.

Industrial refuse is not ordinarily considered a municipal responsibility, although there is a trend toward city collection of it and an even greater trend toward city disposal of some kinds of trade refuse. The disposal of demolition and construction refuse is the responsibility of the contractor in most cities, but it is sometimes accepted at municipal disposal facilities. Disposal of solid sewage wastes is sometimes the responsibility of the refuse disposal agency. Some such wastes can be incinerated at the municipal incinerator or they can be hauled to a sanitary landfill.

Sanitary landfills are also used in some areas for disposing of septic tank sludge and sewage grit.

Special wastes or hazardous materials are nearly always present in refuse in small quantities. Large amounts are sometimes disposed of by special handling procedures at municipal disposal facilities.

The problem of disposing of refuse is not a new one. Nevertheless, solutions to the problem have undergone surprisingly little change in the long interval between the time man first threw an apple core on the ground beneath the tree from which he picked it and the time when he threw it out the window of a moving automobile. During this period, refuse disposal has dealt more with the *where* than the *how*. Evidence of the antiquity of this concept has been found inscribed on an old Roman signpost that warned, "Take your refuse farther or you will be fined."

The Dark Ages ended about 500 years ago, some experts claim, because of what has been called the greatest invention of all time—printing. By means of it knowledge has been disseminated and progress speeded. In modern times, the large amount of printed material has at least indirectly resulted in production of one of the most common and plentiful of refuse materials—paper. It has been reported that the United States government in Washington alone uses 150 carloads of paper each day. Paper and paper products are used in the United States at the rate of more than 500 pounds per person each year—much of it ending up as refuse that must be disposed of.

The idea that the individual can dispose of refuse without creating a greater nuisance than can be tolerated by an urban society long ago was proven unsound. As villages grew into towns and towns into large cities, the disposal of refuse inevitably became a function of local government. And because most residents of a city had no interest in refuse once it was beyond their sight and smell, the government usually had little choice except to concentrate the nuisance by dumping the refuse on the ground at a specific location. Thus because there is an aversion to spending money on materials discarded as worthless, the first criterion that developed for selecting a method of refuse disposal was that it be inexpensive.

Rapidly advancing sanitary standards and increased knowledge of the relation of environmental factors to public health have helped to modify criteria for acceptability until primitive disposal methods are no longer defensible on the basis of low cost alone. As the population of a metropolitan area increases, the number of acceptable dump sites in or near it decreases—almost to the vanishing point.

Aesthetics, water pollution problems, air pollution problems, and a host of other considerations have combined to make refuse disposal a serious engineering and planning undertaking.

The environmental health implications of poor community housekeeping extend beyond aesthetics and nuisances. There are serious health hazards connected with collection and disposal of solid wastes. Probably the first substantial scientific evidence in the United States that implicated

Fig. 2. Changing living habits have an effect on the kinds of refuse produced in a city. The rubbish content of refuse has increased in recent years while the ash and garbage contents have decreased. Paper products and cardboard boxes are a large part of this refuse.

a method of refuse disposal as a cause of a disease in human beings was obtained in the 1930's through studies of the incidence of trichinosis. Using raw garbage as feed was identified as an important factor in the infection of hogs with the parasitic nematode trichinella spiralis. It was also determined that the infection was transmitted to humans when undercooked meat from the infected animals was eaten.

Although the reported morbidity rate for the disease was low and mortality was rare, the economic stakes were high. Many cities depended on hog raising to dispose of garbage. It was honestly believed that the relatively simple remedial measure of cooking the garbage before it was fed to the hogs would bring chaos to the hog raisers and probably create more garbage disposal problems than the step was supposed to remedy. It was not until 1952, when the spectacular epizootic of vesicular exanthema caused an agricultural emergency and raised the economic stakes, that cooking of garbage was required.

Higher living standards and increased production in many ways affect the problem of refuse disposal. Not only is refuse increasing in volume but also the characteristics of refuse are constantly changing. In short, refuse production is directly related to the whole national economy and the behavior patterns of the people. Consequently, disposal facilities must be planned with the ever-changing amounts and kinds of refuse in mind.

Fig. 3. *The New York City East 73rd Street incinerator (above) is a good neighbor, even in this crowded commercial, industrial, and residential area. New apartments in the neighborhood rent for as much as $100 a month per room. Sanitary landfills are also good neighbors. The final layer of compacted earth cover is being put on this one (below) next to a park and an electrical company substation in Memphis.*

Evolution of Disposal Methods

The idea of systematic collection and disposal of refuse is relatively new in the civilized world. Although disposal by dumping and burning was known to ancient civilizations, systematic collection and disposal were not common even in the major cities of the world until well into the nineteenth century. Up until then city dwellers threw refuse and excrement onto unpaved streets and roadways where it mingled with droppings of domestic animals. Even in the Golden Age of ancient Greece "the narrow, crooked streets of Athens were heaped with refuse."[1] The same was typical of European cities and towns in the Middle Ages. In fact, the plagues and epidemics that swept whole countries and continents resulted in large measure because there were no systems of refuse disposal or they were hopelessly inadequate. Although there were local ordinances against dumping refuse in the streets for many centuries in cities of the Western world, there was little popular support or enforcement of them until bacteriology and epidemiology studies laid the foundation for today's sanitary science. It was then that the relationship between refuse disposal and disease-carrying flies, mosquitoes, rats, and other vermin was proven.

Disposal of refuse by open dumping and burning undoubtedly antedates recorded history. Feeding garbage to hogs and the use of inorganic wastes for fill are also ancient practices. Composting of organic wastes has been traced as far back as the Kouloure pits in Cnossus, an ancient capital of Crete, which flourished some 40 centuries ago; and disposal of wastes by burial, the precursor of today's sanitary landfills, dates back at least to Biblical times. Furnaces to burn refuse were designed in the latter part of the nineteenth century; garbage reduction was introduced in the 1880's; garbage grinding began in the early 1920's.

RESEARCH AND DEVELOPMENT

Recognition of the need for intensification of activity in this field is implicit in the Solid Waste Act, which for the first time in history provides federal funds specifically to support training, planning, and demonstration projects on a substantial scale.

A noteworthy accomplishment filling a need for comprehensive basic information is the conduct of the U.S. Public Health Service National Survey of Community Solid Waste Practices, the first report of which was published in 1968. Support of specific research and demonstration projects under this Act has also made possible much fundamentally useful inquiry that would not have been possible otherwise. An example is the project of the APWA Research Foundation, exhaustive investigation of possibilities of incorporating rail haul as an element of urban solid waste disposal. A by-product of this study is development of the concept of preparation of solid wastes under high compression, which suggests and opens the possibility of revolutionary changes in disposal techniques.

Noteworthy, also, is the establishment of the Institute for Solid Wastes by the American Public Works Association and the National Conference on Solid Waste Research (December, 1963) at the University of Chicago, as well as the increased interest and activity of professional groups such as the American Society of Mechanical Engineers Incinerator Division and the reactivated Solid Waste Committee of the American Society of Civil Engineers.

On the international scene, groups such as the International Solid

---

[1] T. W. Wallabank and A. M. Taylor, *Civilization Past and Present*, Rev. ed., Vol. 1 (Chicago: Scott, Foresman and Co., 1949), p. 148.

Wastes and Public Cleansing Association, International Research Group on Refuse Disposal, and the British Institute of Public Cleansing have continued to stimulate programs of research and development, and the World Health Organization and the Pan American Health Organization have sponsored studies designed to be of assistance in Latin America and developing countries throughout the world.

MAGNITUDE OF THE PROBLEM

Although everyone produces solid wastes, their disposal creates a problem primarily in urban areas, and the more concentrated the population the greater the problem becomes. Costs also tend to vary according to the size of the population served. According to reports of the Bureau of the Census, the urban population of the United States is now about 73 per cent of the total—146 million out of 200 million. The rural population of 54 million makes up the remaining 27 per cent. (See Table 1.)

TABLE 1

URBAN AND RURAL POPULATION OF THE UNITED STATES
1950, 1960, AND 1968

Residence	1950		1960		1968 (Est.)	
	Number	Per Cent of Total	Number	Per Cent of Total	Number	Per Cent of Total
Urban	96,846,817	64.0	125,268,750	69.9	146,000,000	73.0
Rural	54,478,981	36.0	54,054,425	30.1	54,000,000	27.0
Total	151,325,798	100.0	179,323,175	100.0	200,000,000	100.0

It is significant that, although the rural population has stayed constant numerically, its proportion of the total has dropped from 36 per cent to 27 per cent, while the urban component has experienced a numerical increase of 51 per cent in 18 years and has risen from 64 per cent to 73 per cent of the total. These figures are based on the definition of "urban" that was used in the 1960 census.[2] Table 2 shows the number and population of urban places by size and type for the United States in 1960.

---

[2] The urban population includes all persons living in (1) places of 2,500 inhabitants or more incorporated as cities, boroughs, villages, and towns (except towns in New England, New York, and Wisconsin); (2) the densely settled urban fringe, whether incorporated or unincorporated, of urbanized areas; (3) towns in New England and townships in New Jersey and Pennsylvania that contain no incorporated municipalities as subdivisions and have either 25,000 inhabitants or more or a population of 2,500 to 25,000 and a density of 1,500 persons or more per square mile; (4) counties in states other than the New England states, New Jersey, and Pennsylvania that have no incorporated municipalities within their boundaries and have a density of 1,500 persons or more per square mile; and (5) unincorporated places of 2,500 inhabitants or more.

TABLE 2

NUMBER AND POPULATION OF URBAN PLACES BY POPULATION SIZE AND TYPE FOR THE UNITED STATES—1960[1]

Population Size	All Places		Incorporated Places		Unincorporated Places		Urban Towns and Townships	
	Number	Population	Number	Population	Number	Population	Number	Population
1,000,000 or more	5	17,484,059	5	17,484,059	0	...	0	...
500,000 to 1,000,000	16	11,110,991	16	11,110,991	0	...	0	...
250,000 to 500,000	30	10,765,881	30	10,765,881	0	...	0	...
100,000 to 250,000	81	11,652,426	79	11,384,755	1	104,270	1	163,401
50,000 to 100,000	201	13,835,902	180	12,511,961	9	585,104	12	738,837
25,000 to 50,000	432	14,950,612	366	12,720,406	26	858,459	40	1,371,747
10,000 to 25,000	1,134	17,568,286	978	15,061,679	101	1,565,850	55	940,757
5,000 to 10,000	1,394	9,779,714	1,282	9,030,786	104	688,135	8	60,793
2,500 to 5,000	2,152	7,580,028	1,763	6,237,739	379	1,304,265	10	38,024
Total	5,445	114,727,899[2]	4,699	106,308,257	620	5,106,083	126	3,313,559

[1] Source: *The Municipal Year Book, 1966* (Washington, D.C.: International City Management Association, 1966), p. 24.
[2] Urban population in urban places only.

The 1968 report of the National Survey shows that the average amount of solid wastes actually collected by public agencies was over 5.3 pounds per person per day, a significantly greater quantity than the 3.9 pounds per person per day estimated in 1959 from an APWA survey. On this basis, in 1968 the urban areas of the United States collected and disposed of an astounding 280 billion pounds or 140 million tons of solid wastes. Placed in a sanitary landfill at an average density this would cover an area of about 35 square miles, 10 feet deep.

Again from the 1968 National Survey, the amount budgeted annually by communities for collection activities averaged $5.40 per capita, and an additional $1.40 per capita was allocated for disposal. This indicates a total of $1.4 billion to which must be added an estimated $100 million for non-budgeted items, some $1.8 billion for private contractor collection and disposal activities, and another $1.0 billion for expenditures in the individual sector—self-disposal by industry and individually owned incinerators, containers, garbage grinders, and the like. This totals to $4.3 billion for the whole job. To give dimensions to this figure, it averages out to $21.50 per capita per year for the entire population.

Fig. 4. The disposal operation must be dependable. If equipment fails, large quantities of accumulated refuse may become nuisances and hazards to health.

National totals and averages cannot be used in determining the amounts of refuse to be disposed of locally, however. Studies show that there are wide differences in amounts collected and disposed of by municipalities because of differences in climate, living standards, and collection and disposal practices. Furthermore, within a city there are marked fluctuations in daily and seasonal amounts.

Refuse Materials Defined

One of the first and most perplexing problems confronting a newcomer to the field of refuse collection and disposal is the vocabulary of the field. To most people in the United States there are "garbage men" who collect "garbage" from "garbage cans" and haul it to "garbage dumps" in "garbage trucks." The public often refers to a sanitary landfill as a garbage dump or to a rubbish collection as a garbage collection.

If a person uses a dictionary, he finds "garbage" means "trash," which is "refuse," which means "rubbish," which again means "trash" or "debris." There are more than 30 synonyms for "garbage" in Roget's *Thesaurus*.

It is common for a city to use one of the many synonyms such as "garbage," "rubbish," or "refuse" to mean all the materials it collects and disposes of. Adding to the confusion in terminology is the wide variation in the refuse collection practices of different cities. For example, some cities collect table scraps, waste paper, tin cans, bottles, and other miscellaneous household wastes and call them "garbage," while other cities use the term "rubbish" to mean the same material. This lack of a common terminology is confusing and leads to numerous uncertainties and even errors in interpreting published information.

Refuse collection and disposal problems must be discussed generally in terms of the collection and disposal of the component substances of refuse. It appears essential, therefore, to define the words and terms used to identify different classes of refuse and to state what materials make up each class.

The terms used in this manual to refer to refuse and its component materials are defined in the following paragraphs (see also Table 3). The definitions are those most widely used among persons engaged in refuse collection and disposal. For purposes of standardization, they are based on those in the 1966 revised edition of *Refuse Collection Practice*.[3]

Waste

The word waste refers to useless, unused, unwanted, or discarded materials. Waste includes solids, liquids, and gases. The gases are principally industrial fumes and smoke; the liquids consist mainly of sewage and the fluid part of industrial wastes; the solids are classed as refuse.

It is difficult to classify municipal wastes or to state absolutely the kinds of materials that constitute the part called refuse. Part of the solid waste materials produced in a city, particularly particles of garbage and rubbish, finds its way into sewers and is disposed of with the liquid sewage wastes. And some semiliquid food wastes are accepted by private collectors of refuse as swill for hog feeding.

Refuse-Solid Wastes

The term "refuse" refers to "solid wastes" and the two are used more

---

[3] American Public Works Association, Committee on Refuse Collection, *Refuse Collection Practice*, 3rd ed. (Chicago: Public Administration Service, 1966), pp. 13-41.

or less synonymously. Because "solid wastes" is somewhat more descriptive and therefore less subject to misinterpretation it is being used more and is supplanting the term refuse. In this book, however, both terms are used interchangeably.

The component materials of refuse or solid wastes can be classified in several different ways. The point of origin is important in solving some problems, so that classifying as domestic, institutional, commercial, industrial, street, demolition, or construction is useful. For other problems, the point of origin is not as important as the nature of the material, and classification may be made on the basis of organic or inorganic character, combustibility or noncombustibility, putrescibility or nonputrescibility. One of the most useful classifications is based on the kinds of materials: garbage, rubbish, ashes, street refuse, dead animals, abandoned automobiles, industrial wastes, demolition wastes, construction wastes, sewage solids, and hazardous and special wastes. Table 3 groups refuse materials by kind and composition and indicates in a general way the source.

Garbage

Garbage is the animal and vegetable waste resulting from the handling, preparation, cooking, and serving of foods. It is composed largely of putrescible organic matter and its natural moisture; it includes a minimum of free liquids. The term does not include food processing wastes from canneries, slaughterhouses, packing plants, or similar industries; large quantities of condemned food products; or oyster or clam shells, which ordinarily are considered industrial wastes. Garbage originates primarily in home kitchens, stores, markets, restaurants, and other places where food is stored, prepared, or served.

Garbage decomposes rapidly, particularly in warm weather, and may quickly produce disagreeable odors. When carelessly stored, it is food for rats and other vermin and is a breeding place for flies.

There is some commercial value in garbage as animal food and as a base for commercial animal feeds. It may also have some value for its grease content or as a plant fertilizer after processing. These uses are fully discussed in later chapters.

The terms "swill," "slops," and "offal," which are frequently found in city ordinances to define garbage, are not synonymous with garbage. "Swill" and "slops" connote semiliquid garbage and free liquids. Where cities do not collect and dispose of such materials, hog raisers operating as private collectors usually collect it from restaurants and institutions for use as hog feed. The word "offal" has had so many different meanings that its use is avoided in this book except as it refers to discarded parts of slaughtered animals.

Market refuse is a special type of garbage that results from the handling, storage, and selling of foods at wholesale and retail stores and markets. It originates principally in meat, poultry, fish, vegetable, and fruit markets, and includes large quantities of putrescible food wastes along with some rubbish, such as wooden crates and cardboard boxes. It also includes some condemned foods but not large quantities of spoiled material.

TABLE 3

REFUSE MATERIALS BY KIND, COMPOSITION, AND SOURCES

	Kind	Composition	Sources
Refuse	Garbage	Wastes from preparation, cooking, and serving of food; market wastes; wastes from handling, storage, and sale of produce	Households, restaurants, institutions, stores, markets
	Rubbish	Combustible: paper, cartons, boxes, barrels, wood, excelsior, tree branches, yard trimmings, wood furniture, bedding, dunnage	
		Noncombustible: metals, tin cans, metal furniture, dirt, glass, crockery, minerals	
	Ashes	Residue from fires used for cooking and heating and from on-site incineration	
	Street Refuse	Sweepings, dirt, leaves, catch basin dirt, contents of litter receptacles	Streets, sidewalks, alleys, vacant lots
	Dead Animals	Cats, dogs, horses, cows	
	Abandoned Vehicles	Unwanted cars and trucks left on public property	
	Industrial Wastes	Food processing wastes, boiler house cinders, lumber scraps, metal scraps, shavings	Factories, power plants
	Demolition Wastes	Lumber, pipes, brick, masonry, and other construction materials from razed buildings and other structures	Demolition sites to be used for new buildings, renewal projects, expressways
	Construction Wastes	Scrap lumber, pipe, other construction materials	New construction, remodeling
	Special Wastes	Hazardous solids and liquids: explosives, pathological wastes, radioactive materials	Households, hotels, hospitals, institutions, stores, industry
	Sewage Treatment Residue	Solids from coarse screening and from grit chambers; septic tank sludge	Sewage treatment plants; septic tanks

As market refuse is usually highly putrescible, the protection of the fresh food supply and the appearance of the community make frequent collection of it necessary. In many cases official city agencies collect and dispose of it.

Rubbish

Rubbish consists of a variety of both combustible and noncombustible solid wastes from homes, stores, and institutions, but does not include garbage. This waste is defined more specifically as "combustible rubbish" and "noncombustible rubbish," but whenever the term "rubbish" is used alone it means a mixture of combustible and noncombustible wastes. "Trash" is synonymous with "rubbish" in some parts of the country, but the term is not used in this book. If garbage is collected with rubbish, it is necessary to have more frequent collections than if rubbish is collected separately.

Combustible rubbish is burnable material. In general, it is the organic component of refuse—paper, rags, cartons, boxes, wood, excelsior, furniture, bedding, rubber, plastics, leather, tree branches, lawn trimmings, and the like. Some cities use this term for only designated burnable materials

Fig. 5. The best disposal system is of little value if collections are inadequate. This accumulation of refuse is so bad that traffic is obstructed. The relationship between good street cleaning, a good refuse collection system, and good disposal methods is obvious from this picture.

that are accepted in regular collections. In such cases some materials, such as food cans and bottles, are specifically included or excluded in the definitions of "rubbish" in the ordinance.

Combustible rubbish, though organic, is not highly putrescible, and therefore may be stored for relatively long periods without becoming a nuisance. It has high heat value and when dry it burns freely without forced draft and without added fuel. Often it is collected with wrapped garbage to provide the fuel necessary to burn garbage in an incinerator. Paper, rags, and cartons may have salvage value.

Noncombustible rubbish is material that is unburnable at ordinary incinerator temperatures (1,300° to 2,000° F.). For the most part, it is the inorganic component of refuse, such as tin cans, heavy metal, mineral matter, glass, crockery, dust, metal furniture, ashes, and the like.

Although some of the metals undergo slow disintegration by oxidation, noncombustible rubbish is stable. When carelessly stored, however, it is aesthetically objectionable and it may harbor rodents and other vermin.

There has been a great deal of discussion among sanitary engineers and public health officials about the proper classification of tin cans that have been used as food containers and, when discarded, have particles of putrescible organic matter clinging to them. Because of this organic matter, some argue that cans should be included with garbage. It is now fairly generally accepted, however, that under ordinary conditions the organic matter desiccates rather than putrefies. For this reason, food cans and bottles may be included with noncombustible rubbish.

The metals, tin cans, bottles, and broken glass in noncombustible rubbish may have salvage value when prices are high.

Yard rubbish consists of tree branches, twigs, grass and shrub clippings, weeds, leaves, and other yard and garden waste materials. When collected, it often contains earth clinging to roots of grass, weeds, and discarded plants. Yard rubbish is usually a part of the combustible rubbish category rather than a category by itself. It is separately defined, however, because many cities make different arrangements for its collection and disposal from those for other combustible refuse and because some municipalities exclude it entirely from their collection service, leaving disposal up to the householder. Collection and disposal of palm fronds in some areas is a problem requiring special techniques.

A considerable part of yard rubbish is green vegetation, which, when kept moist or when stored in large amounts, decomposes fairly rapidly. It is not ordinarily objectionable but under some conditions it may be a breeding place for insects. This green material can be burned in an incinerator but normally it will not sustain a fire alone. Banana stalks are especially troublesome in this respect. Dried vegetation, dead leaves, and plants do not cause a sanitary nuisance and ordinarily will burn readily in an open fire. They can also be disposed of with other rubbish.

Ashes

Ashes are the residue from wood, coal, coke, and other combustible material burned in homes, stores, institutions, and small industrial establishments for heating, cooking, and disposing of combustible waste material. Residues produced in large quantities at steam generating plants are not included within the meaning of the term, since they are normally not the responsibility of a municipality.

Ashes are usually composed of a mixture of fine powdery residue, cinders, clinkers, and small portions of unburned or partially burned fuel or other material. Small pieces of metal, glass, and combustible materials are usually found in ashes when they are collected. Since the mixture is almost entirely inorganic, it is valuable for fills on low land, even in or near built-up communities, and it is acceptable some places for maintaining unpaved streets. Except for the dust that they can cause, ashes are not objectionable from a nuisance or aesthetic standpoint. Among cities in which combustible and noncombustible refuse are separated for collection, many cities ask that such noncombustibles as broken crockery, cans and bottles that are not food containers, and all metals be discarded with the ashes.

The residue in household refuse incinerators and yard rubbish burners is sometimes classed as ash, as are the remains from leaves and other yard rubbish burned in open fires. However, when garbage is only partly burned in low-temperature, inefficiently operated domestic incinerators, local authorities may require that the contents of incinerator pits be stored and collected as garbage or combustible refuse or they may refuse to collect them. In such cases, the incinerator or the operation of it should be modified so that garbage can be burned to ash, or attempts to incinerate garbage should be discontinued.

Household Refuse

Modern municipal incinerators and sanitary landfills can readily dispose of a mixture of the normal household accumulations of garbage and rubbish without any segregation. Ashes in any quantity added to the mixtures are no problem in landfills, and even incinerators can easily handle the present-day, normally small component proportion. Accordingly the predominant collection system now takes all of these unsegregated in one collection from home occupancies in the interest of efficiency and convenience to the public. This mixture is sometimes called combustible refuse, combined refuse, or household refuse. The last term is used in this text.

Street Refuse

Street refuse is material picked up by manual and mechanical sweeping of streets and sidewalks and litter from public litter receptacles. It includes paper, dirt, leaves, and the like. All or part of it is usually disposed of at a municipal disposal facility. Some cities assign the task of collection and disposal of street refuse to the regular refuse collection and disposal agency, while others assign it to the street department.

Dead Animals

As a category of refuse, dead animals are those that die naturally or from disease or are accidentally killed. Condemned animals or parts of animals from slaughterhouses or similar places are not included; they are regarded as industrial refuse.

Dead animals are ordinarily classified into one of two groups—"large" or "small." Large animals are horses, cows, goats, sheep, hogs, and the like. Small animals include dogs, cats, rabbits, squirrels, and rats. Some coastal cities frequently have problems with dead fish and dead aquatic mammals that float ashore at beaches. Collection of large animals usually requires special equipment.

Large animals have value because of the grease and tankage that can be produced from them in rendering plants. Their hides also have some value.

Dead animals are particularly offensive from sanitary and aesthetic points of view and usually must be collected promptly—often on an emergency basis. They putrefy rapidly, particularly in warm, moist atmosphere, and attract flies and other insects. Animal traffic victims are sometimes crushed by vehicles passing over them and therefore must be picked up promptly.

Abandoned Vehicles

Abandoned vehicles include passenger automobiles, trucks, and trailers that are no longer useful and have been left on city streets and in other public places. Usually they are found stripped of tires, wheels,

Fig. 6. Abandoned automobiles are a problem if there is little or no demand for scrap metal. They are bulky and difficult to handle if they cannot be salvaged.

lights, and other easily salvaged parts. While they must be removed from the streets by municipal authorities, the task is not usually considered a part of the work of the regular refuse collection agency, but a duty of the street cleaning, highway, or police forces.

The auto graveyards lining many of our highways have, in recent years, become so overloaded and unsightly that efforts to abate the condition are receiving attention under the Solid Waste Disposal Act from both the Department of Interior and the Department of Health, Education, and Welfare, as well as from the Department of Commerce under the Highway Beautification Program.

Industrial Refuse

Industrial refuse consists of solid waste materials from factories, processing plants, and other manufacturing enterprises. The collection of such matter is rarely regarded as an obligation of the city or a governmental function, but as an obligation of industry. Refuse of this category includes putrescible garbage from food processing plants and slaughterhouses, condemned foods, building rubbish, cinders from power plants, and manufacturing refuse.

Because putrescible industrial refuse may cause serious nuisances and even endanger public health, its storage, hauling, and disposition are subject to municipal control, and many municipalities are now providing for disposal of this type of refuse.

Demolition Refuse

Demolition refuse is the waste material from razed buildings or other structures. It is found mostly in cities in which extensive areas of old or otherwise obsolete buildings are being torn down to make way for new structures. The federally aided program of urban renewal has given impetus to these programs in recent years. The construction of new expressways in large cities also necessitates the destruction of many buildings and adds to the demolition refuse problem.

Demolition refuse is not usually collected by municipal agencies. Usually the company wrecking a building contracts to haul the debris away and dispose of it. In some cities, however, particularly if large landfill areas are available, the city allows wreckers to dump refuse at its disposal facility for a slight charge, or even free. (See Chapter 3, section on special disposal problems.)

Construction Refuse

Construction refuse is the waste material from the construction, remodeling, and repair of houses, commercial buildings, and other structures. It includes a great variety of matter, such as earth, stones, bricks, plaster, wallpaper, lumber, shingles and other roofing, concrete, plumbing parts, old heating systems, and worn out electrical parts.

A small amount of such refuse is usually accepted from households and stores but the bulk of it is considered industrial refuse that contractors

Fig. 7. Serious public health problems may arise if improper refuse disposal methods are used. These rats inhabited an open dump until they were poisoned in a campaign against them.

and builders must remove. A municipality may agree to dispose of it but if it does, it creates problems. (See Chapter 3, section on special disposal problems.)

Sewage

The disposal of some sewage solids is the responsibility of the municipal refuse disposal agency in many areas. Large, coarse solids, mostly organic, are screened from the influent at the sewage treatment plant, and if a municipal incinerator or sanitary landfill is convenient to the treatment plant these solids are disposed of by one method or the other. Solid inorganic matter from grit chambers may also be disposed of in a nearby sanitary landfill. This grit, however, even after going through a washing process, may contain substantial quantities of highly putrescible matter, and it is necessary, therefore, to bury it to effectively prevent an odor nuisance. Septic tank and cesspool pumpings are often disposed of in sanitary landfills in the absence of a sewage treatment plant, again under rigid controls to avoid nuisances. In large jurisdictions with the most modern facilities for digestion of sewage, even the quantity of stabilized sewage sludge produced becomes a disposal problem. Although it has some soil conditioning and minor fertilizing properties, the sheer volume to be disposed of presents a serious problem in many cities.

Hazardous or Special Refuse

Waste material that presents an unusual disposal problem or requires special handling comes within the definition of hazardous, or special, waste. Small quantities of such wastes are usually present in ordinary refuse. A small can of paint or paint thinner, a roll of photographic film, or a plastic household article is not hazardous and can be disposed of by incineration or landfill without special handling. On the other hand, large quantities of the same materials create problems that require special procedures to prevent explosions in an incinerator furnace or a dangerous fire at a sanitary landfill. Even under the strictest safety measures, such explosions occur.

On the other hand, some wastes from industry are hazardous under any conditions, and pathological wastes from hospitals and radioactive materials require special handling no matter the quantity.

2 QUANTITIES AND COMPOSITION OF REFUSE

Any attempt to analyze the dimensions of the solid wastes picture of a community on a comprehensive basis, let alone any effort to compare it with other cities or to produce summarized national statistics, quickly becomes obscured and confused by seemingly endless complexities. Some of the major ones are: definitions and classifications delimiting the parameters of the problem; general scarcity of accurate, reliable, and complete measurements and records on comparable bases; diversity of collection and disposal policies and practices; amount of self-disposal and salvage practiced; geographical situation, including availability, condition, and capacity of land, water, and air resources for solid wastes disposal purposes; daily, seasonal, and other variations in waste production; and other variables involving living standards, climate, type of community, and economic considerations.

In spite of all these complications, for any specific city it is essential to know, within reasonable limits, what the problem involves, both as to quantity and composition, if a reasonable and acceptable solution is to be devised. Regardless of division of the collection problem between public agencies, private contractors, or self-disposal, final disposition of the total solid wastes quantity, with the exception of what is removed from the area as salvaged or as wastes to be disposed of in another locality, is a load on the capacity of the land, water, and air of the community to be absorbed without too deleterious effects. It is the responsibility of government, in the last analysis, to see that reasonable limits of pollution are not exceeded.

QUANTITIES

Some knowledge of total quantities and classifications of solid wastes generated by a community is indispensable for decisions on collection policies as well as for determining the final disposal program. The proportion to be disposed of by public facilities is obviously heavily dependent on how much is handled satisfactorily under private auspices. The total "systems analysis" concept is therefore basically involved with determining public disposal requirements. When it comes to decisions on choice of methods and requirements for land, construction, equipment, personnel, and financing, quantities and composition are primary determinants.

Some cities keep accurate records by categories of the amounts of

solid wastes they collect and make effective use of these data in administration of their collection and disposal programs. For example, the data
can disclose trends that can be used as a basis for determining future
facility needs, and they may provide a basis for helping to judge operational efficiency. Many cities, however, have little or no information on
the amount of refuse they handle themselves, let alone that portion
cared for by the private sector. For these, experiences of other comparable
cities may be of some help, even though experience shows that such outside data must be applied with great caution.

Measuring Quantities

Although it is recognized that weight is the most satisfactory basis
for measuring quantities of solid wastes, there is still a large proportion
of disposal systems where quantities are estimated on a volume basis, or,
if weight is used, it is also only estimated. This is especially true for
sanitary landfill disposal where use of relatively short-lived sites makes
installation of adequate scales somewhat of an expense, regarded as
avoidable. Some cities weigh only selected classes of refuse such as
household refuse and/or commercial refuse—perhaps only those categories
disposed of by incineration—while they estimate volume for the other
classes. Estimated volume is often converted to weight for reporting
purposes by establishing average unit weights from a series of careful
measurements of weights of representative loads.

The short ton (2,000 pounds) is the standard weight unit used most
generally. However, in considering amounts of refuse on a population
basis, it is more convenient and more readily understood when the unit is
pounds, as in pounds per capita per day or per year, and this is the usual
practice.

Where records are kept on the basis of volume, the cubic yard, as
measured in the collecting vehicle, is the unit used. If the volume is carefully measured or estimated the resulting statistics are of value to local
authorities. For comparative purposes, however, there are several reasons
why volume is not as satisfactory as weight. In some places refuse is
loosely thrown into collection vehicles, while in others it is tightly compacted by mechanical compactor-type vehicles or by the collection crews,
which break up bulky articles and compress the loads by trampling. The
weight per cubic yard of a given type of refuse varies greatly with the
type of truck used and the methods the crew uses to load it. An open
truck, for example, may carry from 150 to 300 pounds per cubic yard of
the same type of rubbish, depending on how it is loaded and trampled.
An enclosed truck can vary even more markedly in the weight it carries
per cubic yard. When collected in a modern compaction truck, refuse
can vary from 150 pounds per cubic yard, if the crew neglects to load
it properly, to more than 500 pounds per cubic yard if the refuse is
properly loaded and compacted. A load of noncombustible refuse with
heavy ash content may weigh as much as 1,000 pounds per cubic yard.
Moisture content can also affect both volume and weight by as much as
20 per cent or more.

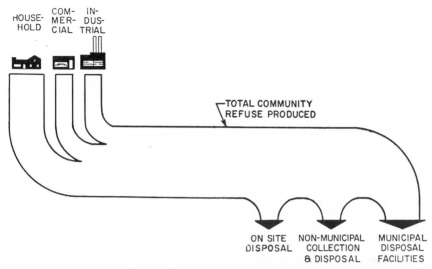

Fig. 8. Private collection and disposal and on-premise disposal and salvage influence the quantities of refuse collected from homes, industries, and businesses and disposed of by a municipality. Consequently, municipal disposal facilities often are provided for only a part of all the refuse produced in a city. Some cities, however, collect and dispose of practically all refuse.

When refuse is taken to dumps or sanitary fill sites, scales are not usually available. Quantities are reported on a volume basis, which is usually estimated by truck body size and at best is only roughly comparable to the weight. When refuse is disposed of in a sanitary landfill it is important to measure the volume of the refuse *after* compaction. This helps to estimate the life of the fill area. In addition, if the weight is known, the density of the compacted refuse can be calculated and compared with other types of disposal operations.

Quantities Produced, Collected, and Disposed of

The amount of refuse picked up by the regular or official collection agency is always less than the total amount produced in the community, the difference being accounted for by the efficiency and extent of the official service, the amount of self-disposal by industry, the amount of private contract collection and disposal used, the extent of salvage operations, and the proportion of on-the-premises disposal practiced.

Any of these can be significant. For example, garbage and combustible rubbish are often burned in household furnaces, stoves, and incinerators, not only because of the usability of the heat produced during cold seasons, but also because it may be more convenient or cheaper for the householder if a charge is made based on quantity. Indeed, some cities actually require installation of household incinerators and do not have a general collection of combustible household refuse. In some cases household and yard rubbish are burned in yard incinerators because it is less objectionable, in spite of their inefficiency, than storing large amounts until the collection day and paying the collection charge. Some garbage and mixed refuse is burned in apartment and home incinerators mainly because of convenience. For the same reason, domestic and occasional commercial grinders account for some of the garbage. Consequently in some cities the amount of combustible refuse collected is relatively small.

Fig. 9. Household refuse is a heterogeneous mass that is extremely difficult to separate after it has been collected together.

The amount of reclaimable material salvaged from household or business refuse is closely related to the market value of the materials. In fact, the proportion of rubbish in refuse is often considered an index of general prosperity. For example, when waste paper can be sold for a high enough price, large amounts will be salvaged by householders and stores and relatively small quantities will be collected as rubbish. Similarly, scrap metal, bottles, rags, bones, and other materials are sold when there is a demand for them by junk dealers. At such times the quantity of refuse collected is considerably less than when the value of salvage material is small. Then it is not ordinarily worthwhile to separate it from other refuse, and large quantities must be collected by the regular forces. Scavengers, when permitted, often pick up part of the refuse that has been put out for collection. Civic and charitable organizations also collect some kinds of salvage materials.

Some commercial garbage (sometimes called "raw garbage" or "swill"), especially that from hotels and restaurants, has value as hog feed and, therefore, is sometimes sold or given to hog raisers even where the city collection agency would remove it without charge. In a few cities this still accounts for a substantial part of the commercial garbage and reduces the city collection load accordingly. However, regulations requiring cooking of garbage before feeding and other increasing costs are tending to make the business less profitable, and the trend is toward more disposal of commercial garbage in public facilities.

The administrator of a refuse collection and disposal agency is primarily concerned with the waste materials he has to handle. Accurate figures on quantities can only be obtained by day-to-day measurements under the operating conditions peculiar to the specific instance, but where such records are not available, as for a study of a contemplated basic change in practices, experiences of other jurisdictions can be useful guides for estimating quantities.

In many places the city collects only from 50 per cent to 75 per cent of the total refuse production even in those categories usually considered primarily the responsibility of a public agency—household or domestic refuse and the commercial load. From the 1968 National Survey of Community Solid Waste Practices it is estimated that the generation of household, commercial, and industrial wastes in this country is about 10 pounds per capita per day, compared with actual collections by all agencies of 5.3 pounds per capita per day.

The amount of solid wastes to be handled at public disposal facilities is, of course, influenced by the quantities collected, but there are also other factors. Existence and use of private disposal facilities is an obvious one. Policies on accepting wastes from private haulers, limitations on classes of wastes that can be handled by the public facility in question, degree of self-disposal by industry, and use of salvage practices are all pertinent. It is usually not possible to determine accurately the amount of wastes salvaged, and quantities disposed of at private facilities are almost equally hard to ascertain.

Refuse Studies

Knowledge of the amount and characteristics of refuse in a city is basic to the design and satisfactory operation of refuse disposal facilities and the application of refuse disposal methods. Data gathered through questionnaires have more or less successfully delineated, on a broad basis, the quantities of refuse collected and disposed of in cities across the country. The interpretation of these data and their application to engineering design problems have been seriously hampered, however, because of the heterogeneous local practices reported, as well as the unreliability of some of the data because of conflicting definitions of terms and incomplete or inaccurate reporting.

In the development of the first edition of this manual it was found that reliable and comparable data were to be obtained only by on-the-spot surveys conducted under standardized conditions. Data in previous editions were based on such a survey of 12 representative cities made in 1959 by the Secretary of the APWA Committee on Refuse Disposal. These have been updated by a 1968 recheck survey made on the same basis. In 1965 a further APWA survey was made by members of the Solid Wastes Committee of APWA, reported in the companion text, *Refuse Collection Practice*, 1966 edition. Still later, the 1968 National Survey of Community Solid Waste Practices, conducted by the Solid Waste Program of the U.S. Public Health Service, provided a wealth of data on a wider base. From all of these, some general basic ranges can be deduced, but they also demonstrate that local idiosyncrasies and aberrations are so marked and so common that it is not wise to apply these figures to a specific situation for design purposes without carefully checking the local conditions. Wide variations from average or normal experience are sometimes found, and the figures shown herein should be used only as guides to solutions.

Total Refuse Collected

Of the 12 cities surveyed in 1959, repeat checks have given up-dated information for other years on some of them as shown in Table 4.

A definite trend to increased per capita collections is indicated from Table 4, even though this is limited to collections under city auspices. It should be noted that, in any specific instance, there may be present influences of changes in policy or rules, and that these figures take no cognizance of collections by private contract which have also increased apace.

The 1968 National Survey covered some minor classes of solid wastes probably not included in the foregoing figures and also was set up to include figures for collections by private contractors as well. Allowing for these major differences in ground rules, it is probable that the average figures derived from the survey of 7.92 pounds per capita per day for the whole country and 8.19 pounds per capita per day for the urban sector for collections of all classes of wastes represent substantial agreement with the more limited APWA studies. A definite trend toward an increase in per capita collections is clearly indicated.

Geographical Differences. The survey does not show a clear-cut difference in total amounts of refuse collected by cities in various geographical locations. There are, however, some differences in the amounts of various components in refuse between northern and southern cities. Yard or garden rubbish and ashes are the two best examples.

In most of the country the season for yard rubbish is from April or May until November or December, with exceptionally large quantities in the early months of the period—the annual clean-up time. In the northern part of the United States there is no yard rubbish at all during the winter months. In the regions that have a mild climate, however,

TABLE 4

PER CAPITA COLLECTIONS OF SOLID WASTES AS REPORTED IN APWA SURVEYS[1]

City	1955		1957-58		1965		1968	
	lbs/cap/yr	lbs/cap/day	lbs/cap/yr	lbs/cap/day	lbs/cap/yr	lbs/cap/day	lbs/cap/yr	lbs/cap/day
Cincinnati, Ohio	—	—	1,103	3.03	1,235	3.4	1,365	3.74
Garden City, N.Y.	1,187[2]	3.3[2]	1,438[2]	3.9[2]	1,308[2]	3.6[2]	1,454[2]	3.98[2]
Los Angeles, Calif.	—	—	1,677	4.6	2,373	6.5	2,536	6.95
New York, N.Y.	826	2.3	1,325	3.6	1,483	4.1	—	—
Seattle, Wash.	842	2.3	1,370	3.8	1,508	4.1	1,431	3.89
Washington, D.C.	—	—	1,638	4.5	1,545	4.2	1,739	4.76

[1]Includes refuse actually collected under city auspices, regardless of method of collection. Does not include automobiles or cinders. In the 1959 survey, apartment house incinerator ash was calculated in terms of equivalent amounts of household refuse.
[2]No industrial refuse.

yard rubbish is produced throughout the year, with the peak amount usually in early spring.

The quantity of ashes resulting from the burning of solid fuel for heating is directly related to the severity of the weather. It is obvious that ash output from burning solid fuel is less in Florida or southern California than it is in the New England states. With the increasing use of liquid and gaseous fuels for heating, however, this factor in the total solid waste picture has diminished to the point of a minor influence, as is shown later in this chapter.

Before the days of mass communication and rail transportation there were areas of the country in which for the most part only people of a single nationality lived. They often adhered to native customs in family and social life and were thrifty according to nationality patterns, which undoubtedly influenced the quantity of refuse they produced. Moreover, most people had to use only the foodstuffs that were produced locally.

Today, because of nationwide radio, newspapers, and magazines, people in one area are much like those in others, in their family and social life and in their recreational activities. A family in Texas reads much the same magazines, wears many of the same brands of clothes, and discards the same kinds of toothpaste tubes as a family in Oregon or Pennsylvania.

A head of lettuce picked in California on Monday can be eaten in Boston the following Friday, a lobster from Boston can be served in Omaha the day after it is caught. Rapid transportation and mechanical refrigeration make it possible for supermarkets in Wyoming to stock the same foodstuffs the supermarkets in Maryland do. The same nationally advertised brands of canned pears can be found coast to coast.

As part of this similarity in living habits, people discard similar types and quantities of refuse in all regions of the country. Differences in collection practices, disposal regulations, and the manner in which the refuse is disposed of (sometimes partially on the premises) account for what appear to be wide differences in quantities of refuse disposed of by municipal agencies in various parts of the United States.

The 1968 National Survey data were collected on a basis that makes it possible to estimate average quantities of refuse collected by categories in the different regions of the country. Table 5 shows figures that bear out the foregoing discussion to some extent.

Seasonal Differences. The extent of seasonal variations in the quantities of refuse produced in a municipality is important, for a variety of reasons, to officials responsible for refuse disposal. A disposal operation must be designed to take care of peak loads. Additional personnel are usually required during the season of high refuse production, and regular employees must often work overtime. By anticipating these labor requirements and hiring additional personnel in advance of actual need, the disposal system can operate smoothly and economically in the rush season. Employees can take leave and equipment can be repaired and major plant maintenance work done during the slack months.

TABLE 5

ANALYSIS OF SELECTED CLASSES OF SOLID WASTES COLLECTED IN SELECTED REGIONS[1]

Class	Pounds per Day per Capita					
	National Average	New England	South-east Region	South-west Region	Great Lakes Region	Pacific Coast Region
Combined household & commercial refuse	4.05	4.60	3.48	3.20	3.73	9.28
Demolition refuse	0.66	0.84	0.16	0.69	1.16	0.12
Tree & landscape refuse	0.18	0.21	0.81	0.40	0.13	0.34

[1] Derived from *Preliminary Data Analysis: 1968 National Survey of Community Solid Waste Practices.*

The amounts of refuse for each season must be determined on the basis of each city's own records, since the pattern of change may differ drastically among cities.

There are several factors besides climate that influence seasonal changes. Most important are the type of fuel used for heating; the amount of vegetation within a city—lawns, trees, and shrubs on private property and along streets and in parks; construction work; and the abundance of fresh fruits and vegetables. In some cities, an important influence on seasonal variations is the number of tourists. This is particularly true in some small resort areas where the population may increase tenfold during "the season." Advance planning for refuse disposal based on past experience of seasonal differences is especially important in these instances.

Figure 10 compares the seasonal variations in the amount of refuse incinerated in Hartford and Cincinnati. The season of highest refuse production in both cities is in the warm months, but the pattern for each city is different.

In Hartford there is an annual spring clean-up campaign, which accounts in part for the high production in March and April. Hartford is a city abounding in trees so that in the autumn great quantities of leaves are collected and incinerated. The second peak shown on the graph reflects the leaf pick-up time in October or November. The below-average production of refuse in July and August in Hartford occurs each year and is thought to come about because many of the large number of white collar workers in the city are vacationing away from the city during these months.

The seasonal pattern of refuse production in Cincinnati is probably more typical of American cities that do not have annual spring clean-up campaigns. It reflects normal increases in summer activities such as gardening, house cleaning, and construction.

Daily Differences. To the municipality that collects refuse weekly,

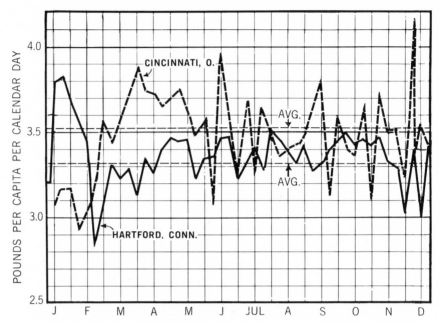

Fig. 10. Seasonal differences in amount of refuse incinerated in Hartford, Connecticut, and Cincinnati, Ohio, 1967.

variations in daily refuse production are not as important as they are to cities that give more frequent service. If refuse is collected weekly, the concern is only with fluctuations from week to week, since the length of the routes covered on high collection days, such as Mondays, can be shorter than the routes followed on days of low production.

If refuse is collected twice a week or oftener, the quantities collected will vary greatly each time. For example, if a route is serviced on Mondays and Thursdays, the amount of refuse collected on Mondays may be double the amount picked up on Thursdays. The reasons are obvious: most housewives do their weekly marketing on Thursdays, Fridays, or Saturdays—after the Thursday pick-up—which means more greens, packages, and bottles in the refuse; more entertaining and more yard work are done on weekends; and there is a four-day accumulation of refuse on Mondays and only a three-day accumulation on Thursdays. The weather also influences the daily output of refuse. If the weekend weather is unusually good there will be far greater quantities of refuse on Monday than if the weather is bad.

Figure 11 shows the daily variations in amounts of refuse in a city that collects three times a week, compared with amounts in a city that collects only once a week. The graph shows that if refuse is allowed to accumulate for a week or longer, variations in amounts collected each day average out and the fluctuations are usually not noticeable. But if collections are more frequent, the differences are more apparent. Daily differences in quantities of refuse are extremely important to the administrator of disposal facilities that are not flexible enough to handle widely varying amounts.

Component Quantities and Their Variations

Up to this point only total refuse quantities and how those quantities are affected by geography and periods of time have been discussed. But the different components of refuse and their quantities and variations are also important.

The traditional measurement of the components of the total solid wastes load under the principal classifications of garbage, rubbish, ashes, and other minor classes of municipal wastes has largely lost significance for solid wastes disposal management purposes with the changes that have occurred in disposal and collection practices. The categories now more applicable include: "household refuse" which consists of domestic garbage and the combustible as well as part of the noncombustible components of the "rubbish" classification; combined household and commercial refuse; noncombustible rubbish which may be of household or commercial origin, but is principally the former; industrial refuse; demolition wastes; tree and landscaping refuse; and municipal wastes consisting of street cleanings, catch-basin cleanings, park and beach cleanings, sewage sludge, and abandoned cars.

The latest and most comprehensive information on component quantities is that gathered by the 1968 National Survey. It was based on

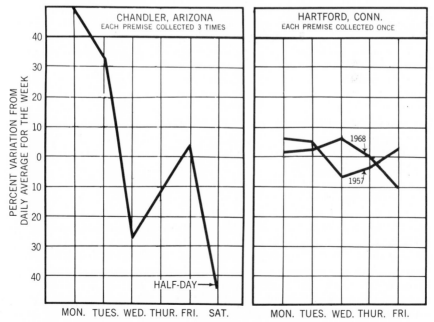

Fig. 11. Comparison of quantities of refuse collected during typical weeks in Chandler, Arizona, and Hartford, Connecticut.

6,259 inquiries covering a population of 92.5 million and has been analyzed and tabulated in great detail in several ways—as to national totals, urban vs. rural areas, and geographical regions. Because of the broad base and the care used it should give the best picture available of the current status. Even so, some estimating is still necessary to reconcile and combine individual reports, since some reported quantities on a weight basis and some on volume.

Table 6 shows the estimated average amounts of solid wastes collected by categories, as derived from this survey, broken down for total population and for the urban sector only. Because reports on all categories were not obtainable from every community the population base for each figure is also shown.

TABLE 6

SOLID WASTES COLLECTED IN THE UNITED STATES[1]

Class	Total		Urban	
	Pop. (1,000) Reporting	lbs/cap/day	Pop. (1,000) Reporting	lbs/cap/day
Combined household & commercial refuse[2]	46,970	4.05	34,213	4.29
Industrial refuse	29,330	1.86	25,213	1.90
Institutional refuse	20,533	0.24	17,337	0.16
Demolition & construction refuse	23,697	0.66	21,716	0.72
Street & alley cleanings	35,340	0.25	32,705	0.25
Tree & landscaping refuse	25,890	0.18	23,405	0.18
Park and beach refuse	17,230	0.16	17,006	0.15
Catch basin refuse	22,010	0.04	20,042	0.04
Sewage treatment plant solids	20,504	0.47	19,100	0.50
Total solid wastes collected		7.92		8.19

[1] 1968 National Survey of Community Solid Waste Practices.

[2] It is of interest to note that the survey indicates that where household wastes and commercial wastes are collected separately, the combined total figure is only 3.76 lbs/cap/day (2.51 household plus 1.25 commercial). For the urban sector only the corresponding figures are 3.71 lbs/cap/day (2.48 household plus 1.23 commercial).

The APWA survey of 1959 for selected cities was updated by a 1968 inquiry. Although the rules were not always identical with those for the 1968 National Survey and there is consequently some disparity, these results are also of interest. In general they point up the trend towards increasing per capita collections, but they also show that local differences or changes in practices and other factors make each community's experience unique and often notably divergent from averages or from figures for other cities. Cities from which comparable figures were obtained for both inquiries are shown in Table 7.

Table 7

QUANTITIES BY CATEGORIES OF SOLID WASTES COLLECTED FROM SELECTED
UNITED STATES CITIES—1957-58 AND 1967
POUNDS PER CAPITA PER YEAR

	1957-58	1967
Atlanta, Georgia		
Population served	560,000	544,000
City & privately collected household refuse	1,104* &**	833*
City collected street sweeping & other debris	123**	302**
Privately collected garbage ("swill")	25**	25**
Total	1,252	1,160
Cincinnati, Ohio		
Population served	547,800	502,550
City collected combustible refuse (garbage, rubbish)	545*	735*
Privately collected combustible refuse (garbage, rubbish)	297*	368*
City collected noncombustible rubbish	129**	98**
Privately collected noncombustible rubbish (commercial, industrial)	132**	164**
Total	1,103	1,365
Garden City, New York		
Population served	23,060	24,926
City collected household refuse	1,040*	1,037*
City collected rubbish (yard wastes, furniture, metal)	327*	393*
Privately collected rubbish	23**	24**
City collected ashes	48*	—
Total	1,438	1,454
Hartford, Connecticut		
Population served	186,000	162,800
City collected combustible refuse (including garbage)	596*	770*
City collected noncombustible rubbish	28*	28*
Privately collected combustible refuse	428*	508*
Privately collected noncombustible rubbish	317*	604*
Privately collected garbage (food wastes)	33*	0
Scavenger salvage before collection (rags, paper, metal)	28**	25**
Total	1,430	1,955
Los Angeles, California[1]		
Population served	2,370,000	2,880,000
City collected garbage (food wastes)	129*	—
City collected commercial garbage (food wastes)	—	5*
City collected noncombustible rubbish	135*	—
City collected residential combined refuse	—	830*
City collected combustible rubbish	568*	—
Privately collected rubbish (commercial, industrial)	845**	1,700**
Total	1,677	2,535

Continued

Table 7—Continued

	1957-58	1967
Omaha, Nebraska		
Population served	299,000	384,425
Contract collection of combined refuse	459*	457*
Privately collected combined refuse	612*	161*
Privately collected noncombustible refuse	267**	271**
Private salvage (paper)	32**	35**
Total	1,370	924
St. Petersburg, Florida		
Population served	154,000	220,000
City collected household refuse	1,037**	1,911**
City collected trash (mostly yard rubbish)	91**	1,082**
Privately collected refuse	562**	6**
Total	1,690	2,999
Seattle, Washington		
Population served	575,000	580,000
Contract collection of combined refuse	1,148**	623*
Commercial & private collection (all classes refuse)	222**	798**
Total	1,370	1,421
Washington, D.C.		
Population served	860,000	800,000
City collected garbage (food wastes)	117*	69*
Privately collected garbage (food wastes)	93**	77**
City & privately collected noncombustible waste to landfill	647**	706**
City & privately collected combustible wastes to incinerators	781**	887**
Total	1,638	1,739

* weighed   ** estimated

[1] There was a substantial change in services rendered in Los Angeles between 1958 and 1967.

Garbage. Separately collected garbage, except for the limited instances where commercial garbage is still collected for hog feeding, is practically a thing of the past. Landfilling and incineration, which account for disposal of by far the greatest part of all refuse, can handle a mixture of garbage with the usual household wastes without segregation, so current data on separate collection of garbage are scarce and not of much significance.

Inclusion of garbage with household refuse makes it necessary to rely on simple analyses of the combined materials for information on the amount of actual garbage collected. Although usually collected separately, commercial refuse still has a relatively high garbage content, but that from residential areas shows a much lower percentage than formerly. This is to be expected with increasing use of food waste grinders, decline in home canning, and much more pre-processing and packaging of prepared foods that leave little household waste but the wrappings.

Rubbish. The trend toward combined collections has made information on quantities of straight rubbish as unavailable as for straight garbage. Of the nine cities in the APWA survey cited in Table 7, all make combined collections of household refuse, although some use different terminology in reporting it. The additional classifications of "combustible" and "noncombustible" refuse reported in some cases are not usually fully comparable because of lack of uniformity in definition of nomenclature among cities.

Accordingly, in any specific instance the composition and component quantities of the solid wastes load can be determined only by a percentage analysis of representative samples. For a final disposal using direct sanitary landfill this exact breakdown may not be of vital importance. If incineration, compression, baling, or shredding are to be used, it may need careful investigating.

Fluctuations in daily, weekly, and other collections of rubbish where it is still taken separately are influenced by climate, growing seasons, holidays, and other factors. Probably the major influence is the fact that rubbish collections can usually be deferred a reasonable time without serious health consequences, unlike refuse containing food or other putrescible wastes. Consequently the major influence on the quantities of this material delivered for disposal may be the exigencies of maintaining regular household refuse and commercial collections, while collections of straight rubbish take second priority. The effect should be a leveling influence, with rubbish deliveries taking up the slack in household refuse schedules.

Total quantities of rubbish to be disposed of by public agencies are continually increasing because of additional restrictions on home burning and self-disposal on land and increasing per capita consumption of all kinds of goods leaving a residuum of wrappings and unwanted materials to be discarded. Since a major proportion of household refuse consists of rubbish, this readily accounts for the increase in collections of that classification as well.

Ashes. Except perhaps in a few cases in or near coal producing areas, the use of coal as a domestic heating fuel has been reduced, often to the vanishing point. The cleanliness and convenience of gas, oil, and electricity have been competitive advantages over coal. Consequently, separate collections of ashes, formerly an important component of the solid waste load, are a thing of the past, and the ashes still produced are largely used as fill without being collected by cities or are included in small quantities with rubbish or other classes. In general, they are no longer accounted for separately.

Obviously, what ashes there are from space heating are produced almost entirely in the winter season, but there are relatively minor amounts of incinerator ashes produced regularly and absorbed in other refuse classes. Residues from coal used in industry are largely cinders. They are normally disposed of by the industry as fill material.

Household refuse. From the APWA survey it appears that those seven cities reporting on a basis permitting identification of quantities of household refuse collected show per capita annual amounts of 618 pounds to 1,911 pounds, with an average of about 1,090 pounds, as shown in Figure 12. This is 3.0 pounds per capita per day on a 365-day year basis.

Seemingly wide differences between individual cities are due to variations in several influences, probably the greatest being collection service regulations. The 1968 National Survey in Table 6 shows the daily average for household refuse plus commercial refuse to be 4.05 pounds per capita per day, which can be considered substantial agreement.

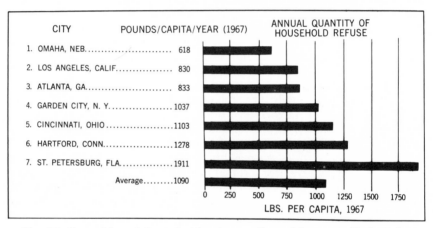

Fig. 12. Quantities of household refuse collected in seven United States cities, 1967.

Since household refuse consists of a variable mixture of garbage, rubbish, and some ashes, the fluctuations in production and hence collections delivered for disposal are not so pronounced as for the components, whose individual fluctuations often tend to offset each other. The capabilities, idiosyncrasies, and schedules of and the effects of weather on the collecting agency may be more of an influence, particularly on short-term variations in quantities, and especially if the collections are made no oftener than once weekly.

Noncombustible Rubbish. The principal reason in the past for requiring separation of noncombustible materials for a separate collection was incinerator design, and some of these old plants are still in use. Large modern incinerators do not require much separation except for relatively large quantities of ashes and bulky objects. Sanitary landfills, of course, need no separation of this sort at all. Bulky objects include items of discarded furniture which may be largely combustible but are considered in this classification anyway.

Accordingly, in the interest of efficiency, separate city collections on regular schedules for noncombustible rubbish from residential occupancies are found much less frequently than formerly, and most of this material is now included with household refuse. Special collections for bulky objects are often available, and there is still considerable service of this type for commercial and industrial establishments through private contractors. In the few instances where noncombustible rubbish is still reported separately, it sometimes amounts to a respectable proportion of the total load. In Omaha, private collections of this class of refuse constitute 29.3 per cent of the total. In Hartford, public and private collections are 32.3 per cent, and in Cincinnati the same classes are 39.0 per cent of the total. The accompanying chart, Figure 13, shows how the noncombustible refuse collections made by the city fluctuated from week to week in 1967 in Cincinnati.

Fig. 13. Comparison of weekly collections of noncombustible rubbish in Cincinnati, Ohio, 1967.

Dead Animals. In most cities, disposal of dead animals does not pose a very large problem. Small animals, comprising by far the greater proportion, can be readily incinerated or buried in a sanitary landfill. Many of these which have been pets never even come to the city for disposal, being buried privately. Large animals such as horses are usually handled by private rendering companies, although even these can be incinerated or buried if necessary.

The city is usually called upon to dispose of animals killed on the streets and will make special collections of others upon request. Only a few cities keep records, but reports have been received showing that

St. Petersburg, Florida, collects 30 per 1,000 population per year, Atlanta collects 80 per 1,000 population per year, and Cincinnati collects 81 per 1,000 population per year.

The 1968 National Survey shows, for urban areas, collections of only 15.9 small animals per 1,000 population and a negligible 0.26 large animal per 1,000 population per year.

The number of dead animals for disposal fluctuates seasonally, with more in the summer than at other times of the year.

Street Refuse. Street refuse includes street sweepings, dirt, leaves, catch-basin dirt, and the contents of litter receptacles. Collection and disposal of this refuse varies considerably among cities. In some cities, street sweeping and catch-basin cleaning, as well as the disposal of the material, are the responsibilities of the street department. However, collection and disposal of leaves and litter is usually the responsibility of the refuse collection and disposal agency.

Divided responsibility within cities, as well as the differences among cities, make it difficult to determine how much street refuse is collected and disposed of.

Among the cities surveyed in 1968 by APWA, street refuse was not reported separately. The 1968 National Survey, however, did include an investigation of this component of the total solid waste disposal load. From this study it is calculated that the average quantity of street and alley refuse collected in urban areas in 1967 was about .0461 ton per capita, or about 0.253 pound per capita per day. This is a small proportion of the total solid waste production, but somewhat significant because it is largely noncombustible outside the leaf season, relatively incompressible, and sometimes suitable for cover material. It may include street sweepings, dirt, leaves, catch-basin cleanings, and the contents of litter receptacles.

Seasonal differences in amounts of street refuse are quite pronounced. Quantities are affected by accumulations of leaves in the fall, greater littering by the public in the summer, and, in some northern cities, street sanding during the winter. Leaves and street sanding also increase the amount of catch-basin accumulations. For a more detailed discussion of street refuse, see *Street Cleaning Practice*.[1]

Industrial Refuse. Wastes from industry for many years were considered the responsibility of the manufacturer. If the wastes were solid, they usually were disposed of in an open dump. Liquids were often dumped into nearby streams.

Anti-pollution measures, for both air and water, as well as fewer dump sites, have influenced a trend toward municipal disposal of industrial wastes. Where industrial wastes are disposed of by a city, they are frequently delivered to a disposal site by the industry or by private contractors retained by the industry, and the city usually charges for disposal, according to the quantity and type of material.

---

[1] American Public Works Association, Street Sanitation Committee, *Street Cleaning Practice* (Chicago: Public Administration Service, 1959), 424 pp.

The 1968 National Survey indicates average urban area collections of industrial wastes of 690 pounds per capita per year, or 1.90 pounds per capita per day.

There is only one accurate way to determine the quantities of industrial wastes within a specific city—by conducting a complete survey of all plants. The types of wastes should be determined, as well as the quantities, so that special disposal problems of incineration or landfilling can be anticipated. For example, if a city is planning to build an incinerator for municipal and industrial wastes, the design could be influenced by large quantities of wet wastes, such as paunch manure, and highly inflammable material, such as some plastics. Also, special provisions may be required for flammable materials, such as cleaning fluids.

Demolition Refuse. Ever-increasing activity in urban renewal programs, in addition to the normal replacements of older buildings, and a trend toward complete prohibition of on-site burning of building debris have all combined to make the quantities of demolition refuse become an important factor in the municipal solid wastes disposal load. The relative incompressibility of demolition materials, and the practical fact that disposal on land by filling is the only feasible solution for much of it, adds to the problem. The rubble component can be a useful landfill material. The wood component, which is considerable, presents a more troublesome disposal problem on a fill where open burning is not permitted.

In the demolition business, salvage was formerly an important factor. With the increases in labor costs and for other reasons it is now less of an influence and substantially everything goes to the disposal point. Fluctuations in the load for disposal obviously depend on urban renewal activity and have no reliable seasonal pattern.

From the 1968 National Survey it is estimated that demolition refuse in urban areas amounts to about 0.72 pound per capita per day, virtually all of which is disposed as landfill. At an estimated density of 1,000 pounds per cubic yard in place, this load amounts to some 0.16 acre-foot of fill volume per 1,000 population annually. This constitutes a significant volume of landfill requirement, for which no feasible substitute is available for the noncombustible part. It should also be stressed that requirements in this sector are highly dependent on local activity in urban renewal projects.

Several large cities, including New York and Philadelphia, have explored the feasibility of using shredding devices to convert combustible demolition wastes into a form suitable for incineration. In Norwalk and Stamford, Connecticut, incinerators burn demolition lumber and other bulky combustible rubbish without shredding. Detroit operates two incinerators for burning forestry refuse, including heavy logs.

Large, Bulky Refuse. Large, bulky objects, particularly beds, mattresses, divans, chairs, and kitchen appliances, present problems in routine collection and disposal. Some cities, such as New York, provide special collection vehicles for such objects. The trucks are routed according to requests from householders. The material is normally disposed of at landfills.

Effects of Collection Methods on Disposal

There are considerable differences among cities in the amount of refuse produced, the amount collected, and the amount actually disposed of by the city. Various combinations of city, city-private, and private systems are used for disposal, as well as for collection. Two cities may produce the same per capita quantity of refuse but the amount collected and disposed of in each city by municipal forces may differ widely.

In Garden City, New York, the city government is responsible for collection and disposal of all refuse produced within its limits, with the minor exception of 23 pounds per capita per year of rubbish collected by private haulers.

In St. Petersburg, the city disposes of all refuse, but about one-third of it is collected by private haulers. Similar systems are used in Omaha and Cincinnati.

Atlanta, Hartford, New York, and Washington, D. C., dispose of nearly all refuse collected within their limits, except garbage used for hog feeding and some other minor exceptions. There are, however, varying amounts of refuse collected by private haulers in these cities.

Seattle has a contract collection system but disposal facilities are operated by the city. About 15 per cent of the refuse produced in Seattle is collected by private haulers.

In Atlanta and Omaha, tin cans from incinerator residue are sold as salvage, thereby eliminating a substantial volume of material.

San Francisco is unique among the survey cities in that it has no direct refuse collection or disposal activity. All refuse is collected by two private scavenger associations. Uniform rates are controlled by the city government and charges are collected by the truck drivers from the householders. As pointed out previously, charges are based on the quantity of refuse collected so that there is a strong incentive for householders to dispose of as much refuse on their premises as possible.

Disposal of refuse in San Francisco is in privately owned and operated landfills. The collection associations pay for disposal according to the weight of refuse. Extensive salvage is practiced in San Francisco. Truck drivers separate salvageable items during collection and drop them off at a depot before going to the disposal area.

Recent action has been taken by the California State Legislature (1965) to restrict the further filling of San Francisco Bay with raw refuse or other material, a practice which has been unabated in the past and which has resulted in this body of water being utilized for the disposal of most of the solid wastes generated in the Bay Area cities at a large number of locations (77 sites). This poses a severe challenge for this area in arriving at practical alternate solutions, even on a regional basis.

Per Capita Quantities

Knowledge of the trends over the past years in the per capita quantity of refuse produced and collected is of great value in planning collection activities and equipment and in planning, financing, and construction of disposal facilities. Various factors increase or decrease the total amount of refuse and the amount of certain types and combinations of types of refuse collected from year to year. The increasing demand for more extensive and better collection service has been pointed out by numerous authorities. Social and economic conditions affect the amount of refuse produced, the amount salvaged, and the amount collected. It is evident that extensive use of canned and packaged frozen foods has caused a per capita increase in the amount of rubbish produced (tin cans, boxes, wrappings, and cartons), while the quantity of garbage has decreased. On the other hand, better transportation facilities for fresh foods have probably increased the amounts of garbage in the winter months in some regions. The effectiveness of the refuse collection system may also help modify the amount collected.

Generally speaking, all studies show that there is a definite downward trend in the total quantities of garbage and ashes collected separately. Conversely, there has been a definite upward trend in the quantity of total refuse collected. Los Angeles, for example, reported that the quantities of garbage collected between 1948 and 1957 decreased from more than 0.6 pound per capita per calendar day in 1948 to less than 0.4 in 1957. The quantity of ashes collected by Garden City during the period 1948 through 1957 decreased from about 250 to 50 pounds per capita per year.

Figure 14 shows dramatically the change that has taken place in

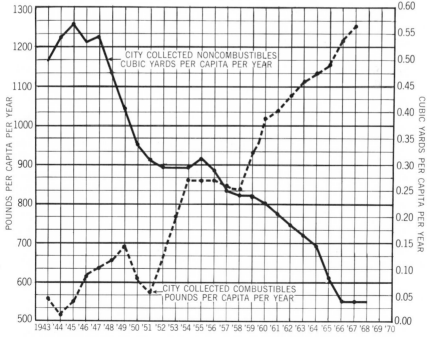

Fig. 14. Yearly fluctuations in quantities of combustibles and noncombustibles collected by city forces, Cincinnati, Ohio, 1943-1967.

Cincinnati as to quantity and type of refuse collected over the period following World War II. During this time solid fuel was almost completely displaced for domestic heating with the result that the few remaining ashes have been utilized for fill and collection of noncombustibles separately has practically ceased. In 1964 rules were changed to eliminate necessity for separation so that the little remaining noncombustible material is largely combined with the combustible for the last few years shown.

Unit Weights

It is obvious that accurate knowledge of unit weights is basic and necessary information in all phases of solid waste management since it is the factor needed to determine size requirements throughout the system. Because the composition of refuse varies considerably seasonally, geographically, and from other influences, some knowledge of density of the principal component parts, as well as general ranges of their more common combinations, is helpful.

Since solid wastes include large proportions of highly compressible materials, unit weights may vary widely even for the same lot of refuse depending upon its condition at the time of measurement. For example, household refuse ready for collection in the householder's container may be poorly compacted and weigh only 150 to 250 pounds per cubic yard. Upon collection and deposit in a packer body the same materials may be concentrated to 300 to 500 pounds per cubic yard or even more. When dumped at the incinerator or sanitary landfill some expansion takes place, lowering the density a bit, but after final compaction and settling in for a period the fill, under pressure of superimposed load and after some organic decomposition, may end up at 1,000 or more pounds per cubic yard. The amount of moisture present is also an obvious factor, affecting compressibility as well as adding weight.

Refuse density in the receiving pit or bunker of a municipal incinerator varies largely with moisture content. Tests[2] in a 30-foot deep pit, filled level full with household refuse, revealed a density of 349 pounds per cubic yard at 26 per cent moisture and 480 pounds per cubic yard at 42 per cent moisture. The density increased to 8 per cent by overnight settling.

Unless some other basis is specified it is customary to speak of unit weights of refuse as those applying when the material is in the transporting vehicle ready to be discharged, and that is the general basis used in this book. It is relatively easy to determine accurate weights and volumes at this stage. In attempting to make comparisons, therefore, the type of vehicle and the treatment the refuse has been subjected to in loading must be considered.

Garbage. As has been mentioned, separate collections of garbage

---

[2] E. R. Kaiser, C. D. Zeit, and J. B. McCaffery, "Municipal Incinerator Refuse and Residue," *Proceedings of 1968 National Incinerator Conference* (New York: American Society of Mechanical Engineers, 1968), pp. 142-153.

only—that is, organic food wastes—are very rare except for those from some commercial establishments, usually where the disposal is feeding to swine. If we are considering the garbage component of general household refuse, its unit weight is subject to several influences. Sanitary ordinances and collection regulations may require draining and wrapping in newspaper, resulting generally in less moisture content and hence lighter unit weight in spite of the additional paper content. Degree of packing for storage and in collection vehicles as well as moisture picked up from rain or snow in storage will be factors.

APWA surveys at various times have shown unit weights for garbage ranging from 798 pounds per cubic yard to 1,540 pounds per cubic yard, with an average of 936 pounds per cubic yard. One survey made in 1956 indicated an average of about 1,000 pounds per cubic yard for unwrapped garbage collected separately.

Ashes. With the widespread shift away from solid fuel for domestic heating, separate collections of ashes are also rarely found any more. Weight of ashes varies with storage conditions since they readily pick up moisture from rain or snow. As usually found they range from 1,150 to 1,400 pounds per cubic yard, with a median of about 1,250 pounds.

Household Refuse. As it is a variable mixture of garbage and rubbish, unit weights of household refuse can also cover a rather wide range. As usually found now in packer trucks it runs from about 300 to 600 pounds per cubic yard, with an average around 400 pounds per cubic yard.

Rubbish and Ashes Together. The unit weight of rubbish and ashes combined depends in great measure on the proportions in which the two categories are combined, for rubbish is quite light and ashes are quite heavy. The differences in unit weights are more marked if the material is exposed to the weather, either before or during collection, and it absorbs moisture. Data collected indicate a range in weight of from 400 to 1,000 pounds per cubic yard, with the average about 700 pounds if ashes are the predominant component. As the amount of ashes in proportion to the amount of rubbish decreases, however, the weight decreases also.

Noncombustible Rubbish. The unit weights of ashes and noncombustible rubbish combined do not vary as widely as those for the other classes of refuse discussed so far. Data available in the late 1950's indicate that unit weights for noncombustible rubbish vary from about 400 to 600 pounds per cubic yard if relatively few ashes are included. The differences in weight can be attributed to the differences in types of coal, the kinds of noncombustible materials included in regular collections, and the amount of moisture in the rubbish.

All Refuse Together. The same reasons for the differences in the unit weights of the various categories of refuse apply also to all types of refuse when collected together. Local collection regulations and practices influence the relative amounts of components in refuse in each community and are, therefore, the most important factors in the weight. The type of collection vehicle used is also important.

The unit weight of all refuse together varies from 300 pounds to nearly 700 pounds per cubic yard; the average is about 350 pounds.

PHYSICAL AND CHEMICAL COMPOSITION OF REFUSE

Most studies made in the past of the physical and chemical composition of refuse have been undertaken to help a city determine what disposal method it should use. They have been done in connection with the design of incinerators, sanitary landfills, and composting projects. Each of these requires different kinds of information, so complete analyses were seldom made. Furthermore, there was little available in the way of standard procedures for analyzing refuse. In 1958, a study at Purdue University resulted in development of standards which have been reviewed, up-dated, and amended by the Research and Development Division of the Federal Bureau of Solid Waste Management. The procedures of analysis in Appendix A incorporate the best standards available for this purpose.

In more recent years, there have been a number of projects conducted under grants from the U.S. Department of Health, Education, and Welfare, investigating solid wastes management in various localities. Some of these have provided useful basic data on quantities and composition of urban solid wastes. Representative of these is one conducted in the "Quad-Cities" area of New Jersey, with a population of 307,255 in a 48.4 square mile area including the cities of Paterson, Clifton, Passaic,

TABLE 8

"QUAD-CITIES" NEW JERSEY SOLID WASTES PROJECT[1]
COMPOSITION OF SOLID WASTES

Waste Composition	Per Cent	Waste Composition	Per Cent
Municipal Wastes (2.74 lbs/cap/day)		*Industrial Wastes (3.31 lbs/cap/day)*	
Physical Composition		Physical Composition	
Paper	45.63	Paper	42.73
Wood	3.00	Wood	7.34
Plastics	2.52	Plastic	12.61
Glass	6.22	Glass	3.03
Stone, sand	7.65	Sand, stone	5.09
Organics	22.62	Organic, chemical	3.32
Rags	4.45	Textiles, rags	3.28
Chemical Characteristics		Ceramics	1.57
as received		Inorganic, chemical	0.19
Moisture	30.1	Petro-chemical	0.23
Volatiles	34.7	Rubber	2.45
Ash	35.2	Mixed commercial	4.15
B.T.U. value/lb	3,364	Food	5.00
Carbon/nitrogen value on day		Miscellaneous	4.43
basis—31			

[1] U. S. Department of Health, Education, and Welfare, *Quad City Solid Wastes Project Interim Report*, HEW Demonstration Grant No. 1-U1-00026.

and Wayne. This area includes highly industrialized sectors as well as residential and even semi-rural locales, and should be widely representative. Table 8 shows the information collected by this investigation as to composition of refuse. Another project[3] investigated household refuse at Hempstead, New York, a predominantly residential community (Table 9).

In another investigation[4] at Johnson City, Tennessee, a similar analysis of household refuse was made with results shown in Table 10. The Hempstead study also investigated the ultimate composition of the components of its refuse on a day basis, as reported in Table 11.

A study[5] of physical composition of household refuse in Berkeley, California, was made in 1967, some of the results of which are shown in Table 12. This study is of particular interest because it can be compared with a 1952 survey of the same areas under identical conditions. This comparison is shown in Table 13.

The discussion of these tables in the study points out the following:

(a) The garbage fraction (included as part of the "compostable material" in Table 13) was only about 50 per cent in 1967 of the 1952 proportion. Since the "compostable material" proportion remained almost constant, a corresponding increase in the proportion of paper is a corollary effect.

(b) The proportions of tin cans, glass, rags, metal, shoes, and wastes of "no salvage value" changed very little.

(c) Plastics were practically nonexistent in 1952, but increased to 1.9 per cent in 1967. This weight relation is not a good indicator of their volume, because they are very light in the usual form of wrappings.

Trends in Composition Changes

A significant thread is traceable throughout any investigation of analyses of refuse. In the household refuse sector the amount of putrescible organic material—garbage—is diminishing while the amount of paper and paper products is increasing. This is readily accounted for by changes in food processing resulting in much less food wastes for the householder and better packaging involving paper products. In other applications also there is a decided increase in the use of disposable paper products.

United States consumption of paper and paperboard increased by 16.6 per cent from 1958 to 1962, from 35 to 42 million tons. This increase was much greater than the comparable population increase of 7.5 per cent.

[3] Kaiser, et al., op. cit.

[4] U.S. Department of Health, Education, and Welfare, *Comprehensive Solid Waste Study, Johnson City, Tennessee, A Technical Services Report (SW-6ts.)*

[5] C. G. Golueke and P. H. McGaughey, *Comprehensive Studies of Solid Wastes Management*, First Annual Report, May, 1967 (Berkeley, Calif.: Sanitary Engineering and Research Laboratory, College of Engineering and School of Public Health, 1967).

TABLE 9

REFUSE COMPOSITION AND MOISTURE CONTENTS

HEMPSTEAD, NEW YORK

Category	Test 1 June 1, 1966		Test 2 June 23, 1966		Test 3 Feb. 21, 1967		Test 4 April 5, 1967	
	Weights Per Cent	Moisture Per Cent	Weights Per Cent	Moisture Per Cent	Weights Per Cent	Moisture Per Cent	Weights Per Cent	Moisture Per Cent
Cardboard	1.59	23.78	6.75	13.22	5.78	16.10	6.81	14.27
Newspaper	8.88	37.77	11.27	19.20	21.35	18.00	12.75	19.05
Misc. paper	22.25	36.93	21.78	24.68	26.20	21.90	24.70	21.88
Plastic film	1.76	18.80	1.77	20.47	1.20	2.85	1.09	12.43
Other plastics, etc.	0.69	20.50	1.67	29.60	2.34	4.38	7.73	6.26
Garbage	9.58	65.25	10.21	73.45	16.70	59.80	7.23	55.75
Grass, dirt, leaves	33.33	62.20	19.00	44.80	0.26	21.08	17.89	23.69
Textiles	3.00	31.40	3.33	22.40	2.24	26.05	3.97	15.30
Wood	1.22	24.98	6.58	8.70	1.46	13.20	3.47	14.80
Mineral (glass, etc.)	9.74	6.00	9.49	1.99	11.87	1.64	7.13	2.23
Metallic	7.96	10.83	8.15	2.76	10.60	4.46	7.23	8.35
	100.00		100.00		100.00		100.00	
Avg. moisture, % weighted		42.10		27.06		21.18		19.57

TABLE 10

COMPOSITION OF HOUSEHOLD REFUSE
JOHNSON CITY, TENNESSEE—1967

Category	Per Cent
Food wastes	25.9
Cloth & synthetics	1.3
Paper products	45.5
Plastics	1.7
Leather & rubber	1.0
Yard wastes	1.6
Wood	0.3
Glass products	10.9
Metals	10.8
Brick, rock, dirt, etc.	1.0
	100.0

Average daily collections—1.1 lbs/cap/day

Table 14 and Figure 15 illustrate past and projected increases of consumption of paper and paperboard products.

It should be noted that the increases indicated have occurred in spite of the facts that 1 ton of paper now covers as much as 50 per cent more than it once did, and that the basic weight of some packaging paperboard has been reduced from 60 pounds to 40 pounds without any reduction in weight-sustaining capacity. These factors indicate a trend to increasing refuse bulk at a faster rate than the increase in refuse weight.

Analyses for Incineration

In the design of refuse incinerators the most important factors in refuse characteristics are the calorific value, moisture content, proportion of noncombustibles, and special components whose combustion could result in problems with flue gases. The general physical condition for design of handling and stoking equipment is also necessary information. A tabulation giving some of these factors for the Hempstead, New York, investigation mentioned above is shown in Table 15.

As in all such analyses the validity of the results of tests of samples is highly dependent on obtaining samples that are truly representative. Since refuse is a highly variable material subject to substantial fluctuations of content from weather, seasonal, and other influences, some care must be used to take account of any significant ranges of variations.

In general the calorific value of household refuse is usually found at present runs of the order of 8,000 to 9,000 B.T.U. per pound on a dry, inert-free basis, and some 4,500 B.T.U. per pound as delivered in average condition with around 30 per cent moisture. These values can vary within considerable ranges under local or temporary circumstances departing from normal.

The moisture content of refuse is made up of bound and free moisture.

TABLE 11

HEMPSTEAD, NEW YORK

ANALYSES OF COMPONENTS OF HOUSEHOLD REFUSE

ULTIMATE ANALYSES IN WEIGHT PER CENT, B.T.U. (HHV) PER POUND DRY BASIS

Category	Carbon	Hydrogen	Oxygen	Nitrogen	Sulfur	Inerts[1]	B.T.U./lb
Cardboard	45.52	6.08	44.53	0.16	0.14	3.57	7,841
Newspaper	48.36	6.13	42.30	0.14	0.11	2.96	8,266
Misc. paper	44.00	6.15	41.65	0.43	0.12	7.65	7,793
Plastic film	67.21	9.72	15.82	0.46	0.07	6.72	13,846
Other plastics, etc.	47.70	6.04	24.06	1.93	0.55	19.72	9,049
Garbage	41.72	5.75	27.62	2.79	0.25	21.87	7,246
Grass and dirt	36.20	4.75	26.61	2.10	0.26	30.08	6,284
Textiles	46.19	6.41	41.85	2.18	0.20	3.17	8,036
Wood	48.30	5.97	42.44	0.29	0.11	2.89	8,236
Mineral[2]	0.52	0.07	0.36	0.03	0.00	99.02	84
Metallic[2]	4.54	0.63	4.28	0.05	0.01	90.49	742

[1] Inerts are ash except in Metallics, where inerts are almost entirely metals.
[2] B.T.U. in labels, coatings, and remains of contents of containers.

TABLE 12

COMPOSITION OF BERKELEY REFUSE IN TERMS OF PERCENTAGES
MAY, 1967

Route	Day of Week	District[1]	Paper Soiled[2]	Paper Clean[3]	Garbage & Garden Debris[4]	Bottles, Broken Glass	Tin Cans	Plastics	Rags	Shoes	Metal	Misc[5]
H-2	Tues.	Low-Med. Resid.	32.6	8.8	19.4	13.9	9.9	2.8	1.7	0.4	0.3	10.2
West Special	Wed.	Low Resid.	35.1	3.8	26.9	11.6	10.7	1.8	1.2	0.5	0.2	8.3
L-4	Thurs.	Low Resid.	40.3	2.7	30.0	10.1	8.4	1.9	1.7	0.5	0.4	7.0
O-1	Mon.	Low-Med. Resid.	37.6	1.9	30.1	11.5	8.8	2.0	0.4	0.1	0.2	7.5
A-2	Tues.	Med.-High Resid.	36.9	3.5	30.1	13.3	7.2	1.9	0.9	0.3	0.5	5.5
R-3	Wed.	Apts. Light Comm.	25.4	42.9	15.4	5.7	3.3	1.2	0.3	Tr.	0.4	5.5
C-4	Thurs.	Med.-High Apt. Resid.	31.7	15.9	24.7	11.8	8.6	1.2	0.8	0.1	0.2	5.0
Average 7 Loads			34.7	9.9	25.1	11.3	8.4	1.9	1.1	0.3	0.3	7.1

[1] Based on income level and type of dwelling.
[2] Paper which has been in contact with garbage; not marketable.
[3] Paper having a market value.
[4] At least 80% garbage.
[5] Dirt, rocks, wood, etc.

TABLE 13

CHANGES IN COMPOSITION OF BERKELEY REFUSE OVER 15-YEAR PERIOD[1]

Route	Year	Type of District[2]	Tin Cans	Bottles, Broken Glass	Rags	Metals	Shoes	Plastics[3]	Compostable Material[4]	Wastes of No Value[5]
H-2	1967	Low-Med.	9.9	13.9	1.7	0.3	0.41	2.8	60.8	10.2
	1952	Resid.	11.0	10.8	1.6	0.8	0.50	Tr.	67.8	7.5
West Spec.	1967	Low	10.7	11.6	1.2	0.2	0.46	1.8	65.8	8.3
	1952	Resid.	8.0	10.0	2.6	1.0	0.04	Tr.	70.2	8.2
L-4	1967	Low	8.4	10.1	1.7	0.4	0.51	1.9	70.0	7.0
	1952	Resid.	12.5	13.5	0.7	0.5	0.03	Tr.	66.6	6.2
O-1	1967	Low-Med.	8.8	11.5	0.4	0.2	0.12	2.0	69.5	7.5
	1952	Resid.	11.0	13.8	1.5	Tr.	Tr.	Tr.	66.3	7.4
A-2	1967	Med.-High	7.2	13.3	0.9	0.5	0.28	1.9	70.5	5.5
	1952	Resid.	10.4	10.9	1.6	Tr.	Tr.	Tr.	69.4	7.7
R-3	1967	Apts.	3.3	5.7	0.3	0.4	Tr.	1.2	83.6	5.5
	1952	Light Com.	7.0	7.0	1.0	2.0	Tr.	Tr.	74.7	8.3
C-4	1967	Med.-High	8.6	11.8	0.8	0.2	0.14	1.2	72.2	5.0
	1952	Apt. Resid.	8.4	13.0	1.5	Tr.	Tr.	Tr.	69.4	7.7
Average (7 Loads)	1967		8.4	11.3	1.1	0.3	0.3	1.9	69.7	7.1
	1952		10.0	11.4	1.5	0.6	0.2	Tr.	69.0	7.4

[1] Values are those for percentage of total load.
[2] Based on income level and type of dwelling.
[3] Plastic content of 1952 refuse was practically nonexistent.
[4] 1967—report on compost figures includes soiled paper, clean paper, and garden debris.
[5] Wastes usable neither for compost nor as a marketable salvage.

TABLE 14

PAPER AND PAPERBOARD CONSUMPTION[1]

Consumption		1963	1980
Total U. S. Consumption—	tons	43,000,000	76,000,000
Per capita consumption—	lbs/cap/yr	460	640
Waste paper re-used—	lbs/cap/yr	96	130
Paper in buildings & storage—	lbs/cap/yr	54	75
Balance to disposal—	lbs/cap/yr	310	435
Percentage increase disposal per capita		—	40%

[1] American Pulp & Paper Association.

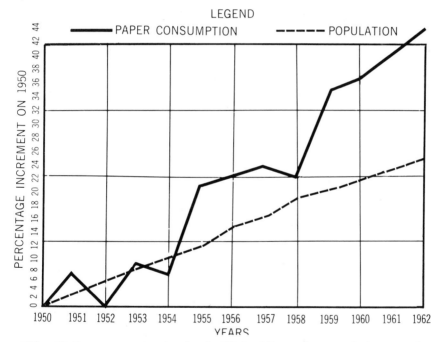

LEGEND

━━━ PAPER CONSUMPTION ----- POPULATION

Fig. 15. *Paper consumption in the United States increased almost twice the percentage of the population increase in the years 1950-1962, thus contributing to the trend toward greater refuse bulk compared to refuse weight. (From Proceedings of 1964 National Incinerator Conference, ASME.)*

Large amounts of vegetable matter result in high bound moisture content, although on visual inspection the material may appear dry because of the lack of free moisture. The net calorific value of refuse is reduced by the amount of heat required to evaporate the water present. Other materials that are noncombustible at ordinary incinerator temperatures likewise reduce the net amount of heat available from combustion of a unit weight of refuse. Coal ash, when considered as a separate component, neither reduces nor increases the calorific value of the refuse, since it normally contains sufficient heating value to raise its temperature independently of the other combustible material.

TABLE 15

EXAMPLE OF DATA ON REFUSE CHARACTERISTICS NECESSARY FOR INCINERATOR DESIGN
AVERAGE ANALYSIS AND CALORIFIC VALUE
HEMPSTEAD, NEW YORK

Proximate	Weight Per Cent	Ultimate	Weight Per Cent
Moisture	28.0	Moisture	28.0
Volatile matter	43.4	Carbon	25.0
Fixed carbon	6.6	Hydrogen	3.3
Glass, ash, metal	22.0	Oxygen	21.1
	100.0	Nitrogen	0.5
Heating Value (HHV)		Sulfur	0.1
Organic	4,400	Glass, ceramics, stones	9.3
Partial oxidation		Metals	7.2
of metal	100	Ash, other inerts	5.5
B.T.U. per lb	4,500		

Analyses for Sanitary Landfill

It is not as important to know the physical and chemical composition of refuse to be disposed of by sanitary landfill as it is for disposal by incineration or composting. The flexibility of landfills in coping with the quantity and quality fluctuations of refuse has played a major part in their popularity.

The two factors of most importance, perhaps, in the quality of the refuse to be handled in sanitary landfills are (1) the amount of decomposable material and subsequently the rate of decomposition, and (2) the density of the material under compaction, both before and after decomposition.

The designer of a sanitary landfill to be used upon completion for some public or other constructive purpose is concerned with ending up with a final surface contour somewhere close to his planned elevations. Data on the ultimate probable density after all decomposition shrinkage and settlement will help him to estimate how much to allow for settlement in setting his grades for the fill operation.

Analyses for Composting

Scientific composting requires a more accurate and detailed analysis of refuse, particularly chemical composition, than any other method of disposal. Modern composting is a method of refuse disposal in which an attempt is made to provide an ideal microenvironment of food, water, air, temperature, and shelter so that microorganisms can break down the refuse. Since food for the organisms is the refuse itself, and because the organisms thrive best within certain physical limits, it is essential that the composition of the refuse be determined so that adjustments can be made in these factors if necessary.

For a successful composting operation an important requirement is a favorable carbon/nitrogen ratio, the optimum range being between 30 and 40. Noncompostable materials such as metals, glass, and tires must be removed. Accordingly, an analysis for composting should show composition by physical categories as well as by ultimate chemical make-up of the portion to be composted. Limits of variations of the vital characteristics because of seasonal or other influences should also be known. Moisture content is also an important consideration in composting, but all plants are designed to control this by addition of water. Only if the material is too wet does this factor become a major one.

Chemical Analyses

Many investigations of the chemical composition of refuse have been made in connection with composting. Because of non-uniform methods of sampling and the use of differing test techniques it has been difficult to make reliable comparisons of one set of results with another. The techniques described in Appendix A of this book have been reviewed and revised by the Research and Development Division of the Federal Bureau of Solid Waste Management. Their use should make possible more uniform test results that can be validly compared with one another.

Chemical composition studies may be of some value in investigating water pollution potentials for sanitary landfills and air pollution potentials for incinerator operations.

Compaction Characteristics

The compaction characteristics of refuse have received increased attention. Changes in composition, desire for better knowledge of behavior in sanitary landfills, concern with improving efficiency of transport, and the interest in high-pressure baling techniques have all been contributing factors.

Since solid wastes, and particularly the important household refuse component, are highly compressible, this factor is a key consideration in any effort to understand performance and to improve practices. For instance, higher compression has been a basic means of increasing the efficiency of collection vehicles, and the use of improved compacting machines has been introduced on landfills with significant results in increases in density and hence capacity. A completely different range of pressures, many times that achieved by foregoing means, has been investigated and employed in a few applications to produce high density bales whose characteristics are hardly recognizable as originating with refuse. By way of indicating the comparative compressive efforts involved, field compaction efforts employ pressures of up to about 100 pounds per square inch, whereas the pressures used in baling machines may go to 2,500 pounds per square inch or even higher and are more evenly applied throughout the refuse mass.

The performance in sanitary landfills of refuse in the form of these high-density bales as well as the potential economic advantages of their use are subjects of a research project conducted by APWA and the Federal Bureau of Solid Waste Management.

The practical consideration in connection with the compaction factor in solid waste disposal management is maximum reduction in volume, consistent with reasonable costs, to assure optimum utilization of disposal space and minimum subsequent settling.

The results of compression tests on household refuse in Chicago are shown in Figure 16. Note the substantial volume expansion of the bales after compaction.

It is of some interest to note that there is a limit to the compressibility of refuse, and that increased pressures beyond some point bring diminishing returns. The compression process largely achieves increased density through elimination of air and sometimes some water. The limit in density is reached when all air and free water is expelled, and is the inherent density of the components. For paper this figure is about 1,500 pounds per cubic yard. For steel it is about 13,000 pounds per cubic yard, although it is obviously not feasible to reduce steel scrap to an air-

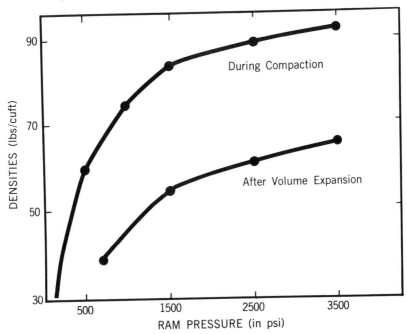

Fig. 16. Average density of residential wastes during and after compaction. Data from report of study of high pressure compaction baling of solid wastes by the City of Chicago, 1969.

free mass by cold compression. Water weighs about 1,685 pounds per cubic yard. A mixture of wastes as normally found in household refuse might be expected to have weights of the order of 2,100 pounds per cubic yard if completely free of voids. Under practical conditions using best equipment for compaction in a sanitary landfill, initial compaction could hardly be expected to achieve more than half this density, and average achievement would be even less—perhaps 800 or 900 pounds per cubic yard. The reason for subsequent settlement is obvious, particularly when it is coupled with some reduction of volume resulting from decomposition of some organic components during which material is lost through escape of gases.

3 SELECTING DISPOSAL METHODS

The selection of the best methods of refuse disposal for a city is of utmost importance. It involves many factors; careful consideration must be given to all and a number of questions answered before a decision can be made:

1. What methods are technically feasible; what are the limitations of each?
2. Do local conditions make some methods particularly suitable or unsuitable?
3. What factors, such as good public health features or fewer potential nuisances, favor one method over another?
4. Will weather, mechanical failure, or other circumstances interrupt disposal procedures and with what results for the city?
5. What are the costs of the various methods; how do they vary and with what factors?
6. What effect do collection procedures have on costs of disposal?
7. What effect will the disposal method have on costs of collection?
8. What methods can be adapted economically to changing conditions in the city?
9. Will salvage or reclamation pay part of disposal costs?
10. What elements in each method are likely to gain public support or meet with antagonism?

Characteristics of Methods

Since each disposal method is discussed in detail in the following chapters, only the essential operations of each are given here as background for the factors that must be considered in deciding on methods.

Sanitary Landfills

Sanitary landfill operations are usually conducted by depositing refuse in a natural or man-made depression or trench or dumping it at ground level, compacting it to the smallest practical volume, and covering it with compacted earth or other material in a systematic and sanitary manner. Before operations begin, a site must be selected and surveyed; geological and hydrological factors evaluated; the site prepared; access roads, control grades, and drainage provided for; and equipment selected. Other steps may be required, depending on climate and the site. In some cases special provisions must be made for controlling blowing papers,

Fig. 17. Disposing of refuse in a sanitary landfill involves depositing the refuse (top left), compacting it to the smallest volume practical (above), and covering it with compacted earth in a systematic and sanitary manner (left).

odors, dust, and fire; and special equipment and personnel facilities may be needed.

Well-planned and operated landfills have several advantages: they are economical and flexible; they require a relatively small capital investment; they may reclaim otherwise useless land; they can accept most classes of solid wastes without segregation, permitting economies in collection systems; they cause practically no air pollution; and they provide a final and complete disposal.

However, landfilling involves substantial volume and hence land area requirements of a depleting nature, considered in relation to the fixed amounts of land existing in any community; resulting long hauls, compared with some other methods; susceptibility to operating problems arising from inclement weather; and susceptibility to serious public relations problems in obtaining rights to fill land to satisfy the continuing requirements for fill space.

Fig. 18. An incineration plant includes equipment necessary to burn combustible refuse without nuisance, reducing it to ash. The scale house and administrative offices for this plant in Jersey City, New Jersey, are shown at the right.

Central Incineration

A central incineration plant, which may be owned either publicly or privately, is one in which combustible refuse is reduced to ash by high-temperature burning. Refuse from collection trucks is dumped on a charging floor or, in newer plants, into a storage pit; it is charged into furnaces where it is burned under carefully controlled drafts, temperatures, and conditions of agitation to insure combustion as complete as possible; and the ashes and noncombustible residues are removed for possible salvage of metallic components and subsequent final disposal, usually in a landfill. Heat recovery may also be practiced through generation of steam, with a potential for some operating advantages as well as for some revenue to offset part of the cost.

Advantages of incineration include reduction of land requirements for final disposal, relatively small plant site and a fully enclosed operation permitting a strategic location to minimize collection costs, and production of a residue of ash that may be useful as fill material. On the other hand, capital and operating costs to comply with air pollution standards and produce nuisance-free results are high; and it is not a complete disposal method, being unable to handle large segments of the total solid waste production and requiring further disposal of a substantial amount of residue.

Incineration should be considered a volume reduction and beneficiating process, applicable to that considerable proportion of the total solid wastes load which is composed principally of combustible materials.

On-Site Incineration

On-site incinerators are those used inside and outside houses, in apartment buildings, stores, small industries, hospitals, and other institutions to burn refuse produced on the premises. They are of many types and sizes for various uses. The advantage is that the amount of combustible refuse that must be collected and disposed of is reduced by the amount that is burned in such incinerators. Householders and others who use them often find them an advantage because refuse does not have to be stored on the premises; it can be disposed of almost as soon as it is produced, reducing possible nuisances and hazards. On-site incinerators do sometimes cause considerable air pollution when they are improperly designed or operated.

Grinding Food Wastes

Garbage can be disposed of by grinding it and flushing it into sewers. There are home grinders; grinders used in restaurants, produce terminals, and supermarkets; and grinders for centrally located stations operated by a municipality. The principle of operation is the same for all. Garbage is kept or collected separately from other refuse, it is ground or shredded in the grinder as water is added, and it is flushed into the sewers.

Household grinders involve very high unit costs for garbage disposal when all elements of expense are considered—capital investment, deprecia-

Fig. 19. On-site incinerators include those used in homes, institutions, industries, and businesses. This portable industrial incinerator will burn 280 pounds of dry wastes an hour. The stack is self-supporting; needs no guying.

tion, repairs, cost of additional water, electric energy, and additional sewage disposal requirements. However, grinders are considered by the housewife as the ultimate in convenience and sanitation, since they practically eliminate garbage storage and much of the handling. Under such circumstances, costs are secondary and domestic garbage grinders are an increasing influence to be considered.

Widespread use of household and commercial grinders reduces the amount of garbage that must be collected and disposed of, and accordingly influences the composition of household and commercial refuse.

Central grinding stations are relatively simple to build and operate, and are sometimes advantageous in cities where there is a great deal of wet garbage that does not burn well and may not be suitable for feeding to hogs. However, grinding requires that other refuse, which may be 85 or 90 per cent of the total load, be collected and disposed of separately. This poses an economic problem unlikely to be offset by savings from central grinding. Accordingly, central grinding finds only very limited application at present.

Feeding Food Wastes to Swine

Garbage can be disposed of by feeding it to swine. It is collected separately, the inedible refuse is separated out, it is cooked to destroy disease organisms, and it is fed to hogs on farms usually especially built for garbage feeding. Municipalities no longer operate such hog farms, but in some cases they contract with hog raisers to use the garbage for feed. In most places, garbage is collected by private haulers who make their own arrangements with restaurants and institutions.

Because all states require that garbage be cooked before it is fed to hogs and because most farms are now far from cities, garbage feeding is not usually as attractive economically as it once was. Health and agriculture department regulations are necessary to prevent or control animal diseases and nuisances created by the disposal process. Furthermore, only edible food wastes are disposed of; other refuse must be collected and disposed of by other methods.

Composting

Composting is sometimes defined as a rapid but incomplete decomposition of moist, solid organic matter—in this case, primarily garbage—by the use of aerobic microorganisms under controlled conditions. The result is a sanitary, nuisance-free, humus-like material that can be used as a soil conditioner but is ordinarily not rich enough in the vital elements to be classed as a fertilizer. Theoretically the advantages are several: the end product has some value and should be marketable, resulting in revenue to the city; the site for the plant can be relatively small; this together with the theoretical nuisance-free aspects should permit a location advantageous to the city's collection system; and the idea of recovering something of value from a troublesome waste problem appeals to many, especially those who are concerned with organic agriculture and the maintenance of natural fertility of the soil.

In spite of these points, the record for composting in the United States is one of repeated failures, even though there have been several well-conceived projects and a good deal of effort has been spent on research and pilot demonstration projects. Most of these failures resulted basically from economic problems arising from uncertain markets and the difficulties in storing, processing, packaging, or distributing and selling the product. Organizing and financing projects on the basis of the expectation that the process could be self-supporting through sale of salvage and compost has resulted in the greatest disillusionment.

By the end of the 1960's only a few full-scale composting plants were in operation in the United States, although a number had been built, operated, and closed up for one reason or another.

Salvage and Reclamation

The term "salvage and reclamation" covers a number of disposal processes: sorting of refuse, either manually or mechanically, for metals, tin cans, glass, paper, rags, and other materials that can be resold; rendering of animal wastes for fats; dehydration of garbage to be used for hog feed; composting; and landfills that reclaim otherwise unusable land. A special but good-sized field for salvage is the processing and sale of scrap automobiles by crunching, baling, or disintegrating.

Garbage reduction, in which grease is extracted from cooked garbage and sold, was once a widely used form of salvage, but it has not been a major disposal method for 40 years or more. No city today uses salvage as a principal means of disposal; it is usually a partial method or sideline of some other method. Decreasing prices for salvage materials and increasing labor costs frequently make it uneconomical.

Dumping

Open dumps for garbage and other refuse are prohibited by law in many jurisdictions. In view of their well-known nuisance features, including air and water pollution, their well-proven health hazards, and the possibility of converting them to suitable sanitary landfills without prohibitive expenses, they are no longer considered an acceptable disposal method and should not be used or permitted by any public jurisdiction.

Legal Restrictions

State and local ordinances may prohibit some kinds of disposal or control various aspects of them. Air and water pollution, health, sanitation, fire, nuisance, zoning, and other laws affect the ways in which various disposal methods can be operated and the extent of cost. All should be investigated before a decision is made on what methods to use. In addition, the agency responsible for disposal may want to get additional regulations and ordinances passed that will help control disposal activities.

Regardless of what they control, the ordinances must be legal. If discriminatory, they may be declared unconstitutional. Typical ordinance provisions for disposing of refuse are given in Appendix B.

Ordinances in many cities make open dumping illegal, for instance, but it is a problem nevertheless. Not only does the producer of large volumes of refuse dump illegally but also the householder who does not want to put beer cans, liquor bottles, or some particularly unpleasant-smelling object in his refuse container. Instead, he dumps them in empty lots or along a roadside.

It is not easy to enforce regulations against illegal dumping because the violator is rarely caught in the act. Furthermore, it may be cheaper and easier for the city to correct the violation than to find and punish the guilty person. Residents of a neighborhood in which illegal dumping takes place are rarely able to tell when the violation occurred or give the names or vehicle license numbers of the violators. However, public concern with dumping violations has increased in recent years and more violators are being apprehended.

The most satisfactory method of punishment is not a fine or imprisonment but widespread newspaper publicity and the requirement that the violator clean up the illegally dumped refuse.

The best preventive measures are good refuse collection services and well-kept city streets and vacant lots. Educational programs appealing to civic pride, in which the newspapers and other mass media take part, are also helpful.

Dumping at sea was fairly common in sea coast cities until 1933, when the United States Supreme Court prohibited it in a decision involving New York City.

With the pressure for moving disposal operations farther from the cities in order to get suitable land there have arisen laws prohibiting disposal of refuse originating outside the legislating jurisdiction. While such restrictions are understandable, they point up the urgent need for solid waste disposal management on a broad enough geographical basis to make suitable disposal sites available to those who must have them.

Public Health Aspects

Most restrictions and regulations applying to refuse disposal are imposed in the interests of protecting and promoting public health, although there may also be some concerned with effects on aquatic life, recreational amenities, or property values.

The term "public health" is used in a very broad sense in this connotation and is generally accepted as a valid and enforceable basis for controls, even some that may be quite rigorous and costly to comply with. Hazards include direct transmission of disease to men and animals and the reservoirs from which disease may emerge, and also such environment-depreciating factors as odor, visible smoke, gases, dust, noise, fly ash, blowing paper, alteration of water characteristics and drainage conditions, heavy traffic, and unsightly appearance. Some of these are more properly classified as nuisances but they are considered for this purpose as sanitation factors of importance to the public health and welfare. The most serious public health hazards have to do with rodent and insect vectors.

Because of the innate nature of solid wastes and their interaction or response to disposal efforts there is always the potential for trouble from one or another of these factors. A well-designed disposal system will control them all within acceptable limits, but it is important to recognize that their complete elimination is not feasible in any practical disposal method.

Sanitary Landfills

The adverse public health aspects typical of open and burning dumps have wide public recognition and justly deserved disapproval. Well-designed and well-operated sanitary landfills will avoid all of these unfavorable features and can be used to actually substantially improve public health conditions, for instance through elimination of mosquito breeding swamps.

It is unfortunate that there is a general lack of public understanding and appreciation of the difference between a dump and a good sanitary landfill. It is even more unfortunate that there are many bad examples wrongly labeled sanitary landfills to give backing to the misconception and lead to confusion. What is badly needed in many localities to gain public acceptance is publicity and demonstration of a good sanitary landfill to alter the unfavorable image, and enforcement of regulations to upgrade the deficiencies of the poor examples. An instance of this approach occurred in Fresno, California, where there was much resistance at first to a landfill located some distance from the city. After several years of careful, nuisance-free operation there was little opposition when a new site was acquired and the disposal operation was moved much closer in.

Some of the possibilities for public health hazards or nuisances that must be avoided in sanitary landfills include air pollution, water pollution, rodent and insect vectors harboring and breeding, unsightly litter, and traffic problems. All of these can be effectively eliminated or controlled within acceptable limits by well-understood and demonstrated design and operation measures. In the few comparatively rare cases where geological, hydrological, or other physical conditions make successful operation unusually difficult, unduly expensive, or doubtful, the site should be avoided for this use. There is no valid excuse for the continued existence of a health hazard or nuisance in connection with a sanitary landfill.

Central Incineration

From the standpoints of public health and sanitation, air pollution presents the most significant problem in central incineration. Careful design and costly removal devices are necessary to prevent entrainment of objectionable quantities of particulate matter in waste flue gases. This can be accomplished to an acceptable degree. The inevitable emission of large volumes of gaseous products of combustion—hydrocarbons and derivatives as well as other oxides—is a matter of concern only in exceptional circumstances.

As in all other solid waste disposal activities, concentration of traffic is a problem that must be dealt with carefully to avoid adverse effects on the public welfare. Otherwise central incineration presents no health or nuisance problems not readily controllable in a well-designed and operated plant. Instances are not uncommon of incinerators operating near high-value residential property without complaint.

Grinding Food Wastes

In new districts of growing cities the use of home garbage grinders has become so widespread that even some very large cities now estimate that 25 to 30 per cent of all garbage is ground and flushed into sewers. The public health aspects of the practice—other than the positive one that garbage storage on the premises is eliminated—are largely those associated with sewage treatment problems. Wherever the method is used, however, its effect on the sewage disposal system must be taken into account. A number of cities prohibit installation of grinders because sewers and other sewage disposal facilities are inadequate.

An enclosed central grinding station must be well operated by a

Fig. 20. Central grinding stations at which garbage is ground and disposed of through the sewage system are used in some cities. Large grinders are especially convenient for disposing of condemned foods. This garbage grinding plant is at the refuse transfer station in Washington, D. C. The storage bin and feeders are at the right.

municipality to prevent the problems and nuisances common to any central disposal plant from developing.

Feeding Food Wastes to Swine

Feeding of garbage to swine is a disposal method in which both disease potential and aesthetics are part of the public health considerations. Health authorities have long been concerned with the reservoir of trichinosis maintained by the practice of feeding raw garbage to swine, even when the strictest precautions are taken to minimize rat and fly infestation of the feeding area. Hog feeders are equally anxious that cholera not wipe out their herds, leaving them without a salable commodity and with contracts that require them to dispose of tons of garbage each day.

While public health officials have been mainly concerned with trichinosis in man, it took an epidemic of animal disease to all but end the practice of feeding raw garbage to swine. The explosive emergence of vesicular exanthema from a California reservoir in 1952 led to the adoption of legislation or regulations banning the feeding of raw garbage to swine in all 50 states. However, if it is cooked enough to kill the disease-carrying organisms, its use as feed is still permitted. The added cost of the necessary processing reduces the profit prospects, but there still remain many such privately operated ventures.

Opposition has grown to feeding garbage to swine in areas that are within economical haul distances of a city. Hog farms are considered a nuisance. Zoning ordinance provisions for them, therefore, are becoming more and more restrictive with the result that, with the need for approval of both health and other public authorities to set up a hog farm, hog feeding as a method of garbage disposal has been eliminated in many areas. With the method eliminated some cities have been forced to combine garbage collection with that of other refuse that previously had been disposed of without undue health hazards or nuisance, requiring a change in disposal practice.

Composting

It has been demonstrated that a good composting operation is a sanitary method for treatment of refuse and that disposal of the end product as a soil conditioner presents no health hazards. Fly larvae and pathogenic organisms are destroyed if the turning process is thorough enough to bring all parts of the refuse into the high-temperature zone at some time.

The very limited use of composting in this country has made it unnecessary to adopt health regulations for these plants other than the general provisions covering health hazards and nuisances. A poorly designed or operated composting enterprise can present serious problems, but under present circumstances the question is academic.

Dumping

Until recently some communities in the environs of the great metropolitan centers were disposing of their refuse by (1) dumping it on a spreading area during the morning; (2) permitting hogs to ferret out garbage during the afternoon, while rags, paper, bottles, large metal pieces, and other objects were salvaged; (3) burning the combustible remains in the evening to reduce the volume and facilitate further salvage of metals; and (4) pushing the residue over the escarpment of a fill before arrival of the first refuse trucks the next morning. Smoke, odors, and other air pollutants accompanied the burning. Flies abounded in the vicinity, although probably to a lesser degree than if the refuse had not been burned daily. Likewise, rats were somewhat fewer than in open dumps, although a sizeable number greeted the arriving trucks each day. Furthermore, trichinosis and vesicular exanthema were perpetuated in hogs (see Chapter 8, Feeding Food Wastes to Swine). And in southern climates, where Aedes Egypti mosquitoes are found, cans and discarded tires partially filled with water were breeding places for the mosquitoes. In some places such operations still take place along a main highway and only a short distance from residences.

Rats, if permitted to do so, will infest a dump as long as there is garbage for food. Any improvement in the disposal method will reduce the food supply for them and they will migrate in search of other food. Consequently, the mere abandonment of the town dump in favor of a more enlightened method of refuse disposal may increase public health hazards unless the rats are destroyed. In fact, there is almost no method of refuse disposal in which good housekeeping practices do not require attention to rodent control measures.

Open dumping of this nature is now forbidden by law in most states. It has no legitimate place in the refuse disposal scene.

CHARACTERISTICS OF THE CITY

The disposal methods used in a city depend to some degree on the "kind" of city it is—because the kind of city affects the amounts and kinds of refuse produced in it. Geographic location, climate, standards of living, density of population, and the main sources of income of the residents are all important.

Geography and Climate

In mild and semi-tropical climates few if any solid fuels are used for heating, with the result that there are few ashes to dispose of. In warm climates there are also large quantities of garden and yard wastes throughout most of the year.

In parts of the country that are cold in the winter there are some ashes part of the year and there are widespread fluctuations in the amounts of refuse produced. Furthermore, frozen ground makes landfills more difficult to operate in the winter months.

Areas in which rain is frequent and heavy may require different techniques for disposal than dry areas. Refuse may have to be predried if it is to be incinerated, for instance.

Frequent smog may eliminate central incineration as a disposal method, or require that special precautions be taken to decrease smoke emissions.

Cities in parts of the country in which earthquakes, floods, hurricanes, and other weather disasters are not infrequent must use disposal methods that are reliable even under such unfavorable conditions.

Population

The number of people living in a city and the number living in large apartment buildings or in single-family or two-family dwellings influence the selection of disposal methods. In cities in which many people live in large apartment houses, for instance, a good deal of refuse is disposed of in apartment-type, on-site incinerators.

In areas in which there are many new houses, a good deal of garbage is disposed of in home grinders.

Standards of living also influence the quantities and kinds of refuse— and in turn the disposal method. The higher the income and the standard of living the more waste there is. Furthermore, in high-income areas, the residents frequently require high-standard refuse collection and disposal services and are willing and able to pay for them.

Sources of Income

Cities in which industry and big business are the main sources of income differ from resort cities, for example, in the amounts and kinds of refuse produced.

Large industrial cities often have to dispose of industrial wastes by special methods. Some industries produce highly mineralized liquid wastes that if deposited in landfills permeate to and pollute underground waters. Others produce explosive or noxious refuse that cannot be burned in incinerators. Still other industries produce large quantities of salvageable refuse and they may be close enough to markets for salvage to make it worthwhile to sell at least some of it.

Tourist and resort centers, on the other hand, often have disproportionate amounts of food wastes from restaurants to dispose of. Large business centers frequently have larger than usual quantities of paper refuse.

CAPITAL AND OPERATING COSTS

The costs of setting up and operating a refuse disposal facility of any kind are specific, but they vary considerably with the methods.

Computing Costs

The financial ability of a municipality to meet both capital and operating costs of any kind of refuse disposal facility is most important. It is certainly unwise to recommend a method beyond the financial capabilities of the city. Besides the obvious costs for the site, construction, and operation, there are other costs, as well as revenues, that are not always considered but should be. Among them:

1. If a bond issue is used to finance capital outlay, the costs of retirement and interest on the bonds must be included as part of the costs of the disposal facility.

2. Since interest paid on bonds is part of costs, it seems logical to some also to include as part of the costs the interest lost to the city on money taken from general revenues to purchase large pieces of equipment. This is a debatable point, however, and frequently the so-called "lost" interest is not included in costs, since a municipality is not a profit-making organization that must show a return on its investments.

3. Some also argue that the amount of taxes lost to the city on property used for a disposal facility should be included as part of costs.

4. It is important to determine the reasonable life expectancy of equipment and include the costs of depreciation and repairs as part of facility costs.

5. In computing operating costs, consideration should be given to increases in salaries and administrative costs in the future and to possible increases in costs of materials.

6. Careful consideration should be given to the costs of the land for a landfill, what its useful life will be as a disposal site, and whether its value can be expected to increase or decrease by the time it is no longer needed as a disposal site. Changing property values are

Fig. 21. Some refuse can be salvaged and reclaimed, and so in most cities there are salvage yards operated by private business, which reduce the amount of refuse the city must dispose of. Salvageable heavy metals are almost always in demand.

important. In Detroit, for example, large tracts of land of relatively little original value were developed through landfill operations and site improvements, increasing their value several times.

7. Population growth should be projected and the increased amount of refuse to be disposed of must be calculated and accounted for in costs.

8. By-products of the disposal process and salvage may have sale value —nonferrous metals, for instance. Revenues from salvage materials and by-products must be included in determining long-term costs, but at the same time the possibility that the market value of by-products and salvage will change must also be considered. (It is almost impossible to predict long-range markets for salvage and by-products with much accuracy.) (Chapter 10 deals with salvage and reclamation operations.)

10. Sufficient money must be allocated for operating and maintenance so that the plant and equipment are kept in good condition and as attractive in appearance as possible. Experience shows that good maintenance pays big dividends.

See Chapter 11, Refuse Disposal Management, for additional information on costs.

Comparative Costs

It is difficult to compare disposal costs from various cities. In fact, it is sometimes difficult to compare costs from year to year in the same city. Comparisons are difficult primarily because of (1) differences in accounting methods, including computation of overhead and equipment amortization; (2) variations in labor rates and employee benefits; (3) differences in conditions (for example, it is necessary to buy and import earth cover for sanitary landfills in areas in which suitable cover is not available); (4) differences in disposal techniques; (5) exclusion from computations of collection costs that are attributable directly to the disposal method used; (6) inability to express the exact work done in a convenient unit of measurement (for example, extraordinary and costly air cleaning equipment needed for an incineration plant in a city where air pollution is a critical problem).

A comparison of costs for the three near-complete disposal methods— sanitary landfills, incineration, and composting—gives a broad indication of the relative economics of each. Partial disposal methods such as feeding garbage to hogs, garbage grinding, and domestic incineration, however, cannot be compared in the same way that the near-complete methods can. Costs of each method are discussed in the chapters on methods.

Initial capital costs for sanitary landfills, including costs of site acquisition and preparation, are roughly one-fourth to one-half of those for central incineration. The modern, fully mechanized composting plant costs about what an incineration plant does.

Operating costs for sanitary landfills are approximately one-third to one-half of those for incineration unless hauling costs for landfills are excessive.

Meeting the Costs

Each year more cities—particularly small ones—discontinue the practice of meeting refuse collection and disposal costs solely from general taxes and instead charge directly for them. There are several advantages to financing disposal facilities as a public utility as opposed to financing by taxes on the basis of assessed valuation of each property:

1. A capital fund can be set up, which permits accumulation of money for large expenditures.
2. Reserves can be established, such as a replacement fund for worn out or obsolete equipment.
3. Long-range planning can be done effectively with the assurance that funds will be available when needed.
4. Revenue bonds to finance large capital expenditures can be issued and sold.

COORDINATION OF COLLECTION AND DISPOSAL METHODS

Disposal methods are influenced by collection methods and vice versa. They must be coordinated. The costs of separate collections of various components of refuse, which are necessary for some disposal methods, and the costs of hauling refuse to disposal facilities are important factors in deciding on disposal methods. In addition, the inconveniences and nuisances created by various methods of collection and hauling must be considered. (Refuse collection problems are discussed in detail in *Refuse Collection Practice*.)

Separate Collections

Separate collections are usually objectionable, particularly to house-holders, so the methods that require the fewest kinds of collections are usually favored because of both convenience and costs. However, separate collections are sometimes necessary for operating, health, and salvage purposes. In fact, some disposal methods are practical only if some components of refuse are completely or almost completely separated from other kinds. Disposing of garbage by feeding it to hogs, for instance, requires that garbage be collected separately from other refuse (see Chapter 8).

Refuse can be separated (1) at the source—by the householder, business, institution, industry, or collection crew; or (2) at the disposal facility—by collection or disposal crews or by scavengers.

Separate storage of various kinds of refuse at the source has obvious advantages. In fact, separation of refuse components after they have once been stored together sometimes is not practical or possible. More important, however, is that the cost of storing refuse components separately at the source is negligible in comparison with the costs of separating it by collection or disposal crews. Of course, costs of separate storage at the source are borne by the producer of the refuse—not by the city—and are not taken into account in computing collection costs. Nevertheless, separate collections increase collection costs over those

Fig. 22. Some disposal methods require that different kinds of refuse be collected separately, and it is important, therefore, that collection and disposal methods be coordinated. If there are separate collections there must be separate storage containers. The small container at the right is for garbage.

for combined collections if the frequency of collections is the same. In some circumstances there may be some cost advantages, however, because separated, nonputrescible refuse can be collected less frequently than combined refuse. Table 16 gives common practices for separation of refuse for various disposal methods.

If refuse separations by the householder or business are to be successful and practical, the regulations for preparation and sorting of the refuse must be reasonable. Experience shows that householders will separate refuse into two or even three kinds and store them separately—but usually only after they are "educated" to the necessity for it. It may take five years to get the public to comply with a new system of refuse separation even under a good administrator; it may never be achieved under mediocre or poor administrative practices.

Merchants are usually less willing than householders to comply with refuse separation regulations for combustible and noncombustible rubbish, primarily because it is difficult to train employees to make the correct separations. Many large businesses prefer to employ private collectors at their own expense to avoid difficult and bothersome regulations.

Regardless of how reasonable the regulations are and how intense an educational campaign is to get people to separate refuse, full compliance is never achieved, so that it is necessary to further separate refuse

TABLE 16

COMMON PRACTICES FOR SEPARATION OF REFUSE FOR VARIOUS DISPOSAL METHODS

Disposal Method	Refuse Suitable for Method	Refuse Unsuitable for Method[1]	Where Separated
Sanitary landfills	Mixed	Tree trunks, stumps; hazardous refuse; offal	Disposal site
Central incineration	Mixed	Large objects that clog hoppers; large metal pieces; heavy wire; hazardous materials; heavy timbers; tree trunks	Combustibles at source; sometimes all refuse collected together
Central grinding	Garbage; some paper	Inert material that cannot be reduced at sewage treatment plant or cannot be carried in sewers; cans, metals, glass, earth	Source; wrapping usually prohibited
Feeding food wastes to swine	Garbage	Paper; citrus rinds; cans; glass	Source; wrapping prohibited
Composting	Organic desirable; inorganic acceptable	Large ungrindable objects—tires, metals, logs	Source or plant
Salvage and reclamation	Materials with resale value	Varies with market for salvage	Source or disposal facility
Open dumping[2]	Some non-putrescibles	Putrescibles	Source or dump
Open burning[2]	Tree branches, trunks; combustible rubbish	Garbage; other putrescibles	Source

[1]Complete or almost complete separation desirable in all methods.
[2]Not a recommended disposal method; acceptable only under special circumstances.

at the disposal point. Usually the more complete the separation is the more efficient the disposal operation is.

Separation of refuse at the disposal facility almost always immediately precedes actual disposal, whether the separation is done mechanically or manually or whether separation is complete or incomplete. Refuse to be separated is usually dumped on a sorting floor of an incineration plant or in an open space adjacent to a landfill. Obviously if the refuse is dumped into storage bins or hoppers when it reaches an incineration plant or into the fill when it reaches the site, there is no opportunity for sorting.

The degree to which refuse components are separated depends largely upon costs. There is usually some latitude in the amount of separation necessary for any method, and costs may be the deciding factor. Complete separation is usually more costly than partial separation, but the savings from partial separation may be cancelled out by increased costs in disposal operations because the refuse is not completely separated.

The costs of space, equipment, and personnel to separate refuse at the disposal facility must be computed, and the possibilities of vermin infestation of sorting areas, injury to employees, damage to equipment, the appearance of the site, and interference with disposal must be considered, in making a decision to use a disposal method that requires separation of refuse at the disposal site.

Hauling

Hauling costs depend on the length of hauls, the type of route the trucks must take, the amount of traffic encountered along the routes, and the kinds and amounts of equipment and the number of employees needed.

The longer the haul and the more traffic encountered, the higher the operating costs. Long hauls also frequently require larger route trucks or transfer trucks, as well as transfer stations, if refuse is taken from route trucks and loaded on transfer trucks, barges, or railroad cars. The number of employees varies with the number of trucks used and the amount of supervision required.

In computing total hauling costs, all expenses from the time refuse is loaded until it is unloaded at the disposal facility must be included: personnel costs and operating expenses. (Personnel costs include not only salaries but also vacation and sick leave pay, health insurance, retirement funds, and other fringe benefits.) In addition, capital costs, depreciation, and maintenance of equipment (or rents, if the equipment is not owned by the city) must be included. If some equipment used to haul refuse is also used for other municipal services, such as snow removal, the costs must be prorated.

Special equipment, although initially expensive, may actually lower hauling costs—particularly those for long hauls. Transfer trucks, for instance, sometimes carry refuse collected by as many as six route trucks from the transfer point to the disposal facility, which cuts down on the number of trucks making the complete haul and frees the route trucks for other collections.

Problems of Long Hauls. Although most refuse is hauled to disposal facilities during off-peak traffic hours, the last trips of the day often coincide with evening rush hours, increasing congestion and the chances of accidents and annoying the public—factors that favor short hauls.

Another objection to long hauls is that more of the public is aware of the collection trucks. Regardless of how good the equipment is, it is difficult to keep refuse collection vehicles clean and odorless and to prevent papers and other objects from blowing or dropping off.

Special Disposal Problems

Special disposal problems arise no matter what kind of collection and disposal methods are used in a city. The unusual must therefore be anticipated, since special disposal problems often require special solutions.

Problems become "special" primarily because of size or infrequency. Disposal of household refuse is routine even with seasonal and other changes in quantities and kinds. But if disaster strikes it may be necessary to change the routine radically and call in outside help. Moreover, some cities, because of geographical location, characteristics of the economy, or unusual construction programs, have other special problems.

Disposal problems are of two kinds: those caused by employees,

Fig. 23. The cost of hauling refuse to a disposal site is important in the selection of a disposal method. Some cities that have sanitary landfills use large collection trucks, which haul the refuse to a transfer station where it is put into tandem trailers (above). The trailers haul the refuse to the site of the fill, where they are unloaded (below). These pictures are of the Los Angeles County Sanitation Districts' transfer station and landfill.

equipment, operating procedures, or the method of disposal used; and those that result from a disaster or because of an unusual or especially hard-to-handle type of refuse. Only the second kind is considered here.

Refuse from Disasters

Not every disposal problem caused by a disaster can be anticipated and planned for, of course, but there is a continuing need for a reasonable measure of preparedness. Reserve capacity at disposal facilities is not the whole answer. Resourcefulness and ingenuity are needed in meeting such problems.

If a tornado, earthquake, or hurricane strikes a city, the refuse disposal agency cannot always handle all of the additional refuse that results. The police and fire departments, safety experts, and public health agencies often help—sometimes by waiving regulations temporarily so that refuse and debris can be disposed of quickly to prevent fire, accidents, and outbreaks of disease. Heavy construction equipment is often used to clear streets and roads and to cut up trees and branches so they can be disposed of. In a major disaster, state agencies often call in federal agencies such as the Office of Civilian Defense and the Army Corps of Engineers.

Condemned Foods

Federal, state, and local health agencies have the authority to condemn foods for human consumption, which, after condemnation, must be disposed of, usually by city agencies.

Federal agencies, under interstate commerce laws, are concerned with foodstuffs that are taken across state lines. The states may and do quarantine infected hogs and diseased plants and fruits. Local health officers may also prohibit the sale of foodstuffs spoiled in transit or kept too long in storage. In any event, all such agencies must work together in condemnation of spoiled foods or infected animals and plants.

Regardless of the method used to dispose of condemned foods, it is desirable that a representative of the condemning agency witness the destruction of the food to be sure that it is not sold or used by the people handling it. A simple treatment, such as spraying with kerosene, is sometimes used to prevent "expropriation" of condemned food before it is disposed of.

Seaport cities probably have bigger problems with condemned foods than inland cities. Sometimes all of the foodstuffs brought in by a single ship must be destroyed. If fire or water has damaged labels on canned goods, they cannot be sold even though the contents are undamaged.

Foods condemned on a ship or other carrier must be disposed of quickly to prevent delaying the operation of the ship, while foods condemned in a warehouse can usually be taken to a disposal facility in quantities and at times that will not interfere with normal disposal operations. Thus a landfill, which is flexible in its capacity and operation, is often the simplest way of disposing of large quantities of condemned foods.

If canned foods are disposed of by incineration, each can must be punctured to prevent it from exploding. If canned foods are disposed of by grinding them and flushing them into the sewer system, each can must be opened and only the contents put in the grinder.

Many foods condemned for human consumption are safe for hogs, but if they are to be fed to hogs, health officials must first give their approval.

Hazardous and Special Refuse

Explosives and inflammable materials are easily recognized as hazardous; others, such as highly alkaline or acidic liquids and toxic wastes such as manganese, magnesium, and cyanides, are not as easily identifiable but can cause damage. Some kinds of refuse also expose collectors and handlers to disease.

Many hazardous wastes come from manufacturing businesses. For the most part, the city disposal agency knows about them and makes arrangements with owners of plants and factories to dispose of the wastes, either at municipal or private facilities. Toxic wastes can be disposed of in carefully controlled sanitary landfills in isolated areas. Waste oil is a problem in some areas. Some cities pond it and burn it at night; others accept it in open ponds at designated sanitary fills. A special charge is usually made for disposal of such wastes.

Pathological wastes from hospitals and other institutions should be incinerated at the source. If they are handled at a municipal incinerator,

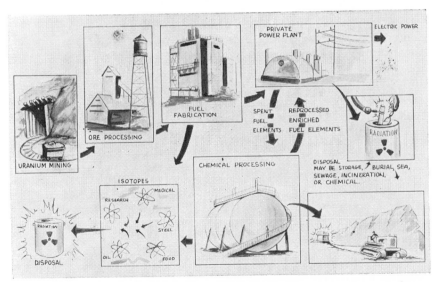

Fig. 24. Radioactive wastes come from a variety of sources, as shown here. Although the disposal of such wastes in 1961 was still the responsibility of federal agencies, disposal of some of them may become the responsibility—and a special problem—of municipalities in the future. (Reprinted by permission of Business Week.)

Fig. 25. Disposal of industrial wastes can be a problem for cities, but many industries dispose of such refuse on the premises. This on-site incinerator built for a rubber company in Willoughby, Ohio, can burn 1,000 pounds of rubber wastes or 1,200 pounds of dry wastes an hour.

extreme care is required to prevent workers from becoming infected.

The growing use of radioactive substances in government and industry is producing ever-increasing quantities of dangerous wastes that cannot be handled as other refuse is but require special disposal techniques. By the late 1960's no municipality was disposing of such substances, but several states had been assigned the responsibility.[1] It appears probable that this pattern will expand and it is unlikely that cities will ever have to assume this touchy and troublesome problem.

Industrial Wastes

Refuse produced by industrial and manufacturing plants is as varied as the raw materials that go into the products manufactured. A good many of the materials that once were "waste" are now by-products, but wastes that are not used as by-products must be disposed of.

Plastics, rubber goods, battery boxes, tar paper, and other refuse that is highly volatile can be disposed of at ordinary incinerators in small quantities. However, if there are large quantities of such materials, they must be burned in special furnaces equipped with after-burners and devices to prevent excessive smoke emissions.

---

[1] Conrad P. Straub, *Low-level Radioactive Wastes—Treatment-Handling-Disposal* (Washington, D. C.: Division of Technical Information, U.S. Atomic Energy Commission, 1964.)

Trash burners are used in some industries—particularly woodworking plants. In addition, landfills are sometimes used to dispose of industrial wastes. (See the section on industrial wastes in Chapter 1.)

Construction Wastes

Construction wastes—whether from new building or repairs—are usually nonputrescible and can frequently be burned or put in landfills.

In large cities there is often so much construction refuse that it is necessary to use private dumps and landfills. In such cases, private collectors usually handle the refuse. (See Chapter 1.)

Demolition Wastes

In most large cities, quantities of wastes resulting from the demolition of old buildings torn down to make way for commercial buildings, housing projects, expressways, and community facilities must be disposed of by the wreckers or by the city.

Some of the materials are salvageable, depending on the type of construction, the local market for the materials, and the urgency for completing the demolition job. But even when conditions for salvage are ideal, more than half the materials in a building have no value.

A large part of a demolished masonry building is rubble which can be used as solid fill material. It is often given away or sold for use in fills on private property or is used in road construction for subgrade. It can also be used for temporary access roads on landfills.

The combustible wastes, mainly wood and asphaltic materials, pose the big problem. The least expensive solution is to burn them on the demolition site.

However, increasing emphasis on control of air pollution has resulted in prohibition of this practice in practically all large and most smaller cities, and even in outlying areas it is hard to find a place where open burning is permitted. Indeed, a few states already prohibit all open burning anywhere in the state. Sometimes burning in relatively inexpensive devices providing quite limited combustion control is permitted, though they provide only little improvement over open burning. These include burning pits and conical steel "teepee"-type structures. The latter can be provided with several degrees of sophistication in additional stack gas washing devices with corresponding improvement in nuisance-free operation.

In a few instances incinerators especially designed to handle only bulky materials are in use and give good results at correspondingly higher costs. Detroit uses such devices for disposal of logs and brush. The New York District of the Corps of Engineers is providing a special incinerator in Jersey City, N. J., for disposal of the sizeable quantities of driftwood (about 22,000 cubic yards per year) collected from New York Harbor. Previously this material was burned in the open on two incinerator barges anchored in the Upper Bay.

The only practical alternative to some type of burning is disposal in sanitary landfills. This poses some problems because of the poor compaction characteristics of the materials and the difficulty of handling them unless they are shredded. Some cities report considerable damage to landfill equipment from demolition wastes.

At the best, large volumes of landfill space are required to accommodate demolition, construction, industrial, and street cleaning solid wastes. Even though these sanitary landfills may be furnished by private operators and are not subject to some of the problems of sanitary landfills involving putrescible components, they do further aggravate the shortage of suitable, convenient sites for sanitary landfills for the solid wastes collected by municipalities and constitute a disposal problem that must be reckoned with in the total picture.

Dead Animals

Several means are used to dispose of dead animals—dogs, cats, chickens, and others. (See Chapter 2 for kinds and quantities of animals that must be disposed of.)

Large central grinders are used in some cities. Only one-stage grinding is necessary. A 150-horsepower hammer-type grinder will handle animals up to 150 pounds, and larger animals can be cut into pieces before they

Fig. 26. Disposal of large dead animals is a special problem, even in large cities that are usually equipped to handle them. The bodies can be buried, sent to a rendering plant, burned in an incinerator, or ground in large grinders.

are put in the grinder. The grinder may be installed at the sewage treatment plant or on an interceptor sewer. It can be made semi-automatic so that the collection crew can dispose of the animals. The grinder and flushing water are started by pressing a button, and the crew can run the unit for two minutes or so after the last animal is disposed of to wash the equipment.

Dead animals can also be disposed of at rendering plants. However, the number of rendering plants has decreased in recent years because of a decreasing market for their products. And many plants will not accept dead animals collected from streets during the summer.

Other cities bury dead animals in special trenches at landfill sites, but the method is not considered a good one for large cities. Still others burn them in incinerators.

A problem unique to coastal cities is that of large dead marine animals such as whales and sea lions that are washed ashore. Some cities dynamite the bodies, placing the charge so that the dismembered animals are blasted back into the water.

Automobiles

Discarded automobiles constitute a troublesome problem of considerable proportions. When abandoned on public property their disposal eventually devolves upon government. Except for a very few incidental units, landfill is not a feasible disposal method. Although automobiles consist mostly of metals having value as scrap, the economics of the processing and transportation involved precludes any small-scale salvage activity, the

Fig. 27. Pollutant smoke and fumes from burning combustibles can be avoided. The picture shows two automobiles burning in open air while simultaneously two automobiles burn in the smokeless incinerator.

result being the thousands of abandoned junked cars that constitute such a widespread national eyesore. The U.S. Bureau of Mines estimates that 6.8 million cars were scrapped in 1964 and that these could provide some 9 million tons of ferrous and non-ferrous metals.

Practical processing of junked automobiles includes removal of re-usable components; burning or otherwise removing most of the non-metallic material, stripping out easily removed non-ferrous metals; and crushing, baling, or shredding the remainder for shipping to steel mills. The equipment to accomplish this must be rugged and heavy and is expensive.

Specially designed incinerators can handle the burning without creating undue air pollution (See Chapter 6, On-Site Incineration). Several manufacturers produce presses, balers, and shears that will reduce the volume, and another type literally tears and shreds the metal into pieces no larger than 3 inches or so maximum dimension.

Fig. 28. Automobile "graveyards" are common near cities, although the metal can often be sold for scrap—if it can be shipped. The baling machine (left) compresses a whole car body to a small bale (right).

Such plants can do much to alleviate this troublesome solid waste problem, but their economics impose limitations on their applicability. Basically they must be located close to a continuing source of a large number of scrap cars and also reasonably close to their steel mill scrap market. Elsewhere transportation costs become prohibitive and make the whole enterprise unfeasible.

Leaves and Trees

Leaves, boughs, and tree trunks are troublesome to dispose of because they are hard to burn and are hard to handle as well as being very bulky for a landfill. In a few cases specially designed incinerators handle stumps and heavy logs satisfactorily, though comparatively expensively. Boughs under 6 inches in diameter and brush are sometimes run through a wood chipper and either burned or buried in a landfill. A portable, multiple-chamber, on-site incinerator has been found to be practical for burning such refuse. Leaves are usually taken to landfills and dumps for disposal, but some cities permit burning of them on the streets, some burn them in incinerators, and some give them away or sell them for humus. Although leaves are burned in incinerators in some cities, furnace operators say they are difficult to burn and it is costly to do so. Leaves —even dry ones—must be stirred frequently as they have a tendency to smother the fire rather than increase combustion.

CONTRACT DISPOSAL SERVICES

Many municipalities rely upon private contractors to provide solid waste collection or disposal services, and sometimes both. The arrangement for collection may be either under a contract directly with the city or a franchise arrangement under which the contractor collects his fee directly from the users of the services. For disposal only, the basis is usually a charge for the quantity accepted, specified in a contract.

The 1968 National Survey includes some information on the extent of use of privately operated disposal facilities in comparison with those operated by the public, summarized in Table 17.

TABLE 17

NUMBER OF DISPOSAL FACILITIES

	Urban		Total	
Number of jurisdictions covered	2,663		6,259	
Population covered	68,000,000		88,000,000	
	Public	Private	Public	Private
Land disposal sites	1,901	1,549	4,811	4,032
Incinerators	201	126	263	162
Transfer stations	70	17	89	25
Hog feeding lots	8	191	15	308
Compost plants	0	9	2	11
Tepee burners	14	25	28	34
Other	27	19	33	51
Total	2,221	1,936	5,241	4,623

These figures indicate, as would be expected, that the average disposal facility in the urban areas is much larger than that in the non-urban localities—16.4 thousand population per facility against 3.5 thousand. From the data reported it is not possible to derive anything on the average capacity of the facilities operated publicly compared with private ones, other than that in urban areas the former serve an average population of 23,700 each, compared with 8,500 for the latter. This is probably not a very good indication of a comparison of size, however, since there is a tendency for private disposal to be used more heavily for industrial and commercial wastes and public disposal more heavily for household wastes. The survey shows that 76.2 per cent of the population in urban areas is served by publicly operated disposal facilities. Interestingly the proportion using publicly operated collection facilities is almost identical—76.8 per cent.

There is a continual shifting among cities both to and away from contract operations for disposal as well as for collection. A principal reason involves availability of and rights to use land for this purpose. As specific sites are filled up or the growth of the city requires new sites, an economic analysis on a systems basis, taking into account the effect on the more expensive collection system, may indicate a change to or from contract disposal. Other influences may also be involved including avoidance of heavy capital financing, legal limitations, problems connected with condemnation, local political changes resulting in new public policies and objectives, temporary exigencies, the availability of a qualified contractor, and other local circumstances.

Local governments of various sizes contract for disposal, often in conjunction with contract collection. Examples of cities currently using contract disposal are San Francisco; Rockford, Illinois; Clifton, New Jersey; Omaha, Nebraska; and Troy, New York. Cities where contract disposal recently has been dropped include Seattle.

In general, private disposal companies use the same disposal methods as do municipalities—principally landfills and incineration—and are subject to the same sanitary regulations and standards under state, county, and city laws. A minor method—disposal, principally of commercial garbage, by hog feeding—is largely confined to private operation, as shown in Table 17.

Advantages and Disadvantages

A major consideration involved in a decision between public or contract solid waste disposal is that of cost, considered in the framework of the total collection and disposal picture. The contractor's primary incentive, as in any business, is profit. The city is obliged to furnish a service to its people of disposing of all solid wastes as economically as possible, consistent with good environmental health practices and reasonable convenience and service to the public. In the long run and with informed, responsible management for both parties, these two interests are not necessarily conflicting.

Whether disposal by contract is advantageous to the city or not from the cost standpoint depends on local circumstances. Under this system, the city's major direct expenditures are the contractor's charge, usually based on quantity, and the cost of city employees' salaries for regulatory, inspection, and administrative services. To whatever extent the solid waste disposal load is handled privately, the city can avoid making public capital expenditures for land, buildings, and equipment, which may be an important factor if capital funds are more urgently needed elsewhere. The city is relieved of much overhead and administrative cost as well as day-to-day operating problems, but not of the final responsibility for results. On the other hand, lack of competition in bidding, a monopoly on available land, or contracts running for terms too short to permit reasonable amortization of necessary plant and equipment may result in high bid prices.

The contractor's inherent advantages revolve largely around his relative flexibility in dealing with employees, in arranging for capital requirements, in arranging equipment rentals, in quickly adjusting to operating changes, and in negotiating for property. The profit incentive provides a strong urge to get best efficiency. This results in frequent and effective use of incentive pay plans and policies aimed at keeping a young, active, productive work force, which are usually not available to public agencies. However, compared with a public agency, he is also handicapped by a number of considerations. He must make a profit on his operations and a return on his invested capital while being obliged to pay taxes (income, sales, and property) not applicable to cities. He is sometimes more vulnerable to labor pressures; his cost of financing is usually higher; he does not have the help of powers of eminent domain; his contract may be too inflexible to permit him to adjust to changing conditions.

The same profit motive that spurs efficiency may also tempt the contractor to cut corners and skimp on the quality of his services, while the city's responsibility for maintaining this quality may be difficult to discharge adequately because of indirect control over employees and inadequate substitute facilities to constitute an effective threat. Very careful contract provisions covering penalties for poor performance are necessary here. Finally, political influence may be involved in obtaining or enforcing the contract, resulting in too high prices, inadequate performance, or other unsatisfactory conditions.

Given equally competent management and equal freedom from political interference, there would appear to be a sizeable cost advantage in favor of public operation, but there are a good many kinds of special circumstances that could make contract disposal attractive to a city administration anyway.

Contract Provisions

If a city decides to contract for even part of its disposal services, it must draw up specifications for the service so that all who are interested can bid on an equal basis. But before the specifications are drawn up, the conditions under which a contractor will operate must be fully analyzed. Careful estimates must be made of all costs under ordinary circumstances and contingencies and emergencies must be planned for.

Contract services often include both collection and disposal and the contract and the regulations governing the services should be spelled out so that the municipality, the contractors, and the public understand them. Health, sanitation, and convenience for the public are the most important considerations for the city.

The term of the contract is important. If contract disposal is new to the city or if the city wants to encourage new bidders, the time the contract runs should be long enough so that companies new in the business can reasonably expect to amortize capital costs. If a city is prohibited by law from writing a contract that is long enough to cover amortization of plant and equipment, the city may be able to arrange for lease or purchase of the facilities at the end of the contract period or to include provisions for extension of the contract if the services are satisfactory. Renegotiation of a contract is also possible.

The contract should provide that the city has control over labor practices: wage increases should be stated in the contract on the basis of a predetermined scale; wage kick-backs from employee to employer should be prohibited and penalties set; and provisions on discrimination because of race, creed, color, and union affiliation should be included.

Increased payments to the contractor to take care of increased operating costs and increased amounts of refuse handled should be provided for in the contract, as well as provisions for controlling salvage of refuse that has resale value.

Enforcing Contract Provisions

Contracts for disposal should include penalties if the contractor fails to perform the services contracted for or performs them inadequately. Prevention is better than cure, however. If inspections or complaints disclose inadequate services, city employees can sometimes see that they are corrected by warning the contractor or helping in other ways. However, if there are widespread and frequent breakdowns in service, city officials are obliged to penalize the contractor, as provided for in the contract.

Regulations for the Public

Regulations for the kinds and locations of refuse containers, for the ways in which refuse is to be separated, and for sanitary conditions to which householders and businesses must comply should be drawn up and enforced by the city. The city should also be responsible for informing the public of the regulations. In addition, city officials should investigate a contractor's complaints about the public and enforce the regulations if necessary.

ADAPTABILITY OF METHOD TO CHANGING CONDITIONS

It is important that the primary methods of disposal that a city uses be adaptable to expansion, modification, or conversion.

The number of people in a city changes, people move to outlying areas, standards of living change, and new industries and businesses start up, all of which change the amounts and kinds of refuse that must be disposed of. Furthermore, the kinds of services needed in one part of a city may be different from those needed in another. Industrial areas may require one kind of disposal, business another, high-density hotel and residential areas another, and low-density residential areas still another.

Although it is impossible to accurately predict where and to what extent such changes will occur, reliable information on trends and future developments is available and should be studied in relation to location and size of disposal facilities. The local planning agency, utilities companies, and business associations are usually able and willing to provide data.

If, for instance, one or both of the two most common disposal methods —landfills and central incineration—are decided upon, sites should be selected that will best serve present and predictable future needs. The site for an incineration plant should be big enough so that the plant can be enlarged if necessary, or a second site should be selected for an additional plant in an area that can reasonably be expected to need one in the future. The same is true of landfill sites.

On the other hand, in an area that is zoned for single-family houses and is to be so developed, household garbage grinders will probably be common. The type of disposal facilities needed for that area will differ from those for an area slated for renewal in which large apartment buildings will be built.

Fig. 29. An easily read sign, a good fence, and a program of public education are needed to assure that rules of operation for a landfill are obeyed.

Hours Disposal Facilities Are Operated

The city must determine whether its disposal facilities will be operated 8, 16, or 24 hours a day, 5, 6, or 7 days a week.

Large cities often operate incineration plants on a 24-hour basis, which permits haulers to deposit refuse at any time. If the facility is not open 24 hours a day, "sneak dumpers" are encouraged to leave odorous or unsanitary refuse in lots and alleys and along streets and roads.

However, landfills and incinerators can often be operated more efficiently if refuse is received only at fixed times. If it is, workmen can keep the premises cleaner and more attractive by tidying up after the last refuse loads of the day are received. A fence with gates that can be locked and prominently displayed signs giving the hours that refuse is received help enforce regulations.

INFLUENCE OF SALVAGE OPERATIONS ON METHODS

Salvage operations can be a part of many refuse disposal methods—landfills, central incineration, composting, and central grinding. Whether they are profitable to a municipality or whether the nuisances and hazards they create outweigh the advantages must be considered before salvage is decided upon even as a partial method of disposal. The problems of salvage operations and their advantages and disadvantages are discussed in Chapter 10, Salvage and Reclamation.

PUBLIC ACCEPTANCE OF METHODS

Acceptability of a method of refuse disposal by the public is of primary importance, since the choice of methods may well hinge upon how easy it is to get approval of it. The public is more likely to disapprove of a method because it believes it will create nuisances than for any other reason.

Public Information Program

To gain acceptance of a proposed refuse disposal method, a program of public information is often necessary. The need for sanitary and efficient disposal methods should be made clear to the public. Especially in large cities, the residents may have little or no idea of what becomes of refuse after it is loaded on collection trucks. The time-worn adage, "out of sight, out of mind" is true of most residents as far as refuse is concerned.

Leadership in an information program may originate in the city council after its members and other community leaders are acquainted with local refuse disposal problems. City officials can begin their own study of the problems by inquiring into commonly used collection and disposal practices. They can visit disposal sites, inspect collection equipment, study the problems of collection methods, and gather other factual data. The study should be made in an atmosphere of inquiry, however, with as little interpretation as possible and with judgment on methods deferred until the study is complete.

While this is difficult and requires considerable time, it pays dividends. Too often facts are lost in a whirlwind of arguments over interpretation, suggestions for solutions to refuse problems based on little or inaccurate information, opposition to sites, explanations of how a system works, who is to blame for present inadequacies, and financial problems. If the council members learn the facts before attacking problems in which differences of opinion are almost certain to develop, however, a solution to disposal problems and public support for it can be achieved.

The advice of interested groups should be sought and data on the success of various disposal methods used in other communities should be collected and made available in nontechnical terms to community leaders and interested citizens. Since there are many facets of the refuse disposal problem that must be considered, the public cannot be expected to understand the problems and solutions and to concur in a decision in too short a time.

A series of feature articles in local newspapers, relating the progress of the study and the preparation of a report on it, is an effective way of informing the public and providing a basis for understanding and evaluating the proposal. Concurrence of health authorities and of the medical profession should be sought and differences of opinion resolved as far as possible before public hearings are held. Premature and irresponsible statements on costs and the technical merits of various methods should be avoided. Too often the public hears first the conflicting opinions of public officials—opinions formed even before engineers have begun an objective study of the problems and solutions.

Public Demands for New Methods

The initiative for different methods of refuse disposal does not always come from public officials. Frequently it comes from a segment of the public that demands action to alleviate conditions that it finds intolerable. Such action does not necessarily imply concern with the overall problems of disposal or lack of concern on the part of the public officials. Often

Fig. 30. Private contractors operate many sanitary landfills satisfactorily. Ravenna fill in Seattle is an example.

it stems from opposition to uncontrolled subdivision of land near a refuse dump, a farm on which hogs are fed garbage, an obnoxious industry, or some other enterprise unsuited to an urban area. Residents of a new subdivision near a dump, for example, may try to get dumping stopped. The outcome may be a long overdue improvement in all local refuse disposal procedures.

Demands for improved refuse disposal methods also come from larger segments of the public than neighbors of a dump, incinerator, or landfill. Smoke or other air pollution or lack of provision for disposing of all kinds of refuse may result in protests. If so, enough of the public may be ready to accept new methods of refuse disposal so that officials can carry out plans without delay.

Public confidence in city officials, community leaders, and health authorities is important in acceptance of any refuse disposal method. An up-to-date and more adequate disposal system often appears to be more costly than the old one, and since most people cannot be well informed on costs and technicalities, they must rely on community leaders to give them correct information. Some people, of course, will oppose any solution that the majority of the public and public officials finds acceptable. Such opposition usually grows out of personal prejudices or vested interests, although sometimes it is based on a sincere belief in an untried and perhaps unpromising disposal method.

Ability and Willingness to Pay

Regardless of where the impetus for change comes from or by whom a change is opposed, the public must be able and willing to pay for the methods decided upon. It is often necessary to convince the people that what is on the face of it a cheap disposal method is in reality an expensive one—in dollars and cents, in health and sanitation problems, in lack of convenience and aesthetics. Once they are convinced that an initially expensive method will bring advantages, they are usually willing to pay for it.

After a new method of disposal has been adopted it is extremely important that the system be operated as efficiently and with as much regard for appearance of the disposal facilities as it is possible. The public must be able to *see* that the new method is an improvement.

THE REGIONAL APPROACH

In recent years, and despite the foregoing, site selection for solid waste disposal facilities of all types has been severely complicated by urbanization and the general failure of comprehensive planning agencies to deal adequately with the knotty problems involved.

In heavily populated areas communities which for many years have indulged in the practice of depositing their wastes "elsewhere" are now finding themselves in the unhappy situation of having "their" landfills exhausted, pre-empted, or abolished by surrounding jurisdictions, with no provision within their own boundaries for final disposal of their own solid wastes. This has led to agonizing reappraisals of method, and attempts to join forces on a regional or "problem-shed" basis for long-range solutions. It has also served to dramatize the problems inherent in site selection for disposal plants and/or transfer stations which suddenly become economically essential under such circumstances. The problems of site selection for solid waste disposal facilities, even under a regional approach, are therefore becoming more intense and critical, in the face of the natural public aversion to the proximity of such facilities.

In addition to good public information programs and adequate project financing, the establishment of future sites for these essential purposes will undoubtedly require:

1. Special attention to specific needs in this area and hard decisions by Regional Comprehensive Planning Agencies; and
2. Upgrading of the performance and appearance standards of solid waste disposal facilities of all types.

4   SANITARY LANDFILLS

Dumping on land was probably the first refuse disposal method used, perhaps because it was the most convenient. As civilization developed and people gathered together in greater and greater numbers, the practice of indiscriminate dumping underfoot became increasingly unsatisfactory. Although the public health aspects of refuse disposal have been recognized only recently, some time ago the quantities and the offensive nature of refuse had created conditions in most cities that were unsatisfactory to all. And so the objectionable dumping grounds were moved from populated areas and more isolated sites were found. Long hauls proved to be costly as well as inconvenient, however, and even in areas where only a few people lived, violent objections were raised to dumps.

There were, however, areas within most cities or near their boundaries that could be put to good use if they were filled. Getting and transporting earth fill to those sites was often prohibitively expensive, but refuse could be used effectively and much more economically, although it was necessary to fill the areas without creating nuisances and endangering the public health. A number of cities developed successful methods—primarily simple burial—of using the garbage component of refuse as fill many years ago: Champaign, Illinois, in 1904; Columbus, Ohio, from 1906 to 1910; and Davenport, Iowa, for some years before 1916. In Davenport, a method of mixing and covering the organic refuse with a sufficient quantity of inert materials such as earth or ash was used to minimize odors in an area being reclaimed along the Mississippi River. At the same time, similar procedures were being tried in England and Germany.

In the 1930's several cities in the United States experimented with heavy equipment to compact the refuse, thereby saving space and developing a means of disposing of refuse on land in an economic, as well as sanitary, manner. One city was New York, which badly needed a different method of refuse disposal, since it was faced with court action initiated by coastal cities in New Jersey to force cessation of dumping its refuse at sea. (In 1933, the United States Supreme Court upheld a ruling requiring that New York City cease this practice.[1])

It was during this period, apparently, that the term "sanitary landfill" was coined at another pioneering operation in Fresno, California, where the "cut and cover" or "trench" method of landfilling was first used in the United States. The term is appropriate, since land is filled with refuse in a sanitary manner.

---

[1] *New Jersey* v. *City of New York*, 290 U.S. 237 (1933).

During the early part of World War II, the Army was faced with the need to develop an economical and sanitary method of handling rapidly changing amounts of solid waste at camps and other installations. Studies revealed the adaptability of a piece of equipment called a "bullclam," which could not only compact the refuse but also pick up and carry earth cover. At the same time it was found that other equipment such as front-end skip loaders and, on large operations, draglines and scrapers could also be used successfully. So the sanitary landfill was recommended as a method of refuse disposal at military installations in the United States.

The successful use of the method by such cities as Fresno and New York, as well as by the Army, influenced its ready adoption by many municipalities. By the end of 1945 almost 100 cities in the United States had adopted it and by the beginning of 1960 more than 1,400 cities were reportedly using it.

Recently, however, use of the method has had to be curtailed in a number of large cities, including New York and Baltimore, because of the difficulty of finding suitable sites within economic haul distances and because of the need to preserve sites for disposal of noncombustibles such as ashes and incinerator residue. Nonetheless, the sanitary landfill method of refuse disposal will continue to find users among small cities and, for that matter, some large cities, so long as suitable sites are available, or until a more economical and sanitary method is devised.

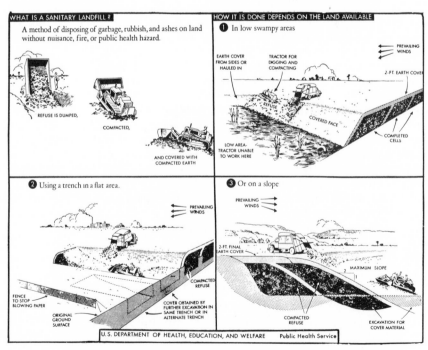

Fig. 31. There are various methods of operating sanitary landfills. How it is done depends mostly on the kind of site available.

SITE SELECTION

Site selection is the process of locating and obtaining the use of suitable land; it is the most important of the pre-operational steps in developing a satisfactory landfill program.

If possible, sanitary landfill sites should be provided for in the comprehensive plan of a city. And it is at times advantageous to buy up sites for landfills at the same time a site for a sewage treatment plant or a sewage lagoon is bought.

Many factors must be evaluated to determine suitability of a site for a landfill. The persons responsible for determining suitability must have knowledge of the public health and nuisance problems of uncontrolled disposal, good operational procedures, the capabilities of the equipment to be used, topography, special climatological problems, drainage, the future use of the land, roads that will facilitate access to the site, availability of acceptable cover material, location with respect to residences and industry, the average length of hauls for collection vehicles, the possibility and significance of underground or surface water pollution, zoning regulations, and the likelihood of public acceptance for a site. Also necessary is a thorough knowledge of the immediate, as well as the long-range, limitations of this method of disposal. These factors are discussed here only briefly; they are elaborated on in other sections of the chapter.

Public Health and Safety

Although the sanitary landfill as a method of refuse disposal was given a clean bill of health many years ago, its acceptance by the public is still far from unanimous. The public has too often heard the terms "landfill," "dump," and "sanitary landfill" used interchangeably and does not understand the difference between a sanitary landfill and a landfill or dump. Unfortunately there are too many disposal facilities labeled "sanitary landfills" which are glaringly deficient in some of the essential elements. The 1968 National Survey shows that 94 per cent of all landfill refuse disposal projects fall short of complying with all criteria for fully acceptable operations. The resulting public image of sanitary landfills has been damaging.

A well-located, well-designed, and efficiently operated sanitary landfill meets public health standards and requirements for control of air and water pollution, fire, and nuisances:

1. Vector breeding or sustenance is prevented by eliminating harborage and food supply for rats, flies, and other vermin.
2. Air pollution by dust, smoke, and odor is controlled.
3. Fire hazards are controlled during operational phases. (They are negligible in a completed fill.)
4. Pollution of surface and ground waters is precluded.
5. All nuisance factors are effectively controlled; i.e., the system is aesthetically acceptable and noise is kept to a minimum.

The U.S. Public Health Service with assistance from APWA in 1957 developed standards by which types of landfills can be rated. Three classifications—A, B, and C—were set up. Landfills rated in the A classification are sanitary landfills. Those in the B and C classifications presently predominate under actual operating conditions. Specifically, the standards for each class are:

A. Operated without public nuisance or public health hazard; covered daily and adequately; no deliberate burning practiced.
B. Operated without public nuisance or public health hazard, but location permits modification of "A," such as burning of certain types of wastes at site, or covering of fill only three times weekly.
C. Operating techniques permit development of public nuisance and potential public health hazards, such as fly breeding, rodent sustenance, and odors.

St. Louis County, Missouri, in 1953 passed a comprehensive refuse disposal ordinance that reflects the recommendations of sanitary engineers and sets high standards for operation of sanitary landfills. It is reproduced as Appendix D.

Landfill Space Requirements

To estimate fill volume required for a community sanitary landfill, it is necessary to know the amount of refuse being produced and the density of the in-place compacted refuse. If the people of a community generate solid waste at the rate of 5.5 pounds per person per calendar day, each will discard 2,000 pounds in a year's time. A reasonably well-compacted sanitary landfill of shallow depth (say 20 feet) should have an in-place density of 1,000 pounds or more per cubic yard. It will, therefore, be necessary to provide 2 cubic yards of landfill space per year for each person living in this hypothetical community. The figures used in this illustration are reasonable, average, and conservative. In the absence of actual figures for a particular community, the rule-of-thumb —2 cubic yards of net fill volume per person per year—will provide an estimate of landfill space required. This is equivalent to 1.25 acre feet per 1,000 population per year.

Topography

Depressed areas such as ravines, swamps, and abandoned borrow pits in which the grade must be raised are usually considered topographically and economically suitable for sanitary landfill sites, providing the fill operations are so conducted that proper surface drainage is maintained.

Availability of Cover Material

The type of earth cover available on a site should be determined by test borings. The most desirable is a sandy loam free of stones bigger than 6 inches in diameter. The cover material may be excavated on the site or hauled in from borrow pits. Cover material also has been economically procured in New York for sites adjoining large bodies of water by hydraulic dredging. A clamshell or dragline is sometimes used on sanitary landfills to excavate suitable earth fill from below water level. Unfortunately, ideal cover soil on the site is the exception rather than the rule.

Proximity to Residences and Industry

It has repeatedly been demonstrated that sanitary landfills can be successfully operated in areas adjacent to residences, institutions, and industry. To be acceptable, the highest level of operations must be maintained: odors must be controlled, dust eliminated, vectors controlled. Good housekeeping and daily covering are musts when solid wastes are being placed close to homes.

Although a close-in site may be more expensive to acquire and to operate, it may be justified because of the expense of hauling to a more remote site and also because the fill may improve the land and make it useful. The public is usually concerned with health, nuisance, and safety aspects of an operation in the neighborhood and is apprehensive that an unsanitary operation will depreciate the value of local property. An exemplary operation will gain public support and will enhance the value of surrounding property if it provides land useful to the home owner or is landscaped and used for a park or recreational facility.

Wrapped household garbage combined with refuse from the home and collected not less frequently than once per week poses no added nuisance problem when placed close to occupied residences. However, separate loads of straight unwrapped garbage should not be received at such locations or, if received, they should be dumped at a location removed a distance from homes sufficient for the odor to be diluted with fresh air and covered immediately.

Fig. 32. A well-operated landfill can be located in the center of a good residential and commercial area without complaints from neighbors; and this site, one of many in Seattle, does not require a long haul for collection trucks. The level area was an unsightly hole before it was filled.

Accessibility

The site should have several access roads so that if one road is temporarily unusable, the site is not isolated. One small town selected a disposal site two miles away on the opposite side of a river that practically always flooded for a week or two in the spring. When the river was at flood, a round-about, 10-mile haul over almost impassable gravel roads was required.

In metropolitan areas access roads that permit trucks to be routed away from residential, commercial, and industrial sections are desirable.

Length of Hauls

The question of whether to use the sanitary landfill method of disposal or another method, such as incineration, is frequently influenced by the costs of hauling. The question is, how far is too far for a haul? Only an engineering analysis can give the answer. For example, it may be more economical to haul refuse a long distance in a 20-cubic-yard compactor-type truck that makes only one trip a day than to haul it a shorter distance in equipment that must make two, three, or more trips. The use of large-volume vehicles for long hauls from close-in transfer stations may increase the distance it is economical to haul refuse by as much as 25 to 50 miles.

However, the cost of owning and operating the transfer station and other nonproductive expense must be regained by the more efficient long-haul vehicle. The APWA companion publication *Refuse Collection Practice* tells how the economic analysis of supplemental transportation systems can be made.

Climatology

Weather is a significant factor in evaluating landfill sites in some areas of the country. Extremely cold weather can prevent excavation for cover, making it necessary to excavate and stockpile it during warm weather. A prolonged rainy spell can flood low areas, making it difficult for refuse vehicles to maneuver at the fill. The intensity and direction of prevailing winds are also important in controlling blowing paper and in determining in which direction odors will be blown.

Local climate conditions may eliminate some sites, require unusual techniques of operation at others, or rule out landfills as the disposal method entirely under extreme conditions.

Drainage

Proper drainage for the landfill itself is necessary, but it is also important to consider what effect the fill will have on natural drainage in the area. For example, filling a ravine that is dry most of the time but which is the channel for a roaring torrent after a cloudburst, without making provision for this peak flow, would be to invite disaster through erosion. Landfill operations in low areas can be potential dams interfering with natural runoff from surrounding property with consequent liability for damages. Planning for sanitary landfill operations must include adequate provisions for handling all drainage peak loads. Diversion around the fill may be feasible at minimal expense, or it may be necessary to construct a costly pipe or enclosed channel of considerable dimensions to be covered by the fill. Such a requirement could be a major factor in site selection.

Future Land Uses

The improvement of property by filling it is one of the chief economic advantages of the sanitary landfill method of disposal. Many cities have turned mosquito producing pestholes into play areas, athletic fields, and parks. Others have used completed sanitary fills to extend airport runways or as sites for industrial buildings. A city must consider how it can use a landfill site when it is completed.

To answer this question satisfactorily it is necessary to consider physical and biochemical reactions of the mass of compacted and covered refuse and the impact of operational practices on it. Construction of houses on sanitary fills is usually discouraged, and heavy construction should be permitted only after careful engineering studies.

Fig. 33. There is little indication at the close of each day that this is a landfill site. Covering the site with earth material each night also helps control fires, odors, and insects and rodents.

Costs

Costs of fills vary widely, even within a city. The cost of the site, site preparation, and operating costs must all be computed to determine which site is economically best. (In Los Angeles, excavations for landfills have cost in excess of $3 million.) The initial cost, however, must be balanced against the value of the land when the fill is completed. Often the land increases in value appreciably.

Zoning Regulations

A survey conducted by the APWA in 1956 showed that a high percentage of cities in the United States are restricted in the acquisition of disposal sites by their zoning ordinances. Where zoning does exist, the rules and regulations vary widely from permissive to very restrictive. The competent engineer or designer will view objectively all the factors controlling site selection, including the prospects of zoning change or exception, when considering the use of a particular site for a sanitary landfill. Master planners, when establishing zoning, should reserve areas to be used for solid waste disposal just as surely as they reserve school sites or commercial areas.

Public Acceptance

The importance of public acceptance of a site for a sanitary landfill cannot be overemphasized. Even though a proposed site is in an uninhabited area, the people who regularly drive past it may think it will be undesirable and protest having it there, sometimes successfully. Some cities—Seattle, Washington, for example—consider that public approval of a landfill site is the most important factor in deciding on its use.

SITE PREPARATION

Site preparation is the readying of an area for sanitary landfill operations. How well it is done spells the difference between success and failure in the operation.

The extent of the preparations for a particular site depends on the nature and location of the site, the size of the operation, and, of course, the amount of money available.

The following steps should be taken or facilities provided for most sites, although not all are necessary for every fill:

1. Make an engineering survey to permit accurate planning for access roads, drainage, lift heights, diversion channels, dikes or levees; to determine soil characteristics; and to estimate the life of the site.
2. Build a semipermanent, all-weather road on the site and a vehicle turn-around if needed.
3. Build an all-weather access road to the site.
4. Take measures to prevent paper from being wind blown.
5. Build appurtenances for aesthetic reasons, such as an earth berm or solid fence around the site to screen the activity.
6. Provide suitable facilities for storing and servicing equipment.
7. Provide facilities for workmen.
8. Install scales to weigh refuse to help determine costs and to improve management practices.
9. Provide utilities—electricity, telephones, water for fire fighting.
10. Do site work: clear trees, divert springs or brooks, and remove and store topsoil for cover material or procure other cover material.

Engineering Survey

To be successful and economical, a sanitary fill should be handled like any other engineering project. Planning should include studies, drawings, and specifications. The survey should result in basic data from which recommendations can be made for construction of access roads, depth of fill, plan of operation, location and amount of stockpiled earth cover material required, provision for proper drainage, and the probable life expectancy of the site for landfill purposes. The planned or potential use of the site must also be considered.

As a first step, a detailed topographic site survey (at a scale of not more than 200 feet to the inch with 2-foot contour intervals for the average level site) is recommended.

Amount of Land Required. The amount of land required for a fill and the length of time it can be used for disposal can be estimated fairly accurately on the basis of data on refuse production, compaction, density, and the amount of settling that can be anticipated in fill sites. The following pointers can be used in making calculations:

1. The compaction ratio (volume of refuse received to the volume after compaction) varies from 1:1 to 3:1, depending on the type of refuse, amount of precompaction in collection vehicles, field compaction procedures, depth of fill, number of layers or lifts, and compactability of underlying earth. The use of collection vehicle volume figures to determine land (or landfill space) required is much more susceptible to error than determination made by actual weighing. The latter should be used whenever available and, if the less reliable truck volume figures are the only information available, spot weighing of some loads should be done to corroborate the volume method.

2. As discussed in Chapter 2, quantities of refuse to be handled at any disposal site are subject to several influences which result in wide variations between cities. The 1968 National Survey shows average generations of household, commercial, and industrial wastes of about 10 pounds per capita per day, compared with average actual collections of 4.74 pounds per capita per day. The range is wide, however. Even household refuse generation is known to vary from a low of about 1 pound to a high of about 6 pounds per capita per day.

   The Los Angeles County metropolitan area, with a population of some 7 million people living in 77 incorporated cities and in unincorporated developments, produces 7.5 pounds per capita per day of all classes of solid wastes reaching disposal facilities through municipal as well as private collectors. Household refuse accounts for about 2.5 pounds of this; industrial, commercial, and agricultural activities, 2.5 pounds; the remaining 2.5 pounds, relatively inert materials, come from construction and demolition work.

   In any specific instance, the quantities to be disposed of are determined by a number of prevailing conditions peculiar to the locality. Specific figures should not be used indiscriminately.

3. The density of mixed solid wastes delivered to the landfill in collection vehicles differs markedly with the type of collection vehicle used. The range can extend from about 100 pounds per cubic yard in non-compaction-type conveyances to 800-plus pounds per cubic yard in vehicles equipped with high-density compacting mechanisms. Also, individual loads can vary greatly. For example, the load collected in the morning is frequently a full load, while later loads are partial loads to complete a work assignment or route. When the load-volume of collection vehicles is used to calculate land space requirements, well-documented back-up data should be obtained to substantiate the pounds per capita figure needed to make the determination.

4. The density of the compacted in-place refuse has an effect on the amount of land required for a sanitary landfill. This element has been the subject of many reports, much speculation, and unsubstantiated equipment performance claims. Unfortunately, few compaction tests have been made that were based on sound engineering practice. However, the reliable information that has been developed by engineering methods indicates that a reasonably well compacted landfill should have an initial density of 1,000 pounds per cubic yard for shallow fills of up to 20 feet in depth. As the depth of fill increases, substantial compaction of the refuse occurs due to the weight of the refuse and daily cover alone, and the density of the refuse in a similarly compacted fill of three or more 20-foot lifts should have a density of 1,250 or more pounds per cubic yard.

5. Earth cover imported to the site or obtained from an excavation within the site (such as the ridge of a hill), which will not later be filled with refuse, uses space in the fill and an allowance must be made for the amount of space so used. To be truly a sanitary landfill, approximately 1 part earth to 4 parts refuse is required for the daily cover. Although this would seem to require a 20 per cent allowance for imported cover, in actual practice the allowance is closer to 5 per cent. In recent compaction tests using household refuse, the Sanitation Districts of Los Angeles County, California, determined that only 25 per cent of the daily cover material used occupied refuse space in the fill. The remaining 75 per cent used apparently sifted into voids between refuse particles or was mixed in with the refuse in the adjacent cells within the test pit. In addition to the conclusion that imported daily cover for a well-operated sanitary landfill uses only approximately 5 per cent of the space in the fill, it should be pointed out that limiting the amount of imported cover to conserve space and thereby operating an unsanitary landfill is not justified by the small amount of space saved.

6. In the case where earth cover is obtained directly from the site, creating space to be filled with refuse, it would appear that the volume of space occupied by the refuse would be measured by that volume lying between the original ground surface and that of the completed fill. If none of the excavated earth is removed from the site and no imported cover is used, the earth should occupy the same volume

after filling as it did before, regardless of how it might be distributed as temporary and final cover throughout the completed fill. However, the factor of commingling of earth with refuse discussed in 5 above applies here also, and the volume available for refuse can be calculated to include part of the excavated earth cover volume as well. There is also the factor of "bulking" of excavated earth compared with its original undisturbed volume to be considered. The tests described in 5 above took "bulking" into consideration, but not all soils bulk the same amount, and bulking may theoretically offset some of the commingling. However, from the data developed to date, 75 per cent of the original volume of excavated earth cover is available for refuse filling and can be added to the volume available for refuse filling and to the volume available between original and final surface. A conservative designer may want to reduce the 75 per cent to 50 per cent pending confirmation tests on various types of earth and their corresponding bulking effect. In the common case involving a combination of use of cover from the site to be filled as well as some imported cover, estimates of the proportions of each class should be made and the appropriate factors applied.

Site Investigations

Site investigations vary according to circumstances. For instance, when Mandan, North Dakota, a city of 7,000, started sanitary landfill operations, engineering investigations included several test borings of a proposed site to confirm that it had satisfactory earth cover available in sufficient quantities, preparation of a topographic map of the site, and plans and drawings for an access road to the site from a county road.

In New York City, on the other hand, an engineering study for a sanitary landfill in a lagoon included data on demolition of condemned structures near the site; data on sand for cover material by hydraulic dredging; information on construction of tidegates and dikes and on extension of water, electric, and telephone lines; and information on installation of truck weighing scales and on construction of a building for equipment and facilities for employees.

The amount and type of earth cover material available should be determined by on-site tests. Ordinarily the tests consist of borings to the depth contemplated for removal of cover material. As many borings as are necessary to get a true picture of soil conditions should be taken. For sites of only a few acres and in which the geological formations are known, only a few confirmatory borings need be made. For large sites on which little geological data are available, a dozen or more borings may be required. Similar investigations may be required of any off-site sources of cover material.

In many cases water pollution aspects may be important. Water table data can be obtained from the test borings. Under some conditions supplemental investigations may be needed to determine migration of ground water as well as provisions for surface runoff, as the basis for a design that will minimize the effects of water contamination.

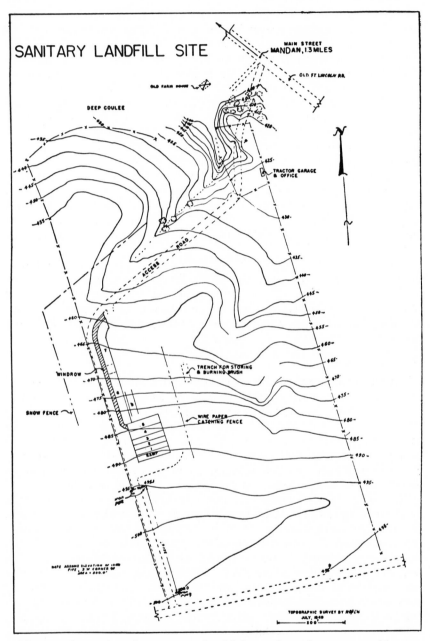

Fig. 34. An engineering survey should be made and a topographic map prepared before landfill operations are started. This map was made of a landfill site in Mandan, North Dakota.

Access Roads

Access roads to a site should be so constructed that traffic is not interrupted by inclement weather or climatological conditions such as spring thaws and rainy seasons. They should be at least 22 feet wide and have a minimum curve radius of 75 feet if use of large transfer vehicles is anticipated. There often is a road meeting specifications adjacent to small fill sites—perhaps a well-drained, graded, gravel road. Depending on the amount of truck traffic and the proximity of the road to dwellings, it may be necessary to control dust by sprinkling with water or treating with calcium chloride, oil, or penetration macadam. Soil cement techniques or a seal coat of penetration asphalt topped with aggregate are often used in contruction of such roads.

On large fill sites, such as those in New York City, a semipermanent, hard surfaced road is built from the point of entry of the site to the dumping point. An all-weather road, extended periodically as work progresses along the face of the fill, will speed up operations and, more important, will pay for itself several times over by reducing damage to trucks.

Overhead lights should be installed along the access road and near the bank of the fill for night operations. Portable generators at the bank of the fill may suffice. Access roads should be kept clear of papers and rubbish, which are fire hazards and are objectionable, and should also be kept clear of glass, scrap metal fragments, and other materials that cut tires.

Fencing

Fences at sanitary landfill sites serve three purposes: (1) cut off the view of the operations for neighbors and passersby; (2) control entry to the site; and (3) control wind-blown paper.

In New York City the view of a fill operation is cut off by an earth berm 8 to 10 feet high, which is topped by an 8-foot wire fence with burlap covering if it is necessary to confine wind-blown debris and dust. Snow fences to catch blowing papers are also sometimes put up temporarily in the immediate vicinity of the dumping operation.

No special effort is made to conceal landfill operations in most cities, however. If sight of the operations is a point of contention for the public, the problem can usually be solved by selecting a relatively isolated site.

Many methods have been devised to prevent wind-blown paper from becoming a nuisance and fire hazard. Use of snow fence in the immediate operating area (about 50 to 75 feet downwind from the operating face of the fill) has been found to be effective and is popular because it is readily available, is relatively inexpensive, and is easily set up and moved as required. In some places, however, snow fences are not permitted because paper cannot be burned off the wood slats.

Metal fencing is often used to catch paper, especially if the fence encloses the entire disposal area. Hogwire-type fencing is generally recommended. It is strong and may be obtained in varying heights. Wire fencing with less strength is not recommended because a strong wind can cause abnormally high pressure on the fence if a lot of paper is "plastered" against it. Portable sectional fencing mounted on skids has been used on sanitary landfills. As the operational area changes, the fence may be pulled by a tractor to a new location.

Fences, it should be realized, are often used to solve a problem that could have been avoided in the first place by selection of a more sheltered site and use of recommended truck unloading procedures. A fill site on a windy plain, for example, presents a much more difficult problem than a site in a valley. One city had to solve the problems caused by a poor site by excavating 12-foot trenches and erecting an earth berm perpendicular to the axis of the prevailing wind as a wind block. All trucks were unloaded in the trench itself on especially windy days.

Fences that help prevent access to a fill by unauthorized vehicles and dumping after hours can be of any of a number of materials and styles, depending on local considerations.

Facilities for Personnel and Equipment

What kinds and how many facilities should be provided on the site for workers and equipment are governed by location and size of each landfill. In the arid southwest states a carport-type structure may suffice as a garage for a tractor, whereas in the northern states a well-insulated heated garage may be needed.

Sanitary facilities for site personnel are desirable even at the smallest site. Arrangements may be made with a nearby business establishment, or at large operations a portable privy may be installed on the site.

Semiportable sheds should be located near the main entrance to large landfill sites for use as operation headquarters and as a base for employees. The sheds should be heated if necessary, have water and sewage facilities, and, when feasible, lights, lockers, showers, and telephones.

Weighing Facilities

Accurate data on quantities of refuse are desirable for cost accounting purposes and as an aid to good management. If the data are to be used for comparison they must be reasonably accurate. Experience shows that the only accurate data for comparison purposes are based on weight—not volume. Few cities in the United States have weighing facilities on landfill sites, however, probably because many city officials do not understand the need for them, making it difficult to justify the cost.

Cities that charge private haulers for depositing refuse in a fill frequently have scales because they charge on the basis of weight. The New York Department of Sanitation uses semiportable weighing rooms with truck scales in the area adjoining the sheds for equipment and employees. Devices that automatically figure charges for disposal on the basis of the weight of the refuse are used by the New York City and the Los Angeles County sanitation departments.

Portable scales may be adequate on temporary disposal sites or arrangements sometimes can be made with a local businessman to rent a scale.

Cover Material

A suitable inert, granular material must be used to cover compacted refuse at the working face and top surfaces of a landfill project. Cover material prevents refuse from blowing and being scattered, helps control odors, helps prevent invasion of the fill by rodents and insects, and lessens fire hazards by sealing "cells" of refuse, thus precluding the spread of internal fires that may occur. A compacted cover also makes the fill firmer and easier for vehicles to drive over.

The most desirable type of earth cover material for a fill is classified in reports of the U.S. Bureau of Public Roads as "sandy loam." Clean earth or its equivalent should be used and it should be relatively free of organic matter, tree roots, branches, stones more than 6 inches in diameter, and bulky building materials, and have a low clay content. Soil that has a low clay content can help prevent quagmires, prevent equipment from bogging down in wet weather, and minimize the formation of cracks in the fill cover. The cracks provide access for rodents and insects to the buried refuse and may permit odorous gases to escape from the fill. Many large stones in the cover material cause similar difficulties. The proper cover material assures good traction for vehicles in all weather, safeguards against unequal settlement and against heaving action of the fill, and reduces surface cracking. Clean ashes or incinerator residue are adequate for intermediate working cover.

The quantity of cover material is customarily expressed as the ratio of the volume of cover material to the volume of compacted refuse. For example, a 1:4 cover ratio indicates 1 cubic yard of cover material for each 4 cubic yards of compacted refuse, although as discussed on p. 100 this does not mean that only 80 per cent of the volume is occupied by refuse. The cover ratio required for results consistent with good engineering practices varies with the type and location of the landfill and the proposed use of the completed site. The most important consideration—public health—requires that at least a 6-inch compacted layer of cover material be put on the top surface of each lift as it is constructed and, in addition, that all exposed refuse be covered at the end of each working period, usually once each day but more frequently if necessary.

The Los Angeles County engineer has determined that a cover ratio of 1:4, or 20 per cent, is satisfactory for the Los Angeles area, and it is required at all landfill sites operating under permits issued by the county engineer. In Burbank, California, a cover ratio of about 1:3 has been found to be satisfactory for a landfill that, because of its proximity to a residential area, must have all surfaces of the refuse covered daily. In very large fills, however, such as those in New York, where compacted depths go up to 40 feet (made in two to four lifts), the cover ratio is substantially less.

The costs of procuring suitable cover on a site by private contract will range from about 30 cents to $1 a cubic yard.

Cover material is usually spread by bulldozer, bullclam, or carryall in a uniform layer over previously compacted refuse. The process of continuous mixing of cover material and refuse for optimum compaction has several disadvantages that make it impractical for large-scale operations and is, therefore, not recommended. Continuous mixing of cover and refuse is difficult with the usual landfill equipment and materially increases costs. Surface layers of compacted cover are required in addition to the continuously mixed cover, thereby increasing the amount of cover material required.

On the other hand, a continuous mix landfill may have less voids than one with conventional cell structure, thus slightly increasing the refuse capacity and minimizing settlement. There may be cases in which the

THE AREA METHOD

Fig. 35. The bulldozer is spreading and compacting a load of solid wastes. The scraper (foreground) is used to haul the cover material at the end of the day's operations. Note the portable fence that catches any blowing debris; these are used with any landfill method whenever necessary.

increased cost of the continuous mixing process is justified, although by 1960 there were no landfills known to be using a true continuous mixing process.

Compactibility of soil depends primarily on the gradient of particle size—that is, soil with a homogeneous particle size does not compact as well as soil containing particles with a wide range of sizes. Nearly pure sands, clays, and silts are not suitable for cover material on sanitary landfills unless especially treated. For example, calcium sulfate has been applied at the rate of 20 pounds per acre for aggregation of silts used as cover on Bergen County, New Jersey, landfills. The final layer of cover is disk harrowed and seeded with rye grass. Crushed rock with no soil binder is likewise unsuitable for fill cover.

New York City has developed a process of converting sand obtained by dredging into cover material by inundating (ponding) the surface of the sand with digested sewage sludge (about 95 per cent liquid). After a drying out period, the sand and sludge are thoroughly mixed by mechanical plowing. The result is excellent cover soil obtained much more economically than if material had been imported.

Landfills in Dry Areas

When sanitary landfills were first used for refuse disposal in the United States, it was convenient to classify the methods of operation as the area method and the trench method. As techniques changed over the years on the basis of experience, the two classifications became inadequate. New names for new methods were thought up and used.

Of the types of landfills in dry areas, two are now common: area landfills—on essentially flat land sites; and depression landfills—on sites that use natural or man-made depressions or irregularities in the terrain, such as canyons, ravines, and pits.

Area Landfills

One of three methods of operation is usually used for area landfills—progressive excavation, cut and cover, or imported cover.

Progressive Excavation. The distinguishing feature of the progressive excavation method is its continuity. Cover material is excavated from the area directly in front of the working face of the landfill and is put over the previously compacted refuse behind. The cover is excavated as required and the process goes on almost continuously.

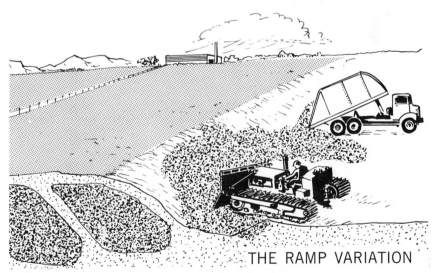

THE RAMP VARIATION

Fig. 36. The solid wastes are being spread and compacted on a slope. The daily cell may be covered with earth scraped from the base of the ramp. This variation is used with either the area or trench method.

Progressive excavation landfills are usually operated with bullclams or bulldozers and have a ramp-type working face (see Figures 35 and 36). Scrapers may also be used on larger operations. It is possible, however, to operate a trench-type or cut and cover progressive excavation landfill with dragline or carryall. This has been done in Fresno, where a dragline operates next to an excavated trench in front of and moving parallel to the plane of the working face while compacting and covering the refuse in a continuous operation.

The original ramp or trench for dumping of cells of refuse may be prepared in any convenient way. If there is a natural bank or other suitable terrain feature on a site, advantage should be taken of it. A bulldozer can easily prepare an earth ramp or cover a windrow of compacted refuse and thus fashion a ramp. Any such scheme is satisfactory.

The point at which refuse is discharged on the working face of the fill has a direct influence on the ease with which refuse is spread and compacted. It has been found by bulldozer operators working ramp-type fills in San Diego and Los Angeles County that it is easier to see the work and to control spreading if refuse is discharged at the base of the working face and spread from the bottom up. Dumping at the bottom of the face has been found to result also in better compaction because collection vehicles drive over the area when it is filled to reach the working area. Discharging refuse at the base of the working face also sometimes hides the disposal operation from the public view and minimizes the amount of paper blown about—important factors at fills near residential areas.

Discharging refuse at the top of the working face requires that loaded collection trucks climb to the top of the fill. Top dumping should be avoided particularly on fills higher than 10 feet because refuse is scattered over a wider area than with bottom dumping. It may be necessary to do so, however, when roads are muddy or for some other reason are impassable.

A 35,000-pound crawler tractor with a dozer blade can dispose of 250 to 300 tons of refuse in each eight-hour working day by this method, assuming that excavation of cover presents no difficulties and requires no extra equipment. Equipment capacities are discussed in more detail later.

Cut and Cover. A cut and cover fill is one in which trench-type excavations are made on the site to hold the refuse and get cover material. The trenches are usually parallel to each other in order to use the site efficiently. The excavated earth, usually stockpiled adjacent to the excavation, becomes the cover material.

With the cut and cover process, the amount of earth excavated may exceed the cover requirements. Such was the case at a Torrance, California municipal landfill, where excess earth was sold as borrow material, providing additional disposal space at the landfill.

The rate of excavation in a cut and cover fill may bear no relation to the rate of disposal. In fact, the most popular practice is to excavate enough trenches at one time to provide space for disposal for a long time. In the northern part of the United States it is customary to excavate enough trenches and stockpile enough cover material to last throughout

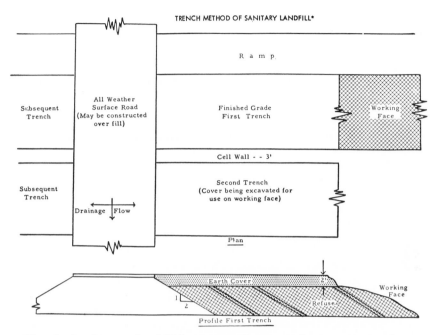

Fig. 37. In the area landfill known as the cut and cover or trench type, earth cover material is obtained on the site either by excavating the trench ahead of the working face or by excavating a trench that is to be filled later. Plans for this fill call for getting cover material from a subsequent trench.

the freezing weather. It may also be advantageous to excavate ahead in areas where periods of heavy rainfall can be anticipated.

Unlike the progressive excavation method, refuse at a cut and cover fill is usually discharged at the top of the working face, although in some cases it may be desirable to discharge it at the bottom. Spreading and compaction of the refuse is usually done by bulldozer, as it was at the Mission Bay site in San Diego, California.

The cut and cover method is well suited to sites on which excavations are made below ground water level, which is common at tideland and mud flat sites. A dragline is essential for excavating on such operations.

Imported Cover. The imported cover method of operating a landfill is not a single method but rather several, and is used when cover material is obtained from a source outside the site. Refuse is dumped and compacted with bulldozer, bullclam, or dragline as it is in other methods of area fill. The volume of refuse that can be disposed of at an imported cover site is a little less than it is when the cover material is excavated from the site.

The imported cover method is used for one of two reasons: (1) if there is excess borrow at a nearby excavation that makes it convenient and economical to use the borrow as cover for the fill; (2) if suitable ma-

THE TRENCH METHOD

Fig. 38. The waste collection truck deposits its load into the trench where the bulldozer will spread and compact it. At the end of the day the dragline will excavate soil from the future trench, and this soil will be used as the daily cover material. Trenches can also be excavated with a front-end loader, bulldozer, or scraper.

terial is not available on the landfill site, such as rock quarry pits or area fills on which one lift has been completed.

Traffic is sometimes a major problem at landfills using imported cover, particularly if the refuse is discharged mostly from collection vehicles rather than from transfer vehicles and if cover is not stockpiled but delivered frequently. In Seattle it was found that traffic congestion at the site caused by refuse collection vehicles and vehicles delivering cover can be reduced by having refuse trucks dump at the bottom of the lift and the cover delivery trucks at the top. Trucks hauling cover material should be routed over roads that create a minimum of dust and noise and over highways that can stand the weight of the loaded trucks.

Although cover material can be delivered as needed, it is good practice to stockpile it against vehicle failure or work stoppages at the source.

Depression Landfills

Depression fills are those that use natural or man-made irregularities or depressions in topography. The methods of operating all depression fills are so nearly alike that it is convenient to categorize the fills according to dominant physical features rather than methods of operation. Depression fills are classified as either canyon and ravine or pit and quarry.

Usually the total depth of the refuse in a depression site is greater than the depth in an area fill. The fill is constructed by dumping refuse in sloping layers and compacting it. Each stratum thus formed has a total depth of from 4 to 20 feet. Each layer must be well covered with compacted, inert cover material; and it is good practice to cover the sloped working face at the end of each work period.

Canyons and Ravines. (Although only "canyons" are mentioned from here on, similar methods are used for ravines.) The two principal criteria

Fig. 39. In the canyon landfill, refuse is placed in the same way that it is in an area landfill; cover material is excavated from canyon walls. The inset shows a cross section of a typical canyon fill in the Los Angeles basin, with access roads built up the sloping face of the fill.

for determining the acceptability of a canyon as a site for a fill are physical configuration and soil type. A relatively flat bottom grade is desirable because it makes it easier for vehicles to go in and out of the canyon. Since all cover material except that for the first stratum is excavated from the canyon sides, it is advantageous if the canyon is long and narrow and has a flat bottom. The type of soil available for cover determines the type of equipment needed for excavating, hauling, spreading, and compacting.

The stability of exposed fill slopes must be considered. Experience indicates that slopes of 2:1 are acceptable and only those approaching 1:1 need be subjected to rigorous analysis. No known attempt has been made to determine shear values or sliding resistance for in-place refuse fill.

The interface between refuse fill and native terrain may be a plane of low shear. If this interface is close to the sliding circle of the fill and reliable shear values cannot be determined, it may prove good practice to terrace the native terrain before dumping refuse.

Usually each lift of a canyon landfill is begun at the head of the canyon and ended at the mouth, which prevents water from ponding in back of the fill and makes it easier for disposal trucks. The first lift of a canyon fill may be carried out by the progressive excavation method if the canyon floor is essentially flat and of reasonable size.

Refuse is usually dumped at the base of the working face of a canyon fill so that refuse trucks do not have to go to the top, and because there is better control and compaction if the refuse is worked from the bottom to the top of the slope rather than from the top down.

The distance between the source of cover material and the working face varies during the operation. Cover material that is 150 to 300 feet away from the face of the fill can be moved most economically by a bulldozer or crawler tractor with shovel attachment. If cover must be moved more than 500 feet, a carryall scraper is more economical for the job, and it can be used to spread cover over the top of the lift or the working face uniformly and efficiently as it unloads. If cover must be moved 1,000 feet or more over an extended period of time, the suitability of various types of haul equipment should be studied and evaluated. For example, a rubber-tired tractor pulling a rubber-tired scraper loaded with the help of a crawler tractor "pusher" might be the most economical equipment.

The nature of the cover material determines the kind of equipment required for excavation and can significantly affect the cost of operating a landfill. Loose sand and loam mixtures, loose sand and clay mixtures, soft decomposed granite, and well-fractured or loosely cemented sedimentary deposits can be excavated easily with a bulldozer or carryall scraper. Clay, adobe, well-compacted sand and clay mixtures, well-cemented sedimentary deposits, partially decomposed granite, and the like often require loosening with a ripper before bulldozer or carryall excavation.

Canyons with geological structures consisting of well-consolidated sedimentary deposits or poorly fractured and poorly weathered igneous or metamorphic formations of solid rock should be avoided if there is a satisfactory alternate site, because blasting may be required before excavation with a bulldozer or carryall scraper. Material that requires blasting is usually poorly suited for cover, and blasting is discouraged near heavily populated areas. At remote sites, blasting may be feasible and prove to be a more economic method of loosening well-compacted material than ripping. Soil borings should be made before a canyon is selected as a landfill site, and if suitable cover material is not available to the extent of about 25 per cent of the volume to be occupied by refuse, the necessity of importing the deficiency must be faced.

Rain water runoff concentrates in canyon sites; consequently, it is important that there be adequate drainage. If the boundary of a canyon site does not include an entire watershed, adequate drainage must be provided for the watershed area above the landfill. In many cases, a diversion ditch may be dug just above the expected final grade of the fill to divert runoff water from that part of the canyon or watershed above the site. This has been done successfully at the Arizona Fill, operated by the city of San Diego. It may prove more economical in some cases to lay a culvert along the centerline of the canyon and thus provide drainage under the fill rather than around the sides or over the top of it. Drainage for the surface of the fill itself must also be provided. The top of a canyon fill may be crowned and drained by a 5 to 10 per cent grade to the sides of the fill or may be drained to the center and faced with a 1 or 2 per cent grade. The latter may be preferred because it assures that settlement, always greatest in the deepest part of the fill, will not result in ponding water.

Surface runoff concentrated at the edges or center of a fill surface must be carried away in such a manner that the fill face does not erode. A drainage ditch along the access road may be suitable, but if the fill face is not traversed by an access road, it must have transverse drainage ditches adequate to prevent erosion by surface runoff. Finished fill faces should be planted with cover crops for surface erosion control. Mustard and wild rye have been found acceptable.

Access roads into canyon sites cannot have a steeper grade than refuse collection trucks can negotiate. A maximum grade of about 7 per cent uphill or 10 per cent downhill for a loaded truck or 10 per cent either way unloaded is recommended. Every effort should be made to minimize access road grades. If access roads are on the slopes of the canyon that are adjacent to the site, they will not take up part of the site that can be filled. An access road on the face of canyon landfills not only reduces the space that can be filled but also requires special care in building.

Dry Pits and Quarries

Pit and quarry landfill sites are lower at all points than the surrounding terrain and consequently are not drained by surface channels; as with canyon sites, pit sites are usually so deep that they must be filled by several lifts or strata of refuse.

Pit and quarry sites are operated in essentially the same way as canyon sites. Refuse is transported to the working face via an access road that should be built on the same principles as canyon site access roads. Refuse is discharged adjacent to the working face, either at the bottom or the top of the lift. Discharging at the top makes the dumping and travel easier and faster for the trucks. If careful control is to be maintained and high densities are to be achieved, however, it is recommended that the fill be constructed of lifts built by bulldozing and compacting refuse from the bottom of the working face up in sloping layers, as shown in Figure 40.

It is desirable that a pit or quarry site have enough excavatable material around its periphery to provide all the intermediate and final cover for the entire refuse capacity of the fill. In most cases this will require a volume of cover equal to at least 25 per cent of the original volume of the pit. In most pits it is economical to operate the first lift of the fill by the progressive excavation method, avoiding transportation of cover material from the periphery of the pit, which is necessary with subsequent lifts. If the pit is very large in area, requiring long cover hauls, or if the amount of cover material is inadequate, it is advisable to consider stockpiling cover material from the pit bottom. The quantity of cover to be stockpiled should be carefully calculated before the fill is begun. If it is impossible to obtain sufficient cover material at the site, a decision to use the pit as an imported cover landfill should be based on a careful economic analysis, as importation of cover material may be prohibitively expensive.

Fig. 40. In the pit and quarry-type landfill, refuse is placed and compacted in horizontal layers, or "lifts," and covered with material excavated from the sides of the pit or brought in from borrow areas. If a pit fill is large, it is necessary to use carryalls to economically transport cover material.

It is desirable that a pit or quarry site be filled to a level slightly above the grade of the surrounding terrain to allow for long-range settling and to obviate problems of surface runoff.

LANDFILLS IN WET AREAS

Wet sites for landfills are of three general types: swamps and marshes; tidal areas with fluctuating water depths; and ponds, quarries, and similar depressions that have standing water in them.

A general plan of the long-range development of the site should be drawn up before operations are started. The plan should include information on the final grades and depths of fill, the drainage system, the amount of cover material required, potential volume of the fill, and its life expectancy. If overall city plans call for highways, bridges, buildings for heavy industry, or other major improvements to be built in the area, it may be necessary to avoid using the area for landfills. Sewers, storm drains, and other large conduits that are to be built in the area of a site probably should be completed before the landfill operation is started.

Swamps and Marshes

For landfills in swamps or marshes it is of utmost importance to construct and maintain a drainage system adequate to handle both ground water runoff from adjoining uplands and surface runoff from newly filled plateaus. The discharge end of the drainage ditches should be equipped with readily cleanable trash screens. If discharge is into tidal waters, the course screen should be supplemented with flap gates to control backflows.

Filling strips should be extended from a previously constructed operating platform. This platform, built up from either compacted refuse or other readily available material to about 5 feet above marsh elevation, facilitates maneuvering of trucks and makes operations more flexible.

Filling operations should be scheduled and controlled so as to preclude, or at least alleviate, mud waves, which may cause structural problems, interfere with normal drainage, and create odor and insect nuisances by stirring up organic silt. The schedule can be carried out by constructing a lagoon with fingers of refuse as described in the following section on tidal areas.

Tidal Areas

Tidal areas used as landfill sites should be divided into several lagoons by means of dikes to better control operations and limit and alleviate nuisances. Only one lagoon should be filled at a time. Each lagoon should be large enough to permit one winter's placing of the initial in-water layer of refuse. The initial in-water layer, built up during the winter, should have a compacted elevation of about 2 feet above maximum high water. (More than 2 feet may be necessary if high winds cause waves of much size at high tide.) The alternative—filling up to water level with clean earth—may be more satisfactory but much costlier.

Lagoon dikes should be strong enough to withstand mud waves and of such materials and proportions as to reduce permeability to the minimum. Malodorous leachings can be prevented entirely by watertight, shallow, lightweight, interlocking steel or wood sheet piling. Where strong currents or high waves are significant factors, outshore faces should be rip-rapped against erosion. Otherwise, flat grades or natural slopes may be a more economical solution.

Seattle has reportedly had good results in constructing dikes in marshy areas by using large masses of rubbish such as trees, tree limbs, lumber, and similar materials. Dikes built of such materials prevent mud and silt from sliding out from under the refuse fill. The large rubbish is brought in by private haulers and is placed by a tractor-dozer. The material, when compacted, is so interlaced and tightly bound together

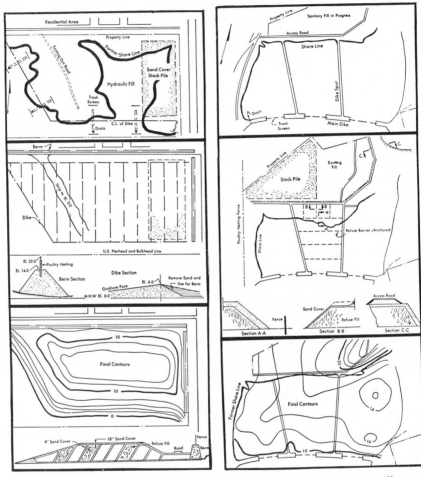

Fig. 41. The New York City Department of Sanitation fills wet areas in three steps: (1) site preparation; (2) construction of berm, barrier fence, and dike, and placing of fill in 150-foot wide strips; (3) site contouring. The plans at the left are for swampy and marshy areas; those at the right for a tidal area. In tidal areas, dikes and spurs divide the site into lagoons. Operational steps are much the same as those for swamps and marshes; the main difference is that in tidal areas the second step includes building anchored refuse barriers to help keep water in the lagoon clean.

that cracking is reportedly almost unknown. Where pollution from leaching is a consideration, a dike should be constructed with an impervious core.

The depth of the first layer of refuse should be the minimum, with deposition in strips, moving out with a pincer operation to confine underlying mud and avoid mud waves. Good compaction is essential to "key" refuse into muck.

Ponds, Quarries, and Similar Areas

Dumping refuse directly into large bodies of deep water such as ponds in quarries often causes nuisances. Biochemical activity of the putrescible component of the refuse creates anaerobic conditions and odors from the hydrogen sulfide given off during the process of decomposition. Relatively shallow ponds may be reclaimed by confining dumping to cold weather. The initial in-water layer should be at a depth slightly above high water during winter; warm weather filling should be limited to the secondary, overlying layers. An oxidizing agent such as calcium hypochlorite can be used to kill odors if there is not a lot of water.

Displaced water should be discharged at low velocities over adjustable weirs preceded by trash screens. A quiescent, shallow, near-uniform discharge will promote settlement of most suspended matter and will reduce carryover of materials to the minimum. Heavy chlorination of effluent may be necessary, depending on temperatures, nature of receiving waters, and other conditions.

Possible hazards of "sloughing-off" of refuse at the dumping face of wet fills cause some problems with equipment. Experience shows, however, that when the top of the first lift is at least 2 feet above maximum water level there is little risk of edge shearing or of losing equipment over the bank. Both rubber-tired and crawler equipment can work safely within a few feet of the bank. Mixed refuse, with its elastic components, interlocks and is also continuously compacted by the heavy operating equipment, developing angles of repose averaging 1 to 1, even when dumped into water.

EQUIPMENT AND PERSONNEL

Equipment and personnel required to operate a fill properly vary with the amount of refuse handled, characteristics of the site, and the fill method used.

Equipment

Five major types of equipment are used in operating sanitary landfills:

1. Track-type tractor that picks up and carries earth and places refuse by pushing with a front-shovel or multi-purpose front attachment.
2. Track-type tractor with bulldozer (and pulling scraper if needed).
3. Dragline.
4. Wheeled-type tractor with bulldozer and scraper.
5. Self-loading rubber-tired scraper.

The standard tractor attachment for landfill use is an oversized bulldozer blade, often equipped with side and top extensions shaped to form a concave face of volume capacity larger than for use with earth only. Often the extensions are of open or grid construction to minimize interference with visibility. In smaller operations where the same machine must be used to spread and compact refuse as well as to excavate, haul, and spread cover earth, a front-shovel is versatile and suitable. A variation is a combination bulldozer with a movable shell-like closure, which combines some of the advantages of the bulldozer and the front-shovel in a single unit. All of these are available in a wide range of sizes and makes.

Generally speaking cities of up to 15,000 population can handle the spreading, compacting, and covering of a landfill with one machine of 1 cubic yard capacity; cities between 15,000 and 30,000 need one larger unit, of 2 cubic yards capacity; cities between 30,000 and 75,000 can do the job with two units of 3 cubic yards capacity each.

Fig. 42. Crawler tractor equipped with special landfill bulldozer blade. This is the type of machine most commonly used for spreading and compacting refuse.

If it is necessary to haul cover material 200 to 500 feet, a wheeled scraper in conjunction with a crawler-type tractor dozer should be considered in communities of 30,000 to 100,000. If water conditions interfere seriously with operation of a tractor at the base of the fill, a dragline and bulldozer may be a good combination. The dragline can operate from firm footing on top of the fill to excavate and place cover material, but the dozer is still required to place and compact the refuse and to spread the cover evenly.

Rubber-tired tractors pulling scrapers and self-powered, self-loading scraper units are useful at sanitary landfills where long hauls on the site are required to provide cover material. They are usually used with track-type tractors that place, spread, and compact the refuse. The self-powered type are high-speed, high-capacity, single-purpose, expensive units that are justified only for larger operations that can make efficient use of their capacities.

Rubber-tired tractors are sometimes equipped with a dozer blade and used for spreading and compacting refuse as well as hauling cover. However, better traction under slippery conditions and invulnerability to tire damage give the crawler-type the edge for general placing, spreading, and compaction duties.

Wheeled-type tractors employing steel wheels with large studs or feet have some advantages in compactive effect, particularly when used on bulky, oversized wastes or on demolition wastes containing wood.

Fig. 43. A steel-wheeled tractor with heavy studs for breaking and compacting refuse. This machine weighs 63,000 pounds and employs a large landfill-type dozer blade for placing and spreading refuse.

Capacities of Sanitary Landfill Equipment

To make cost estimates of landfill operations, it is necessary to know how much refuse various kinds of equipment can handle a day. The Los Angeles County Sanitation Districts made a survey of refuse collection practices among large cities in the western and southwestern states. From the data gathered on equipment usage, the quantity of refuse handled by a piece of equipment was calculated for each landfill operation reported upon. A comparison of the figures reveals an apparent upper limit for the quantity of refuse a unit of equipment can handle.

The survey showed that two landfills operated by the City of San Diego each received about 250 tons of combined rubbish a day, each site operating with one 47,000-pound, 180 drawbar horsepower crawler bulldozer full-time and another part-time. A privately operated landfill in Los Angeles receives about 700 tons of refuse a day and operates with two 180 drawbar horsepower crawler bulldozers full-time and one 180 drawbar horsepower crawler tractor and carryall scraper part-time.

In Seattle, the survey revealed, where landfills were operated on a contract basis, experience indicates that a landfill requires the use of a crawler bulldozer with 180 drawbar horsepower when 2,000 cubic yards or more (truck box measure) of fill a day are handled, 102 drawbar horsepower when 1,000 to 2,000 cubic yards a day are handled, and 75

STANDARD LANDFILL EQUIPMENT

CRAWLER TRACTOR   RUBBER-TIRED TRACTOR

FRONT-END ACCESSORIES

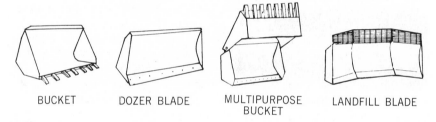

BUCKET   DOZER BLADE   MULTIPURPOSE   LANDFILL BLADE
                                    BUCKET

SPECIALIZED EQUIPMENT

SCRAPER

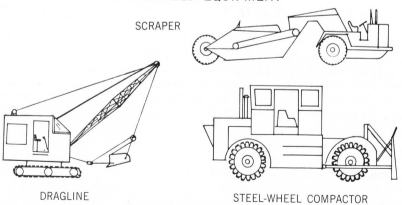

DRAGLINE   STEEL-WHEEL COMPACTOR

Fig. 44. Various kinds of earth moving equipment can be used for sanitary landfill operations. The basic machines usually used are shown above. Under special circumstances those shown in the bottom half have advantageous applications.

drawbar horsepower when up to 1,000 cubic yards a day are handled. The equipment places and compacts the refuse as well as the earth cover that is brought in by truck from other sources.

Based on experience at these landfills, one crawler bulldozer of the 180 drawbar horsepower class and 47,000-pound gross weight size can adequately handle about 250 tons of refuse a day, assuming that excavation for cover presents no special problems and that the cover is hauled no more than 100 yards to the working face. If a ripper is used to loosen cover material for excavation or if a long haul requires a carryall scraper, the quantity of refuse put in a landfill per bulldozer decreases. If a landfill receives many times 250 tons of refuse a day and uses several bulldozers for its operation, the efficiency of each unit can be increased by specializing and coordinating functions.

The Mission Bay cut and cover site operated by the City of San Diego receives about 250 tons of refuse a day, which is adequately handled by a dragline with a 1½-cubic-yard bucket and a 180 drawbar horsepower crawler bulldozer. At another cut and cover landfill, operated by the City of Fresno, a dragline with a 1½-cubic-yard bucket is used 5 days a week and a 75 drawbar horsepower crawler bulldozer 1 day a week to place, compact, and cover about 220 tons of refuse a day.

Based on reports of cut and cover operations, from 5½ to 17 equipment hours per 1,000 cubic yards of refuse may be required. At Riverside, California, two crawler tractors, one equipped with a dozer and the other with a multi-purpose tool, require 8 hours of equipment time per 1,000 cubic yards of refuse handled.

Within its practical range of haul distance one tractor-drawn 15-cubic-yard, self-loading, self-dumping scraper can generally haul enough cover each day to satisfactorily cover 400 to 600 tons of refuse. For longer hauls and a volume of 500 to 1,000 tons per day, one self-propelled, rubber-tired scraper of 15 cubic yards can handle the covering chores with the same degree of satisfaction. As the level of operation approaches 1,000 tons per day, a larger scraper of 24 or more cubic yards is advisable. To provide back-up and flexibility, a site equipped with one self-propelled, rubber-tired scraper could also have a crawler tractor-drawn scraper on standby. The tractor for this unit would normally be used to spread and compact refuse, but, in emergency, it could be used to obtain cover. The tractor need only be equipped with a double drum cable unit in addition to the dozer operating unit to be capable of performing both jobs.

Accessory Equipment

Various types of accessory equipment may also be necessary for a landfill: a ripper may be required if the cover material is difficult to excavate; tractor-towed or self-propelled scrapers if the cover material must be moved more than 150 to 300 feet; a power shovel for operations involving soft or wet soil; a sheepsfoot roller for compacting road fills; a water truck to control dust and supply water for fire fighting; an extra bulldozer tractor to push-load scrapers. Provision should be made for standby equipment that can be used if regular equipment breaks down. Some spare parts may be advantageous if the source of dealer parts is a long distance away.

Personnel

The general public is seldom aware of the detailed planning and design that precedes the establishment of a landfill project. However, the operational phase is in the public eye, and the entire project will be judged by the people solely on the quality of the operation. Competent, well-trained, and motivated operating personnel are necessary to merit continuing public acceptance of a landfill disposal system.

Manpower requirements to dispose of a given volume of solid waste by the sanitary landfill method vary widely throughout the country, on the basis of data reported to APWA. The primary variables are the size and kind of site, the climate, limited use or open to the public, kinds of waste materials accepted, difficulty and method of obtaining cover material, free to users or charges levied for service, and the degree of attention paid to aesthetics, landscaping, and appearance.

Sites serving a small number of people which are open for disposal on selected days are usually manned by employees who perform other functions on the days the site is closed. Some smaller sites, open the normal work week, have contract operators who spread, compact, and cover the waste for a fixed contract cost. A site which accepts only household refuse collected in compaction-type vehicles is easier to operate and requires less personnel than if the site is open free to the public, and less still if the site is open to the public and a fee is collected for dumping. If cover material is readily available at reasonable haul distance from the dumping face, personnel requirements will be much less than if the cover material must be imported to the site by trucks traveling surface streets.

The listing in Table 18 is from the records of the Los Angeles County Sanitation Districts and applies to a sanitary landfill open to the public with all solid waste weighed and disposal charges levied on the net weight of the load.

TABLE 18

LANDFILL SITE PERSONNEL

Classification	Tons per Day			
	200	500	1,000	4,000
Equipment operator	1	2	4	12
Laborer	0	0	1	2
Weighmaster	1	1	1	3
Foreman	0	0	1	1

Additional staff requirements on a part time basis include managerial, supervisory, engineering, planning, administrative, clerical, and legal personnel.

Data on landfill operations reported by 138 cities show that all except 34 cities with populations of 15,000 or less operate fills with 1 man; of 38 cities with more than 15,000 but less than 50,000 residents, 15 used 1 man to run the entire fill operation, 18 used 2 men, and 3 reported they used 3 men. The point at which it was necessary to go from using 1 man to 2 men varied widely, but that point was usually reached in cities in the 16,000 to 25,000 population category. Of 14 cities with more than 50,000 but less than 100,000 population, 7 reported operating fills with 2 men, 5 with 3 men, and 2 with more than 3 men.

Costs

A wide range of costs for sanitary landfill disposal have been reported. The total cost of a fill is the sum of land costs plus site development costs, plus operating and equipment costs, plus landscaping and maintenance costs.

From the long-range point of view, the cost of the land for the site is small; land in a metropolitan area used for fills usually increases in value when the fill is completed; and land in remote areas used for disposal sites may cost less than 1 cent per ton of refuse disposed of.

Land for disposal in the Los Angeles metropolitan area has been purchased for prices ranging from $2,000 to $20,000 per acre since 1965. Land has been leased from private owners for prices ranging from 4 cents to 30 cents per cubic yard of space used. Depending on the degree of compaction obtained in the landfill, the lease cost per ton of refuse disposed could range from 6 cents to 50 cents.

The planner should consider that the economics of a landfill site purchased for, say $10,000 per acre, is dramatically affected by the depth of the solid waste fill. If filled to a depth of only 10 feet, the land cost is 62 cents per cubic yard of space filled. But if the average depth of fill can be increased to 100 feet the cost is only 6 cents per cubic yard of space filled. As a bonus, the average density of the 100-foot deep fill will be considerably greater due to the weight of the refuse itself.

The most recent purchase of land for sanitary landfill use by a governmental agency in the City of Los Angeles cost $2,000 per acre. The fill planned for this site averages 200,000 cubic yards per acre (average depth 124 feet). While the cost of $2,000 per acre might seem quite high when compared to land costs in less populated areas, the 1 cent cost per cubic yard of space to be filled is extremely low.

The economics of the effect of location on collection costs must also be considered in weighing the total systems justification for high site acquisition cost. The site cost of disposal space is a small part of the total cost of collection and disposal in almost any case, and its location may be a major factor in determining collection costs, which are by far the greater part of the total systems cost.

The cost of site development can be analyzed from factors already discussed. Expenditures include those for access roads, water supply, fences, firebreak clearance (if required), landscaping, surface runoff diversion facilities, weighing devices, and an office and equipment shed. The person planning the fill can usually estimate site development costs quite accurately on the basis of physical factors, reasonable standards, and the requirements of government agencies.

With landfill projects serving a city of 50,000 or more persons, it is possible to use equipment advantageously in relation to the amount of refuse disposed of, so that operating costs for a "large-capacity" site are not materially different from those for one of "small capacity." There are so many different methods of operation for landfills, however, that operating costs for large landfills vary widely from place to place.

Experience shows that sanitary landfills are usually operated for from as little as 75 cents to more than $4.00 per ton of refuse handled. The total includes costs of land, equipment, depreciation, labor, operation, and contingencies. Wide variations result from differing operating requirements as well as from the size of the fill. Costs for a small operation (under 50,000 tons per year) run from $1.25 to as much as $5.00 per ton. Larger fills (over 50,000 tons per year) generally fall between 75 cents to $2.00 per ton.

The many variables in operations and their effect on costs are discussed in Chapter 11, Refuse Disposal Management.

SPECIAL PROBLEMS

Winter Operations

Sanitary landfills can be operated in the United States throughout the year, even in extremely cold climates. A landfill was operated as an experiment in Mandan, North Dakota, through the winter of 1949, during which temperatures dropped to as low as 44 degrees below zero. The Mandan project has been continued successfully since and many other

Fig. 45. Even in North Dakota, sanitary landfills can be operated during the winter. In Mandan (upper left), chunks of frozen earth crust are common; in Bismarck (upper right), earth cover material is stockpiled; and in Minot (left), excavations are made through the winter.

cities have also successfully operated landfills under similar climatic conditions.

On the basis of experience with the Mandan project (in relatively sandy soil), the following recommendations for year-around operations in an extremely cold climate have been made:

1. Scarify the area for winter operations before there is a frost and insulate the ground with leaves or similar material (2 to 3-foot depth).
2. Excavate trenches in advance of cold weather and stockpile cover material for use during the winter.
3. Excavate an "undisturbed area," if possible. (An "undisturbed area" is one that has not had the vegetation and earth compressed by, for example, numerous trucks driving over it. "Undisturbed areas" have been successfully used for fill sites in Bismarck, North Dakota.)

It is also recommended that tractor equipment for winter weather operations include ice and snow grousers and a heated cab for the operator. A heated garage for equipment storage and headquarters for personnel are necessities.

Wet Weather Operations

Wet weather operations give rise to problems because maneuverability of trucks as well as landfill equipment is often seriously impeded. The following recommendations have been made for sites subject to even occasional periods of heavy rainfall:

1. Use well-drained sites with sandy loam soil if possible.
2. Build all-weather access roads.
3. Stockpile such materials as cinders, broken asphalt paving, or planking for construction of firm surface lanes from the permanent access road to the area of operation.
4. Dump refuse some distance from the operating face of the fill and bulldoze it to the area of operation under extreme conditions. This practice is advocated in most cases only as a final resort.
5. If a load is not prohibitively heavy, a tractor sometimes can tow refuse trucks to the operating area. (Care must be taken not to damage the trucks, however. On one fill, a dozer pulled the whole front end off a mired vehicle.)
6. Use other sites during prolonged wet periods. In certain places, such as New Orleans, use of alternative sites is a common practice. Techniques for handling wet weather problems vary, of course, according to the location of a fill site.

Dust

Dust can be effectively allayed by periodically sprinkling the site with water. On large operations a tank truck may be assigned to the fill site. In New York City fences surrounding some sites are designed to help control dust. Oiled roadways or the use of calcium chloride minimizes dust from traffic on access roads.

Odors

Malodorous gases are the products of putrefaction and of deep-seated anaerobic digestion, particularly of the protein organic content of the refuse. Ponds with churned-in, high organic content, polluted stagnant drainage ditches, and leaching from refuse fills are sources of objectionable anaerobic decomposition gases. But properly operated landfills are free of odor, and prompt corrective action can forestall complaints from the public if odors do become a nuisance.

The following are recommended to keep odors to a minimum:

1. Promptly, rapidly, and continuously cover freshly dumped garbage with earth or refuse.
2. Cover refuse daily to a depth sufficient to seal in odors, deny harborage to vectors, and prevent fires.
3. Seal surface cracks in completed areas of the site to prevent emission of gases.
4. Eliminate surface pools, side leaching action, and seepages at toes of filled embankments.
5. Spray the refuse with suitable deodorants if sufficient cover has not been used to prevent the escape of malodorous gas.

An emulsion of orthodichlorbenzine, 1 part to 125 parts water, has been found satisfactory as a deodorizing agency. It is largely a masking agent, with some larvicidal properties. It can be sprayed with a conventional fire hose and nozzle at a rate of about 6,000 gallons an acre; the moisture added by spraying promotes more rapid digestion and stabilization of the putrefiables.

Fresh refuse seldom has the unpleasant odor of putrefying material. Therefore, adequate and frequent collection is extremely important. Careful wrapping of garbage by the householder, collections twice a week during warm seasons, and prompt disposal of garbage at the fill should be sufficient to control garbage odors at most landfill operations.

Fire

Fires in freshly dumped refuse or even within a completed fill are possibilities to be reckoned with. Fires in fills are caused by carelessness, by dumping hot ashes or incinerator residue, by spontaneous combustion, and by the presence of highly flammable materials.

When near the surface of a fill, fires can be extinguished by spraying with water, either from large, especially designed mobile tanks or street flushers, or from street hydrants. Deep-seated fires can best be brought under control by excavating them with bulldozers or draglines for surface exposure and spraying. Both surface and deep-seated fires may at times be extinguished economically and successfully by smothering with an impervious blanket of earth.

Fire hazards are negligible on landfill operations in which recommended compaction techniques are used because oxygen required for initial combustion is limited in a well-compacted and covered fill. Good practice calls for earth cover on the face of the fill at the close of each day's operation, which, in effect, creates individual cells that confine a fire, if it does start, to a relatively small area.

Disposal of large quantities of brush, logs, and tree stumps in a sanitary fill is difficult because they are bulky and hard to compact. Sometimes they are burned and the ashes dumped into the fill. If they are, the burning should be done away from the immediate operating area of the fill, or, if quantities justify, even at a completely different site. In cities in which stringent air pollution control ordinances are enforced, this practice is not permitted. However, the use of a wood hog or chipper for processing forestry wastes practically eliminates the problems of handling them in a sanitary landfill.

A water system with at least 30 pounds per square inch pressure is desirable for fire control at a fill site. The system should have a minimum of a 1½-inch diameter line or a 5,000-gallon storage reservoir or tank. A pond or stream may be used as a storage reservoir, but reliable pumps of adequate size must be available.

Ground and Surface Water Pollution

The possibility that a sanitary landfill will pollute ground and surface waters in the area of the fill must be considered. A number of investigations have been made in recent years of the physical "behavior" of landfills and the effects of leachate from fills on underlying ground waters. Briefly, the reports of these studies say:

For pollution of ground water by refuse leaching, three conditions must exist: (1) the site must be over or adjacent to an aquifer; (2) there must be supersaturation within the fill caused by the flow of ground water into the fill from percolation of precipitation and surface water runoff, by water of decomposition, or by an artificial source; (3) leached fluids must be produced and the leachate must be capable of entering an aquifer.

If sound engineering practices are followed, a site that has both conditions one and two would not be selected for the fill. Condition three can be brought about by a combination of water used for refuse compaction (as at the San Diego landfills), water of decomposition, rainfall, and surface runoff. It is highly improbable, however, that any of them except compaction water would provide sufficient moisture to produce supersaturation in the fill. After a site is filled and the area reclaimed, the surface sources of water for leaching are rainfall, runoff, and irrigation; subsurface sources are high ground water levels due to artificial or natural recharge of aquifers and breaks in water mains and sewers.

An investigation at the University of Southern California in which bins filled with rubbish-garbage mixtures were used for tests showed that a total of 15 inches of water applied at the rate of 1 inch a day is necessary to saturate the fill material and produce free water or leachate. Based on a bin depth of 10 feet, the water amounted to approximately 25 gallons per cubic yard of fill, or approximately 65 gallons per ton. It has been determined experimentally that paper and paper products, which constitute approximately 40 per cent of combustible residential rubbish, can absorb 250 per cent to 300 per cent water by weight. Considering also that the average moisture content of typical mixed refuse (including garbage) is only 45 per cent to 50 per cent, it is obvious that a landfill can absorb large quantities of water without becoming supersaturated. In the investigation, a bin of rubbish identical to that to which water was added had no moisture added and produced no leachate, indicating that the water of decomposition plus 3 inches of rainfall during the five months of the investigation were not in excess of what the fill could absorb.

In experiments in San Diego the amount of water used to aid in compaction of a landfill amounted to an estimated 385 gallons per ton of refuse—more than six times the amount used in the University of Southern California test bin to obtain leachate. The addition of such large quantities of water to a landfill for compaction is not recommended for sites in which there is a possibility of ground water contamination, however.

Investigations in Northeastern Illinois[2], where precipitation is about 33 inches per year, show that precipitation is adequate to infiltrate a landfill and to produce a leachate high in dissolved solids. Mineralization of ground water in the fill declines with increasing age of the fill. Hardness is very high in samples from within the landfill but decreases rapidly with distance away from the landfill, although not as rapidly as the organic components do.

If leaching of a landfill does occur and is not corrected or controlled, the ground water in the immediate vicinity of the fill can become grossly polluted, unfit for human and animal consumption or for industrial and irrigation uses.

The effects of pollution may be classified as physical, chemical, and biological. If essentially anaerobic conditions (absence of oxygen) exist in a landfill, the decomposition of organic matter results in the formation of gases—principally methane, carbon dioxide, ammonia, and hydrogen sulfide. Methane diffuses in all directions but the major part leaves the fill through the earth cover. Hydrogen sulfide, even when present in relatively small amounts, gives leach-polluted waters an offensive taste and odor; however, sulfides are oxidized to tasteless and odorless sulfur and sulfates by oxygen-containing ground water and atmospheric oxygen diffusing into the landfill.

Carbon dioxide, due to its high solubility, combines with water to form carbonic acid, which will react with iron from tin cans and lime from calcareous material and deposits. The leachate cannot, however, contain both ferrous iron and sulfides. Chemically, the effects of carbon dioxide, by increasing the hardness and the effects of ammonia on oxidation and by increasing the nitrate content, are the most significant products of decomposition of organic matter in a landfill operation.

In the University of Southern California investigation the leachate from the test bin to which water was applied contained in excess of 200

[2] R. A. Landon and R. N. Farvolden, *Hydrology of Solid Waste Disposal Sites in Northeastern Illinois*, HEW Demonstration Grant No. 5-001-00006-02.

parts per million (ppm) ammonia and organic nitrogen, with peaks of 845 ppm ammonia nitrogen and 550 ppm organic nitrogen. As 1 part organic or ammoniacal nitrogen can produce 4.43 parts nitrate, the concentration present in the leachate, and potentially in lesser amounts in polluted ground water, can thus exceed by many times the 10 to 20 ppm concentration of nitrate nitrogen in water safe for infant consumption. Excess nitrates are also undesirable in the water supply for certain industries and in irrigation water in certain soils, since excess nitrates tend to reduce soil permeability. Their value as a fertilizer probably outweighs their undesirable properties, however.

Pollution of ground water by bacteria from leaching of landfills might seem to be of prime importance. It has been shown, however, that coliform (intestinal) organisms, commonly used as indicators of sewage contamination, even when present in high concentration in sewage effluent as applied to "spreading" grounds for water reclamation, are seldom found below four feet and never below seven feet, even in highly permeable soil. It has been shown that pumped recharge of polluted waters to underground aquifers results in travel of bacteria for less than 100 feet. Considering that it is accepted practice to locate cesspools as near as 300 feet to water wells, safety against bacterial pollution of ground water by leaching of landfills is assured if water is not pumped from a point immediately adjacent to the fill site.

In summary, only where landfills become supersaturated because of artificial wetting, inadequate drainage of surface runoff from the site, or inundation by high ground water is the threat of ground water pollution real. The problem is complex enough, however, to require the investigation and judgment of competent sanitary engineers on whether a landfill could cause contamination. Since the problem is regional in scope, the responsibility for control of pollution should be delegated to a competent government agency, such as the state or local health department or a water pollution control authority. That agency should establish criteria to determine pollution possibilities.

Responsibility for defining reasonable and beneficial use of the natural waters in California is given to regional water pollution control boards. The regional boards review the geological and hydrological factors affecting each proposed landfill site and set criteria for water quality that allow reasonable uses of the natural waters consistent with acceptable standards. For convenience in considering landfill sites, Water Pollution Control Region No. 4, which has jurisdiction in the Los Angeles and Ventura watershed areas, has established the following classifications:

A. CLASSIFICATION OF DISPOSAL SITES

From consideration of the geology, hydrology, topography, nature of wastes and other pertinent factors, three general classes of disposal sites are established:

(A) CLASS I DISPOSAL SITES

Sites located on non-water-bearing rocks or underlain by isolated bodies of unuseable ground water, which are protected from surface runoff and where surface drainage can be restricted to the site or discharged to a suitable wasteway, and where safe limitations exist with respect to the potential radius of percolation.

(B) CLASS II DISPOSAL SITES

Sites underlain by useable, confined, or free ground water when the minimum elevation of the dump can be maintained above anticipated high ground water elevation, and which are protected from surface runoff and where surface drainage can be restricted to the site or discharged to a suitable wasteway.

(C) CLASS III DISPOSAL SITES

Sites so located as to afford little or no protection to useable waters of the State.

B. NATURE OF WASTES ACCEPTABLE FOR DISPOSAL AT CLASS OF DISPOSAL SITE

This list is not intended to be complete or comprehensive but rather an indication of the nature of wastes acceptable at each class of disposal site. Materials, other than those listed, may be considered separately by the interested governmental agencies and the Regional Water Pollution Control Board.

(A) CLASS I DISPOSAL SITES

No limitation as to either solid or liquid wastes.

(B) CLASS II DISPOSAL SITES

Limited to ordinary household and commercial refuse and/or rubbish, garbage, other decomposable organic refuse, and scrap metal of the nature indicated below at safe elevations above anticipated high ground water elevation in the vicinity of the site:

a. Empty tin can
b. Metals
c. Paper and paper products
d. Cloth and clothing
e. Wood and wood products
f. Lawn clippings, sod, and shrubbery
g. Hair, hide, and bones
h. Small dead animals
i. Roofing paper and tar paper
j. Thoroughly quenched ashes from high temperature incinerators
k. Unquenched ashes mixed with refuse
l. Market refuse
m. Garbage
n. All material acceptable at Class III Disposal Sites without regard to elevation of anticipated high ground water

(C) CLASS III DISPOSAL SITES

Limited to non-water soluble, nondecomposable inert solids of the nature indicated below:

a. Earth, rock, gravel, and concrete
b. Asphalt paving fragments
c. Glass
d. Plaster and plaster board
e. Manufactured rubber products

   f. Steel mill slag
   g. Clay and clay products
   h. Asbestos shingles

To minimize the possibility of underground pollution, the Illinois public health department has made the following recommendations (Idaho's are similar):

(a) Do not build on exposed rock strata. Keep a minimum of 30 feet clay-till overburden between strata and refuse, unless studies indicate that a lesser depth is satisfactory.

(b) Locate fill at least 500 feet from drift wells, unless studies indicate that subsurface seepage is not imminent.

(c) Do not place garbage and refuse in mines or other areas where resulting seepage or leachate may carry waste to water-bearing strata or wells. Remember that chemical pollution may emanate from a fill and probably will travel for long distances as compared to organic and bacterial pollution travel.

(d) Do not locate sanitary fills on or near springs.

(e) Consult the state department of reclamation, state geologist, and the state department of public health regarding any problems of possible underground pollution.

Of note in the field of pollution of water by "tipped" refuse is a 1961 report by the technical committee of the Ministry of Housing and Local Government of the United Kingdom. The summary of this exhaustive technical study is quoted, as follows:

We have carried out experiments designed to give information about the risk of polluting ground water by tipping house refuse (a) where percolate from it has access to that water and (b) direct into water communicating with ground water.

The matter has proved exceedingly complex and it is quite impossible to prepare a short technical summary of our conclusions which would be useful and not at the same time liable to be misleading. It is essential that anyone wishing to use our results should read the whole report.

The experiments carried out included a number on a small scale and two on a much larger one, all under as strict scientific control as possible. They also included experiments on the purification by filtration through gravel and sand of water contaminated by having been in contact with tipped refuse.

One larger scale experiment was on refuse tipped dry and the other on refuse tipped into water. In the former case the whole of the percolate was collected, measured and analyzed over a period of 2 1/2 years, at the end of which time it contained little polluting matter. In the latter case, the water leaving the tank into which tipping had been carried out was controlled, measured and analyzed for about 18 months. The filtration experiments covered about a year.

We have measured the amount of pollution in rainfall after percolating through a controlled tip and found it considerable. We have also shown that the liquid undergoes purification during its subsequent passage through sand and gravel. It seems important to emphasize here that, over-all, our work constitutes no condemnation of controlled tipping. It is generally a satisfactory method of refuse disposal and there is no reason why it should not continue to be widely used. We now have more fundamental knowledge which should be of value in the selection of satisfactory sites. Indeed, as a result of our work it may now be possible, with appropriate safeguards, to bring into use sites hitherto considered unsuitable.

Similarly, we have measured the pollution arising through tipping refuse into water under controlled conditions. Here again, the fact that it is considerable does not mean that such tipping would always constitute a danger to underground water supplies. We believe that it should be possible to use the information we have collected to get a better idea than was formerly possible of the risks which may be attached to the use of any particular sites.

We believe the question of pollution should be pursued. The next step would appear to be to collect information, which, as we explain, might easily be obtainable, relating to existing conditions, and to consider it in the light of our findings. It is likely that this will point the way to further full-scale study, probably in cooperation with some local authorities and water undertakings. Because of the difficulties confronting many local authorities in the matter of sites for refuse disposal, the need for reclamation of certain sites, and the necessity of protecting ground water against pollution, we strongly recommend that the whole matter should be the subject for further work. [3]

SETTLEMENT AND DECOMPOSITION

Settlement

The amount that a sanitary landfill settles depends primarily on what kind of refuse is used and how thoroughly it is compacted. Reports of experience in 58 cities with fill depths varying from 4 feet to 20 feet show that 29 cities had only slight settlement and the other 29 had settlements of from 1 per cent to 25 per cent after two years. The average amount of settling reported was 11 per cent after two years.

Settlement generally varies from 10 per cent to 25 per cent within six months to two years, depending on compaction techniques. If the refuse is compacted in thin layers of 1 to 2 feet as it is placed, the percentage of settlement will probably be low and the site can usually be used for recreational purposes two years after its completion, although periodic maintenance may be necessary for parts of the site that settle unevenly.

The City of Richmond, Virginia, has operated landfills since 1947, reclaiming swamps and wasteland for parks and playgrounds. The city operates as many as six landfills concurrently, placing refuse in layers ranging from 6 to 15 feet deep; 5 to 10 per cent settlement has been observed in them after five years.

In New York, where landfills have layers of refuse from 15 to 20 feet deep, it was found that initial shrinkage in dumped refuse is caused by compaction from heavy equipment and the weight of the refuse and cover. Initial settlement reduces 2 cubic yards of truck material to 1 cubic yard in the fill; there is subsequent shrinkage from filling in voids left when semi-compacted tin cans rust out and organic material in the refuse decomposes. There may be even further subsidence from compres-

---

[3] Ministry of Housing and Local Government, *Pollution of Water by Tipped Refuse* (London: 1961).

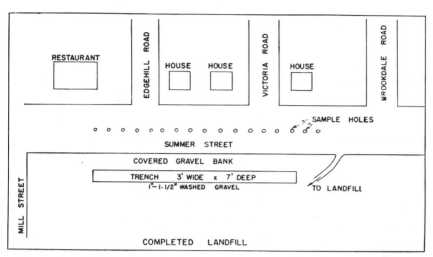

Fig. 46. A hazard of improperly engineered sanitary landfills is accumulation of methane, a gas resulting from decomposition of refuse. When a fill site in Arlington, Massachusetts, was oiled and the cover of the fill thereby sealed, methane gas flowed laterally through a gravel bank toward residences, rather than vertically and harmlessly through the cover of the fill. A washed gravel trench was constructed, as shown above, to intercept the gas and permit it to escape into the atmosphere.

sion or shifting of subsoils and from expulsion of entrapped waters, particularly in water-logged, silty soils. Subsequent compaction and settlement eventually causes 3 cubic yards of refuse in the truck to be reduced to 1 cubic yard in the fill. It was found in New York that about 90 per cent of the total settlement occurs in the first two to five years. The remaining 10 percent may be over such a long period that it has little bearing on the grade planned for the site.

Fills on marshy lands, in boggy areas, and in ponded or open waters settle more and at a faster rate than fills on dry land because of accelerated decomposition, subsurface subsidence, mud wave displacements, and, sometimes, leaching action.

Many landfills must be checked periodically, depending on local conditions. In any event, fills must be regraded occasionally and the surfaces must be maintained until the fill has become reasonably stable.

Decomposition

Decomposition of landfills depends on many factors, including permeability of cover material, depth of burial and rainfall, moisture content and putrescibility of the refuse, and degree of compaction.

In Richmond, Virginia, and in New Orleans refuse in landfills has reportedly been decomposed in three to four years. As a general rule, however, climatological and operational conditions are such that much slower decomposition may be expected.

Garbage and rubbish are made up principally of carbohydrates, fats, and proteins. The elements of carbon, oxygen, hydrogen, nitrogen, and sulfur are most prevalent in organic refuse. Refuse in sanitary landfills decomposes slowly through the anaerobic process of decomposition. Microorganisms of the soil and refuse are responsible for this decomposition. The organic acids of decomposition tend to pickle refuse, especially in deep fills. After many successive breakdowns through the feeding and growth of microorganisms and the action of their enzymes, the end-products are gases and humus material. The gaseous end-products are represented by the diagram in Figure 47.

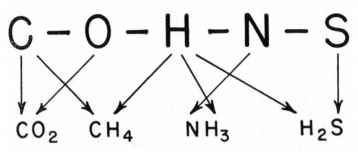

Fig. 47. *Carbohydrates, fats, and proteins, plus micro-biological fermentation, produce gaseous end-products and humus.*

Decomposition occurs anaerobically at elevated temperatures. In a series of studies of landfills made in New York in the late 1930's, temperatures up to 160° F. were generated by the microorganisms operating within the fill. On the basis of subsequent investigations, however, it appears that average temperatures attained in a sanitary landfill may be much less—from 100° to 120° F.

Methane (CH_4) and carbon dioxide (CO_2) are principal gases produced during the process of degradation of refuse in a fill. Studies of a Seattle landfill, made by the University of Washington, indicated that the greatest amount of gas is produced from refuse that is about one-half to two years old if the refuse was placed in layers 20 to 40 feet deep or if there are two or more 8-foot layers. It was also observed that gas production was slowed as the moisture content of the refuse decreased. If completed cells settled below the water level of a swampy area or if surface water percolated into the refuse, gas production increased.

Waste gases were burned at a Seattle fill where earth cover was inadequate (see Figure 48) to eliminate odors. It was found that the static gas pressure developed in the burners was low (equivalent to about ½ inch of water) and an "average" burner was found to give off about 0.7 cubic foot a minute.

On one landfill, workers drove a 1-inch pipe into a decomposing section of the fill, fashioned a tip on the upper end of the pipe, and lighted the gas coming off, providing a continuous flame for boiling

Fig. 48. Studies by the University of Washington indicate that controlled burning of waste gas at a sanitary landfill may be an effective way to control odors where the earth cover is inadequate to do so. This burning of gas was done at the Union Bay landfill in Seattle.

coffee. This gas may be explosive, of course, if trapped in an enclosed space.

Explosive mixtures have gotten into structures built on landfills; the gases have seeped out of the fill and upward along an insulated water or sewer pipe from the fill to an enclosed space in the building. A spark from an electric fixture is all that is needed to ignite the gas. For this reason, all buildings on landfills must be completely vented between the building floor and the landfill surface. A granular material such as crushed stone or slag should be placed over the fill in such situations to permit collection venting of gas into the atmosphere.

Hydrogen sulfide is not a problem ordinarily on dry landfills. The diurnal entrance and exit of sea water high in sulfates into tidal marsh fills, however, may lead to a serious problem from the action of sulfates, which reduce bacteria and which in turn produce sulfides. Diking should be used outside the fill to prevent sea water from going in and out of the fill. A similar problem may arise if a sulfate-containing stream of water passes under or from the fill. The flow of water should be ditched around the fill to prevent contamination.

Other aspects of decomposition are incidental and may have no effect if a landfill site is used as an open area such as a park or storage lot; however, decomposition will affect settling of building foundations. Time of decomposition is unknown. Landfills excavated 25 years after completion have revealed that many materials are virtually unchanged, particularly those that are cellulose, suggesting that fills ordinarily cannot be expected to undergo complete decomposition for generations.

In 1965 the State Water Quality Control Board of California published a report (No. 31) entitled "In-Situ Investigation of Movements of Gases Produced from Decomposing Refuse," a summary of two and one-half years of study beginning in 1961 and extending through June, 1964. These studies are continuing under variably controlled conditions. The conclusions reached in the report are:

1. The test refuse fill, as constructed, has permitted estimates of the rates and quantities of refuse gases passing into the soil and into the atmosphere. Predictions were made pertaining to the active life of the refuse fill and to the concentrations of CO_2 which can be expected in the refuse and in the surrounding soil in the future.

2. The refuse continues to decompose anaerobically primarily, with some aerobism occurring in the top layer of refuse. Inter-diffusion of decomposition gases takes place within the refuse.

3. The maximum concentrations of CO_2 throughout the fill were found shortly after the refuse was placed and covered—within eleven days after the top silt cover was spread. CO_2 concentrations within the fill were found as high as 89 percent, by volume, in the bottom layer; other concentrations throughout the fill were commonly from 60 to 70 percent during the "bloom." Rapid buildup of CO_2 was accompanied by rapid disappearance of O_2 in the refuse during the early period. Only small quantities of CH_4 were detected during the early decomposition.

4. CO_2 concentrations in the fill have decreased since the early "bloom". CH_4 concentrations in the fill began to increase with time and then leveled off. Maximum CH_4 found was 29.6 percent for one probe; most common CH_4 concentrations were up to 11 percent.

5. As of June 1964, the CO_2 concentration in the bottom layer of refuse was 28 percent in contact with the adjacent subsoil.

6. CO_2 was the only gas of decomposition found in significant quantities in the adjacent and surrounding soil. CH_4 was found up to 4 percent (at 40 ft in Well No. 1 directly below the fill).

7. During the initial bloom of CO_2 in the refuse, the velocity of CO_2 in the soil was calculated to be approximately 0.8 to 1 ft/day. As the

CO_2 gradient between refuse and soil decreased, the velocity into the soil also decreased.

8. The quantity of CO_2 passing through the one-foot silt cover of the fill into the atmosphere is about 18 times the quantity passing into the soil, at the present CO_2 concentrations in the fill and soil. About 24 times more CH_4 passes through the cover than goes into the soil. These results are based on an *adjusted measured* rate of passage to the atmosphere in consideration of the rates calculated theoretically.

9. The rate of CO_2 passage to the atmosphere, calculated theoretically, is from four to eight times more than the rate measured with the surface gas monitoring apparatus.

10. The active "life" of the refuse fill was estimated on the basis of the total carbon initially present in the refuse and on the past and present rates at which carbon has passed out of the fill. With the assumption that the calculated initial amount of carbon was "available" the following projections were made:

Per Cent of Initial Carbon Gone	Years	CO_2 Concentration in Bottom Refuse Layers
50	57	12 per cent
90	950	3 per cent

11. A sizeable CO_2 concentration in the bottom layer of refuse can be expected for many years, with CO_2 passing into the ground.

12. The concentration of CO_2 and of other gases that will actually be picked up by the ground water depends on the depth of water and the dilution provided. To determine probable concentrations requires knowledge of ground water flow.

13. CO_2 passes into the ground from a refuse fill; if it is deemed necessary to isolate it from ground water, control methods must be formulated.

14. It is pointed out that extrapolations from the results obtained in the pilot-scale study at Azusa to large prototype landfills need to be done with due consideration for the differences discussed. . . . The data obtained from the small test site showed the possible magnitude of the accumulated CO_2 concentration at the interface between refuse and soil. Because of the shallowness of the test site the CO_2 concentrations and CH_4 concentrations found in the refuse may not be representative of large landfills.

Uses of Completed Landfills

Land reclaimed by landfill disposal operations can be a valuable asset to a city. Many uses—parks, playgrounds, golf courses, parking areas, landing fields, light industrial or commercial buildings—are suitable for completed fills. The use of a site may be restricted by its surroundings, however, and to some extent by the amount of settlement in the fill. A fill several miles from a residential district is not a desirable site for a playground or parking area, and a fill that can be expected to settle

Fig. 49. Landfill sites have been used for many purposes. Above is a baseball field complete with observation tower, batting practice areas, and clubhouse.

rapidly and unevenly is not suitable even for light construction. If a suitable use is decided upon for a fill site before the fill is begun, the method of operation and degree of compaction can be planned to provide for the needs of that use.

Recreation and Parking Facilities

Parks, playgrounds, and ball fields are the most popular uses for landfill sites. Two feet of well-compacted final cover is sufficient for most parks and playgrounds. If trees or large shrubs are to be planted, a deeper final cover may be necessary.

If a site is to be used for a golf course, plans for the finished surface should be decided upon in time to allow fashioning the topography with refuse lifts. Landfill sites used for parks differ only in surface configuration of final grades from those used for golf courses. Degree of refuse compaction, depth of final cover, and other factors are the same for either use. Montebello, California, has a police department-sponsored playground on a completed landfill site; a land reclamation park in Burbank, California, provides both park facilities and access roads to other facilities.

The amount of settlement at a landfill site that is to be used for a parking lot is more important than the amount at a site to be used for a park or playground. If any appreciable settlement occurs after a parking lot has been paved, the paving may crack and drainage may be affected. A final cover of 2 feet on a parking lot site is sufficient if the cover, as well as the underlying refuse, is well compacted. Flexible paving (bituminous binder) is ordinarily recommended for parking lots on land-fills.

Parking facilities and stables have been built on tidelands reclaimed through landfills near the Golden Gate race track on the eastern shore of San Francisco Bay. Reclaimed areas also are used as industrial building sites in the Bay Area. Sand pits reclaimed by landfilling in Dallas, Texas, are now used by a car-transport company and for recreational purposes. In Richmond, Virginia, parking lots for shopping centers have been constructed on completed fills. More than 10,000 acres of tidal and marshy land in New York have been reclaimed, on which streets, parks, airports, industrial buildings, and large housing developments have been built.

Buildings

It is of utmost importance to understand that construction on completed refuse fills can be hazardous if the requirements peculiar to construction on fills are not followed, and that the site may be odorous if the fill is not properly made. Furthermore, although there are many reports of successful construction on fills, further research is needed in the field to encourage more extensive and better use of completed landfill sites.

A landfill upon which buildings are to be constructed should be as stable as possible. A well-compacted final cover 2 or 3 feet deep over a fill of well-compacted refuse should settle no more than 5 to 10 per cent (as in Richmond, Virginia, and other cities). Housing has been built satisfactorily on such fills in Dallas and Richmond, although in Richmond there was some trouble with settlement cracks in foundation concrete slabs. If settlement after construction is anticipated, special attention must be given to the design of sewer and water lines to prevent them from breaking or drainage from being reversed. Foundations and footings should be conservatively designed and no rigid or stucco construction should be used.

Completed landfills provide inadequate support for heavy construction; however, either conventional pile or raft-type foundations, required in any event for an underlying marshy, silty subbase, will normally be satisfactory.

Guides for Construction. Since fills made with ashes, construction wastes, or similar inert materials pose few construction problems and since fills are seldom made of garbage only, the concern is with construction on fills made of mixed refuse.

The following rules, recommended to the 1959 American Public Works Congress,[4] were formulated to help prevent hazards of methane gases in buildings on filled sites. They are based on the concept that:

1. The subsurface gases could be intercepted and dissipated harmlessly into the atmosphere through venting by means of suitably designed porous, gravel filled trenches or by pipes inserted into the body of the fill.

---

[4] Casimir A. Rogus, "Use of Completed Sanitary Landfill Sites," *1959 Yearbook* (Chicago: American Public Works Association, 1959), pp. 129-131.

2. The discharge of landfill gases into structures could be arrested by means of subsurface enclosing envelopes of gas-tight construction.

It was recommended that all structures built on land filled in part or in whole with putrefiable material or that may possibly have been filled with putrefiable material must meet the following minimum requirements:

Houses:

A. No cellars, basements, crawl spaces or similar open spaces shall be permitted below finished grade.
B. The ground floor shall be at least 1 foot above finished grade and shall be of permanently gas-tight construction. The fill immediately underneath shall be of nonporous materials to a depth of 24 inches.
C. All pipes, ducts, and conduits piercing the ground floor shall have gas-tight gaskets of an approved permanent nature.

Multiple Dwellings:

Use any one of the following three alternates.

Alternate I. (Same as for Houses.)

Alternate II. Provide a 3-foot high crawl space—above finished grade—under the entire area of building. This crawl space to be permanently ventilated through fixed louvered openings in the enclosing walls and having sufficient area to provide 10 changes of air per hour. The crawl space shall have gas-tight floor construction at the top and an impervious floor slab at the bottom.

Alternate III. If the structure is to have a basement or cellar, it shall conform with the following minimum requirements:

1. An approved continuous permanently gas-tight envelope shall enclose the entire outside face of the walls and the underside portion of the basement slab.
2. All pipes, ducts, and conduits piercing this protective envelope shall be equipped with gas-tight gaskets of an approved permanent nature.
3. Provide, above grade, fixed louvered openings through the outside basement walls so as to permit at least 10 changes of air per hour.
4. Install around the perimeter of the building a continuous trench, 3 feet wide by 3 feet deep, filled with gravel or similar other approved porous material.

Industrial and Commercial Buildings:

The superstructure construction shall comply with that specified for either Alternate II or III above.

Where undecomposed or partially decomposed putrescibles are exposed, as in the construction of basements and trenches, putrefaction and release of odorous gases take place. The use of an oxidizing agent to control odors may be required.

Bearing Values. Dynamic and static field tests on a refuse fill with an average in-place life of four years and an average compacted depth of 20 feet on top of a 10 to 15-foot layer of weak, compressible organic silt and meadow mat developed the following findings:

Dynamic Loadings: Freshly placed, compacted refuse will support repeated loadings of large rubber-tired equipment in excess of 25,000 pounds per tire. This supporting value is somewhat lower for older refuse fills, particularly when uncovered and wet.

Static Loadings: Well-seasoned refuse fills placed in wet areas will support uniform loads of about 2,500 pounds per square foot if subjected to an equivalent preload for at least one year. Heavier loadings may require special foundation designs; each fill should be studied individually.

Air Fields

Landfill sites used for landing strips for aircraft must be well compacted and able to support, without excessive surface deflection, the wheel loads

Fig. 50. A former sanitary landfill is now the South Coast Botanic Gardens in Los Angeles County, California.

of the largest aircraft that will use the strip. A well-compacted final cover 2 feet thick should be adequate for a light plane strip; however, additional cover may be required if large commercial planes use the field. As with parking lots built on completed landfills, paving for landing strips should be flexible.

LaGuardia Airport in New York was built on a landfill; and in Meriden, Connecticut, a runway at the municipal airport was extended over land reclaimed by landfilling. In Morgantown, West Virginia, where land reclaimed by landfilling was used for a landing strip, the entire fill operation was conducted with a crawler tractor. Tests made after compaction showed no appreciable settlement. A load equivalent to 65.9 pounds per square inch, the equivalent of the load of the main wheel of a DC-4, was applied to the fill and settlement was negligible.

Agriculture

The degree of stability and depth of final cover for a completed landfill used for agricultural purposes depend largely on the kind of agricultural use. Settlement is relatively unimportant if a stockyard is to be built; 2 feet or less of compacted cover is adequate. If crops are to be grown on the completed fill, settlement is important if it affects irrigation channel grades; and final soil cover must be sufficiently deep and of suitable material for growing crops. Surface drainage channels should be paved or stabilized to prevent erosion and fill leaching. The possibility of ground water pollution from leaching by irrigation water must be evaluated before a decision is made to use a fill site for growing irrigated crops.

In Kearney, Nebraska, reclaimed gravel pits are being used as sites for raising alfalfa, with 2 feet of final cover sufficient. The British make liberal use of land reclaimed by landfilling for agricultural purposes.

LANDFILLS IN SMALL TOWNS

With good planning and efficient operation, small towns of 5,000 and less population can operate sanitary landfills effectively and economically.

On such small projects, a tractor is needed only two or three hours a day (or, for that matter, on alternating days if there is alternate-day collection of refuse), so the tractor can also be used for other municipal projects—gravel loading, snow removal, and street excavations, for instance.

It has frequently been suggested that light equipment, costing well under $10,000, can be used to operate a landfill in a small town. Field demonstrations show that light equipment can be used with reasonable satisfaction for compacting and covering household and light commercial refuse in a site excavated with heavy equipment.

The U.S. Pubic Health Service conducted a research project on equipment types in Chandler, Arizona, in 1954, using two tractors: one of class 1, 20 to 25 drawbar horsepower and 2 to 3 tons total weight; the other of class 3, 30 to 40 drawbar horsepower and 4 to 8 tons total weight. Based on the field studies in Chandler, the Public Health Service reported:

1. Spreading and compacting refuse in a sanitary landfill for either a large or small city requires rugged equipment that can withstand the torques developed on the tractor frame when the tractor runs over large, solid objects that are present in refuse from a city of any size. Durability and dependability of a tractor, as well as the purchase price and economy of operation, must be considered when a tractor is to be used for landfills.

2. The class 3 tractor, equipped with an ordinary bulldozer blade, adequately and economically did in a 30-hour week all of the work that must be done with a tractor on a landfill operation for a city producing 69 tons of refuse weekly. It appears, therefore, that 100 tons of refuse can be handled by a class 3 tractor in a 44-hour week, and considerably more in areas where soils are light and easy to excavate.

3. The class 3 tractor used in this study was dependable and durable

*Fig. 51. Landfill sites make use of unproductive, idle land. An apart-
ment-condominium complex (left) rises over a former sanitary landfill in
Chicago, Illinois. The city of Richmond, Virginia, converted a landfill
into a heliport (right).*

and operation costs compared favorably with those for heavy equipment used on large landfill projects.

4. The class 1 tractor is not sturdy enough for all kinds of landfill
   operations. It may be suitable for small towns in which soils are light
   and easy to excavate. It has been used satisfactorily for fill operations
   on sites that were first excavated by heavier equipment and at fills
   for household and light commercial refuse only.
5. Operating costs for a class 1 tractor, when it was the only piece of
   mechanical equipment used to operate a sanitary landfill, were excessive because the rate of disposal was low and repair costs high.
6. A reconditioned, factory guaranteed class 3 tractor purchased for
   about the same amount as a new class 1 tractor performs on small
   town landfills more satisfactorily and economically than a lighter,
   less durable new tractor in class 1.
7. Tests of class 2 tractors and others in class 1 are necessary before
   even broad conclusions can be drawn on what the most economical
   tractor is for small landfills.
8. Small cities initiating a landfill program should make a cautious
   approach to the kinds of refuse accepted for the fill; operations
   can be modified as the work progresses and as operators learn the
   techniques that fit the needs of the town.

Trenching

Small towns can modify the landfill operation by using a form of
sanitary trenching. Often the city dump can be used as the site, although
it is usually necessary to clean up the dump before excavating a trench.
It may be necessary to rent heavy equipment to move the rubbish
accumulated on the site and to excavate trenches. If heavy equipment
cannot be obtained, an ordinary farm tractor and a small, front-end

loading bucket or bulldozer blade can be used after large items such as tree limbs, car fenders, and barrels have been removed. A separate dumping trench or area may be designated for large objects. Although it is not possible to control fires in trenches in this modified fill, a program of burning household refuse is not recommended.

A simple program of sanitary trenching for a small town might follow these steps:

1. Tell the townspeople what you are doing, why, and how.
2. Clean up the old dump and build an all-weather road to the site, renting heavy equipment if necessary.
3. Dig a trench, store dirt at ends or on sides, and designate an area for large objects.
4. Compact and cover the refuse in the trench at least twice a week in warm weather and as often as practical in the winter. Cover the top and face with at least 2 feet of dirt.
5. Each spring use heavy equipment to put into the fill large objects that must be disposed of separately. (Large bulky combustibles can be burned.)
6. Dig a new trench.

The program can be carried out by contract with private operators or by using municipal or county equipment.

Sanitary trenching will not produce the results achieved by a true sanitary landfill and should not be called by that name. However, it is a vast improvement over the usual open town dump and can be used with comparatively satisfactory results in many small communities.

Prospective Developments

There are two current investigations showing promise of important development in the field of sanitary landfilling. These involve exploration of baling and shredding as auxiliary processes.

Baling

Baling under high pressures was looked into primarily in connection with its advantages in economical long-haul transportation of refuse. Its use would have advantages for sanitary landfills used for final disposal as well. A research project of the Department of Health, Education, and Welfare was conducted in Chicago in 1968-69[5], concerning the use of baling.

It demonstrated that high-density bales of refuse can be produced with sufficient stability to stand transportation to a distant disposal site and handling necessary to put them into final position to fill. Advantages for the landfilling aspects, especially for a large-scale operation, are conceived to include some or all of the following:

---

[5] U.S. Department of Health, Education, and Welfare, *Rail Transportation of Solid Wastes—A Feasibility Study—Interim Report, Phase 1*, HEW Demonstration Grant No. 01-00073, and subsequent reports.

1. Elimination of most of the sanitary and aesthetic objections to refuse handling through substantial elimination of odors, blowing paper, fire potential, bulk, and unsightliness of loose refuse.
2. Enabling the use of specialized, efficient equipment for handling standardized, uniformly sized and shaped refuse units.
3. Elimination of compaction effort in the landfill and subsequent settlement.
4. Reduction of earth cover requirements.
5. Enabling the use of remote, lower-cost wasteland sites, with consequent cost advantages and availability.

While the foregoing may provide both cheaper and more satisfactory sanitary landfills, its feasibility is dependent on the total system economics and other system aspects. Final disposal in this case, as well as in any other system, is only a relatively small part of the total costs, although it may pose a considerable proportion of the knotty problems to be solved. Development of this concept, however, is seen as a possible alleviation of the increasingly acute problems of solid waste disposal in metropolitan areas.

Shredding

A demonstration grant project investigating shredding (also termed grinding and milling) as an auxiliary process in connection with sanitary landfilling has been completed at Madison, Wisconsin, under auspices of the U.S. Department of Health, Education, and Welfare, and the city.[6] It indicates that the process may have advantages from certain standpoints and that it may have a definite place under some circumstances. Only household refuse was involved in this project.

Among the conclusions cited in the report are the following:

1. Shredded household refuse has characteristics resulting in substantially different performance in a sanitary landfill from that of raw refuse as collected.
2. It can be landfilled and left uncovered with acceptable sanitary and aesthetic results—little odor, no blowing paper, minimal fire hazard, no rats or flies. Experimental piles have been left uncovered for over a year without creating public health problems. It is suggested that cover requirements may be reduced, although not eliminated, as a general operating procedure.
3. Placing and compaction were simplified and settlement, both total and differential, was greatly reduced.
4. The shredded refuse fill afforded superior traffic-supporting capacity. Trucks may operate easily over the uncovered surface under any weather conditions—and this with complete absence of tire problems.
5. The shredded refuse, soon after placement, was found to have an in-place density of 1,000 pounds per cubic yard, compared with 850

---

[6] U.S. Department of Health, Education, and Welfare, *Interim Report*, HEW Demonstration Grant No. 01-U1-00004, and subsequent reports.

pounds per cubic yard for unshredded material in conventional land-fills in Madison.

6. It was found that rats cannot survive on a diet of shredded refuse as landfilled in Madison and that uncovered shredded refuse was no more attractive to them than raw refuse covered with earth.

7. Under conditions at the Madison project, flies did not breed to any extent in the shredded refuse, although they are capable of breeding in it under optimum moisture and temperature conditions. The ham-mermill kills a large percentage of fly maggots normally found in refuse.

8. Shredded refuse in landfills decomposes faster than unshredded, with the speed of the process increasing with increasing fineness of the grind.

9. Under Madison conditions, where conventional sanitary landfilling of raw refuse costs $2.25 per ton on a 65,000-ton-per-year scale, it is estimated from projections of the pilot plant experience that the cost for shredding and landfilling on the same scale would run about $2.75 per ton.

Grinding mills used in Madison are of the hammermill type. The Gondard machine used has a practical capacity of 8 to 10 tons per hour, while the Tollemache unit can handle 9 to 12 tons per hour. Both machines include a built-in rejection feature to protect against oversized or unusually difficult-to-grind items. Down-time experience averages about 30 minutes out of each 8-hour day for servicing, cleaning, repairs, hammer replacement, and the like.

Machines produced by Eidal International Corp. are much heavier and larger, running up to capacities of 80 tons per hour for a twin mill installation. These are built to handle shredding of such items as automobiles and hence find general municipal refuse easy to handle, including oversize timbers and similar wastes.

In Madison, public officials feel that the use of milling as an auxiliary process will make it feasible to dispose of shredded household refuse at close-in sites where public acceptance could not be otherwise obtained for conventional landfills of raw refuse. As mentioned in the section on *Proximity to Residence and Industry*, sanitary landfills have been success-fully operated close to private residences. The image created by an unsanitary operation, however, is most persistent and difficult to overcome, and the added expense of shredding may be necessary and more economical in the total system if close-in site disposing of milled refuse will be accepted by the concerned citizenry.

5 CENTRAL INCINERATION

Refuse incineration as it is known today is the process of reducing combustible wastes to inert residue by high-temperature burning. "Central incineration" means that the method is used by either a municipality or a private company to dispose of refuse at a plant to which it is delivered.

History

It is a disposal method of recent origin. One of the earliest attempts to incinerate refuse was made in England in 1870. The first incinerator (or "crematory," as it was called) designed specifically for municipal use was built in 1874. Inasmuch as garbage was collected in swill form (wet) and the amount of dry combustible refuse collected with the garbage was extremely small, it was difficult to successfully operate early central incinerators. It was usually necessary to use auxiliary fuel.

The earliest English plants burned refuse at relatively low temperatures, producing a great deal of smoke and unpleasant odors. In 1885, an incinerator was designed that had a secondary fire in the main flue to consume the smoke and odors by assuring combustion at high temperatures. This method proved to be expensive, however, and it was found that acceptable results could be obtained by burning at higher temperatures in the furnaces themselves. Many of the incinerators utilized the waste heat. The low heat value of mixed refuse led to the adoption of a system called "separation-incineration" in which noncombustible material was removed from the refuse for salvage or open dump disposal, leaving only that that could be successfully burned. The first such plant was built in 1919, and most of the plants built in England since have been of the same type.

The first continental European incinerator was built in Germany in 1896. The European plants closely followed the essentials of the English type. A departure was the "Volund," developed in Denmark, which used a revolving, refractory-lined drum in the final burning stage.

The first incineration plant in the United States is said to have been built in 1885 for the Army installation at Governors Island, New York, although there is some evidence that incineration was used at other Army posts before 1885.

Allegheny, Pennsylvania, first used an incinerator in 1885; Pittsburgh and Des Moines in 1887; Yonkers, New York, and Elwood, Indiana, in 1893; and Washington, D. C., in 1896. These early incinerators were of a variety of sizes, shapes, and characteristics. To get the high temperatures necessary to reduce odors and smoke, some used auxiliary fuel and others partly dried the refuse before burning. After 1900, use of incinerators in the United States increased rapidly, and the modern incinerator furnace was developed. The first Decarie furnace was installed in the United States in 1901. It had a water-cooled basket for pre-drying wet garbage and water-jacketed walls, and it produced steam to drive forced draft fans and other appurtenances. Dumping grates and an ash pit were also innovations of this incinerator.

New York City built two rubbish incinerators in Manhattan in 1903 and four garbage incinerators in Queens in 1906. (It was customary to separate rubbish, garbage, and ashes at that time.) The major argument in favor of incineration of rubbish then was that the waste heat from the incinerators could be used as a source of power. But rubbish burning was subsequently abandoned because of operating difficulties and because production of waste heat was undependable. Incineration of garbage, although initially frowned on, was successful when coal was added to the incinerators at the rate of 1 pound of coal to 8 pounds of garbage.

During the early 1900's the Heenan and Froude and Sterling furnaces were introduced into America from England, establishing incinerator practices that were followed successfully for many years in the United States. The furnaces were built on the principles of mutual assistance, air-cooled castings, mechanically operated charging gates, and the flat or suspended arch.

A mobile incinerator was built and tried in Des Moines in 1928; a similar unit had been tried earlier in England. Neither proved to be practical for municipal refuse disposal. A unit built in Chicago in 1960 underwent tests which indicated its ability to meet that city's air pollution ordinance, but it did not prove to be practicable for that city's needs.

In 1929 Carl Ilving of Copenhagen, Denmark, obtained a United States patent on a circular furnace with a rotating hearth and central perforated cone. This general design, in improved form, was in common use in the United States in the 1940's and 1950's.

In more recent years, incinerator design has been markedly influenced by the changing character of solid wastes and need for more efficient operation, lower costs, and less air pollution. This has led to the development of continuous-feed and mechanical stoking, mechanically controlled overfire air, facilities for fly ash removal, systems for continuous quenching and discharge of incinerator residue, and the use of sectionally supported walls and hung arches with high quality refractory linings. These developments have made possible installation of larger incinerators, improved combustion, lower potential for creating nuisances, and the advantage of lower operating costs.

A development gaining acceptance as an improvement of basic design is the use of water tubes (water-walls) in place of refractory linings. The avoidance of costly maintenance problems and the possibilities of sale of the energy recovered from otherwise wasted hot gases present an attractive opportunity for comparatively low net unit costs for refuse disposal in spite of the higher capital expense and more exacting operating requirements. In effect, another form of salvage is practiced. However, from the standpoint of the electric generating industry, the comparatively easy handling characteristics and low cost of coal usually outweigh the "free" fuel aspect. A factor working in favor of refuse is its virtual freedom from SO_2 production, an accompaniment of coal burning coming under increasing pressure in abatement of air pollution.

European experience demonstrates the practicality and soundness of this development. About a dozen large modern plants are in use in Germany, most of them built since 1964. Two older plants and several new ones are operating in Switzerland, two in Holland, two in France, and one in England.

In Montreal, Canada, a 1,200-ton-per-day plant was completed in 1970. A 600-ton plant planned for Hamilton, Ontario, includes innovations such as grinding all refuse before firing and use of an air-swept spout to feed the furnace where burning will take place partly in suspension and partly on a spreader-stoker type grate.

In the United States there are a number of plants which recover heat, some dating back to the 1930's. Plants in Atlanta, Chicago, Miami, and Louisville, Kentucky, have generated steam primarily for space heating and industrial processing. Electric power has been produced at Providence, Rhode Island, and at Hempstead, New York. In each of these cases the refuse is burned in refractory-lined furnaces and the hot gases then pass through a heat exchange section.

A 1,600-ton-per-day plant scheduled for 1970 completion for Chicago is the first large-scale construction in the United States of a refuse burning furnace utilizing water-walls and electronic precipitation. A 600-ton plant at the Norfolk, Virginia, Navy Yard was constructed in the early 1960's. The plant's furnaces are equipped with water-walls, and cyclonic precipitation is used for fly ash control.

Prospective Developments

Innovations have been proposed for basic changes in incinerating refuse. One which is under serious investigation is the use of considerably higher combustion temperatures than the presently used 1,400°-1,800°F. range.

One design has some similarity to a Mono-Hearth type furnace. Refuse is fed into the circular furnace through a top opening, while the outer shell of the section rotates to distribute the refuse evenly about the periphery with the help of distribution plates extending into the feed chute. The refuse is forced into the combustion chamber by vibrating grates where burning takes place at high temperatures maintained by heated combustion air and auxiliary fuel burners. The 2,800°F. to 3,000°F. temperatures attained result in a slag residue which is discharged into an after-combustion chamber and thence through a granulator for crushing. The hot gases discharge through the bottom of the furnace along with the slag residue and then are diverted through a steam-generating boiler.

Another is the proposal that hot gases of incinerated refuse be used to drive gas turbines to recover the power. Another concept, not strictly an incineration process, is pyrolisis or carbonization. In this process, all organic or combustible components of the refuse would be rapidly converted to carbon and/or gas by destructive distillation. This would be accomplished in one version in a sealed, rotating retort under appropriate high temperature and pressure conditions in a continuous-flow, self-sustaining operation. Sixty to 70 per cent of the gas produced would be surplus, adaptable as turbine, diesel, or boiler fuel, or subject to chemical recovery through scrubbing and subsequent use of the refined gas in internal combustion engines.

The increasing emphasis on elimination of air pollution has spurred the search for more effective devices for removing particulates from incinerator stack emissions. Electrostatic precipitators, already well proven in industrial applications, are being incorporated into plants under construction.

The emerging use of water-wall furnaces producing steam and the increasing emphasis on better combustion for improved performance and air pollution control have promoted interest in the feasibility of shredding or grinding the raw refuse fuel to improve its homogeneity and hence its stoking and combustion characteristics. Rugged, practical equipment is already available that can economically improve the problems of nonuniformity that have been a major impediment to good stoking and to obtaining efficient combustion.

Evaluating Incineration As A Disposal Method

The purpose of central incineration is to provide an economic,

Fig. 52. The Southwest Incinerator, Chicago, in which operation began in 1963, has four rotary kiln furnaces that have a total rated capacity for burning 1,200 tons of mixed refuse a day.

nuisance-free, sanitary method of disposing of refuse. Whether it is the right solution to the refuse disposal problem of any particular city must be determined after careful evaluation of its advantages and disadvantages as they apply to the case in question.

Advantages

The important advantages of central incineration are:

1. Much less land is required than for disposal in landfills. If there are insufficient sites available for landfills within economic haul distances, an incinerator in a strategic location may produce the most economical total system of collection and disposal.
2. A central location for an incineration plant is possible. A carefully operated plant in a well designed building that has well landscaped grounds is acceptable in many neighborhoods, and so site selection may not be as difficult as it is for some other disposal methods.
3. An incinerator can produce ash residue that contains a negligible amount of organic materials and thus is relatively nuisance-free and more acceptable as fill material.
4. The modern incinerator can efficiently burn combustibles to ash and can even reduce the bulk of the noncombustible components of mixed refuse. (Special processing or handling is required for objects that are very large, those that cause excessive smoke, and those that are explosive.)
5. An incinerator is not directly affected by climate or unusual weather.
6. An incinerator is flexible. It can be readily adjusted to handle normal fluctuations in quantity and condition of refuse received. A plant operating 16 hours a day can be put on a 24-hour basis, for example, or the rate of firing can be varied within limits.
7. It may be possible to get some incidental income from incinerator operations to partially offset operating costs. Waste heat can be used to generate salable steam or electric power; separable metals can be recovered and sold; residues may have some value for filling purposes or as a construction material if they are well burned or reduced to slag form. In some cases it may be feasible to provide incinerator service for a group of communities, to industry, and to private collectors on a utility basis. Rates can then be set to completely support the operation.

Disadvantages

The disadvantages of incineration in any specific case must be weighed against the advantages, taking into account:

1. An incinerator requires a large capital investment. Increasing public concern with elimination of environmental pollution is requiring ever higher performance standards, achievable largely only by design refinements and additional equipment, all of which add to capital cost.
2. Operating costs are relatively high. Although the number of em-

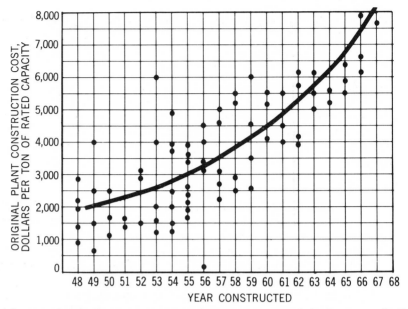

Fig. 53. Original construction costs for 74 central incinerators built for municipalities between 1948 and 1968. Costs were computed on the basis of the number of tons the incinerator can burn in a day. The highest cost plant was built in 1966, the lowest in 1956. (Prepared from data of the Solid Wastes Engineering Section, Committee on Sanitary Engineering Research, American Society of Civil Engineers).

ployees required to run an incineration plant may be less than it is for other methods of disposal, the wages for the skilled employees who operate, maintain, and repair an incinerator are higher than for men who work on a landfill, for instance. Maintenance and repair costs are high. Equipment and machinery are frequently damaged by wires, tramp metals, and fusible, abrasive, and explosive materials in the refuse. The combination of large capital investment, higher labor costs, and costly maintenance and repairs can produce a cost per ton for refuse disposal greater than for other acceptable methods.

3. The economic justification for refuse disposal by incineration often depends heavily on strategic location of the plant to permit substantial savings in collection costs. Acquisition of an acceptable site may be difficult because this often means locating in a densely populated area where refuse operations in any form are offensive to many people. The inevitable attendant truck traffic may be a significant nuisance and hazard factor, particularly in residential neighborhoods.

4. Incineration is not a complete disposal method. Ash and other resi-

due from the burning process, including fly ash, must be disposed of by other means.

Costs

An incinerator plant includes refuse handling and storage facilities, furnaces and chambers for burning the refuse, chimneys, facilities for handling the gaseous and solid products of the combustion process, and buildings and grounds. The amounts and kinds of equipment and facilities in the plant vary widely, and, of course, the costs vary with them.

Construction

In 1959 most incinerator plants fell within the cost range of $3,000 to $4,000 per ton of daily rated capacity, excluding land requirements. By 1966 the average cost had risen to about $6,150 per ton, as reported in a survey of 170 plants made by the U.S. Public Health Service. By 1969 the range for comparable designs was $6,000 to $9,000 per ton. The prevailing need for more sophisticated controls, devices, and equipment for improved air pollution control and operating economies can raise the cost of the upper part of this range to as much as $12,000 per ton.

The cost of plants employing water-wall type furnaces also vary considerably. The 360-ton-per-day Norfolk Naval Yard plant costs about $6,200 per ton. Chicago's Northwest plant of 1,600-ton-per-day capacity is expected to cost about $12,000 per ton including land and engineering fees. Montreal's 1,200-ton plant costs approximately $12,000 per ton. All except the Norfolk plant are equipped with electrostatic precipitators for air pollution control.

Construction costs in general have risen over 100 per cent since 1959 as indicated by the *Engineering News-Record* index.

A typical breakdown of costs by major elements for modern refractory and water-wall furnace-type incinerator is as follows:

Buildings	20 per cent to 40 per cent
Furnace and appurtenances	25 per cent to 50 per cent
Air pollution control devices	5 per cent to 10 per cent
Chimneys	4 per cent to 11 per cent
Shredders	— —

Financing the construction of an incineration plant usually requires a bond issue. If capital costs are amortized over a 20-year period, the annual payments per $1,000 of total cost will range from $67.20 to $80.23 figured at interest rates varying from 3 per cent to 5 per cent.

Costs vary primarily because of:

1. Site preparation peculiarities and foundation conditions.
2. Special requirements including air pollution control equipment and aesthetics.
3. Geographical differences in costs of labor and materials.

4. The extent to which structures must be enclosed because of weather conditions and the need to control nuisances.
5. Special features, such as steam and power generation equipment, and the degree of automation used.
6. The operating schedule—the relationship between the number of hours of plant operation and the rated 24-hour capacity.
7. Provisions for expansion included in original buildings.
8. The extent to which costlier equipment and materials are used for the purpose of reducing maintenance and repair costs.
9. Size of the plant.

The increased use of automatic and semi-automatic labor-saving devices, while raising initial costs, also reduces operating costs and in some cases brings additional economies by saving space.

Operation

Reported operating costs vary from $3 to $7 per ton processed. General evaluation on a uniform basis is not feasible because of the wide differences in local circumstances. Some of the variable influences include: the type of refuse burned and the thoroughness of the burning; the degree of sanitation and pollution controls exercised; the type of incinerator plant and extent of its mechanization; the operating schedule; the market for recovered heat and salvaged materials; the wage scale and amount of fringe benefits; and the productivity of labor and efficiency of management.

TABLE 19

OPERATING COSTS FOR MUNICIPAL INCINERATORS IN THREE UNITED STATES CITIES [1]
(Per ton of refuse processed)

City	Costs Per Ton
Philadelphia (Northwest)	$6.16
Chicago	5.87
Milwaukee	6.04

[1] Costs for the above plants are for the year 1968. The Chicago figure is an average of three plants. Costs include amortization and residue disposal.

In computing and comparing operating costs, it is important to recognize these factors and also to make sure that all of the costs—direct and indirect—are included. Costs must be accurately compiled on a uniform basis and correctly analyzed if reliable comparisons are to be made. These factors are discussed in Chapter 11, Refuse Disposal Management.

Total unit operating costs for comparable modern refractory furnace plants in three cities are given in Table 19. Table 20 shows comparative costs for two basic types of incinerators in use in Chicago.

TABLE 20

COMPARATIVE COSTS FOR TWO TYPES OF INCINERATORS, CHICAGO
(In terms of 1962 costs)

	Mechanized Continuous Type Rotary Kiln	Manually Stoked Batch Type
Total construction costs per ton per day of capacity (including engineering but exclusive of land)	$4,500.00	$3,900.00
Total operating costs per ton of refuse destroyed	5.86	6.06
Operating less residue disposal	1.40	1.62
Maintenance and repair	1.95	1.35
Administration and supervision	.56	.51
Pension	.20	.23
Fuel and utilities	.30	.14
Amortization	.00[1]	1.19

[1] Steam generation and metal salvage profits cover amortization costs.

DETERMINING PLANT LOCATION AND SIZE

Once the decision to use the incineration method of refuse disposal is made, it is necessary to decide where the plant will be located and what its capacity should be.

Location

Selecting a site involves both engineering problems and public acceptance of the location—and public acceptance is often the more difficult.

Engineering considerations include facility of construction and operation at as low costs as possible without creating nuisances for neighbors.

A central location usually cuts refuse collection costs, but the length of the haul to dispose of incinerator residue, although not a major consideration, is also a factor. If some salvageable materials are to be reclaimed, the distance to the nearest shipping point may be a factor. Topography and subsurface soil conditions may also affect costs. For instance, a hillside site may reduce construction costs because access to the tipping floor can perhaps be more cheaply built than if it were a flat site. Similarly, the type of foundations required and the character of subsurface ground waters may have a profound effect on construction costs.

In large urban areas the site problem is usually difficult. To avoid long hauls for collection trucks, a central location is often best, but if the site is near a residential neighborhood it is almost certain that nearby residents will object because they fear nuisances from smoke, fly ash, noise, odors, and heavy traffic. Neighbors also sometimes fear that the plant will deflate real estate values, which may be justified, depending on the type of neighborhood and the route the collection trucks must take to the plant. Furthermore, neighbors often fear that the plant will look like a factory. And although a good architect can design an attractive exterior, the chimney may convince residents that it does look like a factory. If that is true, stub-type chimneys with forced draft may have to be used. In any event, the zoning probably will prohibit an incineration plant in some areas of a city.

Sites are sometimes available in large cities in an industrial or semi-industrial area, where concern about nuisances, real estate values, and truck traffic is not as great as it is in residential areas. For a water-wall furnace plant designed to produce salable steam, proximity to a market for the steam may be a large factor.

In small cities the problem can frequently be solved by selecting a site outside the populated area that at the same time does not increase hauling costs excessively.

Once a site has been decided upon, it is important to institute a program to give the public the facts on it. Public acceptance may be most difficult to get. But a calm, honest presentation of the facts and the reasons for selecting the site and evidence that a well designed building will be constructed help to overcome objections.

Size

In determining the size and number of incineration plants needed in a city, the following must be considered:

1. The amount and kinds of refuse to be burned.
2. Hours of operation contemplated.
3. Seasonal peak loads and stand-by requirements.
4. Optimum relationship to the collection system.

Amount and Type of Refuse. The nature of the refuse (moisture content, combustible content, and weight) affects the size of the incinerator needed, as does the amount of refuse produced in the tributary area. How to determine refuse quantities and kinds is discussed in Chapter 2, Quantities and Composition of Refuse.

Hours of Operation. Most incineration plants are operated for one, two, or three 8-hour shifts a day, and usually for 5 or 6 days a week. Incineration plants in large cities are usually operated around the clock. There are cities—Chicago, Miami, Louisville, and Atlanta, for instance—that operate their plants continuously 7 days a week, mostly because they use waste gases to generate steam for space heating and process use. If the amount of refuse that must be disposed of increases, plants are expanded or additional ones are built.

In small cities, the incinerator is often large enough to dispose of all refuse in 8 hours a day. As the city grows, the plant can be put on a 16-hour or 24-hour basis to take care of increases in the amount of refuse. A plant designed for 8-hour-a-day operation requires almost three times the capacity of a plant designed for around-the-clock operation. Eight-hour-a-day plants are usually found only in small cities. They are

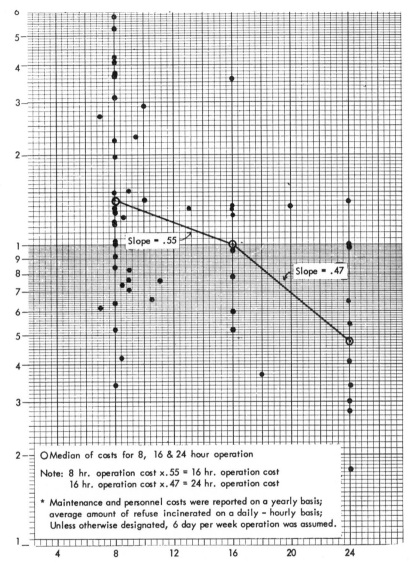

Fig. 54. Effect of one, two, and three shifts on over-all costs for maintenance and personnel in incineration plants in 61 cities in 1956. A re-analysis showed no significant changes in comparative relationships in 1965. Average costs for one shift, or 8 hours of operation, were the highest; those for three shifts, or 24 hours of operation, the lowest. Figures at left start with 10 cents at the bottom; figures across bottom are for hours of operation. (Prepared by Solid Wastes Engineering Section, Committee on Sanitary Engineering Research, American Society of Civil Engineers.)

often the direct-charge type or have only small storage pits that cannot hold more than an 8-hour collection of refuse.

Capital costs of an 8-hour plant may be more than twice the costs of one of similar size designed for 24-hour operation. Continuous operation of an incinerator permits more effective and efficient burning and creates fewer odor nuisances because the incinerator is not heated up and cooled down at the beginning and end of each shift. Damage to the refractory linings of the furnaces and chambers from thermal shock is also reduced.

The effect of operating schedules on overall costs for maintenance and personnel are shown in Figure 54.

Peak Load Requirements. Large incineration plants must have more than one furnace to meet the requirements of peak periods and for stand-by so that major repairs can be made without resorting to incomplete burning (toasting) of the refuse or shutting down the entire plant. It may be necessary during those times of the year when the most refuse is produced to use an incinerator at 100 to 110 per cent of its rated capacity. In off seasons it may be used at only 80 to 90 per cent capacity, which is the time to make repairs. Incinerators should not be built to the capacity of the peak refuse day, since much of the year part of the capacity is not used. It is important, therefore, that the capacity be a balance between the highest and lowest refuse collection periods.

Long-range plans should also be made to take care of increases in amounts of refuse in the future. If only one plant is contemplated, provisions for expansion of it should be included in the original plans for the plant. If more than one plant is contemplated, locations for additional ones should be considered in relation to the first one. It is advisable to project the peak load of refuse for at least 25 years, using the most reliable data available on population growth and changes in living habits of the residents of the city. (See Chapter 3, Selecting Disposal Methods.)

Optimum Relationship to the Collection System

Since collection costs are normally some 75 or 80 per cent of total refuse management expense, it is important to analyze each situation carefully for the most advantageous combination of collection and disposal costs. It may well develop that two or more incinerators, although resulting in higher unit disposal costs than would a single plant, will permit even greater savings in the collection system, resulting in a lower total cost.

FACILITIES FOR HANDLING REFUSE

Besides the furnaces and their auxiliaries, incineration plants must have other components for handling refuse, the kinds and amounts depending on the type and capacity of the plant.

Truck Scales

Scales for weighing refuse trucks and recording other information can be of the conventional mechanical type with manual operation. Or they can be of the more sophisticated type with load cell supports and electro-mechanical equipment that records information on the net load, kinds of refuse, points of origin and disposal of the refuse, truck and driver's identification, weighmaster's number, and the date and time the truck was weighed.

The latter type scales, which are not dependent on manual settings of tare-weights, have been found to be accurate, mechanically dependable, and tamperproof. Although costlier initially than manually operated scales, their aid to better management offsets the cost several times over. They may be particularly useful at incineration plants that serve several cities because costs can easily be allocated from the data automatically recorded.

Truck scales may or may not be inside the incineration building. They should, however, be near the point of entry to the tipping floor and provisions should be made to prevent trucks from by-passing them. There should be good visibility of the trucks and tipping floor from the scale house, and truck drivers and weighmaster should be able to talk with each other easily.

Fig. 55. A water spray system similar to this one in the Brookline, Massachusetts, incineration plant is often used to settle dust and suppress odors after refuse is dumped into the storage pit. The water spray system can also be used to control the temperature of the furnace, which may rise too high when highly combustible refuse is burned.

Tipping Floor

The tipping floor is a paved area on which trucks maneuver when they dump refuse into the storage pit or charge it into a furnace. The floor area should be big enough, especially if enclosed, to permit quick and easy maneuvering of the trucks; and it should extend along the entire length of the storage pit so that several trucks can unload at one time. It may be inside or outside the building, depending on climate, the amount of money available, and the kind of neighborhood in which the incineration plant is located.

Reinforced concrete floors with a highly impervious surface and good drainage are recommended for tipping floors to permit daily flushing to remove debris.

If the tipping floor is a full story above ground level, the space beneath it can be used—at only slight additional expense—for truck or material storage or for a maintenance shop, locker and shower rooms, offices, or assembly rooms. Ramps leading to and from this floor may be used, depending on the designer's decision as to what is most economical.

In direct-charge plants, sometimes used for small operations, the tipping floor is usually small and is located above the tops of the furnaces. Refuse is charged directly into the furnace from the trucks or by use of a small bulldozer that dumps the refuse into the furnace through an aperture in the floor. Sometimes small hoppers equipped with mechanically charging gates are set into the tipping floor—low enough to allow trucks to discharge refuse into the hoppers.

Storage Pits

If not all refuse collected in a day can be burned during the hours the incinerator is in operation, some of the refuse must be stored. The most

Fig. 56. Refuse that cannot or should not be put into incinerators, such as heavy iron, is put into this chute in the Rochester, New York, plant. The chute carries the refuse to ground level, and periodically a truck is backed up under the chute and the contents are removed and taken to a disposal site.

common storage place is a pit that is below the level of the tipping floor so that refuse can easily be dumped into it.

Storage pits are usually constructed of reinforced concrete as a safeguard against rodents and of sufficient strength to withstand both earth and ground water pressures. Surface armoring of light steel rails embedded in the concrete at intervals, rolled T-sections, or a continuous steel plate cover are frequently used to protect against damage by crane bucket corners and teeth. Sidewalls and the floor should have a dense, impervious finish to facilitate cleaning. The floor should be pitched toward drain troughs to simplify the cleaning process and to carry drainage to a dewatering sump pump.

The capacity of the pit may vary from 12 to 36 hours of incinerator burning capacity, depending on collection practices, hours of operation, and the amount of stand-by capacity of the plant.

In recent years there has been a considerable decrease in the density of refuse and a corresponding increase in volume, which in turn has increased the amount of storage space needed. The capacity of the pits in New York City incineration plants has increased with each new plant built—in 1961 they ranged from 65 per cent to 100 per cent of furnace capacity. Thus a 1,000-ton-per-14-hour plant has a liquid level pit capacity of 1,000 tons, or 6,000 cubic yards for truck-compacted refuse.

Chicago's 1,200-ton-per-day Southwest Plant, which burns mixed refuse, has a pit capacity of 1,880 tons and was designed on a basis of 193 cubic feet of volume for each ton of 24-hour plant capacity. Philadelphia's Northwest plant, which burns rubbish only, has a pit capacity of approximately 1,140 tons designed on a basis of 258 cubic feet per ton of 24-hour plant capacity.

Even in the best managed incineration plant there are times when 24-hour operation is not sufficient to meet the demands, which may require that some of the refuse be held in the pit for as long as several days. Since putrefaction of refuse is rapid, especially in warm weather, storing refuse for several days can create strong odors. If odor-free operation is required, special attention must be given to ventilation of the storage pit so that negative pressure is maintained, making it impossible for odors to escape from the building, even when plant doors are open to receive collection trucks. This procedure has often been found impractical, however, and odors must be controlled with deodorants or chemical masking agents.

Charging Equipment

Several means are used to charge refuse into incinerators. Each requires a variety of equipment, including hoppers, charging gates, cranes, and accessories. Skip loaders, oscillating conveyors, rams, and bulldozers also are sometimes used, although not frequently.

Hoppers. Charging hoppers are supposed to keep an even flow of refuse going into the furnaces. They are located above the top of the furnace so that refuse can descend by gravity to the grates. The number of hoppers for each furnace varies with the number of cells; one hopper per cell is customary. Single-cell rectangular or circular furnaces usually have a single charging hopper with a bottom opening of 25 to 35 square feet.

Batch-feed type furnaces require hinged, sliding, or rolling gates to

Fig. 57. Ram-type, hydraulically operated charging gate at Fort Lauderdale, Florida, incinerator.

permit refuse to be discharged from the hoppers into the furnaces and to close the opening at the top of the furnace. These are usually in an inverted steel box lined with refractory material and are manually or mechanically operated. Figure 58 shows a typical charging gate.

In continuous-feed incinerators the hopper discharges into the furnace through a rectangular chute. It may or may not have a closing gate. The chute is kept filled at all times to maintain an air seal, and may be lined with a refractory material or may be water-cooled and steel-lined.

In small furnaces (up to 100-ton capacity) refuse is often charged directly into the hoppers from collection trucks.

Cranes. In medium size incinerators (100 to 300-ton capacity) refuse is often raised from the storage pit to the charging hopper by monorail cranes. Although a monorail crane limits the width of the storage pit and its performance, in some plants it is adequate and more economical than other types of cranes.

In large furnaces (more than 300-ton capacity) a bridge crane is essential to handle the large volumes of refuse and to permit a wide storage pit. The flexibility needed in charging and recasting the refuse, the high speeds necessary, and the strain to which a crane is put in a big plant can be met only by the bridge type. It should be built to the rugged specifications of mill-type cranes.

Cab control for bridge cranes is not essential but it is usually used because it offers better visibility and safer operation than stationary control. Dust and wide variations in temperatures make air conditioning in the crane cab essential. Stationary controls, located at the center or in a corner of the storage pit, are standard with monorail type cranes but are used only occasionally for bridge cranes. However, automated digital magnetic-controlled bridge cranes are now being considered for a number of plants. Savings on manpower with this type of control is the incentive for use.

The size and number of cranes needed is geared to the size of the incineration plant. Stand-by cranes should be available because, if even one of those needed for normal operation breaks down, the entire plant can be put out of operation.

The recommended maximum safe operating speeds for cranes in an average capacity incineration plant (300 to 600 tons) are 300 feet per minute for hoisting and trolley travel and 350 feet per minute for bridge travel. Full magnetic controls are desirable.

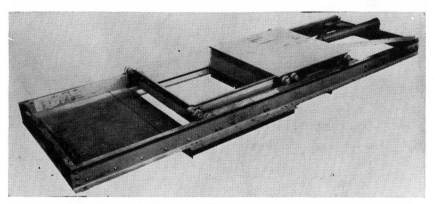

Fig. 58. This five-foot by five-foot charging gate (shown open) is used in the Jersey City incineration plant.

Many crane accessories are also needed. Grapples or buckets of the clamshell type with tines or teeth of good design and manufacture built of steel that will withstand a great deal of abrasion are necessary. Buckets that can open and close rapidly and that have lips so positioned and hinged that they can pick up a full bucketload of refuse with each bite are required for efficient operation. Grapples and buckets ranging in capacity from 1 to 4 cubic yards are in general use in incineration plants. Larger sizes, up to 1½ tons net load, are usually used with high capacity, continuous-feed furnaces. An automatic lubrication system for the crane is also desirable.

COMBUSTION OF REFUSE

There is lack of agreement, even among incinerator experts, as to the correct words and terms for the equipment and structures used to burn refuse. For instance, some use "incinerator" and "furnace" synonymously (as does Noah Webster), while others consider the "furnace" only a part of the "incinerator"; some use "furnace" to include all burning apparatus and structures—drying hearth, grates, ignition chamber, combustion chamber, subsidence chamber, and breeching. Still others use "furnace" to mean only the main chamber in which the major burning takes place.

This confusion stems from the fact that the burning of refuse actually progresses through the steps of drying, igniting, burning of solid wastes, burning of gaseous wastes, and finally settling out of particulate matter before discharging the gaseous end products into the atmosphere through the chimney. Each of these steps overlaps in varying degrees, depending on the characteristics of the refuse burned and the operating methods used. The terms as they are used here—and the recommended definitions—are:

Incinerator—The entire plant (used for burning solid wastes), including refuse handling and storage facilities, furnaces, combustion chambers, subsidence chambers, residue handling and removal facilities, chimneys, and all auxiliaries.

Furnace—An enclosed refractory or water-wall structure equipped with grates.

Combustion chamber—An enclosed, refractory-lined structure, sometimes combined with the furnace, in which the secondary, more complete burning of air-borne particles and gases takes place.

Subsidence Chamber—A large, separate, insulated chamber in which exhaust gases are expanded and slowed down so as to settle out the particulate matter before the gases are discharged into the atmosphere.

Furnace

The furnace as considered here includes the ignition and primary combustion chambers, where preheating, drying, ignition, and most of the burning of refuse takes place. In the furnace are the hearth, the grates, the ash hopper, and gate; stoking may be manual or mechanical. Several different types of furnaces are now in use, with the most common the following:

1. The single-chamber, cylindrical, batch-feed type. This is a refractory-lined furnace charged through a door in the upper part of the furnace. Refuse is dropped into the furnace periodically and stoked to the periphery manually or mechanically by a rotating cone with extended rabble arms. The dumping grates are located around the periphery and are operated whenever the accumulation of ash warrants removal.

2. The single- or multiple-cell rectangular, batch-feed type. This may be a refractory-lined or water-wall furnace with a charging door in the middle or near the back of the ceiling of each cell. It is equipped with either fixed or moving grates set level or inclined.

3. The continuous-feed type. The major mechanical difference be-

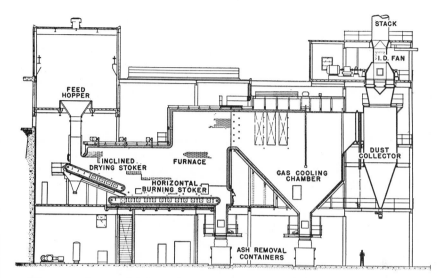

Fig. 59. Cross section drawings of one of the furnaces of the Calumet incineration plant in Chicago (top) and the Northwest plant in Philadelphia (bottom).

tween this and the batch-feed types is obvious from the names: refuse is fed into one in batches; into the other continuously (ashes are also removed continuously and an air seal is maintained within the furnace continuously). The inclined, rotating-kiln type is essentially the same as the continuous-feed type except that it has a refractory-lined, slowly revolving cylindrical kiln that is used in the final burning stage.

In the continuous-feed types of furnaces the grates are of the traveling type, inclined, flat, or a combination; the furnaces require a minimum of manual stoking.

All types of furnaces, except the water-wall design, are lined with refractories and insulating brick or block. However, in many instances water-wall furnaces have a thin layer of castable refractory material covering the side wall tubes to approximately 15 feet above the grate line to prevent erosion and corrosion of the tubes.

Burning Rates. A furnace should operate at temperatures between 1,300° and 2,000° F., with an average of 1,700° to 1,800° F. If temperatures are kept about these minimums, practically all aldehydes, mercaptons, and other malodorous hydrocarbons will break down, thereby eliminating a source of air pollution. The maximum of 2,000° F. should not be exceeded because at higher temperatures refractories begin to deteriorate rapidly, and the high gas velocities reduce the effectiveness of fly ash collection devices. It was thought that water-wall furnaces would be able to operate at temperatures up to 2,200° F., but equipment now in operation indicates that temperatures under 2,000° F. must be adhered to if tube corrosion is to be avoided. Excess air quantities will vary from 80 to 110 per cent or more.

Furnaces designed to burn refuse follow the well-established principles used in designing furnaces for burning such homogeneous solid fuels as sugar cane waste, bark, and wood. Experience with those fuels shows that the two major design elements are the grate areas and combustion volumes. For optimum burning, grate loads are based on a heat release from the burning material at the rate of 300,000 B.T.U. per hour per square foot, while combustion space is based on a heat release at the rate of 20,000 B.T.U. per hour per cubic foot. It should be noted that these basic combustion rates are in close agreement with design criteria used for both refractory and boiler type furnaces using refuse as fuel.

Refuse, however, varies in amounts of combustibles, moisture, density, and chemical composition, and thus requires greater refinements. An

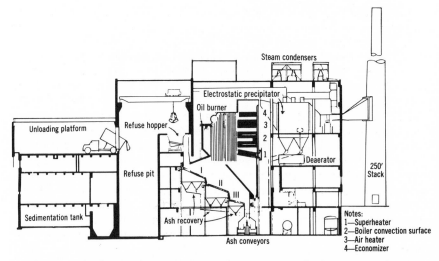

Fig. 60. A three-stage incinerator furnace producing steam for processing. Balance of the incineration function with steam demand is maintained by provision of an oil-fired auxiliary burner for excess steam requirement and three steam condensers for disposing of excess combustion heat.

analysis must be made of each situation. This is best shown in Table 21, which sums up the actual parameters used in the design of refuse incinerators. The values shown are derived from a careful analysis of designs used for 24 large incinerators in 18 United States cities. Of these,

TABLE 21

PARAMETERS OF DESIGN FOR REFUSE FURNACES

| | Type of Refuse[1] | Grate Loadings in Lbs. of Refuse per Hour of Operation per Square Foot of Grate Area | Volume in Cubic Feet per Ton of Refuse per 24 Hours | |
			Furnace (Primary) Chamber	Combustion (Secondary) Chamber
Range of Values	M	58 to 109	8.5 to 25.0	12.1 to 28.0
	R	50 to 72	13.4 to 14.5	26.6 to 31.8
	C	54 to 98	9.9 to 13.8	17.2 to 28.3
Average Values	M	77	12.7	18.5
	R	58	13.6	29.9
	C	77	11.5	21.3

[1] M—Mixed refuse made up of garbage, rubbish, and noncombustibles.
   R—Refuse comprised of burnable rubbish only.
   C—Refuse containing combustibles only, such as garbage and burnable rubbish.

14 burn refuse, 3 burn combustible rubbish only, and 7 burn combustibles only. The furnaces range in rated capacity from 90 to 250 tons per 24 hours of operation.

The grate loadings used coincide reasonably well with the theoretical values of 75, 50, and 65 pounds of refuse per hour per square foot for the three types of refuse mentioned above. They correspond to a calculated heat release of 300,000 B.T.U. per hour per square foot of grate. On the other hand, the total combustion volumes used coincide more closely with the theoretical values of 25, 45, and 35 cubic feet per 24 hours per ton of refuse for the three types of refuse. They correspond to a calculated heat release of about 12,500 B.T.U. per hour per cubic foot rather than the 20,000 advocated for the combustion of homogeneous fuels. When water-wall furnaces are used, however, the 20,000-B.T.U. figure is used for design purposes. Shredding of refuse such as is included in the Hamilton, Ontario, plant design will give a more homogeneous material and use of the 20,000-B.T.U. figure for furnace design seems reasonable.

Although the actual ranges used for the separate primary and secondary combustion chambers vary disturbingly, the ranges for the total combustion space are reasonably close. This points up the need for a better distribution and allocation of combustion space between the two chambers. Many incinerators of recent design have combined primary and

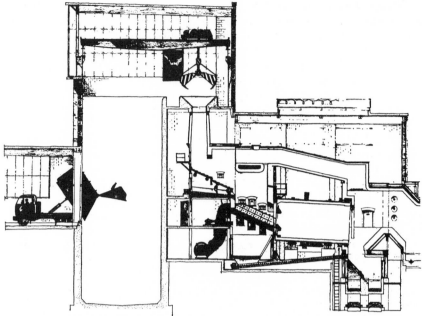

Fig. 61. The Volund rotating kiln incinerator is basically a continuous-feed incinerator, with mechanically reciprocating drying and ignition grates. The grates discharge the partly consumed and burning refuse into an inclined rotating kiln.

secondary combustion chambers into a single chamber based on a heat release of 12,500 B.T.U. per cubic foot to 20,000 B.T.U. per cubic foot.

Designs based on such a broad rule of thumb formula of course must be checked in detail by thermodynamic calculations of heat and mass balances, air volumes and velocities, and operating temperatures.

Combustion Chamber

The combustion chamber as it is considered here is a secondary chamber in which more complete combustion of particulate carryover from the furnace and of volatile gases takes place. It may or may not be within the building that houses the furnace and it may or may not be combined with the primary combustion chamber in the furnace.

How the combustion chamber functions depends on the design and operation of the incineration plant. If the furnace (primary chamber) has sufficient volume so that gases have adequate detention time and the right amount of air is introduced at strategic locations to insure thorough mixing of the gaseous products of combustion, high temperatures will be maintained and practically all combustion will take place in the furnace. Under such conditions, an important function of the combustion chamber, in addition to completing the burning of gaseous and incandescent particulate matter, is to settle out the heavier large particles of fly ash. Gas velocities, therefore, should range from 10 to 40 feet per second.

On the other hand, if the volume within the furnace is insufficient and inadequate amounts of air are supplied, most of the secondary combustion of the particulates and gases will take place in the combustion chamber if sufficient oxygen is present.

Baffles, bridge walls, and similar means to force the gases into a circuitous path in the combustion chamber improve the mixing of gases and increase impingement of fly ash particles.

Subsidence Chamber

The subsidence or settlement chamber is used primarily to complete the removal of fly ash and incidentally to complete the combustion of gases. Wet collectors, scrubbers, checkerwork refractory drop curtains, baffle walls, and other devices for removing particulate matter are used in addition to or sometimes in place of the chamber if a high degree of fly ash collection is required. The chamber is designed to keep gas velocities between 5 and 10 feet per second.

Where baffles or other configurations are used, low velocities at floor level are particularly important so that fly ash that settles there will not again be picked up in the gas stream. Wetting the baffles and floors has quite successfully prevented re-entrainment and promoted continuous discharge of settled particles.

Breechings

Breechings are high temperature ducts lined with refractory material that convey the hot products of combustion to the chimney. The cross-

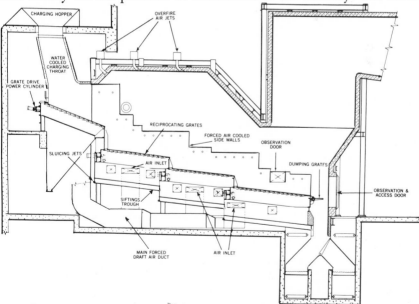

Fig. 62. Section of one of two 200-ton-per-day units in a New Orleans plant. These use Detroit reciprocating grate stokers.

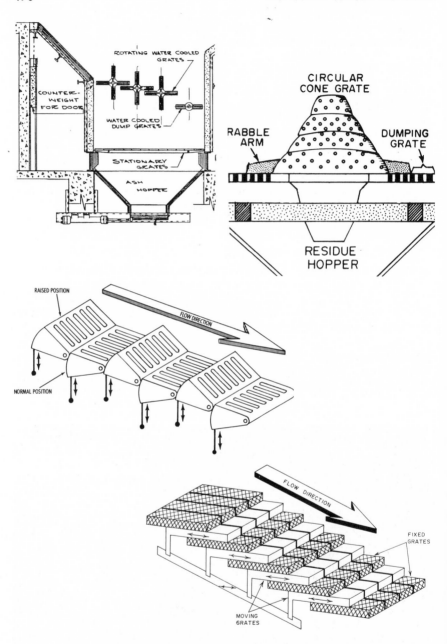

Fig. 63. Among the many automatic and semiautomatic grates used in refuse incinerators are the rotating water-cooled grates (top left), the conical-shaped circular grates (top right), the rocker-type stoker grates (center left), and the reciprocating grates (bottom right).

section should be larger than that of the stacks. Gas velocities should be maintained at 20 to 40 feet per second.

Fly Ash Screens

Large particulate matter may be trapped by wire mesh screens that have openings of one-quarter inch or less, located in the breeching, in the stack, or even at the top of the stack. The preference, however, is for movable screens installed ahead of the stack, which reduces exposure to damaging high temperatures and at the same time provides good accessibility for cleaning and servicing. Double hung, counterbalanced construction permits putting one unit in the gas stream while the other is being cleaned and repaired. Stainless steel construction assures permanency and protection against rapid burn-out and corrosion.

Instrument Panel

The instrument panel is usually a large board of high dielectric strength on which all instruments that record draft, temperatures, and other data on operation and all switches and push buttons for operating the furnaces are mounted. Control panels in many new plants have closed circuit television monitors that view furnace burning conditions and also other strategic locations in the plant.

Air for Combustion

An adequate, correctly distributed supply of air is basic to the combustion process. Air for combustion is referred to as primary and second-

Fig. 64. Control console for an incinerator.

ary: the primary air is introduced under the grates; secondary air is introduced over the fire.

Primary Air. If all other factors are constant and within reasonable limits, the rate of flow of primary air through the fuel bed controls the rate of burning. The grate burning rates in municipal incinerators usually require the installation of forced-air fans. Supplying adequate undergrate combustion air at the correct pressure to maintain burning rates is especially important during periods when wet refuse is charged, because compaction of the soggy material makes air penetration difficult. Stoking and spreading the refuse on the grate are particularly important. Doing so breaks up clotted refuse and clinkers, helps keep all parts of the grate covered to promote uniform burning and keep the grate from being burned, prevents fine ash and particulate matter from being stirred up, and promotes efficiency of the burning by furnishing continuous contact between the refuse and air. In a continuous-flow type grate, such as a reciprocating, rocking or traveling grate, or the reverse-flow type as typified by the Martin Stoker, these problems can be circumvented further by compartmentation of underfire air.

The practice of preheating primary combustion air by heat exchange or intermixing with the combustion gas products has not been used extensively in recent years because refuse is drier and more highly combustible. As a matter of fact, control of furnace temperatures to keep them within refractory limits is now more frequently a serious problem than lack of preheated combustion air; preheated combustion air is only beneficial when very wet refuse is put into the furnace. Then

Fig. 65. This grid type fly ash baffle is used in the secondary chamber of the municipal incinerator in Rochester, New York.

it dessicates the wet material and helps keep furnace temperatures high enough to promote good ignition and combustion. Paradoxically, the need for preheated air develops mostly when it is least likely to be available from hot combustion gases. Under these conditions the use of auxiliary fuels, properly applied, may be helpful.

Secondary Air. The main purpose of secondary or overfire air is to supply the turbulence and oxygen necessary to promote complete combustion of the burnable gases, vapors, and particulates leaving the fuel bed. Under certain conditions it is also widely used for cooling. It is usually introduced into the furnace above the fuel bed, and may be most effective when brought close to the top of the burning refuse. Care must be used in introducing overfire air so that the carryover of particulates from the fuel bed is kept to a minimum.

The best design and placement of overfire air ports or nozzles must frequently be determined by trial and error.

Calculation of Air Requirements. Because of the heterogeneous nature of refuse collected in cities, it is difficult to calculate combustion air requirements. The importance of analyses of representative samples of wastes in the calculation process cannot be overemphasized. Table 22 gives the "theoretical" air needs for complete combustion of various kinds of refuse, including garbage. Previous studies indicate that most refuse that goes to municipal incinerators is cellulosic (moisture and ash-free) and may be so considered in stoichiometric (theoretical complete chemical combinations) calculations of the incineration process.

Enough air is required to completely convert all carbon, hydrogen, and sulfur in the fuel to carbon dioxide, water, and sulfur dioxide, respectively. Ignoring the sulfur content of fuel and assuming that most refuse is cellulosic, calculations show that 5.10 pounds of air are required for combustion for every pound of cellulose. Translating this for the average "as received" refuse and utilizing 200 per cent excess air generally used with refractory-lined furnaces for best results, the air requirements amount to about 7.7 pounds of air per pound of refuse. One of the advantages of the water-wall furnace is the reduction in air requirements to only 80 per cent excess air. The requirements to burn a pound of refuse would thus be only 4.68 pounds of air for this type of furnace.

Air Fans and Ducts. Forced drafts for both burning and cooling are usually produced by a single motor-driven fan and are diverted to above or below the burning grate by a dampering system. If the system is entirely mechanical, modulating motors actuated by thermocouples are used. If more precise control of air is necessary, several fans can be used to provide air at various pressures and locations.

Dampers. The amount of draft in a furnace produced by natural draft stacks and the diversion of hot gases through waste heat boilers can be controlled by dampers. They may be of water-wall steel construction or of refractory and high-temperature resistant steel.

Auxiliary Burning

Because the percentage of garbage in refuse has decreased markedly

Table 22

APPROXIMATE COMBUSTION CHARACTERISTICS OF VARIOUS KINDS
OF MATERIALS AND AMOUNTS OF AIR NEEDED FOR COMBUSTION

Material	High Heat Value[1] (B.T.U. per Lb. of MAF[2] Waste)	Air Needed for Complete Combustion (Lbs. per Lb. of MAF Waste[3])
Paper	7,900	5.9
Wood	8,400	6.3
Leaves and grass	8,600	6.5
Rags, wool	8,900	6.7
Rags, cotton	7,200	5.4
Garbage	7,300	5.5
Rubber	12,500	9.4
Suet	16,200	12.1

[1]Values are necessarily approximate, since the ultimate composition of the combustible part of the materials varies, depending upon sources. The heating value of the material as it is received is obtained by multiplying the moisture-free and ash-free B.T.U. value of the materials by 1 − (% moisture + % ash)/100. For example, garbage with an MAF value of 7,300 and containing 35 per cent moisture and 5 per cent ash or other noncombustible material will have an "as-fired" heating value of 4,380 B.T.U. per pound.

[2]MAF means moisture-free and ash-free if ash refers to total noncombustible materials.

[3]These values are also approximate and are based on 0.75 pounds of air per 1,000 B.T.U. for complete combustion. For various percentages of excess air, multiply these values by (100 plus per cent of excess air)/100. For example, if paper is burned with 100 per cent excess air (5.9) 200/100 = 11.8 pounds of air per pound of moisture-free and ash-free paper will be required.

in recent years, the need for auxiliary burners for incinerators has also decreased, although during the seasons of the year when refuse has a high moisture content they may be necessary. They may also be required to assist natural stack draft and to preheat refractories to reduce thermal shock at the time the furnaces are started. In any event, provision for auxiliary burning is usually considered essential for a municipal incineration plant.

If auxiliary fuel burners are used, they usually are located so that they furnish heat above the grate lines of the furnace for maximum drying of refuse, both by direct and radiant heat.

Oil, gas, wood, and coal have been used extensively as auxiliary fuels, although wood and coal are no longer common. If a municipal incineration plant is near the sewage treatment plant, sewage digester gas can be used satisfactorily.

Auxiliary burners are customary in industrial incinerators, in both the furnace and the section between the furnace and the combustion chamber, because industrial wastes frequently contain materials that require special attention to eliminate odor and smoke. Auxiliary burning

Fig. 66. Facilities for maintenance of baffle water spray system of fly ash removal. Baffles are in raised position; water pipes to spray nozzles are on the roof of the flue chamber (foreground).

increases the high-temperature retention time and creates turbulence for more complete combustion.

REFRACTORIES

Refractories are comprised of various materials, such as fire clay, that are highly resistant to a great deal of heat. In incinerators they are used to line furnaces, combustion chambers, subsidence chambers, breechings, and chimneys because they protect the furnace and other parts of the incinerator against high temperatures and also serve as a reservoir of heat that equalizes internal temperatures.

Refractories can be produced from clay, silica, alumina diaspore, and other materials. Those produced from clay, sometimes known as fire clay bricks, are made in four grades: super-duty, high-duty, medium-duty, and low-duty. Insulating brick is made from the lower grades of fire clay.

Fig. 67. Stainless steel baffle plates at left show the results of an incorrect water spray system. The inadequate spray applied to the steel plates did not reach the top of the baffle system. The 316 stainless steel channel type baffle plates at right have given satisfactory service in the incineration plant in Rochester, New York.

Selection of Refractory Brick

The important factors to be considered in the selection of refractories for incinerators are cost; physical strength; resistance to heat, thermal and mechanical shock, spalling, slagging, and abrasive wear; low coefficient of expansion; and low bonding properties with respect to slag and clinker. To resist the deteriorating effects of heat, a refractory with a low and uniform coefficient of expansion, a minimum of fused glassy material, porous structure, and a high pyrometric cone equivalent will give the best results.

Surface abrasion in incinerators results when sharp objects in the refuse continuously rub against the lining of the furnace. Bricks of high physical strength with a hard, impervious surface offer the best resistance to such wear.

Spalling occurs because of the differences in temperatures between the outer surface and the inner part of the brick, which, aided and abetted by moisture absorption and steam expansion, results in uneven expansion. To resist spalling, a dense brick with a fairly high pyrometric cone equivalent should be used.

Slag—a chemical flux of the oxides of sodium, potassium, iron, or calcium—forms on the surface of the incinerator lining, particularly when temperatures are high. It is deposited on and bonds itself to brick surfaces. As it accumulates, it reduces the volume of the furnace and eventually causes failure in the bricks because of its weight. The refractory material that best resists slagging has high density, low porosity, a

TABLE 23

TYPICAL PHYSICAL PROPERTIES OF REFRACTORIES[1]

Type	Pyrometer Cone Equivalent	Density (Lbs. per Cu. Ft.)	Modulus of Rupture (Lbs. per Sq. In.)	Cold Crushing Strength (Lbs. per Sq. In.)	Thermal Conductivity (@ 1,800 B.T.U. per Hour per F.)	Thermal Expansion (@ 1,800° % Lineal)	Porosity (% Vol.)	Absorption (% by Wt.)	Resistance to Spalling
Super-duty	33-34	140-145	700-850	1,200-2,400	10.6	0.64	10-18	4-7.5	Excellent
High-duty	31-33	140-144	800-1,000	2,100-2,800	10.6	0.64	12-19	5-8	Good
Intermediate-duty	29-31	136-140	1,100-1,400	4,000-5,500	10.3	0.64	13-16	6-7	Good
Low-duty	19-26	160-165	1,000-2,300	2,000-6,000	0.12	0.64	12-25		Fair
Insulating brick	17-32	40-46	60-320	115-380	3.0	0.50	22-26		Good
Alumina, 50%	34-35	130-135	700-1,000	1,400-2,000	10.1	0.60	27-34	10-12	Good
Alumina, 60%	35-37	130-140	850-1,150	2,100-2,500	10.1	0.60	29-36	12-17	to
Alumina, 70%	36-38	125-130	700-1,000	1,400-2,000	9.5	0.60	23-27	13-18	Excellent
Silica	31½-32½	103-107	600-1,200	1,500-3,000	12.4	1.3		13-16	Excellent above 1,200° F.; poor below
Silicon carbide	38	157	2,000		108.0	0.44	13.2		Excellent; slagging resistance excellent

[1]Data, obtained from representative manufacturers' catalogs, determined through tests made according to recommendations of the American Society of Testing Materials.

Fig. 68. The operating floor of an incineration plant must have the correct instruments and control aids for efficient operation, such as these at the Jersey City incineration plant.

high melting point, and a chemical and mineral composition that does not bond or combine with slag.

Obviously, compromises must be made in the types of refractory used in various parts of an incinerator. The choice is different for different parts because the least costly material that will do the job efficiently should be used in each place.

Because silicon carbide has such a high melting point, low thermal expansion, high strength, low spalling loss, and chemical inertness, it may be used in almost any part of an incinerator. However, because of its high cost, it is usually used only in the most troublesome areas. For example, it may be economically used for 3 or 4 feet above the grates, where the greatest abrasive wear and slagging take place.

Insulating brick, which has low resistance to slag, abrasion, and mechanical abuse, should never be used in incinerators for the lining closest to the heat but only as backing for fire clay brick or other refractory material to control heat loss to the exterior. Its additional advantage is that it is lighter than common brick and therefore the supporting structures for it can be lighter.

Typical physical properties of commonly used refractory bricks are given in Table 23. Table 24 lists the conditions to which refractories are subjected in an incinerator and suggests the best quality refractory for each condition.

Costs. Costs of refractory bricks vary widely. In 1968 costs for a

TABLE 24

SUGGESTED REFRACTORY PLACEMENT IN INCINERATORS

Incinerator Part	Temperature Range (Degrees F.)	Abrasion	Slagging	Mechanical Shock	Spalling	Fly Ash Adherence	Recommended Refractory
Charging gate	70-2,600	Severe Very important	Slight	Severe	Severe	None	Super-duty
Furnace walls, grate to 48 inches above	70-2,600	Severe	Severe Very important	Severe	Severe	None	Silicon carbide or super-duty
Furnace walls, upper portion	70-2,600	Slight	Severe	Moderate	Severe	None	Super-duty
Stoking doors	70-2,600	Severe Very important	Severe	Severe	Severe	None	Super-duty
Furnace ceiling	700-2,600	Slight	Moderate	Slight	Severe	Moderate	Super-duty
Flue to combustion chamber	1,200-2,600	Slight	Severe Very important	None	Moderate	Moderate	Silicon carbide or super-duty
Combustion chamber walls	1,200-2,600	Slight	Moderate	None	Moderate	Moderate	Super-duty or 1st quality
Combustion chamber ceiling	1,200-2,600	Slight	Moderate	None	Moderate	Moderate	Super-duty or 1st quality
Breeching walls	1,200-2,400	Slight	Slight	None	Moderate	Moderate	Super-duty or 1st quality
Breeching ceiling	1,200-2,400	Slight	Slight	None	Moderate	Moderate	Super-duty or 1st quality
Subsidence chamber walls	1,200-1,600	Slight	Slight	None	Slight	Moderate	Medium-duty or 1st quality
Subsidence chamber ceiling	1,200-1,600	Slight	Slight	None	Slight	Moderate	Medium-duty or 1st quality
Stack	500-1,000	Slight	None	None	Slight	Slight	Medium-duty or 1st quality

standard size brick (9 inches by 4½ inches by 2½ inches) ranged from $2.68 each for silicon carbide to 25 cents each for silica. The alumina bricks ranged from 44 cents to 50 cents each, depending on the per cent of alumina content. Super-duty bricks through low-duty bricks cost 29½ cents to 19 cents each. Insulating bricks cost 50 cents each.

Plastic Refractories

The clays used in plastic refractories are similar to those in bricks. They are mixed, at the factory, with just enough water to form a stiff, workable mix and are shipped in either metal or waterproof paper containers. When installed, forms are used and the material is sliced, rammed into place, and trimmed smooth. However, instead of being burned in a kiln, as bricks are, plastic refractory develops its ceramic-like structure and bond by gradual, uniform heating up to a certain temperature after it is in the incinerator. Entire linings can be made of plastic refractories; with careful workmanship and correct heating procedures,

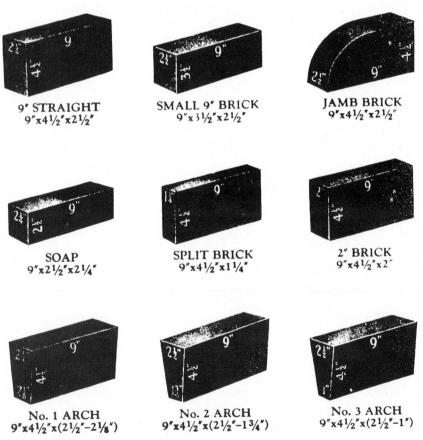

Fig. 69. There are many shapes for firebrick; these are a few of the standard nine-inch series.

good results can be obtained. However, at present plastics are usually used only for lining access, inspection and firing doors, for patching and shaping around curved openings, and for filling and lining other irregular surfaces.

Castable Refractories

Castable refractories are also made of the same clays as those used in firebrick but with bonding additives to impart strength until the temperature in the furnace is sufficiently high to develop a ceramic bond. They can be mixed and poured like concrete. Their use is still usually limited to door and charging gate linings, to spot repairs and patchings, and to special shapes.

Installation

Installation of a refractory lining is as important as the refractory itself. The details depend greatly on whether the wall construction is of the bearing or hung type and whether the roof construction is of the sprung arch or hung type. In any case, the most important factors are expansion and contraction. Firebrick expands in three directions when heated—vertically, horizontally along the plane of the wall, and at right angles to the wall. Vertical expansion is provided for by allowing room for upward movement; but horizontal expansion must be provided for by joints in corners or by expansion spaces in wall panels. All joints must be staggered and header or metal tie courses must be used to interlock the wall transversely. Methods for making and locating expansion joints vary; usually the joints are located at points at which there are radically different temperatures and where there is a major change in the structure configuration. While corner joints allow for differences in vertical expansion, they also sometimes weaken the structure; therefore, a joint is often put in the wall near the corner.

Mortar. The strength and durability of a self-supported refractory lining depend upon the kinds of bricks used, the manner in which they are laid, and the material for bonding them. The mortar materials should be as carefully selected as the brick with which they are used. There are two general kinds of mortars: air-setting and thermal-setting.

The most commonly used is the air-setting type, which hardens at room temperatures and in which some hardening takes place at any temperature.

Thermal-setting mortar forms a strong bond at temperatures between 1,400° and 2,500° F. This characteristic is a disadvantage because before temperatures reach 1,400° F., a great deal of the soft mortar may have been eroded by gases passing over the lining. Furthermore, the brick is bonded only as deep as the high heat penetrates—sometimes not more than an inch.

Since firebrick linings must be laid with thin joints, the bricks should be dipped in a thin mortar; only when fitting or leveling is being done is it necessary to use a thick mortar and trowel.

Fig. 70. The high temperatures produced when refuse containing relatively small amounts of garbage is burned can cause severe damage to refractories if the heat is not controlled.

Refractory Warm-Up

To "set" the brick construction and prevent damage to refractories and refractory mortar because of too rapid drying, too rapid expansion, and spalling it is essential that furnaces, chambers, stacks, and other parts of an incinerator be heated up to progressively higher temperatures for at least five consecutive days before they are used to burn refuse. Improper drying out can ruin the most carefully made and highest quality refractory linings.

Refuse should not be used as fuel during the drying out period. Instead, oil or coal salamanders, gas or oil burners, or waste lumber should be used, and temperatures should be carefully controlled.

The purposes of the drying out period are to drive out moisture from the refractory linings, accelerate bonding and cementing under controlled conditions, and permit gradual and uniform expansion. To do so, temperatures should be increased a few degrees each day. The temperature is usually kept below 150° F. for at least the first day. Thereafter the temperature is increased about 200 degrees every day or every other day until normal operating temperatures are reached and maintained for several days.

CHIMNEYS

A chimney or stack is an upright flue that conveys the gaseous products of combustion to the atmosphere and provides natural draft to assist combustion. When in operation, a chimney is filled with gases that have a higher average temperature than that of the surrounding air. As a result, the gases within are less dense than those of the outer air and the pressure at the bottom of the chimney is less inside than outside. This difference in pressure is the "draft" that can be produced in a chimney, and it is dependent upon height and temperature differential. The height and diameter of a chimney are determined by the amount of draft required, the velocity of the gases passing through it, and the maximum quantity of gas that must be dispersed. Drafts usually range in pressure from 2 to 4 inches of water and in gas velocities from 25 to 50 feet per second.

A trend toward short, stub-type stacks has developed because they reduce the hazards for aircraft and because they are not as detrimental to the value of adjoining properties as high chimneys are.

If low chimneys are used, draft must be provided by induced draft fans. The initial cost of the fans usually offsets the construction savings of the low stack, and operating and maintenance costs are substantial and continuous. Furthermore, even stub stacks must project at least 20 to 40 feet above projections on adjoining buildings to overcome the possibility of down drafts and the dangers of direct discharge of exhaust gases into the buildings.

With induced draft fans, drafts can be controlled, however—a significant advantage under certain atmospheric conditions and particularly in starting operations when natural draft stacks are only partially effective. To avoid rapid deterioration of the fans, exhaust gases must be cooled to temperatures tolerated by metals used in the blowers by water sprays, cold air inflows, or both.

Several types of chimneys may be used for municipal incineration plants: steel, either guyed or self-supporting; masonry, made of either straight or radial bricks or blocks; and reinforced concrete.

Steel Chimneys

The advantages of steel chimneys are many: they can be structurally self-supporting, complying with all building code requirements at a first cost comparable to masonry; they are easily constructed, lightweight in proportion to diameter and height, and require less space than some other kinds; they permit less infiltration of outside air than radial brick or tile chimneys do. The disadvantages are that they are usually unsightly, maintenance costs are high, they must be built of costly heat resisting alloys, and must have special protective coatings to prevent rapid deterioration.

Masonry Chimneys

Masonry construction is most commonly used for high, natural draft chimneys because masonry chimneys can be designed to blend architecturally with the building; they do not require guy wires, brackets, or other ugly exterior reinforcements; they have a much longer useful life than those made of other materials; and maintenance costs are generally lower.

Because of their weight and great exposure to lateral wind forces, both the foundations and general design of masonry chimneys need special

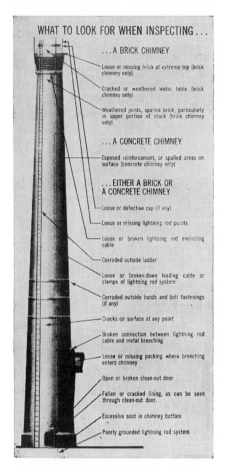

WHAT TO LOOK FOR WHEN INSPECTING...

...A BRICK CHIMNEY

Loose or missing brick at extreme top (brick chimney only)

Cracked or weathered water table (brick chimney only)

Weathered joints, spalled brick, particularly in upper portion of stack (brick chimney only)

...A CONCRETE CHIMNEY

Exposed reinforcement, or spalled areas on surface (concrete chimney only)

...EITHER A BRICK OR A CONCRETE CHIMNEY

Loose or defective cap (if any)

Loose or missing lightning rod points

Loose or broken lightning rod encircling cable

Corroded outside ladder

Loose or broken-down leading cable or clamps of lightning rod system

Corroded outside bands and bolt fastenings (if any)

Cracks on surface at any point

Broken connection between lightning rod cable and metal breeching

Loose or missing packing where breeching enters chimney

Open or broken clean-out door

Fallen or cracked lining, as can be seen through clean-out door.

Excessive soot in chimney bottom

Poorly grounded lightning rod system

Fig. 71. Periodic inspection of an incinerator chimney is important. Repairs require special skills and are almost always done on a contract basis.

attention. They are usually made up of an outer structural shell and separate lining shell that can resist temperatures up to 1,000° F. The two shells are separated by an annular four-inch air space. The exterior shell, varying in thickness from 9 inches at the top to 20 inches or more at the bottom, depending on design, is built of special, wedge-shaped, perforated blocks of hard-burned refractory clay, usually colored to match the building brick.

Reinforced Concrete Chimneys

Chimneys made of concrete are inherently strong, and with properly designed reinforcements they can withstand much higher winds and greater earthquake stresses than other types can. Furthermore, a reinforced concrete chimney may be more economical than other kinds if the chimney is more than 200 feet high and 8 feet in inside diameter. The major disadvantage is that the surface may crack extensively from temperature and plastic stress conditions.

Linings

Steel stacks are usually protected on the inside with a relatively thin, bonded fused-glass lining. Masonry and concrete stacks as a rule are completely lined with firebrick (usually acid-resistant or first-quality) varying in thickness from 4½ inches at the top to 13½ inches at the bottom. The lowest 30 feet have in addition an extra 4½-inch thick renewable refractory lining of firebrick or castables known as a "target wall." Since linings do not affect the strength or stability of the chimney, they are ordinarily only sufficiently stable to support their own weight, and are separated from the outer shell by an annular air space. Some chimney builders fill this space with an insulating material; others leave it open so that circulating air can cool the chimney.

Steel corset reinforcement of chimney linings to restrain "breathing" action under varying temperatures, to strengthen the chimney and reduce the deterioration of articulated masonry construction, is now common. It is also important to provide expansion facilities between the chimney and the breeching and suitable insulation between the chimney and the structural footing.

Accessories

Accessories are necessary for every chimney: equipment to protect against lightning, aircraft warning lights, test openings, clean-out doors, ladders, catwalks, and caps.

Lightning protection is usually provided by ¾-inch lead covered copper rods projecting about 6 feet above the chimney cap and spaced about 8 feet apart. They should be rigidly fastened around the circumference and connected to well-grounded ⅝-inch woven copper down leads. The top 30 feet of the leads should be coated to prevent corrosion.

The height of the chimney must be limited and aircraft warning lights installed according to the requirements of the Federal Aviation Agency.

A test opening in a chimney can be costly if not included during construction. An opening for obtaining gas samples is made by inserting and firmly anchoring a standard six-inch pipe in the chimney. The pipe should extend from a few inches outside the chimney through the inner liner; a means of capping it should be available. Provision should be made for expansion of the inner lining at points where test openings are made.

Openings for test samples should be located where the gas flows in a smooth stream, usually between six diameters above the inlet and eight or nine diameters below the top. Two openings on the same horizontal plane 90 degrees apart are usually sufficient.

Openings for obtaining temperature readings can be made from two-inch pipe projecting through the liner and extending at least two inches outside. They should be located near the ladder at 10-foot intervals for the entire height of the chimney. They too should be capped when not in use.

Many chimneys have a large pocket below the inlet for collecting fly ash, but unless the ash is removed almost continuously, a pocket is not recommended. A clean-out door or other opening at the bottom of the chimney is essential for maintenance work, inspections, and cleaning.

An encaged safety ladder of noncorrosive metal anchored on the outside should extend the full height of the chimney and also connect to at least one catwalk encircling the chimney. Ladders and catwalks facilitate taking gas samples, servicing lights and lightning rods, and inspecting and maintaining the chimney. Inside ladders corrode quickly and are not safe.

A cap is an important accessory because it prevents a great deal of deterioration in the chimney from moisture, especially in high-temperature chimneys. The caps are made of cast iron or special heat-resistant, noncorroding alloys.

Residue Handling

From 5 to 25 per cent of refuse by weight, depending on type, that is charged into an incinerator remains as residue after completion of the combustion process. This residue is a mixture of unburned refuse, ashes, tin cans, and other noncombustibles. It must be removed from the furnace, either manually or mechanically, and thoroughly quenched to eliminate fire, smoke, and odors, and it must be taken to a disposal site. Some components of the residue, such as tin cans and other metals, are sometimes salvaged, either at the plant or at the disposal site.

Batch Type Collection

Batch-feed furnaces are equipped with ash hoppers underneath the

Fig. 72. Ashes can be discharged from incinerators continuously, as they are at the 73rd Street incinerator in New York where a conveyer belt is used to take the quenched ashes to a storage hopper (left). If the volume of ashes and other conditions permit, the ash may be discharged directly into portable containers (right).

grates for intermittent reception of residue, and they usually are also equipped with dumping grates for discharging the ash residue. In the interests of economy and flexibility of operation, ash hoppers should be big enough to store the residue from several hours of burning. Quenching of residue, either with water from spray nozzles beneath the grates or by dumping into a water bath, is essential to reduce fire hazards. To withstand the heat of the residue, the thermal shock resulting from the sudden chilling effect of the quenching spray, and the severe wear from the abrasive residue it is customary to line ash hoppers with a hard-

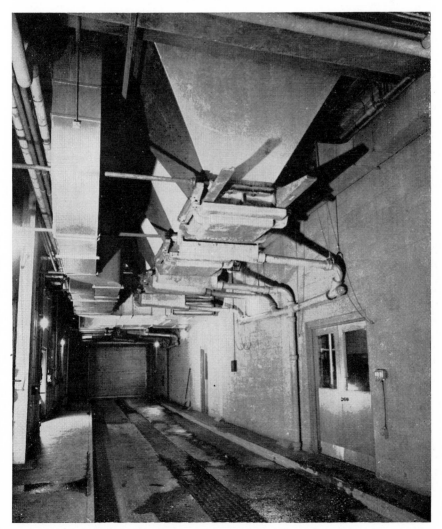

Fig. 73. Overhead discharge hoppers for quenched ashes from batch-feed incinerators, with drive-through so that ashes can be put into trucks directly from the hoppers.

burned, tough, vitrified brick. Usually each hopper is equipped with discharge gates of watertight construction. Plants in which ash hoppers are used usually have an "ash tunnel" so that trucks can be driven directly under the hoppers to receive the residue. This tunnel should be paved, well drained, and well ventilated. The cross-section area should be large enough to permit trucks and equipment to maneuver in it.

Dust and steam are rapidly removed from the ash tunnel by two methods: suction fans or blowers to utilize the exhaust as combustion air, and natural draft through direct duct connections with the annular space in high chimneys.

If final burning of refuse is allowed to take place in the ash hopper or if more residue is allowed to collect in the hopper than the spray nozzles can quench, serious damage can be done to the grates, to the grate supporting members, and to the operating mechanism.

Conveyer Type Collection

In large plants, especially those in which continuous-feed type furnaces are used, residue is discharged continuously into a water trough or tank long enough to receive the residue from all chutes (residue and siftings). An endless conveyer system drags the settled ash from the bottom of the trough up an incline to allow most of the quenching water to run off before the residue is put in trucks or containers. Noncombustible material in the residue, such as steel rods and baling wire or unburnt rags, is removed from the conveyer from time to time to prevent jamming. A rotating screening mechanism and high pressure water spray can be installed at the upper end of the conveyer system to clean and separate ashes and similar materials from tin cans if a salvage operation is desired.

Because the conveyer system is subject to a great deal of wear and requires more than occasional repairs, a stand-by conveyer should be available to assure reliable operation. The conveyer should have wearing shoes, replaceable rails and bottoms, and hard alloy steels for the chains. Some plants, depending on the type of furnace ash discharge equipment, use belt or apron-type conveyers.

Hauling

The transportation of incinerator residue in open trucks through city streets, especially for long distances, is a potential nuisance and may cause complaints. Care should be taken with quenching, draining, and cooling operations so that residue does not drip, smoulder, or give off offensive odors while it is being hauled to a disposal site. Some cities have solved this problem and reduced the cost of residue handling by using demountable, drainable, and watertight containers that can be placed beneath the ash hoppers, transported, and dumped with fork lift or hoist trucks.

For hauls of 20 miles or more it is advisable to explore the possibilities of using a truck transfer station or transportaion by rail or by large semi-trailer over-the-highway vehicles.

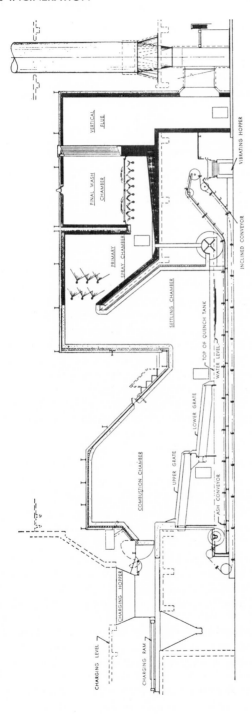

Fig. 74. Cross section through Fort Lauderdale incinerator shows relative position of ram-type, hydraulically operated charging gate and vibrating hopper receiving residue. Note inclined conveyors for reverse quenching.

The best design and construction for an incineration plant are simple, functional, economical, and attractive. Although technicalities of incineration plus the usual economies expected of a city impose restrictions, they also present a challenge to the architect to design a plant that is pleasing to the eye. Parts of the incinerator and equipment that are not usually housed within the main building—fly ash collectors, expansion chambers, fans, and storage bins, for instance—are often unsightly. However, plant design and layout can be such that the components become a part of the over-all design and do not detract from well proportioned and good looking buildings.

Since incineration is an industrial-type process, the first step in design and construction is a mechanical engineering one. Agreement must be reached on what kind and size plant is necessary and what kinds and amounts of furnaces and equipment are to be used. Architectural plans must be based on engineering layouts.

Most municipal engineering staff members do not have the specialized knowledge necessary to plan an incineration plant, so a consulting engineer is usually retained. What is expected of the consultant? First, a plant that operates well at full capacity with as little maintenance and repair as possible; second, a plant that is nuisance-free—that meets all locally imposed regulations and is acceptable as a good neighbor.

A good consulting engineer will also see to it that city officials are reasonably well informed on the design and operational problems of various types of plants and equipment so that those best suited to a city's needs can be built.

Construction involves the plant buildings, the furnaces, and other parts of the incinerator.

Plant Building

Foundations. Reliable soil samples and tests to determine bearing values are extremely important in designing and constructing a foundation. With average soil conditions, simple, reinforced concrete spread footings provide ample support for furnaces, combustion chambers, breechings, boilers, outer walls, and interior columns. If, however, the soil is relatively unstable, it may be necessary to use pilings to provide sufficient bearings, through "skin friction" or by sufficient depth to reach a firm stratum of earth or a combination of both. Frequently the site for a municipal incineration plant was formerly a dump, a marsh, or both.

The most difficult part of the foundation excavation is for the storage pit. The storage pit is nearly always built before the excavation is done for the rest of the building. The earth from the pit excavation is used to fill adjacent areas; thus the foundation adjacent to the pit can be built on firmly compacted ground. If the pit is considerably lower than the normal ground water table, the pit may have to be pumped until enough of the building above the pit has been built that hydrostatic pressure has been balanced. Filling the completed storage pit with water has also been used successfully in place of pumping. Watertight construction of the pit through the use of dense concrete, temperature reinforcement bars to prevent cracking, and water stops at all expansion and construction joints below ground water level is important. Waterproofing that part of the exterior of the storage pit that is below ground level is also recommended.

The foundations for chimneys are a special design problem and are not considered here.

Supporting Structure. Steel framing in standard shapes for beams, columns, purlins, and so on is preferred for the supporting structure of the average municipal incineration plant because it is economical. Reinforced concrete usually is not suitable because it cannot withstand the rapid temperature changes, intense heat, and vibration to which incineration plants are subjected.

Steel shapes are usually delivered with a coat of protective paint already applied. Before they are put into use they should be given a second coat of protective paint to help prevent corrosion and to cover unpainted parts such as welds and bolts. Structural members that are used in building rectangular furnaces, combustion chambers, breechings, flat arch refractory ceilings, and suspended refractory sidewalls must be protected from the heat and changes in temperature by refractory materials, fiberglass blocks, asbestos blocks, or other noncombustible materials. Temperatures vary widely in incineration plants. In northern climates the temperature of the plant near the furnaces at the end of the operating week may be as high as 130° F., while on weekends when the furnaces are not in operation the temperature may be near freezing. Provision must be made in the structure for expansion and contraction caused by these changes to prevent buckling and warping.

Structural parts that support the traveling crane, the tipping room floor, and charging gate mechanisms are subjected to live load stresses of considerable intensity and to concentrated static loads, as well as changes in temperature. They must also be able to accommodate expansion and contraction caused by incinerator operation. Furthermore, after several years of operation, crane rails become uneven and crane wheels become "egg-shaped," which may, by vibration, impose additional stress on the supporting structure.

Some special problems, such as support of the tipping floor roof with long span beams or provision of adequate rigidity against wind stresses, may require especially designed steel framing, which usually proves more satisfactory and more economical than standard steel shapes.

Interior Walls and Ceilings. Easily cleaned, impervious surfaces are important in the maintenance of the interior walls and ceilings of an incineration plant. Concrete block with an impervious surface or hollow structural tile with a salt glaze finish are economical and serviceable materials. Ceramic tile has been used with good results in many plants but it is usually too expensive for general use. It is ordinarily justified only in washrooms, showers, locker rooms, and lunchrooms.

Whatever material is used, it is important to choose colors that are both practical and pleasing to look at. Attractive appearance does much to boost employee morale.

Floors. The most economical as well as the most practical kind of floor for a municipal incineration plant is reinforced concrete or flat slab construction. In areas of the plant where the floor is exposed to a great deal of moisture and abrasion, such as the tipping floor, stoking floor, ash tunnel, and maintenance shop, it is well to consider using one of the many surface hardening and waterproofing compounds that help preserve the top layer of cement and fine aggregate.

Ventilation and Heat. The ventilation of an incineration plant is much more than a matter of opening doors and windows and allowing the air to circulate.

To safeguard the neighborhood from odors and dust, a plant should be operated with slight negative pressure in those areas where nuisances are likely to originate. It is necessary to bring air into the building, however, to prevent more negative pressure than is wanted, especially during the winter when the doors and windows are usually closed. By taking most of the combustion air through a duct at the top of the storage pit, it is possible to draw in some of the dust and odors produced by the refuse dumping and handling and to prevent them from spreading.

The ash removal floor may be a particularly steamy and dusty one. However, by taking part of the combustion air from this area or by providing an exhaust fan and duct system, dust and steam can be cut down a great deal.

Offices, lunchrooms, locker rooms, and washrooms should be ventilated independently of the rest of the building, with a slight positive pressure at all times. Plants in cold climates must be heated in some parts—offices; lunchrooms; washrooms; maintenance shop; scalerooms; charging, tipping, and stoking floors; ash handling areas. Air taken into the plant to alleviate excessive negative pressure must also be heated.

Heat may be provided by separately fired boilers or by using waste heat from the furnaces. (The sale of waste heat from incinerator furnaces is discussed in Chapter 10, Salvage and Reclamation.) If furnace heat is used, the hot exhaust gases are diverted to a low pressure boiler and from there to the chimney by means of dampering devices or induced draft fans. If waste heat from the furnaces is not used, small oil burning boilers can furnish heat for offices, lunchrooms, washrooms, and locker rooms. In cold climates the equipment can be used to provide heat on weekends when the plant is shut down. Offices and other areas away from the furnaces should be heated and air conditioned to about 70° F. and other spaces to about 55° to 60° F.

Lighting. Good lighting in an incinerator building need not be expensive if it is well planned. The most important thing is the correct amount of light for each area to promote efficiency and safety. Excellent lighting must be provided near the storage pit, moving machinery, hot surfaces, ladders, stairways, and other hazardous locations—an intensity of about 50 foot-candles is recommended.

A lighting intensity of 7 to 10 foot-candles is sufficient on the tipping floor; on the charging and stoking floors an intensity of 25 foot-candles should be maintained. Offices, lunchrooms, locker rooms, and washrooms require an intensity of 50 to 75 foot-candles.

Local switches, rather than a few main switches that control large banks of lighting equipment, are an operating economy and cost little additional to install.

Facilities for Employees. Ample and comfortable facilities should be provided for employees. Impervious and noncorrosive materials, such as stainless steel and ceramic tile, should be used in washrooms, shower rooms, and locker rooms; sanitary facilities must be installed in compliance with local plumbing codes. The locker rooms should be big enough for two metal lockers for each employee (one for work clothes and one for street clothes) and for dressing space.

In many new plants, cooking facilities—stove, refrigerator, sink, tables, and chairs—have been provided for employees who want to prepare their own meals.

Drinking fountains, strategically located, usually pay big dividends in time saved.

A freight elevator is most advantageous in large plants with many floors.

Safety Facilities. Accepted safety practices used in industrial plants should be used in incineration plants also. Wherever possible, catwalks and stairs should be provided instead of movable ladders. Railings and toeboards around all upper level walkways and stairs also help prevent accidents, especially from falling tools. If ladders are necessary, they should be fixed and provided with hoop enclosures; they should also be long enough to extend two or three feet above the landing place in order to help prevent falls.

Safety equipment such as hip-height railings and chain and waist belt should be mandatory for employees working around charging doors in direct overhead charge type plants.

Special-purpose fire extinguishers and fire hose stations should be strategically located throughout the plant, as recommended in local fire control regulations. Fire occasionally breaks out in the storage pit and it is essential to have fire fighting equipment, including fire hose and appurtenances, to control pit fires. Carbon dioxide extinguishers have been effective in extinguishing small pit fires. Large plants may have a separate water standpipe system for such emergencies.

Some refuse causes explosions and fire, especially when batch-fed into a furnace. Naphtha and lacquer thinners in a free state or in combination with other materials, for instance, are naturally hazardous. But some substances that normally are not dangerous, such as flour and sawdust, may cause violent explosions when dropped into a blazing furnace. Moreover, sealed containers develop tremendous pressures when subjected to furnace heat and also explode.

It is recommended, therefore, to protect plant employees and equipment, that such materials be rejected for incineration but if they are not all employees exposed to such dangers be required to use safety goggles or face safety shields.

Exterior Walls and Windows. Face brick has been preferred for the exteriors of incineration plants for many years. It is usually a veneer backed up with hollow structural tile. Concrete block and stone veneer are also used. Trim is usually of cut stone or precast concrete.

If an incineration plant is to be built in an industrial area, economies are possible if an industrial-type material, such as transite or sheet aluminum, is used. Before final selection of the exterior material is made, however, it is essential that the limitations of inexpensive materials be understood.

The important thing about the outside of the building is that it be easy to clean and impervious to water, dust, and gases if it is to be satisfactorily maintained.

An important factor in the appearance of an incineration plant is the windows. Although adequate ventilation can be supplied by air conditioning, for psychological reasons it is well to have windows that open, especially if the plant is in a part of the city where escaping odors do not cause a serious problem.

Glass block gives a plant a modern, dressed-up appearance and the light that filters through it is soft and pleasing. It also is durable, easily installed, and not expensive.

In the operations parts of the plant, projecting industrial type steel or aluminum sash are suitable; double hung or casement type windows are often preferred for offices, lunchrooms, locker rooms, and washrooms.

Noncorrodible screens should be provided for all ventilating sash, and window shades or venetian blinds are recommended where protection against sun glare is important.

Roof. The roof of the building is usually made up of precast slabs of lightweight concrete or other fire-resistant material, a three-ply hot asphalt mopped roofing application, and a layer of fine gravel.

Landscaping. Every municipal incineration plant, no matter how large or small, should be pleasingly landscaped. Shrubs and grass, relatively inexpensive to plant and maintain, pay big dividends in public relations in the neighborhood and in the entire city. The layout of the walks and driveways is important. Permanent materials, such as concrete, are recommended for lasting appearance and ease of maintenance.

Large plants may require professionals to plan the landscaping and an experienced gardener to maintain the grounds, depending on location of the plant and the size of the grounds.

Furnace Construction

Walls. For many years solid gravity type walls were almost always used for furnaces and chambers because labor and material costs were low for this type of wall. However, incinerators are much larger today, which makes high walls necessary and construction and maintenance of gravity type walls too costly.

Hung type walls were first tried about 1924. Essentially they consist of a series of low walls, one above another, completely supported on steel or cast iron shelves or hangers supported by steel columns. Each section or "wall" is independent.

The construction principle is entirely different from those used for gravity type walls. Heavy structural steel columns, spaced 3 to 5 feet apart, are framed on the outside of the chamber. A framework of horizontal and vertical heat resistant castings is securely fastened to these columns to support and retain the refractory. A shelf on the horizontal bar supports the entire weight of each wall section. Refractory brick and tile are designed with interlocking treads on the sides and slots or offsets at the back. The first row of tile is set on the shelf and the tiles are held to the framework by castings engaging the back slots. The second row rests on the first and the tiles are held by the interlocking treads. At intervals, as a section is being built, a row of tiles is attached to the framework by castings or fingers engaging the back slots. All tiles are dipped in a thin mixture of fire clay and water to fill irregularities before setting in place.

The height of the section depends on the weight supported; it can vary from 12 to 48 inches. There is a small gap between the top of one section and the bottom of the next to provide for vertical expansion. This opening is packed with a soft asbestos cement.

Details of wall construction vary with location of the wall in the incinerator and therefore the service required of it. In the most troublesome area—the 4 feet of wall above the grate bed—the wall may be up to 24 inches thick (7-inch air cooled silicon carbide brick, 2-inch air space, 4½-inch firebrick, 4½-inch insulating brick, 2-inch insulation, 4-inch ceramic glazed face tile). The combustion chamber walls and hung

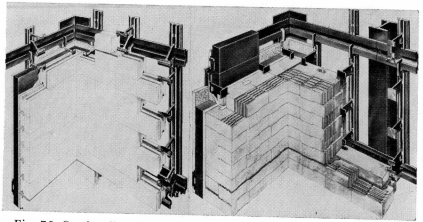

Fig. 75. Sectionally supported hung walls are usually used in modern incinerator refractory construction. They may be insulated or air-cooled. The wall shown right is for use in ignition and combustion zones of the incinerator; the one at the left is for use in zones in which temperatures are lower, such as the flues.

arches require only a 9-inch firebrick wall, a large air space, and an insulating casing of facia (aluminum plate faced with bonded insulating material or a ceramic glazed tile). The subsidence chambers and flue linings, which are subject to much lower temperatures, need to be built only of 4½-inch brick with 2½-inch insulating block or castable material on the outside.

Suspended type walls can be justified for present day incinerators on the bases of longer life and lower repair costs alone. There are other advantages, however. Since the tiles are dipped only in a fire clay mixture, they do not adhere to each other and so can expand or contract in all three dimensions relatively free from interference. Since the vertical sections are low, the amount of expansion upward is small and amply provided for by expansion joints. Nor is the refractory subject to the expansion problems of a solid brick wall. Expansion cracks are not likely to develop and tiles are held in plumb. Spalling usually occurs only in limited areas of a refractory wall, and since a suspended wall consists of sections, it is possible to remove and replace a section or even a part of a section without disturbing other sections. A solid brick wall cannot be repaired or rebuilt in part; the whole wall must be rebuilt.

The original cost of a suspended wall may be less than that for the gravity wall because the thickness of the suspended wall is determined by the refractory and insulating needs and not by stability, as it is with a gravity wall. For example, the wall of a flue 12 to 15 feet high requires a 13½-inch refractory plus insulation and steel for a gravity wall, but only a 4½-inch refractory plus insulation and steel for a suspended wall.

Plastic refractories can also be used in suspended walls. Sectional supports and tiebacks to the steel framework are used with them.

In most large incinerators it is necessary to protect the refractory lining from external damage. This is done by an outer brick wall, a ceramic tile facia, or removable metal plates fastened to the buckstays.

Floors. The floors of the furnace, combustion chamber, subsidence chamber, breechings, and chimneys, when built of firebrick, are usually made up of three parts. A layer of hollow structural tile is laid on the concrete floor or footing in such a manner that air can circulate through the tiles and cool the floor and insulate the supporting structure. The tiles are covered with a layer of insulating brick over which the firebrick is placed. Silicon carbide brick is preferred in fly ash settlement chambers in which a wet floor system is used. If circumstances warrant, the tile layer may be omitted. Also, the firebrick floors may be laid without mortar if there is no risk that the open joints will fill with fine ash, causing the floor to "creep" and eventually fail.

Arches. Every chamber and flue ceiling must be lined with refractory materials. The lining of the ceiling, known as the arch, can be of the sprung type or the suspended type.

The sprung arch is supported by abutments at the sides or ends only. It is used for short spans in which the weight at the ends of the span are not excessive. It is also used over openings for doors and observation ports. Before 1913, all arches were of the sprung type, and they required

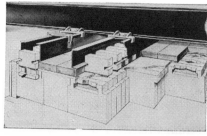
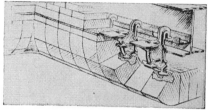
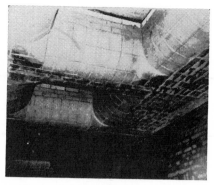

Fig. 76. A refractory arch: the flat suspended arch (top left); details of nose construction (left); interior of charging holes (above).

expert craftsmen to build them. There are serious disadvantages to them: unreliability, repair difficulties, and span limitations.

Suspended arches, introduced in 1913, are now used in construction of all large incinerators because of their many advantages. They are similar in principle to suspended walls in that a steel framework is supported by columns and the refractory is hung on anchors attached to the framework. The top of the refractory is usually covered with insulation to reduce the heat loss and air infiltration. The thickness and quality of the refractory are determined by service needs, not by stability needs, as they are with sprung arches. Suspended arches are cheaper for the long spans, provide better for expansion, require less skill to build, usually last longer, allow for more flexibility in the design of the furnace, and are much easier and cheaper to repair.

Water-Wall Furnaces

Where water-walls are used, only a small amount of refractory material is required in the furnace lining. There is generally a castable refractory lining for the reflecting arch at the discharge end of the furnace, and a thin castable layer covers the side wall tubes to a height of approximately 15 feet above the grate line.

OPERATION AND MAINTENANCE

Operation

Incineration can be efficient. Refuse can be reduced to a minimum through a combination of high burning temperatures, semi-automatic temperature and air controls, controlled feeding, and mechanical stoking. Production of residue acceptable as fill material without cover is primarily a matter of correct burning temperatures, time, and adequate agitation of the refuse while it is burning. A well operated incinerator produces residues that vary from 5 per cent by weight of refuse relatively free of noncombustibles to 25 per cent by weight of mixed refuse, and from 3 per cent to 15 per cent by volume. The amount of unburned organic matter in a good residue varies from 2 per cent to 7 per cent by weight, with approximately 0.2 per cent to 0.4 per cent subject to decomposition under putrescent conditions.

High-temperature combustion effectively destroys odors and reduces noxious gases to tolerable traces. Particulate matter can be trapped so that the amount that escapes through the stack is within limits set in air pollution control ordinances. The noise from a fully enclosed incineration plant is not loud enough to be objectionable in most neighborhoods.

Maintenance and Repairs

The modern incineration plant is dirty, dusty, odor producing, and requires more than normal routine care to even approach a power plant in spit-and-polish appearance and trouble-free operation.

An annual budget for maintenance and repairs approximating 5 per cent of the total capital costs of the plant usually is adequate, particularly if the plant is well designed and constructed; if it was properly tested, adjusted, and broken in; and if it is always kept in good condition. Maintenance and repairs can be expected to cost between 10 per cent and 15 per cent of the total cost of operation, depending on the size and type of plant. Approximately half the cost will be for labor and the other half for materials.

Routine maintenance is preventive. Weekly inspections, cleaning and greasing, removal of clinkers and slag, minor repairs to easily accessible parts of the plant and machinery, and less frequent inspections and repairs to hard-to-get-at parts of the plant will help prevent major damage and emergencies.

In addition to routine maintenance and repairs, major repairs are needed occasionally; reconstruction and modernization of furnaces, cranes, and other parts of the plant are needed less frequently; and a complete overhaul and modernization of the plant is necessary perhaps every 25 years or so.

For routine maintenance and repairs it is necessary to stock firebrick and insulating brick, refractories, parts and links for grates and chains, and other parts of the plant components and equipment that break or wear out frequently. If extra pieces of equipment, such as cranes, are kept on hand, efficient and complete repairs can be made to parts that break without having to shut down the plant.

Even an average size incineration plant should have a machine shop, an electrical shop, and a welding shop for repairs and maintenance work.

The most important factor in good maintenance of an incineration plant is well trained, conscientious employees. If the plant is to operate efficiently, they must take personal responsibility for tending the plant and equipment and for reporting defective parts and faulty mechanical operations. Such employees will concern themselves not only with replacing worn out or defective parts, but will also try to analyze the reasons why equipment wears out or breaks and suggest improvements in operation and maintenance.

Air Pollution Control

Since the municipal government is usually responsible for the enforcement of local air pollution control ordinances, it is important that municipally operated facilities be examples of compliance. Indeed, considerable attention has been focused on air pollutants discharged by central incinerators.

Local Ordinances

Many cities have air pollution control ordinances. Almost all include provisions for the control of smoke, odors, and fly ash; a few also include provisions for control of gaseous discharges.

Local air pollution control ordinance provisions cannot be standardized because local conditions differ. Nevertheless, most ordinances are based on uniform recommendations for combustion of fuels.

The heterogeneous character of refuse, its low unit weight, its changing combustibility, and the amount of cool air needed in an incineration plant make it difficult to set uniform standards for excess air and temperatures.

The situation is further complicated by the fact that even if an incineration plant does, during a test period, meet the standards set by law, the results are for that test period only. It is necessary, therefore, that emission tests cover a wide range of operating conditions to insure, as far as possible, that a plant operates satisfactorily under all conditions.

The advent of water-wall furnaces requiring less excess air for good combustion promises improvement of this situation. Shredding of refuse material will insure more homogeneous fuel charged into the furnaces, which will further reduce excess air requirements. Perfection of high-temperature furnaces will improve burnout of material and produce less particulate matter for removal from the gas stream.

The lack of a simple, reliable method of measuring particulate discharge from municipal incineration plants has been a handicap. However, a recent APWA Research Foundation project has developed a continuous monitoring device for particulate loading from incinerator stacks. This will soon be available on the market and will materially improve air pollution control. Recently tests have been conducted on the use of pulsed laser and infra-red beams for monitoring of stack emission.

Smoke

Smoke of the visible black type is only occasionally a serious problem with central incinerators. Most cities use the Ringelmann Chart for Grading Density of Smoke (described in the United States Bureau of Mines Informational Circular 6888) as the standard for determining visual smoke emissions.

To use the chart, the color and density of smoke emitted from a chimney are compared with black cross-hatched lines of various widths on the Ringelmann Chart and the emission is given a number accordingly. If the number is greater than that permitted by local ordinance, the incinerator is in violation of the law. The chart has been reproduced in a number of handy devices, such as the one shown in Figure 77.

While most cities use the Ringelmann Chart as the basis of ordinance standards, it is not a universally adopted measuring technique. And in most cities no limits have been set in the ordinance as to how long smoke of a certain color and density can be emitted, although the trend is toward more such provisions.

The most serious effort to standardize time limits on visual black smoke emission was made by the American Society of Mechanical Engineers in a 1949 information bulletin, "Example Sections for a Smoke Regulation Ordinance," drawn up by the Model Smoke Law Committee of the Fuels Division of the society.

The society's recommendation on smoke emission reads:

No person shall cause, suffer or allow to be emitted into the open air from any fuel-burning equipment, internal combustion engine, premises or open fire, smoke the shade or appearance of which is equal to or darker than No. 2 of the Ringelmann Chart excepting:

A. Smoke the shade or appearance of which is equal to but not darker than No. 2 of the Ringelmann Chart for a period or periods aggregating 4 minutes in any 30 minutes;

B. Smoke the shade or appearance of which is equal to but not darker than No. 3 of the Ringelmann Chart for a period or periods aggregating 3 minutes in any 15 minutes, when building a new fire or when breakdown of equipment occurs such as to make it evident that the emission was not reasonably preventable.

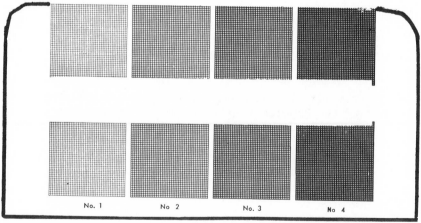

Fig. 77. Smoke emitted from a stack is compared with this chart to determine if it is light enough to meet standards. The Power's Micro-ringelmann Chart above, a direct facsimile reduction of the standard Ringelmann Chart, is reproduced by permission of McGraw-Hill Publishing Company.

Fly Ash

Limited data have been published on the amount of fly ash emitted from industrial and municipal incineration plants. However, design factors, as well as operating conditions, have a marked effect on fly ash emission. For example, the greater the burning rate per square foot of grate surface, the greater the amount of fly ash emitted. Data also show that when other factors are constant in an incinerator, fly ash emissions can be expected to increase if a forced draft system is used instead of a natural draft system.

Burning temperatures and the corrosive nature of incinerator gases limit the types of fly ash control systems that can be used.

Tables 25 and 26 give particle size and chemical analysis, respectively, of fly ash emitted from the Gansevoort Incinerator, New York City, and Tables 27 and 28 give the same information for the South Shore Incinerator in New York, which is also given by source.

TABLE 25

PARTICLE SIZE OF FLY ASH EMITTED FROM
GANSEVOORT INCINERATOR, NEW YORK CITY

Size	*Per Cent by Weight*
Plus 120 microns	5.8
Plus 90 microns minus 120 microns	6.5
Plus 60 microns minus 90 microns	17.7
Plus 40 microns minus 60 microns	13.2
Plus 30 microns minus 40 microns	12.5
Plus 20 microns minus 30 microns	1.9
Plus 15 microns minus 20 microns	3.4
Plus 10 microns minus 15 microns	21.2
Plus 5 microns minus 10 microns	5.8
Minus 5 microns	12.0

TABLE 26

CHEMICAL ANALYSIS OF FLY ASH EMITTED FROM
GANSEVOORT INCINERATOR, NEW YORK CITY

Component	*Per Cent by Weight*
Organic	14.5
Inorganic	85.5
Silica as SiO_2	36.0
Iron as Fe_2O_3	10.0
Alumina as Al_2O_3	27.7
Calcium as CaO	8.5
Magnesia as MgO	3.4
Sulfur as SO_3	9.7
Sodium and potassium oxides	4.7
Apparent specific gravity	2.58

TABLE 27

PARTICLE SIZE OF FLY ASH SAMPLES FROM
SOUTH SHORE INCINERATOR, NEW YORK CITY, BY SOURCE
(Per cent by weight)

Sieve Size[1]	Source of Sample			
	Upper Flue	Expansion Chamber	Base of Stack	Emitted
Plus No. 20	1.4	1.0	0.9	0.4
Plus No. 60 Minus No. 20	31.5	34.5	31.8	4.1
Plus No. 100 Minus No. 60	24.8	31.4	32.6	8.8
Plus No. 200 Minus No. 100	25.4	22.9	25.1	20.2
Plus No. 325 Minus No. 200	8.5	5.6	5.6	38.4
Minus No. 325	8.4	4.6	4.0	28.1

[1]Numbers refer to United States standard sieve; the higher the numbers the smaller the openings.

TABLE 28

CHEMICAL ANALYSIS OF FLY ASH SAMPLES FROM
SOUTH SHORE INCINERATOR, NEW YORK CITY, BY SOURCE
(Per cent by weight)

Component	Source of Sample		
	Upper Flue	Expansion Chamber	Emitted
Organic	0.5	0.6	10.4
Inorganic	99.5	99.4	89.6
Silica as SiO_2	50.1	54.6	36.1
Iron as Fe_2O_3	5.3	6.0	4.2
Alumina as Al_2O_3	22.5	20.4	22.4
Calcium as CaO	7.9	7.8	8.6
Magnesium as MgO	1.8	1.9	2.1
Sulfur as SO_3	4.3	2.3	7.6
Sodium and potassium oxides	8.1	7.0	19.0

Dry Collection. Most municipal incineration plants cannot meet the ASME-recommended fly ash limitations by using the usual dry fly ash collection systems alone, and therefore require special fly ash removal equipment. However, some incinerator fly ash has been controlled both by the use of refractory baffles, which settle fly ash in large, low-velocity subsidence chambers, and by mechanized collecting systems, such as

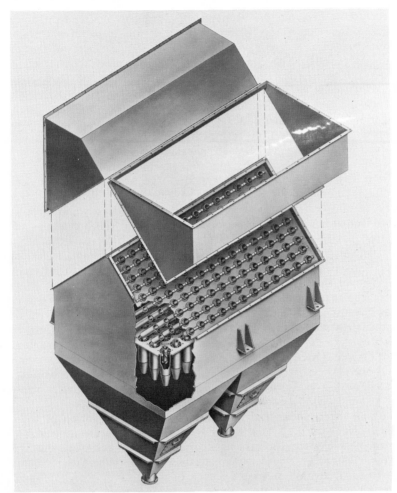

Fig. 78. Shown above is a multicone mechanical collector for the removal of fly ash.

multicone centrifugal separators, which have been operated successfully in a number of large plants. Gravity settling of fly ash by low velocity sedimentation methods—with or without baffles, checkerwalls, and the like—requires unusually large chambers and a large plant site, which for some cities are impractical and costly.

The use of bag filter dust collectors has been proposed but not used in a full-size plant. They are capable of high-efficiency particles removal, producing emissions of the order of 0.035 pounds of particulates per 1,000 pounds of flue gas at 50 per cent excess air. However the accompanying rather large draft loss, requirements for low-temperature operating conditions, and cost of bag replacements appear to make other types of equipment more attractive.

Electrostatic Precipitators. Removal of particulate matter from the flue gas stream by electrostatic precipitation appears now to offer a practical solution for high performance. Removal of 99 per cent of the grain loading is possible, and emission of gases containing weights of only 0.05 to 0.10 grain per cubic foot at standard temperature and pressure conditions can be met with good furnace combustion. This will comply with any present code requirements in the country. Although such an installation will add some $300,000 to the cost of a 300-ton-per-day incinerator, many of the newest plants are incorporating electrostatic precipitators. A number of such installations in European plants are reported to be giving high efficiency and trouble-free operation.

Wet Collection. Water spray systems have been used in incinerator breechings to control fly ash but they are relatively inefficient. The probability of a dust or fly ash particle colliding with a water droplet is remote. Furthermore, the high gas temperatures in the breechings (900° to 1,500° F.) may vaporize the water containing dust particles and the particulate matter may be re-entrained in the gas stream. In addition, the velocity of the gas prevents the water from falling uniformly so that some parts of the gas stream are not subjected to any wetting at all.

Wet impact collection devices have been used effectively for fly ash control in municipal and industrial incinerators. This method is more effective than water sprays because the gas stream is brought into close contact with water film that eliminates the possibility of re-entrainment of the fly ash. There are a number of types of wet collection systems in use. Among them are wetted metal or refractory impact baffles and enclosed tank type scrubbers. Such devices operate under a medium draft loss and produce satisfactory fly ash dust loadings.

With any wet collector system, the problem of separation of the collected solids from the water slurry is important in preventing a sewage disposal problem and preventing recirculation or reuse of the water. Figure 79 shows gravity settling tanks used in a municipal incineration plant to settle fly ash from the slurry of an efficient wet impingement collection system. The water can be reused or wasted, depending on the local water supply and costs.

The main disadvantages of wet collectors are that they use a lot of water and create corrosion and maintenance problems.

Induced Draft Fans. Some types of fly ash removal equipment cause such a high draft loss that the draft at the furnace is not sufficient to properly operate it. If such is the case, it is necessary to install induced draft fans to boost the chimney drafts.

Testing Procedures. The ASME Test Code for Dust-Separating Apparatus and a Western Precipitation Corporation bulletin on gas and dust measurement are the two standard documents on test procedures and techniques.

The ASME code has been described as the best set of standards adaptable to industrial and municipal incinerators. It describes procedures, techniques, and equipment to meet four basic testing requirements:

Fig. 79. A wet type fly ash collection system. The fly ash gravity settling tanks are upper right.

1. Securing a truly representative sample of the effluent gases and particulates. This is done by "isokinetic" sampling equipment and techniques. This is best done by using the static balanced tube sampling techniques.
2. Accurately filtering and weighing the samples of particulates.
3. Accurately measuring the samples of gas volume.
4. Devising methods, equipment, and techniques to measure con-

Fig. 80. Tests for particulate matter discharge at the municipal incinerator in Rochester, New York, require that scaffolding be put up. Gas flow measurement instruments are read during an air pollution test at an incinerator (inset).

tinuously temperatures, pressures, gas composition, velocity, and gas density of the samples of gases and of the main effluent gas stream.

Figure 80 shows part of the instruments needed to perform a field stack test in conformance with the ASME test code.

As part of the performance tests for a new incineration plant and to demonstrate compliance with local air pollution control ordinances, it may be necessary to require air pollution dust-loading emission tests. (Appendix E contains design and testing standards for incineration at federal facilities, issued by the National Air Pollution Control Administration.)

6　ON-SITE INCINERATION

On-site incineration is a widely used method of disposal for combustible refuse for two principal reasons: (1) it is often desirable to dispose of refuse as soon as possible after it is produced to eliminate the need for storage facilities; (2) it does not require collection services. As discussed in this chapter, on-site incineration applies to houses, apartments, stores, industries, hospitals, and other institutions.

Pros and Cons

The storage of refuse often causes nuisances, particularly odors. Covered containers and wrapped garbage minimize some odors but under some conditions all odors cannot be reduced sufficiently. Usually there are not unpleasant odors when wastes are first put into refuse containers but they develop from bacterial action during storage. Facilities in which food wastes are improperly stored also attract rodents and offer breeding places for flies and other insects.

If, however, instead of putting refuse into a storage container and having it collected, it is put into an incinerator and burned, it can be destroyed before nuisances or hazards are created.

If it were possible to have efficient, nuisance free incinerators for an entire city that would burn rubbish, leaves, grass clippings, and yard trimmings, as well as food wastes, collection of combustible refuse could be eliminated. The ash residue is so small that only infrequent collections of it would be necessary. Much of the noncombustible refuse could be salvaged as metal and the rest could be disposed of in sanitary landfills.

A study made in New York City indicates how much municipal refuse collection and disposal could be reduced if on-site incinerators were used citywide. Data were collected from three large apartment house developments with tenants of three different economic levels and extrapolated for the entire city for 1970, with these conclusions: there would be 13,000 domestic incinerators that would serve 1,935,000 people; the incinerators would burn 2,250 tons of mixed refuse a day, of which 550 tons would be residue; and the city would collect 1,700 tons less refuse a day than it did in 1960. In other words, the amount of refuse collected would be reduced each year by about 620,000 tons at an approximate annual savings of $18 million.

Unfortunately, on-site incinerators do not always dispose of refuse without trouble. Many incinerators operate at temperatures too low to destroy odors. Odors consist primarily of oily vapors that burn completely only if combustion temperatures reach 1,200° F. or higher. To insure complete odor elimination, incinerator temperatures should be above 1,300° F.

It is possible to maintain temperatures above 1,300° F. even in a single-chamber incinerator by providing adequate air and combustion volumes and by using sufficient auxiliary fuel. The incinerator must be built to safely withstand high temperatures, however, and the auxiliary fuel burners must be located so that they can produce the required results. In any case, the use of after-burners and of adequate size subsidence chambers assures that smoke, odors, and fly ash emissions are cut down. These facilities increase installation and operating costs, however; the extent of their use must be tailored to local conditions.

The method by which refuse is put into the incinerator often has considerable effect on whether nuisances are created during burning. If any refuse is stored in the incinerator, as in a flue-fed incinerator, and later the refuse is ignited, it is extremely difficult to get efficient, nuisance-free combustion. If, however, refuse is collected in cans and brought to the incinerator for controlled charging, it is possible for the operator to burn lightweight materials first to raise furnace temperatures and to put in garbage and other odor producing refuse after the temperature is high enough. Unfortunately, not all operators know of this process of charging and some who do are too indifferent to follow it.

Refuse incineration requires supervision during the entire burning process if there are to be no nuisances. Often an on-site incinerator operator starts the incinerator and then leaves it. He may come back once or twice during the burning period, but perhaps only to shut off auxiliary burners. But other procedures and manipulations are required with modern incinerators to insure correct temperatures at all times.

Weather plays an important part in detecting odors from incinerators. Gases are discharged from chimneys, usually a considerable distance from the ground. If an incinerator is operated only when there is a wind, there is little danger of any odors being detected in the atmosphere, because the gases rise and are carried away. On the other hand, if refuse is burned on a humid day when smoke settles to the ground, odors can easily be detected in the air. Odors can be reduced by confining burning to days when weather conditions are favorable, but this is seldom expedient.

Domestic Incinerators

Domestic incinerators are used for the bulk of on-site incineration—on the basis of the total number of incinerators, on the number of tons of refuse burned, and on number of hours operated. There are two broad classes of domestic incinerators: outdoor and indoor.

Outdoor Types

The outdoor or back yard type is by far the most common. The simplest burners consist of a metal drum with air holes punched into the sides near the bottom. Those that have a wire burning basket are probably the next most common type. Back yard burners can be quite elaborate, varying from simple concrete boxes to refractory-lined units with substantial cast iron grates and a short chimney.

Regardless of type, outdoor incinerators are not suitable for present-day living in urban areas. Combustion temperatures and the amount of air needed for combustion cannot be regulated effectively or economically. The burners produce smoke, odors, and fly ash and are fire hazards to nearby buildings. This was dramatically demonstrated in the Los Angeles area in 1957 when back yard burning was limited to the hours of 4 P.M.

Fig. 81. Domestic incinerators are widely used where there is inadequate or infrequent collection of combustible refuse. Their appearance is comparable to other household appliances.

to 7 P.M. Pictures taken just before 4 o'clock showed the area to be relatively free of smoke and haze. But pictures taken at one-minute intervals after the burning was started showed the area gradually blanketed with smoke; visibility was reduced from several miles to only a few hundred yards. Back yard incinerators have since been banned in the Los Angeles area.

In fact, the practice of burning refuse outdoors is gradually being prohibited in most large cities. Outdoor incinerators cannot be manufactured nuisance-free at a price that interests householders and justifies discontinuance of refuse collection and disposal systems.

Back yard burning may be justified in sparsely settled areas where smoke and odors are quickly diluted and it is unlikely that the burners will cause any significant air pollution problems.

Indoor Types

Indoor domestic incinerators, usually called home incinerators, are of many types, but they can be classified broadly as those that burn refuse without the use of auxiliary fuel and those that use auxiliary fuel.

Burners Without Auxiliary Fuel. Home incinerators operated without auxiliary fuel work much like outdoor incinerators. The simplest and cheapest type consists of an iron grate built into the base of a chimney. A charging door is built into the chimney above the grate and an ash pit door below. Often a complete unit is bricked into the base of the chimney. The actual burning takes place in the chimney, where there is little chance to regulate the draft. Other types are burners connected to the house chimney by a length of vent pipe. They may be simple sheet metal units or elaborate refractory-lined ones.

The advantages of this type of home incinerator are that smoke and odors are discharged from the top of the house chimney and fire and odor hazards are substantially reduced. The refuse mixture burned in them is usually a better fuel than that in outdoor burners, because leaves, grass clippings, brush, and other garden trimmings are not ordinarily carried into the house for disposal. If the burning is restricted to papers and cardboard, smoke and fly ash are the only probable nuisances. If garbage, rags, wool, rubber, plastics, and similar materials are put in with paper and cardboard, disagreeable odors result because the papers burn up quickly and high enough combustion temperatures are not maintained to burn the other refuse satisfactorily. The possibility of odor nuisance is then entirely dependent upon atmospheric conditions, which determine whether odorous gases from the chimney are blown away and dissipated or descend to the ground.

This type of home incinerator is rapidly losing its appeal to the householder. It cannot burn large quantities of garbage under normal circumstances without causing odors. The increased use of home garbage grinders has greatly reduced the refuse problem in many homes.

Burners With Auxiliary Fuel. The most widely used home incinerators are those that use gas as an auxiliary fuel. Many models have been marketed during the 1950's. All can be classified in three general types:

(1) dehydrating units, (2) high B.T.U. input units, and (3) units equipped with after-burners.

1. The dehydrating type home incinerator consists of a round or rectangular combustion chamber large enough to hold one or two bushels of refuse. The charging door is usually at the top and an ash-pit door is near the bottom. A small gas burner is located near the bottom of the chamber and is protected by a tube or deflector so that the refuse cannot interfere in any way with the gas flame. Combustion gases exit from the rear at or near the top of the burner and are vented to a chimney (Figure 82).

The operating principle of these incinerators is simple. The gas flame burns continuously and is adjusted to a gas input of from 1,500 to 3,500 B.T.U. per hour, depending upon the manufacturer's recommendation. The burner and shield heat up the air in the combustion chamber. When refuse is placed in the unit, the warmed air circulates through the material and picks up moisture before passing to the chimney. The refuse is thus dehydrated. As it dries, its temperature rises until it ignites. With combustion started, the refuse burns to ashes.

In practice there have been a number of difficulties with this type of incinerator. Food wastes dehydrate slowly at temperatures below 200° F. and at temperatures below 150° F. the process requires days. As a result, incinerators of this type cannot economically burn an appreciable quantity of wet refuse. If the refuse consists primarily of combustibles such as papers and cardboard, the paper next to the burner reaches ignition temperature in from two to eight hours. The flames ignite all of the papers and similar materials in the combustion chamber and the temperature within the unit rises rapidly to a peak within two to five minutes after ignition. Paper and similar materials burn comparatively quickly, however, so that the temperature drops as soon as they are consumed. It has been found that 10 minutes after ignition the temperature is usually below 500° F. No appreciable amount of garbage can be burned in so short a time and even little drying takes place. Only the hot ashes from the paper and the continued burning of partially dried garbage from previous charges provide dehydration for the freshly charged food wastes. The temperature of the combustion gases from a charge of mixed refuse usually falls below 200° F. in 15 minutes and gradually returns to a steady operating temperature of about 140° F. for the next two hours. This final dehydrating and burning period, extending over several hours, produces little smoke or fly ash but produces strong burning-garbage odors. A dehydrating incinerator cannot completely burn a refuse charge in one operation unless the material is practically all paper.

Home incinerators of the dehydrating type produce the most smoke and fly ash within the first five minutes of ignition. The air supply, which is relatively constant, is regulated by the size of the air in-take holes and the chimney draft. At the start of ignition, there is usually insufficient air for complete combustion and some smoke may result. As soon as most of the paper and other high combustibles are consumed, the air supply becomes adequate for the combustion rate and the smoke practically

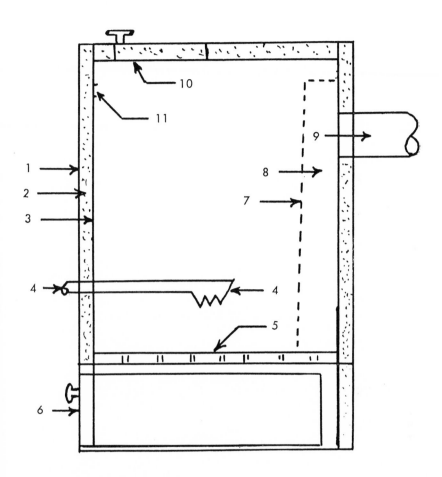

1 - Outer Metal Shell
2 - Insulation
3 - Inner Metal Lining
4 - Constant B. T. U. Gas Burner (1800 B. T. U.)
5 - Grate
6 - Ashpit Door and Pan
7 - Perforated Metal Retainer Plate
8 - Passage for Gases of Combustion
9 - Vent to Chimney
10 - Charging Door
11 - Overfire Air Ports

Fig. 82. A schematic drawing of the dehydrating type of household incinerator.

disappears. The disappearance of the smoke makes it difficult to locate the source of odors, however. The strongest odors, as mentioned previously, usually come from burning garbage at low temperatures, which continues long after all of the paper has been destroyed.

A typical curve for an ignition cycle in this type of incinerator is shown in Figure 83. The initial and final temperatures are determined by the amount of paper and similar highly combustible materials in the refuse.

The dehydrating type incinerator has not yet been demonstrated to be a good general solution to home refuse disposal problems.

The electric heater home incinerator, which is in the dehydrating category, was developed for use in areas that do not have gas available for fuel, although many have also been installed in cities where there is gas. They are designed and operate on the same principle as that of the gas dehydrating type except that a hot plate is used in the electric burner.

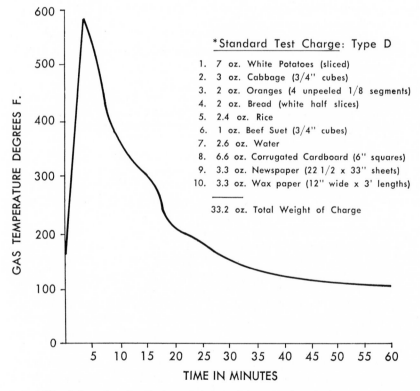

*Standard Test Charge: Type D

1.   7 oz. White Potatoes (sliced)
2.   3 oz. Cabbage (3/4" cubes)
3.   2 oz. Oranges (4 unpeeled 1/8 segments)
4.   2 oz. Bread (white half slices)
5.   2.4 oz. Rice
6.   1 oz. Beef Suet (3/4" cubes)
7.   2.6 oz. Water
8.   6.6 oz. Corrugated Cardboard (6" squares)
9.   3.3 oz. Newspaper (22 1/2 x 33" sheets)
10.   3.3 oz. Wax paper (12" wide x 3' lengths)

33.2 oz. Total Weight of Charge

* "Regulations for the Testing of Indoor Refuse Burning Equipment - Type D". Ordinance Number 77-F. Department of Buildings and Safety Engineering. City of Detroit, Michigan, May 3, 1956.

Fig. 83. Chart showing ignition-temperature cycle of a dehydrating household incinerator.

Electricity has serious limitations as an auxiliary fuel for a home incinerator. The heater must first cook the refuse to dry out the moisture because the refuse cannot be burned until its temperature is raised to the ignition point. If a large amount of garbage is put in the incinerator, or little or no dry combustible refuse is included, it may be a long time before the garbage will be dry enough to ignite.

The cost of operating and maintaining electric units is usually comparable to a gas-fired unit, although it can vary with local conditions.

2. The majority of home incinerators installed in the 1950's were of the high B.T.U input type. The unit usually consists of a round or rectangular chamber that holds from one to two bushels of refuse, and is equipped with a charging door and an ash-pit door. The gases of combustion exit from the rear at or near the top. The burner is installed near the grates and is protected so that the gas flame cannot be extinguished by falling refuse (Figure 84).

An incinerator of this type also is, in practice, a storage container for combustible refuse. Refuse is put in the unit until it is full; the main gas burner is then lit, which in turn ignites the charge; the refuse is burned and the incinerator is ready for use again as a storage container. The frequency of burning is entirely dependent upon the amount of refuse; it varies from daily operation in large families to weekly operation in small ones.

A timer is often installed on the main gas burner line so that the gas will go off automatically in the burner when the predetermined time has elapsed, eliminating the need for any further attention once the incinerator is ignited.

In practice, lighting the main gas burner ignites the dry paper in the incinerator and the temperature of the gases leaving the combustion chamber rises rapidly. At this point most of the combustion chamber air space is occupied by the refuse. The air supply is limited by the size of the air holes and therefore is insufficient for the amount of refuse during the initial combustion period. The temperature rises during this period but is below the desirable minimum of 1,300° F. The small combustion chamber volume, the limited air supply, and the low flue gas temperature make starting the period of greatest potential smoke production. As the temperature rises, gas velocities increase and the fly ash discharge increases. In about 10 minutes most of the dry paper and similar materials have burned and the flue gas temperature begins to decrease. The heat dehydrates the fresh garbage and also the garbage that remains from previous charges. Some of the garbage burns and produces odors at this point because the combustion chamber temperature is considerably below that required for odor-free burning. This condition continues for a considerable time—usually for several hours and sometimes even after the main burner is shut off.

The primary purpose of the gas burner is to supply a flame of sufficient heat (from 9,000 to 35,000 B.T.U.'s per hour) to dehydrate and burn all wet refuse. Theoretically, the wet materials fall into the flames and are eventually destroyed. In practice, the paper and other combustibles

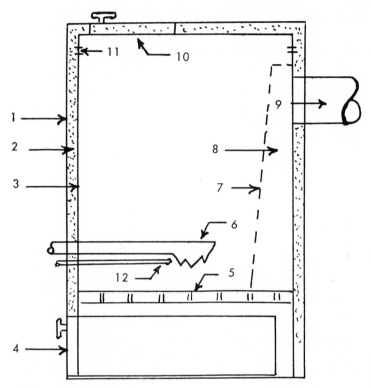

1 - Outer Metal Shell
2 - Insulation
3 - Inner Metal Lining
4 - Ashpit Door and Pan
5 - Grate
6 - High B. T. U. Input Burner (9,000 to 35,000 B. T. U.)
7 - Perforated Metal Retainer Plate
8 - Passage for Gasses of Combustion
9 - Vent to Chimney
10 - Charging Door
11 - Overfire Air Ports
12 - Pilot Burner

Fig. 84. A schematic drawing of the high B.T.U. input type of household incinerator.

burn out quickly and leave channels through the unburned refuse. The flames from the burner travel through these channels without coming in contact with the wet refuse, and at times, it has been observed, the burning of the garbage has practically stopped. If the unburned materials are agitated to break the crusted or coked surfaces and the channels are closed, the gas flames must pass through the unburned refuse and burning is speeded up considerably. It is possible to completely burn all refuse if the gas burner is operated for long enough and the unburned refuse is agitated several times. A typical curve for an ignition cycle in this type of incinerator is shown in Figure 85.

3. The performance characteristics of the dehydrating and high B.T.U. input types of home incinerators have made those incinerators unsatisfactory in cities that have and enforce effective air pollution control ordinances. This led to their prohibition in some areas and the development in the late 1950's of after-burner units that meet requirements of air pollution control ordinances.

The after-burner type is similar in appearance to other home incinerators. The principal difference is that the combustion chamber is baffled so that the gases of combustion from the primary chamber must pass down and under the baffle to reach the secondary chamber. A typical unit is shown in Figure 86. The gas burner is designed so that it discharges about one-third of its B.T.U. output into the primary chamber and about two-thirds into the secondary chamber.

Operation of after-burner type incinerators is similar to that of the

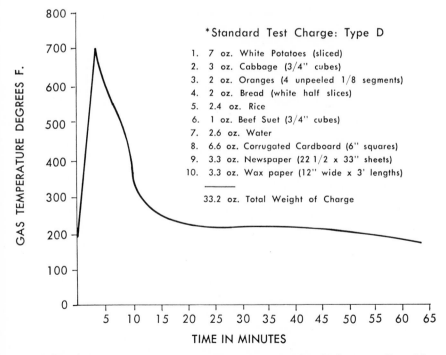

*Standard Test Charge: Type D

1. 7 oz. White Potatoes (sliced)
2. 3 oz. Cabbage (3/4" cubes)
3. 2 oz. Oranges (4 unpeeled 1/8 segments)
4. 2 oz. Bread (white half slices)
5. 2.4 oz. Rice
6. 1 oz. Beef Suet (3/4" cubes)
7. 2.6 oz. Water
8. 6.6 oz. Corrugated Cardboard (6" squares)
9. 3.3 oz. Newspaper (22 1/2 x 33" sheets)
10. 3.3 oz. Wax paper (12" wide x 3' lengths)

33.2 oz. Total Weight of Charge

* "Regulations for the Testing of Indoor Refuse Burning Equipment - Type D". Ordinance Number 77-F. Department of Buildings and Safety Engineering. City of Detroit, Michigan, May 3, 1956.

Fig. 85. Chart showing ignition-temperature cycle of a high B.T.U. input household incinerator.

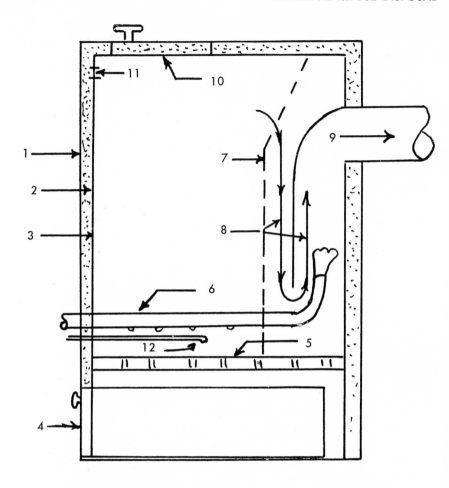

1 - Outer Metal Shell
2 - Insulation
3 - Inner Metal Lining
4 - Ashpit Door and Pan
5 - Grate
6 - Primary Burner and Combined Afterburner
7 - Metal Retainer Plate - Perforated at Top
8 - Passage for Gases of Combustion
9 - Vent to Chimney
10 - Charging Door
11 - Overfire Air Ports
12 - Pilot Burner

Fig. 86. A schematic drawing of the after-burner type of household incinerator.

high B.T.U. input type, but in general has a considerably greater heat input than the older types. This is because the major portion of the gas flame is discharged into the secondary chamber for smoke and odor destruction. Some units have timers on the main gas burner line so that the burner must stay on for at least two hours after it is ignited.

The products of combustion from the primary chamber go into the secondary chamber just above the grates. As they enter, they pass through the flame of the burner projecting into the secondary chamber. This flame increases the temperature and burns smoke and oily vapors.

In practice, when the main gas burner is ignited, the dry papers in the incinerator are ignited and the temperature of the gases leaving the unit rises rapidly. This increase in temperature is often less rapid than that of the high B.T.U. type, so the secondary burner is relied on for smoke and odor reduction. The temperature in the combustion chamber should rise to 1,200° to 1,400° F. to control odors. Most of the dry paper and similar materials are destroyed in about 10 minutes and the remainder of the refuse burns slowly.

After-burner incinerators may take almost twice as much time to burn a given amount of refuse as a high B.T.U. input unit does, even though the after-burner type may have about 25 per cent greater heat input. The main reason is that only about one-third of the heat input of the after-burner type is used to dry and burn the refuse. Two-thirds of the gas input is used to destroy smoke and odors. Additional fuel can be directed into the primary combustion chamber to speed up the combustion rate, but that, of course, increases the amount of gas consumed considerably. Also, if the burner is to be operated within the 1,200° to 1,400° F. range, the burner must have a refractory lining adequate to withstand such temperatures.

EVALUATING HOME INCINERATORS

The indoor type of home incinerator must be evaluated in terms of costs, safety, nuisances, and performance. Standards have been set up to measure some of these factors and tests have been conducted by several groups studying different phases of operation.

Costs

The initial cost of home incinerators that use auxiliary fuel varies considerably. Some are made so that they can be built into the base of the chimney when the house is constructed. Others, intended for basement installation, may be designed with exterior simplicity or may be as well finished as the best refrigerator or stove. Automatic controls, such as pilot lights and timers, add to the cost. The price of indoor incinerators varies from about $50 to $200, with after-burner types in the $100 to $200 range. Installation costs vary from $15 to $30, and again, costs for the after-burner type are usually in the upper range—from $20 to $30. Local wage scales affect installation costs, obviously. Assuming that a home incinerator lasts 15 years, annual capital costs range from $5 to $15.

Operating costs of home incinerators are determined by many factors, including the size of the household served; the cost of gas; the size of the burner; and to a large degree, particularly in the after-burner type, by operating practices. If the unit is charged and ignited manually and no auxiliary fuel is used, there is, of course, no cost for auxiliary fuel. On

TABLE 29

ESTIMATED ANNUAL CAPITAL, INSTALLATION, MAINTENANCE, AND
FUEL COSTS FOR THREE TYPES OF DOMESTIC INCINERATORS, 1959

Type of Unit	Capital and Installation[1]	Maintenance	Auxiliary Fuel	Total
Dehydrating	$12	$10	$24	$46
High B.T.U.	8-12	10	18	36-40
After-burner	15	10	18[2]	43

[1]Assuming unit can be used for 15 years.
[2]May be much higher, depending on operating practices.

the other hand, if the gas burner is left on until the charged refuse is completely incinerated, auxiliary fuel may be required continuously, in some cases for as long as 10 to 15 hours. Manufacturers of some units have incorporated a "no cheat" timer in their burners so that once the burner is lighted, it cannot be shut off for at least two hours. Assuming an incinerator of this type with a burner input of 35,000 B.T.U. was operated every other day for at least two hours each time, more than 1 million B.T.U. of gas would be used in a month.

Maintenance costs for the dehydrating, the high B.T.U. input, and the after-burner types of incinerators are similar. The vent pipe for each is usually constructed of metal with a life expectancy of not more than five years. In most cases, the liner of the combustion chamber is sheet metal, which rusts and burns out. Charging doors warp from the heat of combustion when large amounts of combustibles are charged and need replacing. It is difficult to generalize on maintenance costs, but they probably are about $10 a year for 15 years.

Safety

There are two broad categories of safety factors: (1) those that affect the safety of the house directly and the occupants indirectly, and (2) those that affect the safety of the user directly and the house and its occupants only indirectly.

To burn garbage and similar refuse without producing odors, it is necessary to heat the gases in the incinerator to at least 1,200° F. and preferably 1,300° F., which is recommended. When large quantities of highly combustible refuse such as paper, excelsior, and wood are put into a home incinerator, the temperature of the gases of combustion may be as high as 1,500° F. A home incinerator is frequently connected to a conventional chimney designed to withstand temperatures of less than 1,000° F. Thus, to protect the chimney and reduce fire hazards, cooling air must be mixed with the products of combustion. This is done by installing a barometric damper.

The metal vent pipe and metal incinerator linings, however, must withstand red hot heat. Even the tops of some units become red hot, which is hazardous to the home unless safety precautions are taken. Ceilings above an incinerator vent pipe must be protected with suitable insulating material, such as asbestos millboard, if the clearance is less than 36 inches; flooring under the units must also be protected if it is combustible; combustible side and rear walls must be protected if they are less than 18 inches from the incinerator.

Surface temperatures of an incinerator are also important from a safety standpoint because there is always the danger that occupants of the house will touch hot surfaces.

Since some of the refuse put into an incinerator may be explosive, provisions must be made for explosion relief in the primary chamber. That can usually be done by constructing the charging door so that it is self-opening and self-closing.

The greatest danger to the user of a home incinerator is flashback, which can only be countered through education. When the unit is charged with a large amount of combustible materials, such as papers, and then ignited, the fuel supply exceeds the air supply by a considerable amount. If someone opens the charging door too soon after the refuse is ignited, there is considerable danger of flashback as fresh air reaches the burning paper. Flames coming through the door are hazardous, of course, to people and property.

Nuisances

It is difficult to measure the nuisance potential of a home incinerator. Because of the difficulty of maintaining a flue gas temperature of at least 1,200° F. continuously, offensive odors may be produced when garbage and similar materials are burned. But an incinerator can easily be tested for odor creation by operating it so that at least part of the flue gases are discharged into a room where they can be smelled.

Odors can sometimes be detected if there is an insufficient stack draft. If smoke leaks from around the edges of the charging door, strong odors are usually present. Operating an attic cooling fan without opening a window produces a back draft and causes combustion gases from the incinerator to go through the house. The odors under such circumstances may be no different from those discharged from the top of the chimney but they are much closer.

The chances of odors becoming a nuisance outdoors are also hard to determine. The products of combustion are discharged from the chimney, a considerable distance above the ground. If the top of the chimney is also above the roofs of surrounding houses, the chances of odor nuisances are reduced a great deal. If the chimney top is lower than neighboring houses, however, the neighbors can expect odors frequently, especially if prevailing winds blow from the incinerator towards their houses.

Actually, it is unusual when odors from a home incinerator settle so quickly that they can be detected on the user's property. Usually smoke and odors travel 100 feet or more before they settle to the ground, even under adverse atmospheric conditions.

It is possible for the user of a home incinerator to minimize or practically eliminate odors by using care and judgment in charging the unit; using it when weather conditions, particularly the wind direction and velocity, are right for burning; allowing the gas burner to run until all refuse is destroyed to prevent smoldering; and learning techniques for getting good combustion. Whether it is reasonable to expect such careful operation from many householders is a matter of conjecture.

A few incinerators in a neighborhood may be an occasional nuisance to some residents. But if everyone in an urban neighborhood has an incinerator, the potential for nuisances is multiplied; thus the widespread use of incinerators should be avoided unless their design and operation are carefully controlled.

Considerable smoke, condensible tars, and greases may also be emitted during the operation of a home incinerator. Sunlight reacts with the discharged gases to form more troublesome gases (as demonstrated in the Los Angeles area with smog). The volume of particulate matter and gases coming from a single house chimney is small, however, and therefore is not usually detrimental, at least in rural areas. Since the condensible tars, greases, and smoke are end products of incomplete combustion at low temperatures, it is possible to reduce them by using skill and judgment in charging and firing the incinerators and by using after-burners.

To alleviate fly ash and particulate emissions, suitable controls must be built into the incinerator. High air and gas velocities in the furnace and in the chimney stir up light particles and carry them in the air stream into the chimney discharge. The use of subsidence chambers to reduce these gas velocities is most helpful but, of course, increases costs and the amount of floor and roof space required.

Meeting Household Needs

To be useful, a home incinerator must burn refuse almost as quickly as it is produced—at least without having to store it. The dehydrating type has a fixed B.T.U. heat input and therefore its burning rate is fixed. If there is more wet refuse than the unit can dry and burn, the unburned residue accumulates on the grates until the incinerator is completely filled with unburned garbage. The high B.T.U. input incinerator and the after-burner types more nearly meet family needs because they can be operated sufficiently long to insure that the refuse is completely destroyed each time the incinerator is used.

Effect on Municipal Disposal Costs

Elimination of or reduction in the amount of refuse collection services in a city does not necessarily reduce costs of refuse disposal of the householder. If the elimination of municipal services is dependent upon purchase, operation, and maintenance of home incinerators and garbage grinders but the municipality must provide other special facilities to handle the increased sewage wastes, the householder may ultimately pay considerably more than he would for conventional municipal services. Of course, if all combustible refuse, including garbage, is burned in back yard incinerators without the use of auxiliary fuel, such is not the case. While this latter disposal method is cheap, it is neither sanitary nor conducive to good neighborhood relations.

There are many local conditions that must be considered whenever comparisons are made of disposal systems. Not the least of these are costs, which vary with the many needs of communities. Frequency of collections, types and locations of containers, types and quantities of refuse acceptable for collection, types of collection equipment, size of lots, disposal methods, and geographic location are primary factors in determining municipal costs. For example, in urban areas the cost to the householder of collecting and disposing of combustible refuse may vary from $25 to $75 a family per year. On the other hand, if a householder provides and maintains his own disposal facilities, the cost may vary from $16 to $50 a family per year.

In an effort to get maximum convenience and avoid some problems, garbage grinders and home incinerators are sometimes both used. But even with the high costs involved the combination does not solve all disposal problems. Some type of collection and disposal service is still required for ungrindable, noncombustible solid wastes, for ashes and residue from domestic incinerators, and for bulky wastes that neither of the two disposal units can handle.

In cities that have an efficient, frequent refuse collection system, the home incinerator is a luxury and convenience for the housewife. Thus cities that have adequate or better collection and disposal systems may evaluate home incinerators differently from cities that do not. They also are in a better position to determine the over-all effect of home incinerators on the community and on the collection and disposal systems, including costs.

Effect on Municipal Disposal Practices

In cities where central incineration is the major method of refuse disposal, widespread use of home incinerators may have a considerable effect on the efficiency and efficacy of central incineration. The destruction of the easily burned paper, wood, crates, and similar materials in the home may reduce the "fuel" content of the remaining solid wastes that go to the central incineration plant to a point where auxiliary fuels, special designs, and special operating techniques are required in the plant, increasing the cost of central incineration considerably.

On the other hand, if sanitary landfills are used as the major disposal method, on-site incinerators, if properly used, not only reduce the putrescible components of refuse taken to the fills but also reduce the total amount of refuse that must be disposed of, thereby decreasing the nuisance potential and the amount of land required for fills.

Municipal Regulation of On-Site Incinerators

Several types of ordinances have been adopted by municipalities to regulate home incinerators or some factor in their use. Some ordinances prohibit or require incinerators; some regulate design, construction, installation, and performance; and some control air pollution from incinerators.

Most incinerator ordinances protect against unsafe construction and air pollution, but to be effective an ordinance should also cover other aspects of design, installation, and operation, and should require tests and licensing. An incinerator ordinance has other benefits, too; all installations are inspected, which makes for greater safety, and a list of incinerators approved to burn various types of refuse helps the usually uninformed householder who is often taken in by false claims such as "no odor," "complete, rapid combustion," and so on.

Prohibiting or Requiring Installation

Obviously, if a city prohibits the use of on-site incinerators there is no need for other regulations. A city may require incinerators for new construction, however, as a means of reducing and eventually eliminating the combustible wastes the city collects.

Design, Construction, Installation Standards

The design, construction, and installation requirements are easiest to understand and agree upon. For the most part they are intended to keep incinerators safe and prevent air pollution. While a great deal of research is still to be done in this field, it is generally agreed that design and construction that permit vermin infestation, require excessive maintenance, or are dangerous to the user are not acceptable.[1]

Most ordinances specify chimney height and construction, flue size, draft control, distances from incinerator to combustible walls and ceiling, piping, gas connections, and other factors.

The public's concern with air pollution has had a definite effect on design and construction of home incinerators. The problem of designing one to meet modern air pollution control laws is basically one of producing combustion temperatures sufficiently high to completely destroy all odorous gases inside the unit. Accordingly, the incinerator must be constructed so that it can withstand the high temperatures required, retain the products of combustion for a sufficient time to assure complete combustion, and satisfactorily control the emission of fly ash.

Operating Standards

Although many ordinances include broad standards for operating home incinerators (operated so as "not to create a nuisance," "fly ash discharge is not to be excessive," and so on), no rigid tests have been developed to determine performance characteristics of various incinera-

---

[1] See Appendix E for approved standards for design, construction, and installation of incinerators at federal facilities.

tors. Most ordinances do require that instructions for igniting and shutting down the incinerator be put on a permanent rust-resistant plate fastened to the unit where it can be read easily.

Actually, the development of performance standards is not particularly difficult technologically, but the capital, operating, and maintenance costs of a unit designed and operated to meet such performance standards under all conditions probably would be considerably greater than most householders are willing to pay.

Air Pollution Control

Provisions in air pollution control ordinances that are supposed to regulate incinerators are much more difficult to write and administer than other types of incinerator regulations. Since atmospheric and other conditions vary from city to city, each city must develop its own control provisions.

Odor is the most important factor that must be controlled, but since no method has been developed to measure odors scientifically, the human nose must be relied upon. And there are those who say that it is noticeable that the offensiveness of an odor decreases in proportion to the financial gain from an odor-producing business.

Combustible refuse produced in a household can be classified into at least four groups on the basis of the amount of odor and smoke produced when it is incinerated:

1. Class A refuse: wood, paper, cardboard, and other materials that when incinerated do not usually produce excessive smoke or offensive odors.
2. Class B refuse: rags, rubber, leather, plastics, lint from vacuum sweeper bags, and similar materials that are not in themselves odorous but which often cause offensive odors when burned at low temperatures.
3. Class C refuse: food wastes resulting from preparation and use of foods in the home, normally known as garbage.
4. Class D refuse: grass clippings, weeds, leaves, brush, and similar materials.

Wood, paper, and cardboard—Class A refuse—does not usually cause offensive odors when burned at relatively low temperatures in a home incinerator. If an incinerator is properly charged and ignited, the amount of smoke emitted will usually be acceptable.

The inclusion of Class B refuse with Class A refuse changes the problem. Rags and leather burned at low temperatures produce offensive odors. Burning rubber at low temperatures produces both strong odors and dense black smoke.

A home incinerator that can burn Class A and Class B refuse without creating odors can probably burn garbage. Because of the difficulty of burning garbage without creating odors, however, many ordinances regulate the kinds of food wastes that can be incinerated.

Class D refuse creates odor and smoke problems if it is burned in a home incinerator. However, it is unlikely that anyone carries yard wastes into the house for disposal.

Testing and Licensing

Classification of refuse is also necessary if incinerators are to be tested and licensed on the basis of what kinds of refuse can be burned in them satisfactorily without producing odors, smoke, and fly ash.

Manufacturers, distributors, and salesmen, as well as others who are interested, are usually permitted to watch the tests made by licensing authorities.

In recent years the quantity of garbage included in a standard test charge has been reduced for home incinerators, which has been justified on the basis that each year the average family produces more combustible rubbish but less garbage. The primary purpose of the tests, however, is to determine the air pollution potential of a given incinerator. Since air pollution results from not only usual conditions but also from unusual ones, test charges should be used that duplicate as closely as possible the unusual: garbage and refuse from large dinners or canning, for instance. If an incinerator operates well when there is an unusually large amount of garbage, it is almost sure to operate well with normal amounts.

Upon satisfactory completion of tests, an incinerator is certified as to the types of materials for which it may be used. A permanent metal plate should be fastened to the unit stating exactly what kinds of refuse can be burned in it.

INCINERATORS FOR COMMERCIAL ESTABLISHMENTS

The refuse incineration needs of commercial establishments such as stores, small manufacturing plants, and restaurants vary greatly. A small neighborhood shoe store, for example, may have only about two bushels of waste paper and cardboard a day; a large supermarket may produce several tons a day of more troublesome wastes.

Municipal refuse collection systems are not ordinarily set up for the type of service required by large stores; they are primarily intended for residential areas. But commercial establishments usually have limited storage space for refuse; furthermore, some of their storage practices are hazardous. Nor are the services of private collectors always a good solution. Such services are expensive in some cities and sometimes are too limited as to time and frequency of collections.

All of these factors make on-site disposal of refuse a desirable solution to the problems of some commercial establishments. If other disposal methods are expensive and only partially meet the need, the costs of a satisfactory incinerator are almost insignificant.

Many small stores use incinerators that are similar to but larger than the high B.T.U. input home incinerator. Unfortunately, the operational problems are also similar to those that must be solved to achieve satisfactory performance with domestic incinerators. However, since each store produces much the same type of refuse each day and the operating personnel may be trained in and required to use approved charging and operating procedures, it is somewhat easier to establish good operating practices than it is at home.

Fig. 87. An incinerator used in a large supermarket has a rated capacity for burning 1,200 pounds of dry refuse in an hour.

It is usually not difficult to incinerate satsifactorily in those businesses in which only waste paper and cardboard are burned and if there are no residences within 75 feet of the stack outlet. There are many incinerators that can burn materials of this type satisfactorily, since they do not produce offensive odors while burning and quickly burn to ash if properly charged and exposed to sufficient heat and oxygen. The size of the charge must be limited, however, so that the primary combustion chamber is not overloaded and auxiliary fuel is not necessary for smoke destruction. A subsidence chamber also should be provided or the combustion chamber must be large enough to reduce gas velocities so that fly ash is minimized.

Food stores, supermarkets, restaurants, produce terminals, and similar businesses have an entirely different and much more serious incineration problem. They must burn highly combustible refuse, as well as food wastes, which contain from 50 to 90 per cent water. The problem is to design an incinerator that will successfully burn both types of refuse.

The largest portion of the refuse from a supermarket, for instance, consists of cardboard boxes, wood boxes, and paper. This material is light, bulky, and readily combustible, although thin wood boxes are almost impossible to burn without producing smoke. An incinerator for this type of refuse should have a large charging door, a large primary combustion area, an ample supply of air, a large settling chamber, and a low flue gas velocity, as well as an after-burner. The other part of the refuse is vegetable wastes, such as lettuce and celery leaves, which do not have enough heating value to burn themselves. Thus auxiliary fuel must be used to maintain a temperature of from 1,200° to 1,400° F. for the gases leaving the unit. Dehydration and combustion of these materials is slow, so to conserve heat only a small amount of air should be used. Frequent agitation of the refuse on the fuel bed is desirable to close up the holes and to increase the burning rate. Because of the lower air requirements for combustion, the gas velocities through the unit are lower and fly ash discharge is considerably less until the grates are almost bare.

The incinerator that will burn both types of refuse successfully must be a compromise that permits operation at both extremes or any place between extremes. But doing a satisfactory job depends to a large extent on the way an incinerator is operated, and unfortunately the unit that eliminates all skill and judgment on the part of the operator has not yet been built.

Costs

Commercial incinerators vary in price according to size. An incinerator used solely to dispose of waste paper from a small office may cost about $100. But a warehouse for a supermarket chain may require one as large as those used by small cities, which cost more than $50,000.

Operating costs vary considerably with the type of installation and the materials burned. Almost all commercial incinerators must use auxiliary fuel. Gas consumption depends upon the size of the burner to some extent, but the greatest variable is the judgment of the operator who determines the length of time the gas is used.

Maintenance costs for commercial incinerators are usually high. Most incinerators are subjected to high temperatures because of the quantities of paper and cardboard burned. Intermittent operation and rapidly rising and falling temperatures shorten the life of brick work, vent pipes, and chimneys.

Nuisances

Commercial incinerators that are improperly designed or improperly operated are a source of smoke, odor, and fly ash nuisances. Many cities have ordinances controlling their installation. Usually the regulations require adequate temperatures for odor destruction (which vary from 1,200° to 1,500° F.), heavy duty construction to withstand continuous temperatures as high as 2,000° F., settling chamber gas velocities from 5 to 15 feet per second, drying hearths for wet materials, secondary air, auxiliary fuel burners, and an adequate chimney.

The data supplied when applying for a permit to install a commercial incinerator indicate only in a general way what operating results may be expected. Many of the factors are so interdependent that a series of tests is often necessary to determine the limitations of a given incinerator.

INCINERATORS FOR INDUSTRY

Many factories and industries incinerate refuse and trade wastes in small or medium size incinerators on the premises. A study of the kinds of wastes to be burned usually indicates in a general way the procedures that must be followed to get satisfactory combustion.

Trade wastes that produce strong odors or heavy smoke are difficult to burn in a small incinerator. It is usually cheaper to dispose of them by taking them to a landfill or municipal incinerator. If they are burned in a small incinerator, however, an operator should be present the entire time to keep the combustion temperatures above 1,300° F., to limit the size and frequency of the charges, to provide sufficient aid for complete combustion, and to regulate the draft properly. A small incinerator must be well designed and well constructed to meet these requirements; operating costs will be relatively high.

Fig. 88. Some hospital incinerators must burn a large amount of refuse. The incinerator above is of the pit and crane design; gas scrubber equipment is at the right. The incinerator is scheduled for a modern replacement.

Hospital Incinerators

Hospitals must have sanitary disposal facilities readily accessible at all times. The disposal problem in hospitals is complicated because the refuse usually has a high garbage and moisture content and the anatomical wastes are malodorous and germ-ridden. At the same time that the need for nuisance free disposal operations is the greatest the tolerance for a badly operated disposal system is the least. So when on-site incineration is used, the equipment must be correctly designed and operated. Flue-fed incinerators should never be installed in a hospital. The usual practice is to use an incinerator consisting of a furnace and combustion chamber, although large hospitals may use one similar in design to a small municipal incinerator. Use of auxiliary fuel is essential. Most important, regardless of the size of the hospital, are prompt and thorough burning and a minimum of storage.

Some hospital refuse does not burn readily and close supervision is needed during burning. If insufficient auxiliary fuel is used, odorous gases are sure to be present. Frequent agitation of the refuse on the fuel bed is also necessary when burning hospital refuse; but since hospitals are usually understaffed they often do not give incinerators the attention they need.

TABLE 30

AVERAGE DAILY PRODUCTION OF HOSPITAL WASTES FOR 29 HOSPITALS
WITH AVERAGE OF 224 PATIENTS[1]

Type of Waste	Average Weight per Capita[2] (Lbs. per day)	Average Volume per Capita[2] (Cubic ft. per day)	Average Weight per Patient (Lbs. per day)	Average Volume per Patient (Cubic ft. per day)
Garbage (Specific weight: 53 pounds per foot³)	1.86 (8)[3]	0.035 (15)	3.28 (8)	0.064 (15)
Noncombustibles (Specific weight: 9.24 pounds per foot)	0.83 (5)	0.090 (17)	1.10 (5)	0.111 (17)
Combustibles (Specific weight: 4.85 pounds per foot)	1.67 (5)	0.344 (21)	2.61 (5)	0.521 (21)
Surgical			0.11	
Autopsy			0.03	
Total	4.36	0.469	7.13	0.696

[1]Computed from weekly waste production data in a report of the Committee on Hospital Facilities, Engineering and Sanitation Section, American Public Health Association, November, 1955.

[2]Average equivalent population of 29 hospitals sampled was 393.

[3]Figures in parentheses indicate number of hospitals included in averages.

In an effort to reduce hospital personnel costs there is an increasing use of throw-away items—sheets, pillow-cases, trays, dishes, hypodermic needles. Much of this material is made of paper, so the composition of hospital refuse is changing to include more combustibles.

Operating room wastes, experimental animals, and cadavers create problems different from other hospital refuse disposal problems. They are ordinarily disposed of in a separate incinerator designed especially for this purpose. The usual installation consists of a furnace with auxiliary fuel burners and a combustion chamber heated by auxiliary fuel and equipped with after-burners to insure that the gases leaving the chamber are heated to at least 1,300° F. A washer for reducing the fly ash to acceptable levels may also be provided.

Cadavers and operating room wastes are put into the furnace proper. The after-burners and the combustion chamber burners are ignited and the brickwork heated up until the gases leaving the chamber reach 1,800° F. The washer is then started and the burners in the furnace are ignited. By preheating the combustion chamber, complete odor destruction is assured.

Table 30 reports quantities of hospital wastes in 29 hospitals during 1955. Recent studies indicate that 19 pounds of solid waste are generated daily for each hospital patient.

The costs of operating such incinerators are high because it is necessary to preheat the combustion chamber and maintain high furnace temperatures. The brickwork maintenance costs are correspondingly low, however, because the incinerator is fired infrequently. The only routine servicing required is one that keeps auxiliary fuel burners and gas temperature indicators operating satisfactorily.

Incinerators for Other Institutions

Other institutions are also confronted with refuse disposal problems. When located in a large city, institutions usually use municipal services, but if they are in outlying or rural areas, as is often the case, it may be necessary to use on-site disposal. Incinerators can be designed for satisfactory service in institutions because charging of the refuse can be controlled. Under no circumstances should a flue-fed type of incinerator be used, although separate refuse chutes may be considered.

A typical incinerator in an institution consists of a furnace and a combustion chamber, which should, of course, be correctly designed. In many, no auxiliary fuel is used and so the operator has no means of controlling the temperature of the gases that leave the incinerator.

Many institutional incinerators cause air pollution problems. Some problems result from careless or uninformed operation, but usually they result from installing a "cheap" unit in the interests of "economy."

The cost of a suitable incinerator depends to a great extent upon the size of the institution and the type and quantity of refuse burned. Auxiliary fuel burners should be used to insure satisfactory combustion temperatures and odor destruction when necessary. The combustion chamber must be designed for low gas velocities to insure that fly ash is trapped or a wet collector must be used. Equipment meeting these requirements costs several thousand dollars. Operating costs vary with the size of the unit, the amount of auxiliary fuel required, and labor costs.

APARTMENT HOUSE INCINERATORS

Large apartment buildings have special problems in connection with solid wastes disposal. Space stringencies, efficiency, and sanitary considerations make storage on residential floors impractical. The need for prompt removal to a central storage area can be most easily solved by a chute system. The economics and convenience of combining this with the chimney of an incinerator and thus disposing of the whole refuse production with a minimum of handling and expense have led to the widespread use of the single-chamber, flue-fed incinerator. For some 40 years it has been a standard, integral part of apartment buildings, and to some extent of schools, hospitals, and office buildings.

Flue-Fed Incinerators

A typical flue-fed incinerator of the most elementary type is shown in Figure 89. The operating process is simple. Refuse is dropped through a charging door on each floor into a chimney which acts as a chute leading to the incinerator grate. Here it may be stored for a time and is then ignited and burns, hopefully with the assistance of some manual stoking and attention from an attendant. The heat and products of combustion pass over the fresh refuse and up the chimney, accomplishing some dehydration. Ashes are periodically dumped from the grates and removed from the ash pit.

Unfortunately this arrangement constitutes a collection of poor combustion practices leading almost inevitably to highly unsatisfactory results—production of smoke, particulate matter, odors, and incompletely burned ash. In densely populated apartment areas the concentration of air pollution from this source sometimes reaches serious proportions of major concern to agencies responsible for air quality.

Upgrading Existing Flue-Fed Incinerators

An existing flue-fed incinerator often can be equipped to meet air pollution control requirements. A minimal addition is the installation of an auxiliary burner above the grate and provision of a second flue in the chimney. The second flue permits use of one for charging and the other for discharge of combustion products. Even with these minimal additions, the system is still subject to deficiencies that include lack of adequate draft control; inability to develop, maintain, and control temperatures high enough to accomplish complete combustion; unsatisfactory stoking performance and disruption of the burning mass by dropping onto it fresh charges from above; and flashbacks or smokebacks from disturbance of draft by opening of charging doors.

Performance improvement of units lacking a secondary combustion

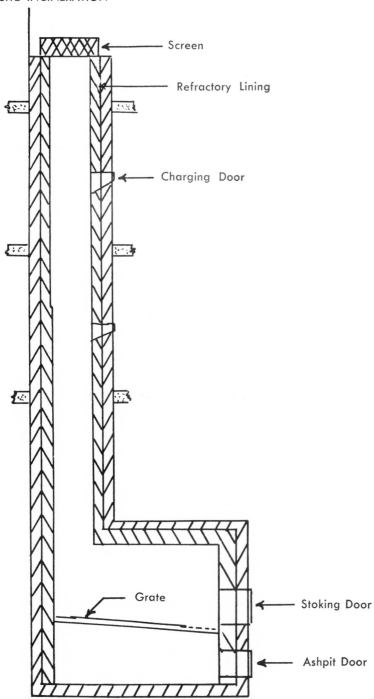

Screen

Refractory Lining

Charging Door

Grate

Stoking Door

Ashpit Door

Fig. 89. A schematic drawing of a basic flue-fed incinerator of the type still in use in older apartment buildings.

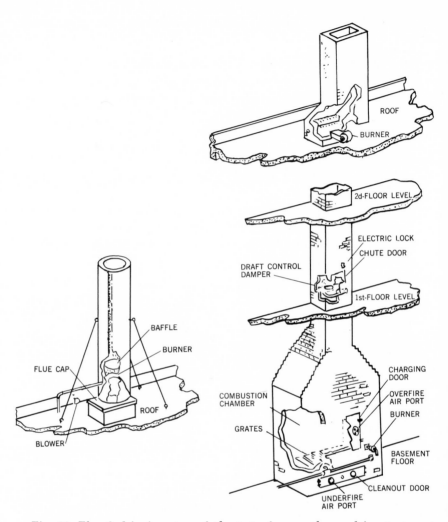

Fig. 90. Flue-fed incinerator of the type frequently used in apartment buildings, modified by a roof after-burner and a draft-control damper. Another after-burner is also shown.

chamber can be achieved through the addition of an after-burner. Figure 90 shows such installations on the roof. If space is available in the basement, installation of an additional multiple-chamber incinerator may be a further improvement, separating burning from storage but introducing an additional factor—manual transfer from storage to incinerator as shown in Figure 91.

Some improvement in draft control can also be obtained by installation of better dampers and of a chute door locking system to prevent charging of refuse during the burning period. A gas scrubber can be a roof addition, as shown in Figure 92, to remove excessive particulate matter.

Improved Designs for Apartment House Incinerators

The potential public and private advantages of on-site incineration of apartment house refuse are so great that it is important to explore carefully the continued use of this disposal method. Technically, compliance with air pollution standards is achievable.

Principal design features recommended for new installations include the following:

1. The basic provisions mentioned above of double flues and auxiliary heat source.
2. Use of a multiple-chamber furnace designed to assure that all stack emissions are subjected to satisfactory high temperatures.
3. Design proportions and arrangement to minimize flue gas velocities to avoid excessive entrainment of fly ash.

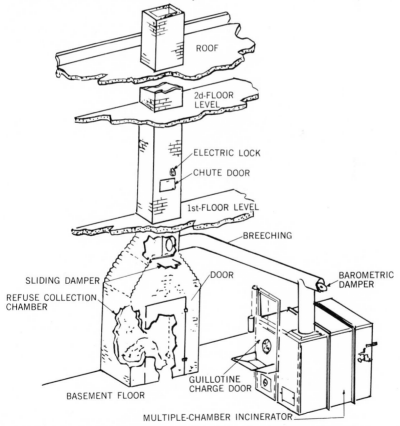

Fig. 91. Flue-fed incinerator modified by the basement installation of a multiple-chamber incinerator.

4. More sophisticated draft control devices.

5. Chute door locking systems to prevent interference with combustion from charging at inopportune times.

6. For incinerators burning some restricted classes and quantities of refuse for which an integral secondary combustion chamber is not necessary, a roof settling chamber may be required to trap fly ash.

A carefully designed and operated flue-fed incinerator may provide advantageous final disposal within acceptable air pollution limits. A poorly conceived installation can be the source of an intolerable nuisance and health hazards. Because of the formidable task of adequately enforcing pollution regulations for the myriad of such installations arising in a large city, each of which is more or less susceptible to production of poor results because of improper operation, many air pollution control officials look with disfavor on permitting any flue-fed incinerators.

On-Site Compaction Devices. As an alternate to on-site incineration, a system that has gained favor in Sweden and has recently been introduced in the United States, is on-site reduction by packaging refuse under compression into paper sacks. It is claimed that with their extremely high compaction ratio, packing machines can cut the space needed for

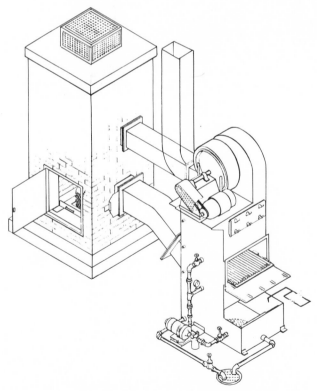

Fig. 92. Gas scrubber for a flue-fed incinerator.

Fig. 93. Semi-automatic refuse packaging machines, which hold 3.5–cubic-foot paper bags. Refuse is loaded manually. A ram under 3,000 pounds of air pressure descends and packs the contents. Filled bags weigh about 75 pounds. Food service establishments and institutions favor this type.

waste storage by 75 per cent or more, and also that they are generally adaptable for use (with chutes) for centrally located storage areas in apartment houses and institutions.

Both automatic and semi-automatic types are illustrated and briefly described in Figures 93, 94, and 95.

Several United States manufacturers provide stationary equipment in various sizes for compressing commercial, industrial, or apartment wastes into storage containers, often designed for mechanical transfer of contents into self-loading collection vehicles. Figure 95 shows such a device, which is produced with variations by several manufacturers.

Incinerators For Special Purposes

There are many industrial salvage and waste disposal operations that require special incinerators. Those designed to burn automobile bodies, those that burn combustible demolition debris, and those that burn forestry refuse are sufficiently widely used to warrant consideration here.

Automobile Bodies

An automobile body contains a considerable amount of high-grade

Fig. 94. Automatic refuse compressor used in apartment buildings. Refuse comes down a chute and is automatically compressed by air-operated ram.

Fig. 95. Stationary refuse packers are available in a variety of sizes and styles from several manufacturers.

scrap metal that can be sold at a profit if it can be salvaged economically. However, it also contains large amounts of upholstery, plastics, under-coating, grease, paint, and paper products, none of which is acceptable to steel mills.

The practice in the past was to burn automobile bodies in the open after spraying them with fuel oil. This produced large clouds of dense black smoke and strong odors. The method is so obnoxious that most cities prohibit it. However, the cost of labor is so high that if objectionable materials must be stripped from cars by hand, salvage is uneconomical.

To meet this need incinerators have been developed which incorporate combustion features and equipment for smoke and fly ash control that accomplish the burning in compliance with air pollution control regulations. Two principal sizes are in use, the larger being designed for continuous flow and capable of burning up to 300 cars per 8-hour day. Use of after-burners in secondary combustion chambers and use of other devices provide adequate control of stack emissions.

A smaller incinerator burning two cars at a time can handle about 28 cars in 8 hours. This capacity is great enough for most such businesses and the comparatively low cost (about $25,000) with good operating results make this a practical unit. It employs sound combustion design with an after-burner supplied with auxiliary heat to provide stack emissions complying with air pollution ordinances. This unit is shown in Figure 96. It was developed under a grant from the National Institutes of Health, U.S. Public Health Service, and basic plans are available.[2]

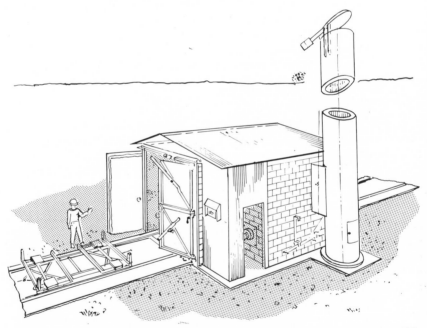

Fig. 96. This incinerator, especially designed to burn combustibles from automobile bodies so that the metal can be salvaged, can handle 28 cars in eight hours. It uses an after-burner to control stack discharges.

Demolition Debris

Increasing activity of cities in slum clearance, highway construction, and other rebuilding projects results in substantial quantities of building

---

[2]E. R. Kaiser and J. Tolciss, *Smokeless Burning of Automobile Bodies*, Technical Report 764.2 (New York: New York University, College of Engineering, 1961).

debris from the demolition of old structures. With methods currently being used this consists principally of a mixture of wood and rubble, the proportions depending upon the construction of the old buildings. Often they are of wood frame construction, and the debris is largely wood which can easily be burned and is a nuisance material in a sanitary fill. The former widespread practice of handling this through open burning on the site provided a convenient solution, but also resulted in air pollution. This practice is now widely prohibited.

The use of "tepee" or conical shaped burners that are adaptations of sawdust burners long used in the lumber industry was tried for this purpose. At best this method is controlled open burning with usually unsatisfactory control of combustion and resulting poor performance. It is not considered as a satisfactory method, although several kinds of supplementary aids are available to improve performance.

The idea of running the material through "hogs" or chipping machines to reduce it to a size that can be handled in conventional municipal incinerators has also been tried. Problems with separation of rubble, damage to chipping equipment from foreign materials, and general economics discourage this practice.

The net result is the predominant current practice of disposing this material in landfills, despite increased hauling and handling costs.

Forestry Refuse

In many parts of the United States the disposal of debris accumulating from normal growth of trees and other vegetation is a significant problem. When this becomes aggravated by special circumstances, such as the impact of the Dutch elm disease on the Midwest in recent years, the disposal problem may become a major one.

For example, for Des Moines, Iowa, a city of 288,000 population, it was calculated that in 1967 there was a total of 562,000 tons of wastes of all categories accumulated.[3] Of this amount, 103,600 tons or 18.5 per cent were accounted for by "special tree wastes," consisting of the removal of 28,000 trees killed by Dutch elm disease. This general situation will prevail over a period of several years and constitute a serious refuse disposal problem for Des Moines. Many other eastern and midwestern cities are similarly confronted.

Forestry brush is relatively easily burned but produces much fly ash. Heavy logs and large limbs are more difficult but can be satisfactorily consumed in well-designed furnaces. A city confronted with the prospect of disposal of significant quantities of tree wastes may well consider the possibilities of especially designed incinerators to handle this material only. The application of recognized principles of combustion design can produce incinerators capable of disposing of this kind of refuse reasonably, economically, and in compliance with air pollution requirements.

---

[3]U.S. Department of Health, Education and Welfare, *Report for the Des Moines Metropolitan Area—Collection and Disposal of Solid Wastes—1968*, HEW Demonstration Grant No. 1-U1-00060-01.

Fig. 97. A special incinerator for disposal of driftwood collected in New York Harbor was constructed at the Caven Point Marine terminal, Jersey City, New Jersey, for the New York District Corps of Engineers. The incinerator is of the open pit type with controlled overfire air.

A good example is the specially designed installation of the New York District Corps of Engineers, used for disposal of the 600,000 cubic feet of driftwood collected annually from New York Harbor, shown in Figure 97. This is a $2 million installation designed to handle about 10 tons per hour input, in compliance with New York air pollution regulations.

In another example, Detroit has operated a brush and tree debris burner successfully for several years, disposing of 171,944 cubic yards of such materials during a single year. This unit uses primary and secondary combustion chambers with four baffles and a "wet-bottom" system to trap fly ash. It is not recommended for demolition refuse because the intermittent firing and consequent fluctuations in temperatures produce smoke from the waxes, varnishes, paint, tar paper, and roofing materials included with demolition materials. Large logs, however, which are troublesome to burn in most incinerators, are handled quite well in this unit.

A large new multipurpose incinerator in Stamford, Connecticut, and a smaller one in Norwalk, Connecticut, have demonstrated successful burning of oversized wastes in a tractor-charged furnace.

"Tepee" burners have also been used for disposal of forestry and oversized refuse. They are subject to the same limitations here as were noted in connection with their use for demolition debris. At best, they afford only limited improvement on open burning and cannot be counted upon for dependably satisfactory performance.

The Future of On-Site Incineration

There is increasing concern about and regulation to prohibit the production of air pollution. On-site incinerators of flue-fed and other obsolete designs have been contributors to air pollution and should properly be the target of regulations designed to improve environmental quality.

However, it is perfectly feasible, technically and economically, to provide incinerators for on-site burning of apartment, commercial, industrial, and hospital wastes that incorporate well understood principles of combustion and that can produce results in full compliance with applicable air pollution standards. Such equipment is on the market from numerous sources. There are many cogent warrants for on-site disposal if it is handled properly. Normally it is more economical; transportation of wastes, with attendant load on public streets and resulting costs, are avoided; air pollution is controlled as it would be at a central plant; and the public agency is relieved of the necessity for providing for the additional increment of refuse to be handled.

Municipal ordinances should prescribe adequate performance standards for on-site incinerators. Any further restrictions leading to unnecessary curtailment of their use may work to the disadvantage of the public and serve only to aggravate the already acute solid waste problem.

As better information on physical requirements for incinerators to meet prescribed performance standards becomes available, it may be expected that regulations will include more minimum design and construction standards. However, such requirements should never become so rigid and detailed as to freeze all production into a set pattern and stifle innovation completely. Creative improvements are always possible and necessary if economic competition and progress are to be attained with resultant general benefits.

7   GRINDING REFUSE

The disposal of food wastes by grinding—the process by which garbage is changed into small particles and flushed into the sewers—has been widely accepted in recent years. Eliminating garbage on the premises as it is produced is considered the ultimate in convenience and sanitation. The on-site grinder reduces the time garbage is stored on the premises to an absolute minimum.

The over-all benefits of garbage grinders to a community must be carefully evaluated, however. Grinders are useful but they do not eliminate the necessity for collection of most refuse. Garbage usually is less than 10 per cent of the volume of refuse collected. Yard wastes such as wet grass and weeds, which are not put in the grinder, can produce odors that are as obnoxious as those produced by garbage. Furthermore, not all garbage can be disposed of through a grinder; some must be stored for collection.

Garbage grinders are usually divided into three classes according to their use. Home grinders are exactly what the name implies. Commercial and institutional grinders are large units used in restaurants, hospitals, and food processing establishments such as a produce center or super-market. Municipal grinders are even larger and are used to dispose of garbage collected by conventional means and taken to a central grinding station.

In addition there is the developing concept of grinding or shredding all refuse to be disposed of by incineration and also by sanitary land-filling. Grinding is, of course, an integral necessity for composting. Machines for handling mixed refuse must be heavy and rugged.

HOME GRINDERS

The millions of home garbage grinders already in use have become a symbol of convenience and sanitation to many housewives. The 1968 National Survey of Community Solid Waste Practices discloses that there are 63.5 home grinders installed per 1,000 population on a countrywide basis. In urban areas this figure is 61.0 per 1,000, but in nonurban areas it is higher—76.0 per 1,000. It is obvious that their number will increase considerably in the future.

The grinder is located in the most convenient place for disposing of food wastes—in the kitchen sink. This is where food is prepared and the housewife decides which lettuce leaves will be eaten and which thrown away; it is the place where dishes and cooking utensils are stacked and where the housewife determines which leftovers will be thrown away. Thus the transition from food to garbage is rapid; and disposal by grinding is equally fast. The refuse is scraped into the grinder, a twist of the wrist locks the cover, a water faucet is turned on, and in a matter of seconds the garbage is ground and flushed into the sewer system.

Types and Safety Features

Because of the growing acceptance of home garbage grinders, there is an increasing number of companies manufacturing them. The units vary in appearance, size, and operation but the design principles are about the same. All are installed in the sink and are equipped with a refuse chamber that holds about a quart of garbage. Cutters, or shredders, are rotated at high speed by an electric motor. Cold water from the faucet is required to flush the ground garbage through the grinder and into the sewer system. (Cold water must be used so that grease will congeal before it enters the sewer system.)

Fig. 98. There are many types and makes of household and commercial garbage grinders. Above are household grinders made by Westinghouse, General Electric, Hotpoint, and Frigidaire. A commercial and institutional type grinder is shown at lower right.

A sink garbage grinder must grind the food uniformly fine. Large particles sometimes lodge in the drain pipes or settle in the sewers. Grinders vary considerably in this performance, depending on the design and manufacturer. It is desirable for a city to set up performance standards

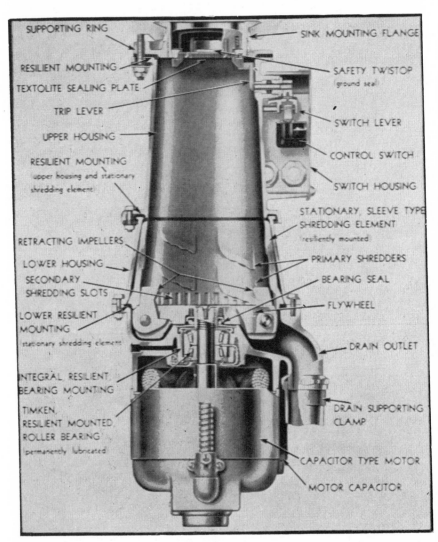

Fig. 99. A cross section of a household garbage grinder. This grinder has a top control that must be put into the sink opening and turned to the "on" position before it will operate. It is also equipped with a flow interlock valve, which prevents the motor from operating unless an adequate amount of cold water is running through the mechanism. Newer units are equipped with "anti-jam" devices; in some models the direction the blades rotate is reversed each time the unit is turned on.

for size of grind and to require that the standards be met before a grinder can be installed.

There is considerable difference in safety features of grinders. Some have an electric switch that is actuated by locking the cover in place—a type that cannot be operated when the cover is open, thus making it impossible to get fingers in contact with the revolving shredders. If large quantities of garbage are ground in this type, however, it is necessary to stop the grinder to recharge it.

Some grinders have covers that are not interlocked with the electric circuit; others have an open top protected by rubber "fingers." Garbage can be put into these two types of grinders while they are running. But it is also possible for children to put their hands into the revolving cutters.

Any type of home grinder can be equipped with a water flow control switch that is operated by turning on the cold water faucet. When the flow reaches the desired volume, the grinder starts. This procedure insures an adequate flow of water before the grinder can operate and minimizes the danger of plugging the drain lines with ground garbage. The switch increases the cost of the grinder, however, and so it often is not included.

Portable Grinders. Portable grinders do not appear to have sufficient advantages to justify their becoming important in the refuse disposal field. They are self-contained units that are placed in the sink and plugged into an electric outlet. Water from the faucet is used to grind and flush ground garbage down the sink drain.

Portable grinders are not widely used. They weigh about 21 pounds, so that it is difficult for a woman to lift them; and flushing garbage down a conventional drain also presents difficulties. They cost about what a low priced permanently installed grinder does, but they can be used in old houses where it is difficult and expensive to install permanent ones.

Effect on Municipal Services

Cities that permit or encourage the installation of home garbage grinders must plan for the changes that they require. The effects of the first few grinder installations are so insignificant that little thought may be given to what may happen when there are a lot of them. The need for additional water, sewer, and sewage treatment facilities can develop so rapidly that the problem may become acute before steps are taken to correct the situation. If a city has financial difficulties also, a satisfactory solution is even more difficult.

Water Supply. During grinding, water is used at the rate of 1.5 gallons a minute or between 1 and 2 gallons per capita per day. The installation of home grinders does not materially affect the municipal water supply (except in critical areas), since grinders increase the use of water by only 2 or 3 per cent.

The water supply does affect the use of garbage grinders, however. Units equipped with a flow control switch will not operate until a predetermined amount of water is flowing from the faucet. In areas where the water pressure drops appreciably during periods of heavy demand, it may be impossible to operate a grinder during some parts of the day.

Elimination of the flow control switch does not solve the problem in such cases, because the water flow would probably also be insufficient to properly flush the drain lines. The result of insufficient flushing is clogged drains—an expensive and inconvenient problem to solve.

Sewers. Experience with domestic grinders shows that the admission of finely ground garbage to house plumbing does not clog it; in fact, there is a tendency for the garbage to keep the inside of the pipes clean.

Normal domestic sewage and most industrial wastes are so dilute that if there is an average of 50 per cent increase in the amount of suspended solids in sewage caused by citywide installation of garbage grinders, there will be little more deposition than under normal conditions. Therefore, if a sewer system is free of deposits, it is reasonable to expect that it will remain so after the addition of ground garbage. However, if a sewer system is inadequate to handle the deposition of sewage solids before there are many home grinders, the addition of ground garbage may in-

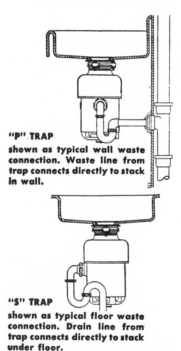

"P" TRAP
shown as typical wall waste connection. Waste line from trap connects directly to stack in wall.

Fig. 100. Most domestic home grinders can be installed under any standard sink that has a 3½-inch drain opening.

"S" TRAP
shown as typical floor waste connection. Drain line from trap connects directly to stack under floor.

crease the amount of deposition in some parts of the system a great deal. Furthermore, inasmuch as garbage is higher in volatile solids than sewage is, the volatile content of the deposits is increased, thus increasing the putrescibility and the likelihood of obnoxious odors. The frequency with which the sewers must be flushed is increased; if they are not, sewage reaching the treatment plant is more septic than normal.

Problems of this kind may warrant prohibition of home grinders. The blame should not be placed on the grinders or the garbage, however, but on the faults in the design or construction of the sewers.

There can be trouble in even well designed sewer systems with deposition of solids at the upper ends of laterals, where the volume of sewage is too small to maintain adequate flow, causing solids to become stranded along the pipe. If domestic grinders are installed in houses tributary to the upper ends of lateral sewers, such difficulties may be increased. Flushing is the only remedy.

Sewage Treatment Plant. If sewage is discharged into a stream or large body of water without treatment, the installation of home grinders does not increase the cost of disposal for the municipality. However, the practice of discharging raw sewage into water (except perhaps in some special cases) is a questionable one. It is only a matter of time before some sewage treatment is necessary for almost every community.

The effect of introducing ground garbage into a sewage treatment plant depends upon the method and point of introduction, the type of treatment plant, and the quality of effluent desired.

If all garbage were ground at the point of origin and flushed through the sewer system, the suspended solids content would increase by up to 100 per cent, with an average 50 per cent increase for any one system. The biochemical oxygen demand (B.O.D.) of the sewage will increase up to 65 per cent, with an average of 30 per cent. Ground garbage may

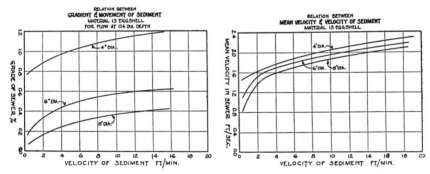

Fig. 101. The relationship of sewer grades, mean velocity of sewage, and sediment velocity of garbage was studied at the University of Texas in the late 1940's. That and other studies showed that the slopes of sanitary sewers then in use could satisfactorily transport the solids produced by domestic garbage grinders. (Reprinted with permission of The American City.)

increase the amount of grit in sewage by about 40 per cent where home grinders are used and by 80 per cent where central grinding stations are used. Grit tends to have a high volatile content and is potentially offensive.

In primary tank operation, the volume of scum and sludge can be expected to increase up to 100 per cent, partly as a result of the increase in suspended solids in the raw sewage and partly as a result of an apparent increase in removal efficiency caused by the addition of garbage solids.

Primary effluent may increase in suspended solids by 5 to 10 per cent and in B.O.D. by 15 to 30 per cent, requiring corresponding enlargement of secondary treatment facilities.

Increased facilities for sludge digestion, sludge handling, and digester-gas collection are necessary if ground garbage is added to either the sewage or the digester directly.

The introduction of ground garbage into the sewage system usually increases the treatment plant loading. If a treatment plant was built to handle future needs and is not operating at capacity, obviously expansion is not required. On the other hand, if the treatment plant is working at or near capacity before grinders are installed, it will be necessary to build additional facilities before there are many grinders.

The cost of processing ground garbage in a treatment plant is difficult to determine. In plants in which the gas produced in the plant is used as fuel, savings in operating costs reportedly have been realized by processing ground garbage at the sewage treatment plant. The costs of sewage treatment for a home garbage grinder are usually about 50 cents to $1.50 per capita per year, depending upon the type of treatment plant and economic factors.

Municipal Collection System. The effect of garbage grinders on the municipal collection system may be great or almost negligible, beneficial or detrimental, depending on local conditions.

Cities that sell garbage for hog feeding notice a marked decrease in the amount of garbage collected as more and more people install grinders. Cities that operated self-supporting garbage collection and disposal systems before grinders were widespread may find that it is necessary to make a collection charge to those households that do not have grinders.

If a city has many old dwellings and little room for new construction, it is unlikely that home grinders will be installed in sufficient numbers to materially affect collection practices, since under such conditions, grinder installations are usually spotty. Installation of home grinders will cause no appreciable change in cities that have a one pick-up collection system, either, particularly if residents put all refuse out at the curb. The total weight of the refuse collected may drop as much as 20 per cent but the volume will be practically the same. The elimination of household garbage from refuse disposed of in a sanitary landfill or incinerator reduces collection and disposal costs relatively little.

In the few cities that use separate garbage and rubbish collections, and especially those in which the garbage is taken from yards in tubs, a considerable change in the collection system will be noticed if many home grinders are installed. Houses equipped with grinders can be omitted from garbage collection routes, speeding up service to other homes and reducing collection costs. If all the houses in an area have grinders, garbage collection can be discontinued there entirely. But surveys of all garbage collection routes must be made frequently if savings to the city are to keep pace with grinder installations.

Effect on Home Disposal Practices

The installation of a home garbage grinder has a number of effects on home refuse handling practices. The conventional covered garbage can usually is done away with because the garbage that is not put in the grinder is too small to require a large container; in most cases that garbage can be stored with the rubbish.

But home garbage grinders are not used for large bones and peach pits because the noise is more than most people will tolerate. Some food wastes, such as gristle and fish heads, which are rubbery, bounce around inside the grinder and require a long time to grind. Fibrous materials such as corn husks can stall the grinder unless they are fed into the grinder correctly. Seafood wastes, such as clam shells, can plug the drains and sewers.

Furthermore, not all food wastes that can be ground reach the grinder for one reason or another. During warm weather many people eat outdoors and dispose of food wastes on paper plates in a nearby rubbish container. In cities in which it is permissible to store rubbish in open containers, the practice of dumping ungrindable garbage into them can be a nuisance and a health hazard, since food wastes attract insects and rodents and cause unpleasant odors.

In any event, the installation of a home garbage grinder does not completely eliminate the garbage storage problem, and good housekeeping requires other means of disposal for some refuse although on a smaller scale.

Costs

The costs of buying, installing, operating, and maintaining a home grinder vary according to the costs of the grinder, freight, labor, and building code requirements.

Grinders are easily and economically installed when a house is under construction because plumbing pipes, electrical circuits, and the sink itself are designed for a grinder.

The cost of installation for an average quality grinder in a house under construction is sometimes as little as $90, but the same installation in a house already built may cost $125 to $200 or more.

The problems and costs of installing grinders in old houses vary between houses. Those five to ten years old usually have a sink designed for a grinder; most have adequate plumbing so that changes are few; and many have ample electric circuits. But in some old sections of a city, the cost of installing a grinder is almost prohibitive. Some of the houses do not have adequate sewer lines to city mains; and in some the sinks and plumbing are so old and in such poor condition that it is necessary to install all new plumbing.

The practice of using basements for recreation rooms or laundries sometimes makes it difficult to install a grinder after a house is built. Installation usually requires that a portion of the basement ceiling be removed and sometimes a part of a wall or walls, which also requires redecoration. The cost of the grinder itself may be insignificant compared with installation costs.

A grinder can be installed in the laundry room of an old house at a fraction of the cost of kitchen installation. However, the main appeal—that of disposing of garbage at the point of origin—is lost.

A home grinder has a useful life of 10 to 20 years although with good care and maintenance it can last longer. Some servicing is required over the years because water seals wear out, electrical switches fail, rubber gaskets deteriorate, and motors fail.

Average annual costs to a householder for a $150 garbage grinder with a 20-year life expectancy installed when the house is built, if the costs are included in the mortgage, are about $10.30 for purchase and installation at 5 per cent interest, $10 for repairs, $1 for water and electricity, and 75 cents for sewage treatment, for a total of about $22 a year. Costs for the same installation in an old house are probably about 50 per cent more, bringing annual costs to about $27.

Since local conditions affect costs, the figures given above are only general; they are not costs for any particular city or kind of grinder. In many cities the minimum charge for a service call is $10 regardless of how minor the repair is. In any event, the cost to the householder of a home grinder is usually greater than that of efficient collection and disposal systems.

Municipal Regulation

Experience shows that the installation of home garbage grinders should be regulated through local building codes or other ordinances. Since problems vary from one city to another, regulations also vary.

It may be necessary to prohibit by ordinance the installation of home grinders until adequate sewers are available or until the sewage treatment plant is enlarged.

If grinders are permitted and encouraged, their installation should be regulated for everyone's protection. Regulations give the city the power to control the types of grinders installed, assure compliance with the building code, assure the most favorable grind for the sewer system and treatment plant, and grant the right to inspect installations. Cities allowing installation of grinders without permits have no way of knowing about them and inspecting plumbing changes and additional wiring. The slight increase in cost to the householder for a permit is justified.

One of the most controversial requirements for home grinders is the flow control switch that assures an adequate flow of water every time a grinder is used. If it could be installed without additional cost, it would probably be required by most cities to protect the householder, but in most cases it is not.

Many cities require that to be approved a home grinder must grind the garbage to a certain particle size for given amounts of garbage. The size of the particle is important in the movement of ground garbage through a sewer system and to the sewage treatment plant, but testing for particle size is difficult because of grease and other refuse in the garbage. Uniform standards for grinding have not been established, but a manufacturer of household grinders has drawn up these standards:

The food waste shredder shall discharge shredded wastes at a reasonably uniform rate, in a fluid form, which shall flow readily through an approved trap, drain line, or soil line in a manner which will prevent clogging or stoppage of drain line. The food waste shredder shall shred food waste to a uniform size to meet the following requirements: 100 per cent shall pass a ½-inch screen, at least 90 per cent shall pass a ¼-inch screen, not over 5 per cent shall pass a No. 40 sieve. Screens shall be the U. S. Standard and weight shall be taken on a dry basis.

Some ordinances adopted for the purpose of encouraging or forcing installation of home grinders are both unrealistic and impractical. Premature abandonment of a garbage collection system even when householders are required to dispose of garbage in a manner approved by local health authorities can cause serious sanitation problems. In a large city such a requirement can create intolerable conditions. However, as already pointed out, the requirement that garbage grinders be installed in all new houses has met with success in some cities. Installation in some old houses can also be expected, but requiring installation in all old houses is considered impractical.

Public Acceptance

Garbage collection and disposal are not ordinarily subjects of general interest. They are necessary parts of housekeeping but of little public interest unless something is wrong with the systems. However, a well planned and conducted campaign to encourage installation of food waste grinders may make a substantial impact on a city. This has been demonstrated in Detroit; Jasper, Indiana; and Shorewood Hills, Wisconsin.

A well conducted campaign can also speed up installations in old houses in small cities. The same efforts are much less effective in large cities, however, because a smaller proportion of the residents are home owners. Grinders are a fairly expensive convenience and their installation, therefore, is directly related to family finances, as well as to the effectiveness of the campaign, whether it is sponsored by equipment manufacturers or by local government.

GRINDERS IN COMMERCIAL ESTABLISHMENTS AND INSTITUTIONS

Grinders are proving an excellent solution to the food waste disposal problems where large quantities of garbage are produced. Speed of operation, compactness, low operating costs, and freedom from nuisance assures that more and more will be installed in hotels, restaurants, food markets, hospitals, and other institutions and businesses. Relatively small grinders with 1½, 3, or 5 horsepower motors are commonly used.

The storage of food wastes in such establishments has always been a problem, especially from the sanitation standpoint. Garbage is produced in large quantities and in a relatively short time. Storage facilities are often inadequate and frequently are in the same area in which food is prepared. Problems with insects and rodents develop quickly unless sanitary measures are employed at all times. Usually daily garbage collections are required to eliminate odors. But the installation of a garbage grinder has substantially eliminated such problems for many businesses and institutions.

Fig. 102. There are two basic types of commercial garbage grinders: the swing hammer mill type with rotating hammers that tear up the refuse and beat it to a pulp against a side plate (top), and those that use rotating knives, or shredders, which operate on the same principle as home grinders (bottom).

The grinder can be installed in a restaurant so that it serves both the food preparation area and the dish washing area. Garbage is ground as fast as it is produced. As with home grinders, however, oyster shells, clam shells, and large bones cannot be ground and must be stored and disposed of by other means. But they are only a small part of the wastes produced (except in sea food restaurants) so that for all practical purposes, garbage storage is eliminated, which raises sanitation standards considerably in food preparation areas. Hotels have also found that use of grinders reduces the amount of silverware lost.

Centrally located grinders in large supermarkets are quite satisfactory. Supermarkets must dispose of large quantities of produce and produce wastes daily, and storage space is almost always limited because as much space as possible is used for the sales area.

Grinders have also been used effectively in food processing plants. It is relatively easy to install a grinder so that it is a part of the production cycle in such plants. Usually a conveyer belt carries all waste products to the grinder and the grinding and flushing process is automatic. Such a system requires a minimum of labor. Both hammer mill and shredder type grinders are used in processing plants, and they are usually larger than those used in most other businesses.

Produce terminals have large quantities of food wastes because most produce is perishable. It is sometimes necessary to dispose of an entire shipment of fruits or vegetables that arrives in poor condition—100 or more tons of only one product. It is not feasible to store such large quantities of spoiled produce; instead it is necessary to get it to a disposal point as quickly as possible.

A grinder centrally located on the premises of a produce terminal reduces hauling distances to a minimum. Fruits and vegetables are easily ground so that a relatively small grinder can dispose of large quantities of them in a short time. The grinder is usually equipped with a hopper and a conveyer system so that large truck loads of produce can be dumped without overloading the grinder. It operates continuously, controlled by the conveyer, without constant attention.

Because only a relatively small space is required for a grinder, several are sometimes installed in a large terminal; different sizes and types are used for different needs.

Types and Sizes

Commercial and institutional grinders are of two general types. One uses rotating knives, or shredders, and operates on the same principle as a home grinder. The food particles are ground between the rotating shredder plate and a stationary wear ring; water is used to flush the ground garbage into the sewer. The fineness of grind is controlled by the amount of space between the rotating and stationary sections. Grinders of this type may have vertical shafts like those in household grinders or they may have horizontal shafts. They are usually manufactured in small sizes, with motors up to 5 horsepower.

The other common type of grinder has rotating hammers that tear up the garbage and beat it to a pulp against a side plate; the garbage is flushed through a screen to the sewer. Hammer mill grinders can be built in small sizes but they are usually large, using motors of 5 to 150 horsepower or more.

Effect on Municipal Services

Water Supply. It is difficult to generalize on the quantity of water required to operate commercial grinders. Some grinders require more water than others and the type of garbage ground affects the amount used. Furthermore, the size of the sewer into which the grinder discharges affects the amount of water needed. If the normal flow in the sewer is small, considerably more water must be used in the grinder to assure proper flushing and to prevent heavy solids from settling in the sewer pipes.

The amount of water used varies from about 5 gallons per minute for a small unit using a 1½ horsepower motor to about 20 gallons per minute for a unit with a 10 horsepower motor. About 1 gallon of water is required for each 1 to 2 pounds of ground garbage. Commercial grinders are usually operated only a small part of the day so that the amount of water needed daily is comparatively little.

Many cities charge for sewage treatment on the basis of the amount of water used. Commercial grinders put a high concentration of suspended solids into sewers and treatment plants without using an appreciable quantity of water. If the charge for sewage treatment is based on the amount of water used, it is possible for a produce terminal or food processing plant to install a grinder and get disposal service for only a fraction of its actual cost.

Sewers. Commercial grinders should not be installed in areas in which sewers are inadequate or faulty. A restaurant near a residential area sometimes has this problem. The lateral sewer may have insufficient flow or pitch to permit garbage from the restaurant grinder to flow to the main sewer. If a sewer stoppage results, not only the restaurant but often residents of the area are inconvenienced.

Sewage Treatment Plant. Ground garbage from commercial grinders does not present any unusual problems at sewage treatment plants. Restaurants, hospitals, food processing plants, and produce terminals put the same types of garbage through the grinder that householders do. The particle sizes may be larger than those from home grinders but they are usually small enough for efficient treatment. Commercial grinders differ from home grinders in that they put large amounts of suspended solids into the sewer system over an extended period of time. This is usually not noticeable at the treatment plant because of the dilution and leveling out processes as the ground garbage travels through the sewers. However, a produce terminal may contribute such large quantities of ground garbage that the treatment plant becomes overloaded. This problem can be solved, however, by regulating the time and the extent the grinder is used.

The comments made previously in connection with the effects of ground garbage from household units on the costs of sewage treatment are equally applicable, of course, if the source is commercial grinders.

Municipal Collection System. Most municipal refuse collection systems are unaffected by installation of commercial grinders because commercial establishments are usually serviced by private collectors. Hog feeders often collect garbage from restaurants and hospitals even in those cities that provide collection services for businesses and institutions.

In many communities, however, the practice is to permit private collectors to dispose of refuse at municipal incinerators or sanitary landfills, either free or for a fee. The installation of commercial grinders reduces the need for such disposal services.

Limitations

Some garbage, such as oyster shells, large bones, and banana stalks, mentioned before, should not be ground. Neither can chicken feathers, hog bristles, and wool be ground successfully; if they are ground, they plug the unit. Thus a poultry processing plant, for instance, can use a grinder for only part of the waste produced; a collection service is needed for the remainder.

Costs

The cost of a 1½ horsepower commercial grinder is about $600 and a 5 horsepower grinder costs about $1,600. The expected life is from 10 to 20 years. Maintenance costs are relatively low because the grinders have only a few parts that wear.

The grinder itself is usually only a small part of the costs, because

Fig. 103. Spoiled fruits and vegetables are conveniently disposed of in this grinder, installed by the United Fruit Company at its ship terminal in New Orleans.

additional facilities such as metal chutes, sorting tables, storage hoppers, and conveyers are often needed.

Electric power used for a commercial grinder is relatively insignificant because the grinder is used only intermittently. Assuming an average charge of 2 cents a kilowatt hour, a grinder equipped with a 1½ horsepower motor uses 3 cents worth of electricity an hour; it would cost 10 cents an hour for power for a 5 horsepower grinder. In restaurants and other places where food is served, the total time a grinder is in operation is probably considerably less than one hour a day.

Municipal Regulation

Ordinances pertaining to commercial grinders are of two types: (1) those dealing with approval of grinders, sizes of water lines, plumbing, and installation procedures; (2) those dealing with the broad field of refuse disposal. The second type either permits or prohibits the installation of commercial grinders because of their effect on the sewage disposal system.

A national model code for commercial grinders has not been developed; each city must work out its own standards for fineness of grind, standard refuse test mixture, and water. An acceptable model performance code would help eliminate confusion and help municipalities set up regulations.

Ordinances encouraging or requiring the installation of central grinders are usually only applicable to new buildings or to remodeled buildings in which production of food wastes is expected to increase. Some cities have explored the possibility of requiring installation of grinders in all commercial buildings where food wastes are produced; all have determined that such a requirement is not feasible.

Most ordinances that have to do with grinders but do not prohibit them are concerned with all kinds of on-site disposal; they are usually written to cover both grinders and incinerators.

Installation. Permits should be required for the installation of commercial grinders because records of permits are the most important single means of locating the sources of ground garbage in the sewer system. Many kinds of garbage that should not be ground may get into sewers if permits—and thus inspections—are not required. Furthermore, a permit requirement makes it possible to prohibit connections to sewers that are known to be inadequate. One city requires the business or institution installing a grinder to be responsible for damage to sewers.

The department responsible for issuing permits and inspecting installations should pay particular attention to the quantity of water supplied to the grinder. The amount is usually controlled by specifying the minimum size water pipe that can be used for a grinder and requiring an electrically operated water valve. A grinder so installed cannot be operated unless the right amount of water is flowing.

If limits on particle size are included in the ordinance, the responsibility for testing the installation rests on the department issuing the permit. The tests are performed after the installation has been inspected and approved as far as other ordinance requirements are concerned. Testing large commercial grinders for fineness of grind is difficult because a large quantity of test refuse is required and it is difficult to get a representative sample.

Use

Grinders are being installed in most new commercial buildings in which food disposal facilities are needed unless grinders are prohibited by law.

A commercial grinder is easy to maintain, gives long service, requires little space, and is a comparatively inexpensive method of disposing of garbage.

Many grinders have been installed in older buildings because they are convenient, and many more such installations will be made. The commercial grinder has solved the problems of garbage disposal in hospitals and other institutions so efficiently that it is considered almost a necessity.

Grinders are usually installed in large, successful restaurants for convenience and to improve sanitation. The small neighborhood restaurant that constantly changes ownership is a different problem, however. The business may not be profitable enough to warrant installation of a grinder.

The benefits of grinding stations at produce terminals and food processing plants have been quickly recognized, especially in cities in which the only disposal charge is included as a small part of the water bill. Probably the single most important factor that has prevented 100 per cent installation in areas where grinders are permitted is that they cannot grind all food wastes.

MUNICIPAL GRINDER STATIONS

Centrally located municipal garbage grinder stations are in use in a number of cities. If garbage is collected separately from other refuse, grinding is a convenient way of disposing of it, particularly wet garbage not suitable for incineration or hog feeding.

Types and Sizes

The garbage from a city of 80,000 people can be disposed of daily at a station that grinds 5 tons an hour or even less. An installation of this size requires little equipment and facilities in addition to the grinders. The garbage can be dumped on a concrete floor, sorted for objects that cannot be ground, and the rest manually pushed into the grinder. Where only one or two loads of garbage are collected each day, it may be much more economical to use part-time labor than to mechanize operations.

Grinder stations in large cities receive large quantities of garbage in relatively short periods of time, which has led to the development of grinders that can process 30 to 50 tons of garbage an hour. Such installations are highly mechanized.

How well garbage is prepared and separated from other refuse by the householder largely determines the type of plant that should be built.

Garbage with a high moisture content (swill) that is free of cans, glass, and other ungrindable objects is the most suitable for grinding. The equipment usually needed consists of a receiving hopper, a conveyer, and a grinder. Some sorting is done on the conveyer line to remove an occasional can or bottle. The initial cost for such a plant is low, maintenance costs are low, a minimum of labor is required, and the plant has a high disposal rate per hour. Plants of this type have been built in cities in which the practice of feeding garbage to hogs has been abandoned or to dispose of garbage that is surplus from a hog feeding program. Grinders of this type are sometimes installed in an incinerator plant to handle spoiled produce or swill, which is easily ground but difficult to incinerate.

Wrapped garbage requires a much more complicated grinder plant. Packages of wrapped garbage usually contain ungrindable materials that must be exposed before they can be removed.

The plant designed to grind wrapped garbage should have two sections. The first section includes a receiving hopper where trucks dump their loads, a conveyer that carries the garbage at a uniform speed to the primary grinder, and the primary grinder that shreds the packages and exposes the contents. This grind is extremely coarse, and only a small amount of water is used because the garbage must be sorted before the final grind. The primary grinder discharges its material to the second section. The second section consists of a conveyer that carries the refuse to a picking belt; the picking belt, which discharges the sorted

Fig. 104. An attendant inspects garbage being carried on a picking belt from a storage hopper to a grinder at the Washington, D. C., refuse transfer station. Objects often found in garbage that are harmful to grinders, such as heavy metals, should not be put into grinders.

refuse to the final grinder; and the final grinder, where garbage is reduced to the correct size particles and flushed into the sewer. On the picking belt, ferrous metals are usually removed by a magnetic pulley and nonferrous metals, concrete, and other objects are removed manually.

The large grinders used in municipal plants are usually of the hammer mill type. There is considerable wear on the hammers because all municipally collected garbage contains some ungrindable objects, especially if wrapped garbage is processed.

Location

Municipal grinder plants may be located near load centers to reduce hauling costs or they may be at the sewage treatment plant where the ground garbage can be deposited directly in the digesters. This requires less investment in treatment facilities than if the ground garbage must be processed through the entire treatment plant. Each city must make studies to determine what location is most economical for it, however.

In large cities, grinder stations are usually located along main sewer interceptors. Hauling costs become important as the number of trucks and driving distances become greater. Several grinder plants can be so located that hauling distances to each are minimum. Furthermore, by putting the ground garbage into the sewer system at several locations, the load at the sewage treatment plant is leveled out over a period of time and problems of treatment are not as great.

Small cities usually find the most economical location for a grinder is at the treatment plant. If only a small amount of garbage is ground daily it is often possible to use the workers at the treatment plant to grind the garbage, which results in considerable savings. Another advantage is that the people responsible for grinding also learn the limitations of the treatment facilities and are able to work out the most desirable techniques for both grinding and treatment.

Effect on Municipal Services

Water Supply. The water requirements of a municipal grinder station vary considerably with type of station, location, and the kind of refuse processed. Grinders located in sewage treatment plants can use the effluent from the secondary treatment for all operations, and the amount of water needed is reduced considerably when the garbage is pumped directly into the digester. Grinder stations on main sewer interceptors that have a high normal flow rate can use sewage to supply a good share of the flushing water. When city water is used for the grinding process, it usually requires about 1 gallon for each pound of garbage ground. The quantity varies considerably, however, if flushing problems are severe and higher flow velocities are required.

Electric Power. The cost of the power consumed by a municipal grinder station is relatively low. If city water is used, most of the power is for the grinders, with a small portion for the conveyers. If power is charged for at the rate of 2 cents per kilowatt hour, power costs for grinder stations vary between 10 cents per ton of garbage ground for a simple station to 30 cents for one using primary and secondary grinders and an elaborate conveyer system.

Sewage Treatment Plant. The discharge of ground garbage from a central grinder station into the sewer system presents additional problems at the sewage treatment plant. The problems are similar to those with home grinders. There is a marked increase in the amount of suspended solids received at the treatment plant when the grinder station is in operation; there is a noticeable increase in grit unless the grinder station is equipped with a grit chamber to wash the slurry before discharging it into the sewer; there is an increased organic load on the secondary treatment process. If a plant is operating at or near capacity before a grinder station is built, the treatment plant must be enlarged before the station can be operated.

If the grinder station is built at the sewage treatment plant, the slurry from the grinder can be pumped directly to the digesters, thereby eliminating the need for increased plant facilities other than on the digesters and for sludge disposal.

Some cities still dump sewage into streams of water without treating the sewage. Those that do can build a grinder at any convenient location without giving thought to fineness of grind, grit, grease, and increased suspended solids. However, the practice of dumping untreated sewage in water is rapidly being eliminated, and it is doubtful if any new plants will be constructed for direct discharge into streams.

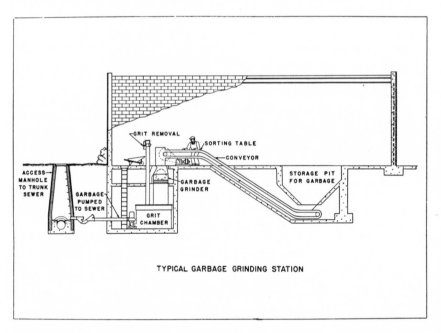

Fig. 105. A cross section of the layout for a central garbage grinding station.

Safety

Municipal grinder stations are relatively safe. Experience shows that when reasonable care is exercised in removing materials such as heavy metals that are unsuitable for grinding, the possibility of injury from flying objects rejected from the grinder is remote. The concrete walkways are usually wet and slippery, so employees must be careful when they walk around the equipment; guard rails should be provided.

Odor Control

A grinder station can cause considerable odor unless the air is deodorized before it leaves the plant. To do this, equipment must be housed in a building maintained under negative pressure while garbage is being ground. This prevents air from escaping together with garbage odors except through the air purification equipment located on the exhaust side of the ventilation system. The discharge of the purified air through a stack extending some distance above surrounding buildings also helps eliminate odors.

Costs

There are many factors and variables involved in the costs of a municipal grinder station.

If a small, five-ton-per-hour grinder is installed in a sewage treatment plant, the total cost of the installation may be less than $10,000, and the equipment should last for at least 15 years. Assuming that 10 tons of garbage are processed daily, the costs will be about 25 cents a ton.

Costs for a large municipal grinder station located on a main interceptor are at the other extreme. A 300-ton-per-day plant consisting of an enclosed dumping area, primary and secondary grinders, conveyers, stand-by equipment, air purification equipment, employees' facilities, and so on requires a sizeable capital investment. The building would probably cost in excess of $300,000 and could be expected to last at least 30 years. Equipment would cost about the same amount but it would be depreciated in 20 years. Costs for such a plant would be about 40 cents a ton of ground garbage. Operating and maintenance costs would vary between 50 cents and $1 a ton.

The type of sewage treatment plant and the degree of treatment influence costs. Cities in which garbage is ground at the treatment plant and pumped into the digester and in which the gas produced in the digester tanks is used as fuel in the operation of the plant have reported savings in treatment plant operating costs. Other cities have reported a cost of more than $3 a ton of garbage processed. In view of the conflicting reports, each city must study its own conditions and evaluate the cost of grinding in terms of known costs of operating collection and disposal systems and a sewage treatment plant. Garbage disposal is only one small part of refuse disposal. The best solution is the one that conforms to sanitation standards at the lowest cost.

Evaluating Grinding as a Disposal Method

If garbage is to be ground it should be collected separately from other refuse, so a city must have at least two collection systems. Plant construction is simplified and operation is more economical if only garbage that is free of hard-to-grind objects is ground. Sanitary landfills or other methods of refuse disposal are also necessary to dispose of ungrindable refuse.

If disposal sites are some distance from the city, the installation of a central grinder plant may reduce hauling distances so that garbage can be collected with fewer trucks and fewer man-hours. The savings may more than offset the cost of the grinder plant.

Large cities that use incineration as the primary means of refuse disposal also use grinders to advantage for some refuse. It is difficult to burn large loads of tomatoes and watermelons, for instance, from produce houses. A grinder makes it possible to dispose of such refuse quickly, easily, and economically.

It is doubtful if a large city can justify use of central grinder stations for all garbage disposal. The need for only one collection system with either incineration or landfill disposal offsets any possible savings of central grinding.

The Future of Food Waste Grinding

Any attempt to prognosticate the future of garbage grinders must be based to a large extent on experience during the past 10 years. The effects of grinders on sewers are well known; it is unlikely that grinders will ever be limited because of sewer problems except in special cases. Ground garbage behaves much like sewage solids in treatment plants, so no new and startling discoveries can be expected there that would greatly influence the acceptance of grinders.

It has been suggested that grinders could be developed to handle other solid wastes and thus increase their effectiveness and appeal to the householder, although such a grinder probably could not be installed in the kitchen sink because of the heavy-duty work it must do. By the late 1960's, however, there was little promise that a feasible and practical grinder of this type would soon be ready for marketing.

Built-Up Cities

Cities that are almost completely built up will not be affected to any great extent by the installation of grinders during the next 10 years. Most new houses in the middle and upper price brackets and some low-cost houses will be equipped with grinders. Experience indicates that approximately 75 per cent of the houses in the middle and upper price levels that were less than 10 years old in 1960 will have grinders by 1970; and 20 per cent of the houses from 10 to 30 years old in 1960 will have grinders installed in 10 years. Houses over 30 years old are a poor market— less than 5 per cent will add this improvement. In a city that is 80 per cent developed and in which about 10 per cent of the houses are equipped with grinders, it can be expected that in 10 years 40 per cent of all new houses will have grinders.

Many hospitals, restaurants, produce houses, and other businesses that produce large quantities of food wastes have already installed grinders, and most businesses that need grinders will include them in new buildings if they are permitted under local ordinances.

Cities that are growing little probably will not have a big enough increase in the number of grinders to change collection and disposal systems, but changes in sewage treatment facilities may have to be made.

Growing Cities

Most growing cities must plan for a large increase in the number of home garbage grinders. Unless a city prohibits them, it can anticipate that most new houses in the middle and upper price brackets will have grinders. All will have disposal units if installation is required by ordinance, of course.

A growing community can predict reasonably accurately the saturation limits of acceptance. Where installation of grinders is controlled by ordinance, estimates of future use can be made reliably. Promotion campaigns with or without ordinance assistance affect the number installed.

About 50 per cent of the older houses in growing cities probably will have grinders. Houses built for low income groups, where the selling price is important, probably will not have grinders unless they are required.

Suburbs

The number of home grinders that can be expected in suburbs is difficult to assess. Most suburban houses are on large lots, so that storage of refuse is not as difficult as it is in a city. Many suburbanites hire private refuse collectors, usually for both garbage and rubbish, who charge a monthly fee. In some areas in which air pollution problems are not critical both garbage and rubbish are burned outdoors. Furthermore, septic tanks are used for sewage disposal in many suburban houses and although grinders can be used with septic tanks if both the tank and the tile field are large enough, a grinder may increase construction costs of the septic tank system by as much as 50 per cent.

On the other hand, most suburbanites probably can afford garbage grinders better than most city dwellers.

SUMMARY—FOOD WASTE GRINDERS

Food waste grinders are neither a panacea nor a passing fad. They have been in use for more than 40 years. While many household grinders have been installed in the past 20 years and they have grown in popularity, they cannot be expected to compete with refrigerators and washing machines in acceptance.

The acceptance or rejection of appliances normally concerns only the manufacturers and distributors. Garbage grinders are an exception, since acceptance or rejection can be important to a city. If a city wants 100 per cent use of grinders so that it can do away with garbage collection, refusal by 25 per cent of the home owners can nullify the program. On the other hand, a city that has inadequate sewers or sewage treatment plant cannot depend on home owners *not* to buy grinders; it must prohibit their installation.

All cities have a garbage grinder problem in one form or another, whether it is recognized or not. Sooner or later each city has to evaluate grinders in terms of city needs and conditions. Some cities under some

Fig. 106. The twin Eidal shredders are reported to be capable of shredding 80 tons of domestic refuse per hour.

conditions will have 100 per cent use of home grinders. But even those cities will not grind all the garbage produced; the amount probably will be less than 10 per cent of the total refuse normally collected and disposed of by the municipality.

Home grinders are usually considered a luxury, but as living standards continue to rise, more and more people will reach an income level at which they become a household necessity.

GRINDING MIXED REFUSE

The nonuniform nature of refuse is a major complicating factor affecting the efficiency of its handling and disposal. More specialized, better adapted equipment could be used in many applications if it were not necessary to accommodate such a wide range of sizes and other physical characteristics. In an effort to improve this situation, the idea of grinding or shredding all refuse as an auxiliary process has been an intriguing one which is beginning to receive increasing attention in the United States.

In connection with incineration, the advantages of firing a more uniform fuel are readily apparent. Advanced combustion techniques involving burning in suspension and pneumatic charging could be considered and the problems of uneven fire beds and requirements for agitation of the fire beds could be minimized. The plant being built for Hamilton, Ontario, is designed to utilize ground or shredded refuse.

In landfills the handling, spreading, compacting, and cover requirements would all be benefitted likewise and problems of settlement—particularly uneven settlement—would be minimized.

The demonstration project at Madison, Wisconsin, conducted under a grant of the U.S. Department of Health, Education, and Welfare, shows decided benefits from shredding or "milling" household refuse to be landfilled. The characteristics of the raw refuse are changed significantly insofar as they affect its behavior in landfilling. Sanitary aspects are much improved as are also the requirements for satisfactory operation. High compaction and uniformity of the fill are obtained comparatively easily, while the need for daily cover is materially reduced.

A significant problem with any grinding or shredding process is that of cost. The nature of the material being processed calls for heavy, rugged machines. Wear on grinding parts is high and power requirements are heavy. Machines are available and being improved with practical capacities and better reliability. For instance, machine wear and damage are materially reduced in both the Gondard and Tollemache hammermill type grinders used at Madison by reason of features built into the designs to reject heavy and oversized objects, which cause most of the damage, before they reach the grinding section. The Eidal machine, which is used also for tearing automobiles into shreds, features grinding wheel elements held against the refuse material by centrifugal force but free to retract on loose fitting shafts when encountering over-

 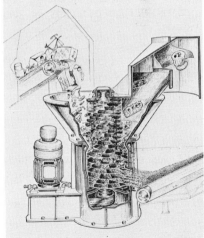

Fig. 107. The Tollemache hammermill type grinder features a vertical shaft and gravity feed with ballistic rejection of oversize, heavy items.

size pieces. In any case, however, there is still necessary a heavy investment, stand-by capacity, and regular replacement of wearing parts.

The cost of present grinding as an auxiliary process, when added to the normal cost of incineration or sanitary landfilling, has usually been deemed prohibitive. However, until incinerators are modified to comply with federal air pollution standards and sanitary landfills are operated in compliance with the rules and regulations that are being promulgated by various state agencies, the additional cost of milling or shredding is reasonable. Current investigations point toward additional justifications of the use of grinding through improvements and to some extent through savings achievable in the final disposal methods.

8 FEEDING FOOD WASTES TO SWINE

In colonial times the problem of garbage disposal in large cities was "solved" by turning pigs loose in the streets to serve as scavengers. In view of today's sanitary practices, such a system seems remote, indeed. However, in small communities a pig or two is still frequently the garbage disposal plant for a family. Traditionally, farmers have kept a few hogs that were "slopped" after mealtime with the leftovers from the table, trimmings from the preparation of food, and other edibles. Into this melange were sometimes thrown a few handfuls of grain.

As cities grew, owners of small farms in outlying areas found it profitable to collect all or part of a city's garbage as food for their livestock. When cities became so large that hundreds and then thousands of families were living in close proximity, the garbage disposal problem became acute, and regular garbage collection and disposal became a matter of public health.

It was about this time that city governments began to contract with private individuals to collect all of the garbage in the city. The garbage often was used for hog feeding by the contractor himself or resold to the contractor's customers. With this arrangement, the city retained control of the operation and could demand that pickups be made at regular intervals and that all parts of the city be served by the collection trucks. Other cities found it more convenient to collect and dispose of garbage with their own crews and equipment.

Despite the fact that there is a statistical correlation between the practice of feeding raw garbage to hogs and the relatively high incidence of trichinae infection in humans in the United States, the practice was not changed for many years. The rapid spread of a virus disease of swine between 1953 and 1955—vesicular exanthema—prompted the states to enact legislation prohibiting feeding of raw garbage to swine. Agricultural authorities had said that the disease was spread largely because raw garbage was fed to swine. The United States Bureau of Animal Industry reported that more than 400,000 swine had to be slaughtered because of the outbreak.

When laws required that garbage be disinfected before it could be fed to swine, the problem of how to do it arose. Cookers of every type and size were soon developed, but a great deal of experimentation was necessary to find the best method of both thoroughly and economically cooking the garbage. Many questioned whether feeding garbage to swine could be continued economically.

However, the feed value of commercial garbage has been enough to

induce continuance of a surprisingly substantial amount of swine feeding.
The United States Department of Agriculture reported for June, 1968,

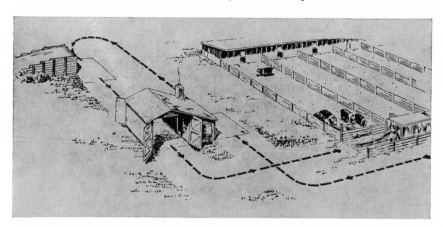

*Fig. 108. Although municipalities do not operate farms on which hogs
are fed garbage, the officials responsible for refuse disposal often find it
a good method of garbage disposal and are concerned with the layout,
operation, and cleanliness of such farms. This layout consists of a ramp
for dumping garbage from collection truck into cooking truck, a cooking
shed with a boiler where steam is turned into the load of garbage, and a
drive-through alley 10 feet wide, with a feeding trough in the center, as
shown below. This design was based on an allowance of 15 inches of
trough space per hog to finishing weight.*

that there were 8,794 premises on which 842,911 hogs were being fed garbage. Of the 90.7 per cent of these animals inspected during that month, 98.2 per cent were fed cooked material. At an estimated 24 pounds per head per day, this amounts to over 10,000 tons daily.

PROBLEMS AND NUISANCES

Feeding garbage to swine causes problems—some for humans and some for the swine. Some of the problems result from the operation of a farm on which swine are fed garbage, some result from the pork products put on the market.

Problems for Humans

Trichinosis in humans is a disease caused by a round worm contracted when people eat raw or insufficiently cooked meat that is infected with the worm. Pork is a common source. Swine become infected by eating raw pork scraps or infected rats but usually no symptoms are evident in the live animal and the trichinae may even escape microscopic examination of muscle tissue after death. In humans, however, trichinosis is characterized by the onset of symptoms of varying intensity, according to the amount of infected meat eaten and the abundance of trichina in it.

At one time between 6 per cent and 11 per cent of the pigs fed raw garbage were infected with trichinae. However, the incidence has declined since laws require that garbage be cooked. Studies by the United States Department of Agriculture show that the proportion of garbage-fed hogs in Massachusetts infected with trichinae dropped from 11.2 per cent in 1952 to 2.7 per cent in 1958.

Hog farming is an agricultural pursuit and has no place in a built-up area, and particularly not in a residential area. Odors cannot be eliminated from even the best operated and cleanest farm, and although odors are not a hazard to health, they are objectionable and a public nuisance.

Flies are attracted in large numbers wherever livestock is kept, and particularly where garbage is fed to swine. Feeding and watering areas, pens, sheds, and compost piles are potential fly breeding areas. Sanitation practices, use of insecticides, and disposal of manure and other wastes are necessary for control. But it is impossible to completely eliminate flies, and since they are a threat to health, they are not acceptable, particularly in heavily populated areas.

Wherever garbage is kept or fed to animals, rodent infestation is a possibility. Feeding areas and shelters of piggeries must be properly constructed and sanitary measures used that will prevent rodents from gathering and feeding.

Animal Problems

Swine that are fed food wastes are susceptible to the same diseases as those fed grain, and in addition they are susceptible to vesicular exanthema, hog cholera, and enteritis diseases, which may be spread by the consumption of infected raw pork scraps.

Vesicular exanthema, which is clinically indistinguishable from the dread hoof and mouth disease, occurs mainly in swine fed on raw garbage. It may also infect grain-fed pigs but it does not normally attack other domestic animals and it has never been known to attack humans. Obviously, cooking of garbage is essential to control.

Hog cholera causes an estimated $50 million a year loss to swine raisers in the United States. Vaccination against the disease is necessary in almost all sections of the country. Since the virus can be carried in raw garbage, swine so fed are continually exposed to infection. Probably the most important benefit to hog raisers from the laws requiring that garbage be cooked is the possibility of eventual eradication of hog cholera.

Swine fed on garbage often get one of the diseases in the enteritis group because they are more often exposed to bacterial infection than those fed on grain.

Pork from Garbage-Fed Swine

Pork quality is based on the type of fat found on the carcass of the pig—hard, medium, soft, or oily. Barley usually produces hard fat, corn the lower limit of the hard grade, and soybeans and peanuts produce soft or oily fats.

According to studies made by the University of California Agricultural Extension Service, most of the pork production of 92 pigs in three herds fed cooked garbage was hard. Of the 92 pigs, 73 produced pork graded hard; 13, medium hard; 3, medium soft; and 3, soft.

Abnormal odors or flavors do not occur any more frequently in pork from garbage-fed swine than in swine raised on grain or other feed.

The type and grade of meat produced in garbage-fed swine are influenced by the same conditions and factors as those fed on grain. Breeding is of prime importance in producing a good meat hog with a high-grade carcass. Good husbandry and sanitary surroundings also play a part.

The feeding time required to reach an average market weight of 220 pounds is somewhat longer for a garbage-fed pig than a grain-fed pig. Six to eight months is average for grain-fed pigs. However, the cost for each pound of weight gained is the main factor in determining whether grain feeding or garbage feeding is more economical.

Local, State, and Federal Regulations

Local. Most local health agencies require that premises where animals are kept be sanitary and that odors, flies, and rats, which may be nuisances and a threat to the public health and welfare, be controlled.

Local zoning ordinances usually permit hog farms only in certain districts. Some local governments require that a license be obtained before a garbage feeding hog farm can be operated. Los Angeles County has had such a requirement since 1926. Plans for construction and maintenance of such a farm must be approved by the county livestock inspector before a building permit can be obtained. Weekly inspections are made by veterinarians of the county livestock department to check the health of the animals and to insure compliance with county and state regulations.

State. All states require that garbage fed to swine be cooked. In addition, many have minimum construction and sanitation requirements for piggeries.

Federal. The federal government prohibits movement across state lines of animals that have been fed raw garbage, as well as pork and pork products from such animals. It also prohibits movement across state lines of garbage that is to be fed raw to swine. In cooperation with the states, the United States Department of Agriculture and the Public Health Service of the United States Department of Health, Education, and Welfare encouraged legislation requiring that garbage be cooked; the recommendations of these departments are the basis of most state laws.

CHARACTERISTICS OF GARBAGE USED FOR FEED

Neither the quantity nor the quality of garbage remains stable long. Geography, the season of the year, frequency of pickups, and even the economy of the city affect the composition and quantity of garbage.

The United States Department of Agriculture, reporting on studies of the chemical composition of garbage in New Jersey and Virginia in 1956, said that in both states samples collected from restaurants, households, and institutions were judged to be nutritious. In New Jersey, samples were tested before and after cooking, which was found to have little effect on the nutritive value of the garbage. A vitamin analysis was also run on the samples and it was found that there was no significant change. However, keeping the garbage at high temperatures overnight caused a slight decrease in vitamin content. This decrease was not important unless the garbage contained insufficient vitamins before it was heated.

The amount of garbage required to feed an animal depends on the size of the animal and the type of garbage it is fed. Less garbage is required if it comes from a military installation than from households because there is more inedible material in household garbage.

There are three principal sources of garbage: residences, businesses and institutions (including restaurants), and markets. In some localities military installations also are a source of garbage.

Residential Garbage

Residential garbage ordinarily has the poorest value as hog feed. It invariably has in it significant amounts of inedible materials such as glass and razor blades. However, the quantity of garbage is steadily decreasing with modern packaging and refrigeration. More garbage is wrapped, too, which increases the paper content of the garbage.

Commercial and Institutional Garbage

Commercial and institutional garbage also contains inedible materials—paper, china, lamp bulbs, silver, napkins, cigarette and cigar butts. In fact, they are the rule rather than the exception. Restaurant garbage exceeds residential garbage in nutritional value as hog food, however, primarily because of the larger quantities of inedibles in residential garbage. Also, garbage is usually collected more frequently from commercial establishments and institutions and is in better condition than residential garbage, especially in summer.

Market Garbage

Garbage collected from markets is predominately fruits and vegetables. It is not unusual to receive entire carloads of squash, melon, and other

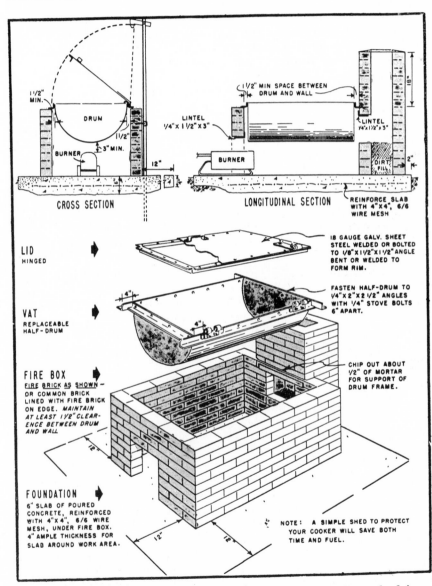

Fig. 109. Garbage is often cooked by the "direct fire" method in an outdoor cooker.

foodstuffs that are unsaleable and thus become garbage. Trimmings alone from a large city market can make up several truck loads of garbage a day. However, garbage from markets is made up of foods that have almost the same nutritional values and so it must be mixed with other foods to make it suitable for hog-feeding.

Garbage from Military Installations

Military installations are usually a good source of food wastes for swine feeding. The garbage is from well balanced meals, and the inedible wastes, such as coffee grounds and egg shells, are separated from edible wastes better than in other sources of garbage.

METHODS OF COOKING GARBAGE

Swine feeders have tried various methods of cooking or treating garbage before it is used as feed. One method is to dehydrate, another to remove the grease; but cooking is the most effective. Equipment is readily available and hog raisers are familiar with it.

Several methods of cooking garbage have been discontinued because they were unsuccessful. Pressure cooking is one. Dry garbage sticks to the sides of the cooker with the result that all the garbage scorches, making it unpalatable. Dry steaming in a jacketed kettle also has largely been discontinued.

Garbage is usually cooked by one of two methods—direct fire or wet steam injections.

The direct fire method is merely cooking it in a vat set in a walled-in firebox (Figure 109). About 90 per cent of the equipment used to treat garbage is of the direct fire type. It is popular because it costs less than $100, can be built by the hog feeder, and different types of fuels can be used. The trend now is to use liquid fuel or gas instead of wood or old tires. A great deal of improvement is necessary to make many of these cookers efficient, however.

The wet steam injection method is commonly used with large loads hauled from cities by private contractors. It consists of injecting steam into the load of garbage through perforated parallel pipes at the bottom of the body of the hauling vehicle (as in Figure 110). The steam comes from a boiler on a truck or from a vat. If the boiler supplies about 270,000 B.T.U. of steam for each ton of garbage treated, it takes 2½ hours to cook the garbage.

Much of the equipment used for this method of treating garbage could be improved by putting a tight lid on the vat and adding valves at the end of the injector pipes so sediment can be removed. Either high or low-pressure boilers are suitable, although more water is added to the load when low-pressure boilers are used.

Heat treating in truck bodies is common because a cooking vat is not necessary. In addition, less labor is required because the raw garbage need not be taken from the truck and put in a vat. Concrete tanks are not suitable because the garbage that is in contact with the concrete does not cook thoroughly.

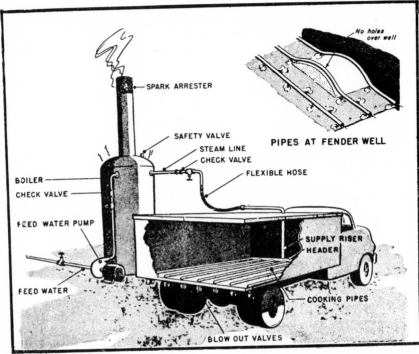

Fig. 110. Garbage can be cooked by injecting steam into the especially equipped trucks that collect it.

Stirring the garbage occasionally evens out the temperature of the garbage and shortens the cooking time. Stirring is simple with a small vat, although it is difficult with truck loads of garbage. Some trucks are equipped with a center shaft with agitator arms that stir up the top and bottom of the load. The shaft is slowly turned by a truck power take-off or an electric or gasoline motor.

The garbage should be cooled and fed to the hogs as soon as possible after it is cooked. Although it is not good to run cold water into the vat to cool the garbage, the garbage can be spread in a trough immediately after cooking instead of leaving it in the heating vat to cool.

Economics of Feeding Garbage to Pigs[1]

Reliable cost data are essential to intelligent and profitable management. Information on the costs of every phase of operation—collection, cooking, veterinarian supplies and services, supplemental feed, labor, land, and maintenance of the farm—is necessary.

---

[1]Cost figures presented in this section are for comparison purposes only. Because of the limited use of this method of disposal by cities, up-to-date statistics are difficult to obtain.

It is axiomatic that costs must be related to the selling price of the pigs. It is important to consider how much pork can be expected from each ton of garbage fed to a pig. It has been reported that hogs fed on cooked garbage gain more rapidly and produce more pork per ton of garbage than those fed on raw garbage. A weight gain of 1.44 pounds a day for the pig and a pork production of 193 pounds per ton of cooked military garbage have been reported. Experience in Canada shows that one ton of good quality cooked garbage produces an average of about 80 pounds of pork; each hog eats between 20 and 24 pounds of garbage daily and gains approximately one pound each day. Studies made in California indicate a yield of 70 to 75 pounds of pork per ton of cooked residential garbage. Records kept at the Kansas City penal farm piggery showed a pork production of about 100 pounds per ton of cooked commercial garbage.

Assuming the price of hogs is $20 a hundredweight, one ton of garbage

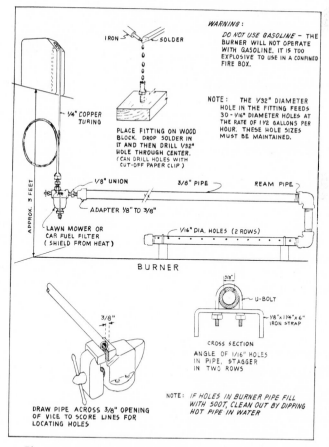

Fig. 111. Oil can be used as fuel for "direct fire" cooking of garbage by converting the fire box.

delivered at a hog farm is worth from $15 to $39 gross to the hog raiser, depending on the type of garbage. Costs vary, however, and must be analyzed carefully for each case. For example, the haul from a city to the hog farm may be 10 miles or it may be 50 miles, with costs varying accordingly. Furthermore, costs of constructing a piggery that meets local standards vary considerably because local standards vary.

Usually the cost of facilities should be paid off in approximately 10 years—the average life expectancy of the structures and equipment required for this type of operation. Costs are substantially less if second-hand equipment is used. Assuming that new equipment and facilities are used, however, and that two herds of hogs are fattened from 100 pounds to 250 pounds and marketed each year, the capital investment would amount to 25 cents per hundredweight over a period of 10 years.

Cooking garbage increases costs, of course. A cooker must be bought and maintained and men must be employed to operate it. Cookers come in all types and sizes and are frequently modified, so costs for them vary greatly as do labor and fuel costs.

The cost of garbage heat treatment in New Jersey in 1955 was about one-half that in Massachusetts, primarily because the equipment used in New Jersey was much more efficient and economical. The equipment used in New Jersey was similar to that recommended by the United States Agricultural Research Service and the United States Public Health Service. It had closely fitted lids on the trucks and efficient boilers. The cost of cooking garbage in 1955 ranged from $1 to $2 a ton; or at 70

TABLE 31

AVERAGE GARBAGE COOKING COSTS IN NEW JERSEY AND MASSACHUSETTS, 1955
(Per cubic yard: about 1,200 lbs.)

Cooking Method	New Jersey	Massachusetts
Direct-fire	—	$1.12
Small boilers and vat (less than 50 boiler hp)	$0.56	1.05
Larger boiler and vat	0.45	0.92

pounds of pork produced for every ton of cooked garbage, the cost varied from $1.40 to $2.80 per hundredweight.

Proximity to a shipping point or meat packing plant is important to the hog raiser when his hogs have reached marketable size. In many localities, meat packers who are prejudiced against garbage-fed hogs penalize the hog raiser a cent or two a pound.

Fluctuations in the price of grain for feed are sometimes a cogent argument in favor of garbage-fed swine, since the supply of garbage and the price of it is constant, except for seasonal fluctuations.

Although the number of municipalities that have contracts to dispose of garbage for hog feeding has decreased rapidly, there are still a number of private operators who supply hog farmers with garbage from commercial establishments.

EFFECTS OF GARBAGE FEEDING ON REFUSE COLLECTION

If garbage is fed to swine there is considerable effect on the municipal refuse collection system. Garbage must be separated from other refuse before it is collected, separate collections must be made at different frequencies, and specially designed collection equipment is needed. It may also involve different collectors for different kinds of refuse.

Systems of Collection

Garbage to be fed to hogs is collected under one of three systems: by the municipality itself, by a private collector who contracts with the municipality to make the collections, or by private contractors who contract with companies and individuals to collect it.

At present, garbage collection is divided between municipal, municipal-private contract, and private contract methods. Household garbage is usually collected by municipal crews, but garbage from restaurants is often collected by private entrepreneurs who contract with the restaurants directly as there are large quantities that should be collected daily and the rich quality of the garbage makes it valuable for hog feeding. Furthermore, such collections often require special equipment, special timing arrangements, and special locations for containers.

Various local conditions determine who should collect the garbage, but the most important is whether there is a market for the garbage. Obviously, if garbage is fed to hogs there is a market for it, and private contractors frequently do at least some of the collecting. In some cities separate collection of garbage by private collectors is a major advantage to the city because it makes municipal collections easier, helps eliminate odors, and cuts costs of disposal of other refuse by incineration or sanitary landfill.

Storage

Garbage that is to be fed to hogs should be stored separately from other refuse, although in the past many cities permitted householders to store them together. This made it difficult to use garbage as feed unless at the hog farm it was scattered over a large area and the hogs rooted through it, which created nuisances and unsanitary conditions. Since garbage must now be cooked, it is no longer stored with other refuse.

Garbage feeding to hogs also brought the practice of wrapping garbage into question. Garbage that is well wrapped is less likely to cause odors during storage than unwrapped garbage, it reduces the likelihood of flies breeding in it, and makes it easier to clean the container. Furthermore, in the North wrapping garbage prevents it from freezing to the container in the winter. On the other hand, if garbage is to be fed to hogs, wrapping is undesirable. It makes the cooking process difficult and adds a great deal of material to the garbage that has no nutritional value. A successful

Fig. 112. The collection of garbage for hog feeding requires the use of special trucks designed for that purpose.

compromise is lining garbage containers with newspapers or paper bags.

The size of household garbage and refuse containers should be controlled by the city. The container should not be so small that the collection crew must empty many of them at any one residence but it should not be so large that it is too heavy for a collector to handle. Most garbage weighs from 800 to 1,200 pounds per cubic yard. Thus a five-gallon container and the garbage in it weigh from 25 to 45 pounds and a 55-gallon drum from 275 to 475 pounds. Household containers should be between 3 and 16 gallons. Containers for restaurants usually range from 20 to 32 gallons. If mechanical equipment is used to lift the container and dump the garbage into the truck, the capacity of containers may range from 3 to 16 cubic yards.

Frequency and Kinds of Collections

If garbage is collected separately from other refuse, it is usually done because there is an advantage as far as the disposal method is concerned, because it is economical, or because the public wants it. In times of national emergency, several types of collections to separate salvage materials from other refuse may be necessary, regardless of the cost.

Combined collection of residential refuse is usually considered more economical for the municipality than separate collections. That is not necessarily so, however. A final conclusion can be reached only after all factors and problems peculiar to the city are studied—costs of separate collections, savings from less frequent collection of rubbish, costs of special collection trucks for garbage, and the cost to the householder of separate containers.

Studies show that it requires less equipment and man-days to collect rubbish and ashes together once a week and to collect garbage separately twice a week than to collect all refuse together twice a week. If rubbish-ash collections are made weekly and garbage twice weekly one or several different disposal methods can be used.

There are, of course, other factors that must be considered: capital investment in collection and disposal plants and equipment on hand; availability of storage space for rubbish and ashes for a week; extra containers required for separate garbage storage; and seasonal changes in amounts of refuse. Seasonal changes can indicate, for instance, combined

Fig. 113. If large quantities of garbage are collected from restaurants and institutions, it is sometimes worthwhile to use garbage receptacles that can be lifted and dumped by collection truck mechanisms.

collections twice a week for four months of the year and once a week the other eight.

Some public works officials are convinced that most cities in the United States can collect well wrapped garbage mixed with rubbish once a week without causing health and nuisance problems. In Los Angeles County, for example, it was found that collecting garbage separately twice a week for disposal by hog feeders cost about $3.50 a ton more than it did to collect wrapped garbage with other refuse once a week. Thus separate collection of residential garbage in Los Angeles County represented a subsidy to the hog feeder and a loss to the community of some $600,000 a year.

If garbage is not well wrapped and is stored and collected separately, it is especially important that it be collected at least twice a week in residential areas during the warm, fly-breeding season. In some southern cities in the United States, garbage is collected three times a week. If the garbage is fed to hogs, collections twice a week keep the garbage more palatable to the hogs and less likely to putrefy.

Table 32 shows that garbage is collected more frequently when it is

TABLE 32

FREQUENCY OF REFUSE COLLECTION FROM RESIDENTIAL AREAS IN 1964 BY 924
COLLECTION SYSTEMS INCLUDING MUNICIPAL, CONTRACT, AND PRIVATE COLLECTION
ARRANGEMENTS, BY CLASS[1]

Frequency of Collection		Number of Collection Systems				
		Combined Refuse	Garbage	Ashes	Rubbish	Other
3 collections per week	S	27	12	0	0	1
	W	19	10	0	0	1
2 collections per week	S	309	101	6	15	2
	W	289	75	10	16	1
1 collection per week	S	288	45	44	84	45
	W	363	71	48	84	34
1 collection ea. 2 weeks	S	2	0	13	21	7
	W	3	1	13	21	7
1 collection per month	S	1	1	8	11	13
	W	1	2	7	11	13
Cleanup drives	S	—	0	1	0	45
	W	—	0	1	0	34
Variable	S	11	1	12	8	33
	W	22	1	12	7	32

S = Summer
W = Winter

[1] Data from American Public Works Association, Committee on Solid Wastes, *Refuse Collection Practice*, 3 ed. (Chicago: Public Administration Service, 1966), p. 88.

collected separately. One hundred and thirteen cities, or over 70 per cent, reported at least twice-weekly garbage collections in residential areas in the summer, and 85, or 53 percent, reported twice-weekly collections during the winter. Comparison of data collected in recent years with that collected in 1939 shows that the practice of using residential garbage for hog feed is decreasing. Nevertheless, the practice of feeding garbage to hogs probably will continue to be economically sound for private haulers in many cities because of the quantity and quality of food wastes from restaurants and food processing companies.

TABLE 33

FREQUENCY OF COMBINED REFUSE COLLECTIONS FROM RESIDENTIAL AND COMMERCIAL AREAS DURING THE SUMMER BY MUNICIPAL COLLECTION AGENCIES IN 1964[1]

Frequency of Collection[2]	Residential	Commercial
(Number of communities responding)	(418)	(359)
Once a week	46.7%	8.1%
Twice a week	48.5	11.4
Three times a week	3.6	3.6
Four times a week	0.0	1.1
Five times a week	0.0	11.7
More than five times a week	0.0	29.3
Fortnightly	0.5	0.0
Monthly	0.0	0.0
Variable	0.7	34.8
Cleanup drives	0.0	0.0
	100.0	100.0

[1] Data from American Public Works Association, Committee on Solid Wastes, *Refuse Collection Practice*, 3 ed. (Chicago: Public Administration Service, 1966), p. 87.
[2] The frequency of collections during the winter varies only slightly from that in the summer.

Cities that combined refuse either collect once or twice a week (see Table 33). It is worth noting (Table 34) that Washington, D.C., as other places with separate garbage collection, has experienced a progressive decline in the total tonnage collected from residential areas.

Collection Equipment

The separate collection of garbage from other refuse requires equipment designed for the job. Because of the relatively high density of garbage compared with rubbish and the relatively small amount of residential garbage per capita (about one-eighth of a gallon per capita per day), a truck with a heavy-duty chassis and a 5- to 10-cubic yard body is usually ample. The body should be covered, watertight, and so constructed that garbage can easily be unloaded from it.

Public Acceptance

Regardless of costs, any public service is successful only if the public

TABLE 34

TONS OF GARBAGE COLLECTED ANNUALLY IN WASHINGTON, D.C., 1964-1967, BY MONTHS*

RESIDENTIAL GARBAGE ONLY

Year	Jan.	Feb.	March	April	May	June	July	Aug.	Sept.	Oct.	Nov.	Dec.	Total
1964	2,785	2,490	2,700	2,746	2,831	3,339	3,806	3,988	3,439	2,982	2,694	2,821	36,621
1965	2,628	2,255	2,730	2,699	2,848	3,302	3,892	4,135	3,563	2,812	2,877	2,537	36,278
1966	2,162	2,305	2,483	2,375	2,394	3,030	2,974	3,152	2,892	2,415	2,263	2,193	30,638
1967	2,254	1,752	2,293	2,028	2,511	2,637	2,808	3,248	2,716	2,473	2,119	2,027	28,866
Avr.	2,457	2,201	2,552	2,462	2,646	3,077	3,370	3,631	3,153	2,671	2,488	2,395	—

*As of 1971, Washington, D. C. adopted combined collection.

likes and accepts it. This is especially true of refuse collection and disposal systems because they affect every resident of the city. The public wants and usually demands prompt services that are perhaps best described as "the simpler the better."

It is relatively easy to change a collection system that requires that garbage be stored separately from other refuse to one in which combined storage is permitted. But the opposite is not as easy. Unless there are special circumstances, such as a national emergency, getting the public to change from a combined refuse collection system to a separate one is an almost impossible task. In fact, even in a national emergency, a persuasive public relations program is necessary to get the public to separate salvageable refuse from the rest of it. Cities that now have separate collection systems but may be considering a combined system will find it is not difficult to decide one way or the other on an objective, economic basis.

LAYOUT AND DESIGN OF PIGGERIES

Although only a few cities have ever directly operated pig farms to dispose of refuse, all cities that dispose of garbage to hog feeders—directly or indirectly—have a responsibility to see that farms on which hogs are fed garbage are well built, regulated, and properly operated. State, county, and local government agencies usually have an interest in them—enforcement agencies, health and sanitation agencies, planning and zoning boards, and agriculture departments.

All too often ordinance provisions covering piggeries are vague and confusing and responsibility for enforcement is widely scattered. However, if several different agencies and departments are involved, their functions can be consolidated. In Los Angeles County, for example, the county livestock inspector, the county health department, the county engineer, the regional planning commission, and the state livestock disease control bureau were all involved in regulation and inspection of pig farms. To avoid duplication of services, the Los Angeles County Livestock Department was designated to carry out and enforce the regulations of all the agencies.

Preliminary Planning

Before a prospective pig feeder selects a site for his farm, he and the contractor who will build it should—to acquaint themselves with all requirements—consult local agencies responsible for regulation. Once the site is selected, it should be inspected by all responsible officials. Plans for the piggery should be submitted to the control agency for approval before construction is started. (Most building codes require submission of plans when application for a building permit is made.)

The responsible agency should inspect each phase of the construction so that violations can be prevented or easily corrected before the piggery is completed. Once the ranch is in operation, it should be inspected routinely and a copy of the written report of conditions given to the owner. Figure 114 is an example of such a report.

LOS ANGELES COUNTY LIVESTOCK DEPARTMENT
203 Administration Building   Telephone:
Union Stock Yards   Jefferson 3233
  Los Angeles 58, California

MONTHLY INSPECTION REPORT
_____, 19__

Ranch_____

Number of inspections during month_____Condition of swine_____

	Very Satisfactory	Satisfactory	Fairly Satisfactory	Un- satisfactory	RECOMMENDATIONS
Fattening Unit - General Feed Floors					
Pens, Fences, Alleys					
Drinkers					
Breeder Unit - General Feed Floors					
Pens, Fences, Alleys					
Drinkers					
Water Drainage General					
Grease Traps & Drainfields					
Bone Receptacle					
Vehicle Wash Rack					
Garbage Cooking					
Feed Floor Refuse					

REMARKS_____

The recommendations above must be complied with promptly.
REPORT IMMEDIATELY any case of suspicious lameness to Livestock Department or Inspector.

                              County Livestock Inspector

                          By_____
                                Deputy Livestock Inspector

*Fig. 114. City, county, and other officials are often responsible for in-
specting farms on which hogs are fed garbage. The Los Angeles County
Livestock Department used this form to report on inspections of such
farms.*

A suitable location is of prime importance if a pig farm is not to be declared a nuisance. It should be accessible in all kinds of weather; be well drained, either by natural or artificial means; and have an adequate supply of potable water.

Basic Design

Piggery design obviously depends on the size and type of operation, but also to a large extent upon climate. If snow and freezing temperatures are usual, design problems are greater than if the climate is mild the year around. Feeding and housing areas must be enclosed, as must areas for cooking garbage and for storing vehicles and implements. Provisions should be made for artificial ventilation when doors and windows must be kept closed. If the climate is especially cold, heat should be considered for areas where the pigs are housed, particularly if early spring and late fall or winter farrowing is advantageous.

The farm usually consists of feeding and fattening units, farrowing units, breeding sections, and dry sow pens. Garbage cooking units, parking lots, garages, storage areas, and waste disposal facilities are accessory sections.

The farm should be designed to provide "production line" movement of pigs from the breeding section to the farrowing units and through the feeding and fattening units to the market.

Feeding and Fattening Units. Feeding and fattening units are those in which the pigs are kept from the time they are weaned to the time they are ready for market.

Feeding floors and platforms where garbage is fed to the pigs must be constructed of concrete or other equally impervious material. They should be smoothly finished for easy cleaning, well-drained into grease traps and drainfields, and have 18-inch "rat walls" on all sides to prevent rats from getting in. Approximately 5 square feet of floor area should be allowed for each animal. A feeding floor 10 by 50 feet is commonly used for 100 pigs.

The feeding area should be enclosed with solid concrete or fenced with chain link or wood on steel posts set in concrete curbing. Chain link or wood fencing on steel posts set into a concrete curb may also be used around the edge of the feeding floor. The curbing should be 8 to 12 inches high and should be reinforced and fastened securely to the feeding platform.

A feeding floor can be adequately drained by allowing a 1-foot drop for every 100 feet of floor. The runoff is collected in a gutter at the end of the floor and passed through screens to remove solid material. It is then directed through a grease trap and finally spread underground through a drainfield.

Design of drinking equipment for the feeding unit varies. All drinkers should be equipped with a float-type valve. They must be easy to clean, be set on a concrete platform to provide approximately 6 feet of floor space on each side, and the platform so constructed that overflow water drains onto the feed floor. They should not be large enough to allow animals to lie in them; a space large enough for the pigs to put their snouts in is sufficient.

Pens should be at least 50 feet by 150 feet for 100 hogs and larger if possible. Fences should be made of wooden panels or chain link set in concrete. Chain link fencing is especially desirable because it is difficult for pigs to root up. All pens should have gates that can be latched between them and the feeding floor so that the animals can be shut into the pens while the floor is being cleaned and while they are being fed. When closed, the gates should be completely off the feeding floor to prevent damage to them during the cleaning operations. Easy access should be provided in the back of each pen for cleaning.

Construction of shelters for the feeding units varies, depending on the

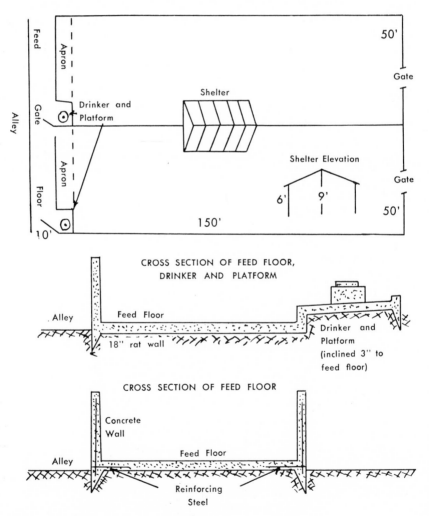

Fig. 115. Cross section of a feeding unit of a piggery.

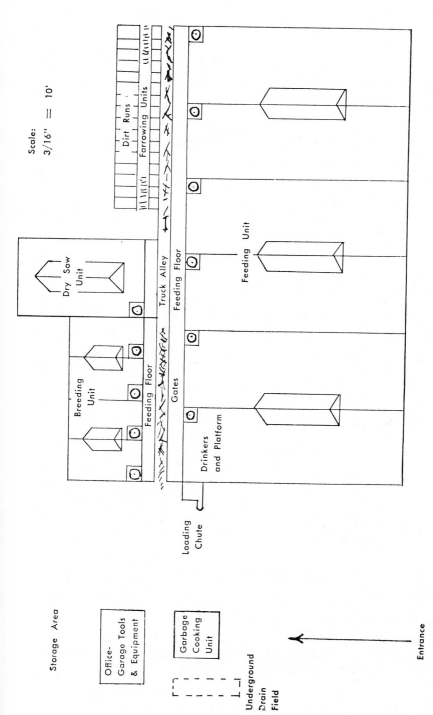

Fig. 116. Hogs can be fed garbage on a "production line" basis if the piggery is efficiently laid out.

weather, but they are usually built of wood with corrugated iron, aluminum, or tar paper roofs. One shelter approximately 1½ times the area of the feeding floor can usually serve two pens. It should be high enough to permit a cleaning vehicle, such as a skip loader, to enter. If the sides of the shelter are hinged they can be closed during inclement weather.

Pigs often defecate and urinate immediately after feeding so that if they are forced to enter the shelter from the rear, the shelter can be kept cleaner, because the animals will usually relieve themselves before entering. Crushed rock or cinders 1½ to 2 feet deep are excellent for the shelter floor and provide good drainage. Cement floors are cold and hard and require a large amount of bedding material.

Farrowing Units. Many pig farmers find that they cannot always buy suitable feeder pigs and therefore must breed their own.

The kind of construction used for farrowing units probably depends more upon the weather than does any other part of the farm. Breeding must be carried on throughout the year to produce feeder pigs regularly. During freezing weather, new-born animals must be kept dry and warm or the mortality rate is disastrously high. Farrowing units consisting of a feeding floor, shelter, and dirt run, should be big enough to accommodate a sow and her litter.

Farrowing floors are similar to floors in the feeder unit except that they are smaller (8 feet square), and, depending on climate, they may or may not be covered. Gates rather than division fences are built between each feeding floor for easy cleaning. Shelters can be either single or double. Double shelters have two rows of units with an alleyway between them. Floors in the shelters should also be 8 feet square and should be of concrete so that they can be cleaned easily.

Protectors, made of two-by-fours placed about 6 inches from the floor and 8 to 10 inches from the wall, should line all walls of the brooder to prevent the sow from crushing the small pigs. A warmer for the baby pigs can be built in a corner by boarding it across to form a triangle 8 to 10 inches high. The front is not enclosed so the baby pigs can easily get to the sow; the top is hinged so it can be opened. An electric light bulb in a one-gallon tin that hangs down into the enclosure from the top provides the heat.

Wood, coal, or gas stoves may be used to heat the farrowing unit if the weather is especially cold. In recent years, radiant heat has been used. Pipes are embedded in the floors and steam or hot water is run through. If the units are heated, however, the pigs must be protected against sudden changes in temperatures because sudden changes make them susceptible to pneumonia and other infections.

Good ventilation is especially important in farrowing units. The partitions between units should not be more than 4 feet high and should have enough openings for air to circulate. The ends of the shelter should be so constructed that they can be opened in good weather and closed in bad weather. Roof ventilators equipped with dampers are often practical.

Straw, shavings, or other bedding material must be provided to help keep the farrowing units warm, dry, and clean.

Accessory Units. Many accessory units must be considered in the construction of a hog farm on which the animals are fed garbage. One is the garbage cooking area, which is discussed in the section on treating garbage.

A suitable area for cleaning and washing vehicles is near the cooking platform, where hot water and steam are available and refuse from the trucks can be washed into the cooking unit drainage system.

Disposal of wastes from the feeding floor is one of the worst problems of piggeries. Disposal is influenced by: (1) the amount of wastes, (2) the

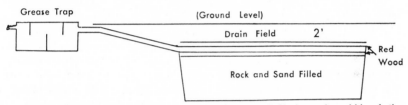

Drain Field should be approximately one and one half times the width of the grease trap and at least twice as long. (A standard type leach line may be substituted for the drain field. More detailed information is available from local health departments.)

CROSS SECTION OF GREASE TRAP

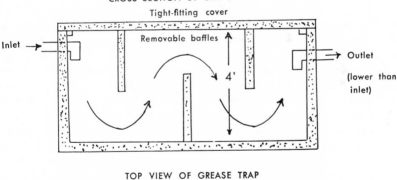

TOP VIEW OF GREASE TRAP

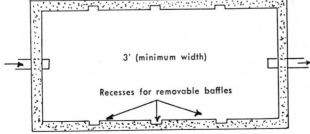

Fig. 117. *Cross section of a grease trap and drain field for disposing of liquid wastes at a piggery.*

amount of space available, (3) the season of the year, (4) proximity of the piggery to dwellings.

Waste from feeding floors is excellent fertilizer if it is properly processed. If space and other conditions permit, it can be thinly spread over a large area and dried quickly, keeping odors to a minimum. If space is not available and weather does not permit drying, it can be composted or buried. If it is hauled away to be composted, strong odors create a real nuisance for nearby residents. As a last resort wastes can be buried by a cut and fill operation.

Large quantities of bones are usually found in feed floor refuse. Since they can be sold, they are usually separated from the other refuse and stored. The area for bone storage should be screened, be at least 18 inches off the ground, and be kept sanitary at all times.

The best place to store materials is at the rear of the farm. Boards, posts, and similar materials should not be stacked on the ground, however, because if they are rats can easily use them for harborage.

9   COMPOSTING

Composting is the biochemical degradation of organic materials to a sanitary, nuisance-free, humus-like material. Modern scientific composting has been described as a rapid but partial decomposition of moist, solid, organic matter by the use of aerobic microorganisms under controlled conditions.

Although in the late 1960's there were only a few composting plants in which municipal refuse was treated in the United States, experiences in Europe and with experimental operations in the United States indicate that capital and operating costs of a compost plant may, under favorable conditions, be similar to costs for an incinerator. The major advantage of the process appears to be that it produces a potentially marketable and useful product. However, unless some economically beneficial use is actually made of the end product, composting will be of limited value as a means of municipal refuse disposal.

There is considerable skepticism among public works officials over composting as a method of refuse disposal. A lack of confidence in the process is understandable and to some extent justified in view of the failures of certain widely heralded composting plants that in the past have processed refuse for cities in the United States.

Actually, little scientific investigation was made of composting of municipal refuse in the United States before 1950. It was largely through the efforts of the University of California, Michigan State University, and the United States Public Health Service that research was begun. As a result, the basic principles of composting refuse for municipalities are now sufficiently well understood to effectively use the process under favorable circumstances on a full-scale basis. Although a decision to use the method should be approached with caution, it is possible that at least at times the economic advantages of it will be considerable. If composting is to be a successful method of disposal, however, several factors must be considered. It should be decided upon only after an engineering survey is made to determine if it is economically and scientifically feasible under local conditions; the plant and equipment should be designed on the basis of modern, scientific principles; the plant should be operated on a scientific basis; and there should be a satisfactory market for the product.

There is reason to believe that early in the development of agriculture, man learned to use leaf mold, animal manure, decayed fish, and other decomposed organic matter in husbanding his crops. However, only in quite recent years has the biochemistry of composting been sufficiently well understood to apply it to municipal refuse disposal problems.

Perhaps the first significant development in composting as an engineered process took place in India in 1925. At that time Sir Albert Howard, in collaboration with others, systematized the procedure by which farmers and gardeners had for many centuries produced humus for use on the soil. Sir Albert's process, known as the Indore process because of the country in which it was developed, is simple. Organic wastes such as garbage, straw, and leaves alternated in layers with night soil, sewage sludge, or animal manures were put into pits or trenches two to three feet deep or piled on open ground to a height of about five feet. The mass was turned twice during a period of six months; and the drainage was utilized on the pile to keep the compost moist. Because the process uses principally hand labor, it has been widely used where manpower is cheap and plentiful.

In some places the Indore process has been modified, chiefly by turning the compost material more frequently to hasten the aerobic action and to lessen the odors. The Indian Council of Agriculture Research improved the method and has used it widely under the name of the Bangalore process.

Composting processes in which the principal objective was to dispose of refuse rather than to produce a humus were begun in the early 1920's. These processes, several of which have been patented, were aimed at rapid production of compost, mechanized handling of materials, and less objectionable methods.

The most important of the early patented processes was developed by Dr. Giovanni Beccari of Florence, Italy, in 1922. It combined an initial anaerobic fermentation with a final stage in which decomposition proceeds under partially aerobic conditions. A modification of the Beccari process, known as the Verdier process, provided for the recirculation of gases or drainage liquors. A further modification of the process was made in 1931 by Jean Bordas, who sought to eliminate the anaerobic stage.

The first full-scale composting plant in Europe and at the time the largest in the world was begun in the Netherlands in 1932 by a non-profit utility company formed by the government for the disposal of city refuse. It used the van Mannen process, a modification of the Indore process, in which refuse is composted in large windrows.

The Dano biostabilizer system and the rasping system of windrow composting are the two most widely used processes in Europe. The Dano system consists of a single slowly revolving, horizontal cylinder that holds the material from one to five days. Material is finished by windrowing, with or without turning, in two to four weeks. The rasping system involves grinding the refuse before the composting process is started and turning the compost piles during a three- to six-week period (instead of sprinkling the piles and composting it for four to eight months, as had been done previously).

By early 1960 there were 25 Dano biostabilizer plants and 12 rasping system plants in use or under construction in Europe, most of them built in the 1950's. These systems provide for more rapid composting

Fig. 118. Typical 25-ton-a-day Dano composting plant in Europe. Refuse is kept in digester five days followed by two to four weeks of windrowing in the open.

than former methods because aerobic decomposition is more closely maintained during the process. Furthermore, special equipment for composting refuse was developed. (In the United States attempts have been made to adapt equipment used in other processes for refuse composting.)

There are also a number of single installations of cell-type or enclosed composting involving the intermittent disturbance principle: the John Thompson system plant at Jersey, Channel Islands, Great Britain, and one in Bangkok, Thailand; the Dumfriesshire system plant at Kirkconnel, Scotland; the Tollemache system plant at Mabelreign, Southern Rhodesia, South Africa; and the Calais system plant at Calais, France. The same principle has been used in plants in the United States. These systems are not as efficient as those providing continuous mixing, aeration, and particle size reduction but they may be somewhat more efficient than windrow composting.

Composting processes were not developed in the United States at the same time they were in India and western Europe. Before 1950 only a few municipal refuse disposal officials gave attention to advocates of composting. Without a process of proven worth or even a basic understanding of the science of composting the advocates of composting could at best offer only enthusiasm. Most often they tried to sell an untried process or a special inoculum. Most claimed that their process would be profitable. However, little came of such efforts because no well tested process was offered. Besides, city officials in the United States consider disposal the problem—not making a profit—and they are reluctant to become involved in uncertain composting ventures. Nevertheless, a few attempts were made to import European methods. The Beccari process and its modifications, tried for a short time in Scarsdale, New York, in the late 1920's did not prove adaptable to municipal composting of refuse on a large scale and under conditions peculiar to the United States, although there were a number of plants in Europe by that time. Furthermore, garbage and other putrescible components of refuse in United States cities, together with environmental problems, also made impractical any simple adaptations of the procedures used so successfully in the van Mannen system.

To suit United States conditions it was thought desirable that composting be done mechanically in completely enclosed structures. A multiple-deck digester of the silo type was patented in 1939. Aeration involved a combination of rotary plows and air flues, the material moving downward from deck to deck on a continuous flow basis. Some work was done in a pilot plant but mechanical weaknesses were encountered. Furthermore, advocates of the process claimed that it was dependent upon the use of a secret and expensive inoculum.

In 1949 a process patented in the United States was introduced in which shredded organic matter was put into a fully enclosed, semimechanized digester intended to produce compost in 28 days under aerobic conditions by intermittently dropping the material from one level to another, which permitted contact with the bases of decomposition—a salient feature of the process. Reportedly, each of four small experimental plants had technical problems, including difficulty in keeping the material aerobic, and was closed.

The University of California in 1951 began a two-year study of the principles of aerobic composting, which terminated in a pilot demonstration carried out in cooperation with the City of Berkeley. The study went into the feasibility of composting refuse using open windrows. The process requires sorting and shredding the refuse, putting it in windrows five to six feet high, and turning the material about three times in a 15- to 21-day composting period.

While the University of California was making its study, the Compost Corporation of America began a pilot plant operation in Oakland, California. During the year it was in operation, many of the problems of shredding refuse and handling compost were uncovered, the lack of justification for adding inoculum was demonstrated, and the practicality of the windrow method as recommended by the university was verified for California conditions. The pilot project led to the design of a workable plant but local problems prevented its construction.

Between 1953 and 1956 a team of researchers at Michigan State University conducted extensive laboratory and field experiments on the composting of municipal wastes. The effects of temperature, pH, moisture, and other variables of the composting process were studied and solutions to problems were investigated by actually composting four to

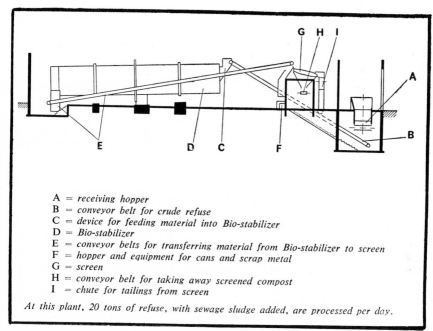

A = receiving hopper
B = conveyor belt for crude refuse
C = device for feeding material into Bio-stabilizer
D = Bio-stabilizer
E = conveyor belts for transferring material from Bio-stabilizer to screen
F = hopper and equipment for cans and scrap metal
G = screen
H = conveyor belt for taking away screened compost
I = chute for tailings from screen

At this plant, 20 tons of refuse, with sewage sludge added, are processed per day.

Fig. 119. Diagram showing composting process in a 25-ton-a-day Dano plant.

five tons of garbage a day from the City of East Lansing. An eight-deck silo type digester was operated for two years after which a three-deck horizontal mechanical digester was developed. Windrowing of ground garbage was aided by a front-end loader and a shredder. Experiments using forced air, with or without turning, in barrel and bin-size units led to the development of processes described as "modified windrow," "bin," and "area" composting. Some of the details are reported in other parts of this chapter.

The United States Public Health Service initiated two research projects on composting in 1953—one in Savannah, Georgia, and the other in Chandler, Arizona, near Phoenix. Both have contributed substantially to the basic knowledge of composting. The Phoenix studies included the development, construction, and operation of a 70-ton-a-week experimental plant at Chandler in which aeration, bin, and windrow composting was used. The operation of this plant produced substantial information on the cost of refuse grinding and other material handling aspects of composting. The Savannah project has made excellent contributions through its basic laboratory scale research. An additional demonstration project is in operation at Johnson City, Tennessee, and continues to contribute useful information on the operation.

In 1956 a widely advertised composting plant with a capacity of about 100 tons a day began operation at McKeesport, Pennsylvania. Apparently efficient grinding and mechanical handling devices were used in the plant, but after a year's operation the plant was closed, reportedly because of technical problems and economic difficulties.

Among the other U.S. plants which are no longer operating, a Dano plant was built near Sacramento, California, in 1957 to treat 40 tons of refuse a day with a 48-hour retention period. By 1959, the plant was processing 80 tons a day with a 24-hour retention period. The "green" compost produced required further maturing by windrowing or removal for direct curing on the farm.

A 40-ton-a-day mechanical digestion plant constructed by the Naturizer Corporation in Norman, Oklahoma, in early 1959 employed primary and secondary grinding and large digesters in which the ground material is moved by pan-type conveyers through six decks; the plant is presently not operating. This same principle was used on a smaller scale for composting stockyard and manure and ground leaves in Toronto in 1954 and 1955. The original Naturizer design was abandoned in favor of horizontal rotating agitators, reported to produce more efficient and higher rates of digestion. It is reported that a local adaptation of this later design proved biologically successful but mechanically deficient in a 20-ton-a-day plant built in Kobe, Japan, in 1956.

Some More Recent Developments. An interesting new modern plant has been constructed at Leicester, England, for handling refuse and sewage sludge, involving a combination of salvaging, composting, and incineration (described in detail in the Spring (1965) issue of *Compost Science*, Vol. 6, No. 1). Experience in Italy is outlined in a paper by Prof. E. de Fraja Frangipane (*Proceedings-Trento Congress*, 1965).

Composting developments in the United States are discussed at some length in a joint paper [1] by John S. Wiley (USPHS) and O. W. Kochtitzky (TVA) in a joint research venture by these agencies to determine the intrinsic and potential market values of compost as well as some of the hygienic safety factors involved in the process and the product. A historical record (since 1950) of composting plant experience in the United States was included (see Table 35).

THE VALUE OF COMPOST

Reliable data are available to prove that many farmers in the United States have worked the soil to such an extent that organic matter in it is depleted and productivity of the soil is greatly reduced. In some areas productivity has been cut by as much as 50 per cent. Sometimes a farmer has added chemical fertilizers to the soil, but soil scientists point out that this may ultimately do more damage than good. They say that the solution is to replace the organic matter in the soil. There are two major ways that this can be done: (1) plant green crops and plow them under, and (2) add compost or animal manure in one form or another. The farmer, however, must weigh the costs of purchasing and spreading compost against the costs of raising a crop and plowing it under. He

---

[1] John S. Wiley and O. W. Kochtitzky, "Composting Developments in the United States," *Compost Science* (Summer, 1965), pp. 5-9.

TABLE 35

MUNICIPAL SOLID WASTE COMPOSTING PLANTS IN THE UNITED STATES

Location	Company	Process	Capacity Ton/Day	Began Operation	1965 Status
Altoona, Pennsylvania	Altoona FAM, Inc., Fairfield Engg. Co.	Fairfield-Hardy	45	1951 1963[1]	Operating
Largo, Florida	Peninsular Organics, Inc., National Composters Co.	Peninsular Organics	50	1963	Operating
Norman, Oklahoma	International Disposal Corp.	Naturizer	35	1959	Closed 1964
Chandler, Arizona	Arizona Biochemical Co.	Dano	300[2]	1963	Closed 1963[3]
Sacramento Co., Calif.	Dano of America, Inc.	Dano	40	1956	Closed 1963
San Fernando, Calif.	International Disposal Corp.	Naturizer	70	1963[4]	Closed 1964
Springfield, Mass.	Springfield Organic Fertilizer Co.	Frazer-Eweson	20	1954[5]	Closed 1962
Williamston, Mich.	City of Williamston	Riker	4	1955	Closed 1962
Wilmington, Ohio	Good Riddance, Inc.	Windrow	20	1963	Closed

[1] Date of initial operation of the original Hardy plant is unknown; plant rebuilt in 1963.
[2] According to European Dano practice, the plant capacity is about 175 T/day.
[3] Reported to be back in limited operation, March 1965.
[4] Date of initial operation is unknown; continuous operation began in July 1963.
[5] Partially burned in 1958; rebuilt in 1961.

Note: Since the preparation of this table by John S. Wiley and others, composting plants have been constructed at St. Petersburg and Gainsville, Florida; Mobile, Alabama; Houston, Texas; and San Juan, Puerto Rico. The Largo and St. Petersburg, Florida plants have been closed.

probably spends from $20 to $25 a ton for the organic matter produced by raising and plowing under a cover crop—often called "green manure."

The value of organic matter can also be evaluated by actually adding it to crops and determining the increase in yield. Although the increase in yield is frequently the only factor evaluated, there is also reported to be a marked increase in the quality of the crops—in protein, vitamin, and mineral content.

Addition of organic matter to the soil is reported to have several benefits:

1. It markedly improves the physical properties of the soil; makes it easier to till, more porous, and easier to keep aerated. It also helps the soil absorb precipitation. Organic matter holds water like a sponge (it retains up to 300 per cent moisture by weight) so that in periods of drought a field that contains a large amount of organic matter may be productive when soil without it is valueless. Organic matter also supports earth worms, which in turn keep the soil porous and improve aeration. The worm holes increase percolation during heavy rains, which reduces runoff and soil erosion.

2. According to the results of tests run in California, organic matter in soil reduces the amount of chemical fertilizer required by as much as 40 per cent. This is largely due to the mechanics of leaching or the prevention of leaching. If organic matter is present in the soil, water does not wash away chemical fertilizers as it does in barren soils.

3. Experiments by soil scientists indicate that the presence of organic matter is a prerequisite to healthy biological activity of the soil, and healthy biological activity stimulates plant growth, especially the roots. Roots have been known to grow eight times as fast in soil in which there is a lot of organic matter as it does in soil in which there is little or no organic matter.

4. Healthy biological activity is also reportedly important in the breakdown of insoluble mineral compounds such as the phosphates, which are required for plant growth.

5. Soluble nitrogen used as a fertilizer can be easily leached away. In the presence of organic matter and biological activity, however, a portion of this soluble nitrogen is converted into organic nitrogen of the microorganisms' bodies. As the microorganisms die, the nitrogen again becomes available to the plant roots. In the interim, it is less likely to be lost by leaching or to the atmosphere as ammonia.

6. The same phenomenon occurs with phosphorus. Tests show that about 95 per cent of soluble phosphorus can be converted into organic bodies and living protoplasm and released slowly to the plant as an organic complex, thus reducing loss by leaching.

ADVANTAGES AND DISADVANTAGES

It is difficult to tell exactly what the advantages and disadvantages are of a disposal method that has considerable potential but has not been adequately used and proven on an operational basis in the United States. There apparently are, however, advantages and disadvantages, if experiences with recently operated plants in Europe and in the United States are evaluated.

Advantages

1. Composting is the only presently operational technology which provides for the recycling of organic residuals.
2. Composting can be used to dispose of many industrial wastes such as those from meat packing plants, paper mills, saw mills, tanneries, stockyards, and canneries; also dewatered sewage solids, especially if they are mixed with ground refuse; and cans and bottles that have no salvage value can be ground and disposed of with the remaining refuse. When large grinders are used (plants of more than 100 tons a day) even large, bulky objects may be handled. A municipal refuse composting plant can dispose of all these wastes.
3. Normally composting plants offer favorable conditions for salvage of rags, glass, cardboard, paper, cans, and metals.
4. A well located refuse composting plant may reduce the cost of hauling refuse to the point of disposal.
5. Flexibility of operation permits a 100 to 200 per cent overload in design capacity for several days by increasing the time the receiving bins and grinders operate.
6. Weather does not affect an enclosed composting plant, although heavy rain adversely affects most kinds of outdoor composting.

Disadvantages

1. Capital and operating costs apparently are relatively high.
2. Whether the end product can be marketed is not yet proven and seasonal use of the end product may require special marketing procedures or outdoor storage.
3. Trained personnel to operate composting plants are not readily available.
4. Refuse that damages grinders must be removed and disposed of separately—tires, pipes, heavy stones, mattresses, for instance.
5. If cans and bottles have no local salvage value they must either be removed and disposed of separately or ground with the organic matter, thus somewhat reducing the quality of the finished compost.
6. Site procurement for a composting plant is difficult because any type of refuse disposal facility is considered a nuisance in most neighborhoods.

FUNDAMENTALS OF COMPOSTING

Modern composting is an aerobic, thermophilic, biochemical process that with the assistance of mechanical equipment and controls is faster and more effective than older, relatively slow, mesophilic and anaerobic processes. The stabilization of organic matter in a modern composting process is accomplished by bacteria and other microorganisms that use large volumes of oxygen and produce considerable quantities of heat.

Temperatures of 160° to 170° F., which can destroy disease producing organisms, are maintained relatively easily.

The following conditions have been found to be desirable for efficient aerobic composting:

1. Raw materials should have a carbon to nitrogen ratio of 50 to 1 or less. They should have no serious deficiency of essential food elements and should be within a normal pH range (5.5 to 8).
2. Material should be mixed and ground (fine grind for mechanical composting, medium to coarse grind for windrow or area composting).
3. Moisture should be controlled to 50 to 60 per cent throughout the process.
4. Air should be thoroughly dispersed throughout the composting material with an excess of oxygen remaining.
5. Seed compost should be recycled in the amount of about 1 to 10 per cent by weight.

Fig. 120. A view of the tower of the composting plant at Jersey, Channel Islands, Great Britain. Aerobic fermentation takes a week in the tower, the refuse being dropped one floor a day from the six self-emptying floors; windrowing takes four to six weeks.

If high-rate composting is used, the following additional conditions have been found desirable:

1. Constant slow stirring or intermittent stirring every 5 to 10 minutes or a combination of forced air and less frequent stirring.
2. Temperatures should be controlled throughout the process.
3. The pH should be controlled to prevent nitrogen loss.
4. Digestion should be a continuous flow process in three or four stages, including recycling of seed and thorough mixing for each

stage. The last stage may combine slower digestion with natural drying from the heat.

High-rate composting can be done in two to five days using selected materials but requires a properly engineered mechanical digester. Refuse can be composted without a digester but may take 10 to 15 days. It is not necessary to compost all organic matter—only the putrescible material that attracts rodents and insects or creates odors. The remaining resistant material can be broken down in the soil where its further decomposition stimulates soil bacteria and plant growth.

The major objectives in composting are:

1. To stabilize putrescible organic matter.
2. To kill all pathogens and weed seeds.
3. To conserve the nitrogen, phosphorus, potash, and resistant organic matter found in the raw material.
4. To produce a uniform, relatively dry end product, free from objectionable and harmful objects.
5. To conduct the process in a sanitary manner, free from insects, rodents, and odors, and an inexpensively and in as dependable a manner as possible.

Types of Biological Decomposition

There are two general types of biological decomposition: aerobic and anaerobic.

Aerobic (with oxygen) decomposition is efficient and rapid, resulting in the oxidation of organic matter primarily to minerals, humus, carbon dioxide, and water. The aerobic process, properly carried out, does not produce foul odors; it is the one employed in most modern scientific composting.

Anaerobic (without oxygen) decomposition is slower and less efficient, resulting in the reduction of organic matter primarily to minerals, humus, methane, and carbon dioxide. This process is similar to the digestion of sludge in sewage treatment, and if it is not properly controlled causes offensive odors by release of sulfides and mercaptans.

There are also two other general classifications of biological decomposition: thermophilic and mesophilic. Thermophilic (high-temperature) decomposition occurs at well above body temperatures and is the result of the action of "heat-loving" microorganisms—bacteria, actinomycetes, and fungi. The energy produced by aerobic composting is sufficient to heat the mass to the high temperatures shown in Table 36 if conditions are correct for it. Mesophilic (moderate-temperature) decomposition occurs widely in nature at lower temperatures. Heat is also liberated by aerobic or oxidative decomposition in the mesophilic range. The most rapid composting is accomplished by aerobic, thermophilic microorganisms.

Raw Materials

The primary purpose of a municipal refuse composting plant is to

TABLE 36

MINIMUM, OPTIMUM, AND MAXIMUM TEMPERATURE RANGES
FOR THERMOPHILIC AND MESOPHILIC BACTERIA

Bacteria	Minimum	Optimum	Maximum
Thermophilic	25-45°C.	50-55°C.	85°C.
	77-113°F.	122-131°F.	185°F.
Mesophilic	15-25°C.	25-40°C.	43°C.
	59-77°F.	77-104°F.	109°F.

treat solid wastes. Therefore, if refuse is collected together, provision must be made at the plant to dispose of components that cannot be composted, such as metals, tires, and glass. The great variety of refuse materials that has been composted indicates that the raw materials are not greatly restricted. For example, materials with carbon to nitrogen ratios (C/N) varying from 20 to 78 were successfully composted at the University of California. While it is desirable to keep the C/N range in raw materials from 30 to 40, it is not essential. Somewhat longer composting time is required with a high C/N than a low one. The desired end C/N is about 26 to 31. Mixed refuse (garbage and rubbish) composts better than separate garbage or rubbish. Garbage often is too wet; rubbish has too high a C/N. The optimum mixture for composting is a well blended mixture of refuse and partially dewatered raw sewage solids plus suitable organic industrial wastes.

A single type of industrial or agricultural waste may not be sufficiently balanced to compost well alone; if so, it may be necessary to add other wastes. If carbonaceous matter is required, sawdust, paper, or straw may be added. High nitrogenous wastes include fish scraps, fowl manures, and sewage sludge. It should be unnecessary, except in extreme cases, to buy supplemental materials.

Particle Size

Refuse as it is collected in a city is much too coarse and irregular for efficient composting and should be ground at least once, if not twice. Grinding accomplishes several things:

1. It vastly increases the surface area available for the microorganisms to attack.
2. It mixes the refuse into a more uniform mass.
3. It breaks down the cell structure, releases fluids, and in general makes the material more susceptible to decomposition.

Grinding does, however, reduce the permeability of the mass. The finer the grind the more difficult it is to aerate. How fine the material should be ground depends on what composting process is used. Fine grinding is recommended for mechanical composting with constant or intermittent stirring. A medium grind is recommended if forced air is

Fig. 121. Earp-Thomas composting plant in Verona, Italy, has a capacity of 50 tons a day.

used with either windrow or bin-type composting. Turning and shredding during the course of digestion further reduces the particle size. Low permeability may, under the right conditions, be overcome by positive air pressure from beneath. Coarse grinding is recommended for windrow or bin composting if forced air is not used and if natural ventilation or turning alone is used to aerate. Even with coarse grinding, natural diffusion of oxygen into windrows is far slower than the organisms demand it and the rate of decomposition is slowed.

Moisture and Liquid Contents

Experiments at the University of California indicate optimum moisture for aerobic composting of coarsely ground refuse in windrows or open bins, using aeration by turning and natural ventilation only, to be 40 to 60 per cent (moisture content computed on a wet basis by oven drying). Similar experiments with mechanical composters and continuous aeration of refuse at the United States Public Health Service laboratory at Savannah, Georgia, indicate 55 to 69 per cent moisture as optimum. Yet 60 per cent was found to be too wet for wet garbage at a plant in San Diego and for wrapped garbage at Michigan State University. Thus it has been determined that other factors also affect the optimum moisture content: (1) the rate of digestion is affected by the adequacy of the air supply by natural ventilation, which in turn is adversely affected by finely ground materials; (2) aeration is hindered by filling of voids with all liquids, not just water; (3) ash or mineral matter does not absorb water as well as organic matter; (4) lipids (fats and oils) are liquid at normal composting temperatures and are present in substantial quantities in garbage; (5) fine grinding releases more liquids than coarse grinding, further restricting air flow through the material. A formula for liquid content has been proposed that should be more representative of the materials composted and should narrow the ranges reported for liquid content by workers with different materials and techniques. On the basis of this formula the estimated "effective liquid contents" of raw materials used at Savannah and Michigan State University ranged from only 68 to 70 per cent. The formula (all values on a wet basis) is:

$$\text{Effective \% liquid} = \frac{100\ (\%\ \text{moisture} + \%\ \text{lipids})}{(100\ -\ \%\ \text{ash})}$$

Mechanical digestion with continuous or intermittent mixing to assist in aeration can efficiently compost materials with a higher liquid content than windrow or bin composting employing forced air for aeration. Windrows relying on natural ventilation or periodic turning for aeration should have the lowest effective liquid content.

Low moisture retards or stops microbial action, but whereas some authorities have specified the lower limit for composting to be 40 per cent moisture, activity in composting has been observed in a windrow (temperature over 154° F.) at a moisture content as low as 24.5 per cent. For compost that is to be shipped in unlined bags, it is desirable to reduce moisture to about 10 per cent. If polyethylene lined bags are used, moisture content can be 20 per cent without causing deterioration. At these low moisture contents nearly all bacterial action is arrested, thus cutting down on odors and the dangers of heating, spontaneous combustion, and rotting bags.

Aeration

Aerobic organisms require oxygen just as they require moisture and food. In composting, oxygen is usually supplied by atmospheric air, by forced aeration with a blower or fan, by stirring, or by a combination of forced air and stirring. Natural aeration is dependent primarily upon convection and diffusion and is undependable and less efficient. In theory, the carbohydrates are decomposed by oxidation in accordance with the following hypothetical formula:

$$2C_{13}H_{20}O_7 + 29O_2 \rightarrow 26CO_2 + 20H_2O + \text{heat}$$

There are many intermediate steps and the formula given above includes only lost volatile solids and excludes all elements except carbon, hydrogen, and oxygen. However, it indicates a need for considerable oxygen from an outside source and also the production of appreciable amounts of carbon dioxide, water, and heat. In mechanical units with continuous aeration, the amount of air found to be desirable was 10 to 30 cubic feet per day per pound of volatile solids (in the initial charge). This provided more than twice the amount of oxygen needed for the oxidation of the organic matter but was desirable because lower rates resulted in prolonged composting and higher rates resulted in rapid cooling and drying of the refuse. The maximum rate of oxygen utilization measured at Michigan State University was 0.0244 parts of oxygen a minute per 100 parts of dry weight. On the basis of 50 per cent of the oxygen remaining in the air that was used, 37 cubic feet of air per day per pound of total dry solids, or about 44 cubic feet of air per day per pound of volatile solids, would be required.

Windrow composting also requires oxygen but the amount required or used is difficult to measure. However, use of an oxygen analyzer with sampling probe can measure the oxygen present at various depths within a windrow, pile, or bin. Normal atmospheric air contains about 21 per cent oxygen by volume; thus, a value of 3 per cent oxygen indicates that approximately one-seventh of the oxygen in normal air is present in the atmosphere within the compost windrow. The studies made in Chandler, Arizona, by the United States Public Health Service in which this technique for oxygen determination was used, show that for coarse grind, low moisture, natural ventilation conditions and at the one-foot depth, oxygen was lowest about one day after turning but recovered to 5 to 7 per cent. However, at the two-foot depth the oxygen value was consistently below 2 per cent and usually below 0.9 per cent. It was

Fig. 122. *Left, composting plant in Bangkok, Thailand (330-ton-a-day capacity), in which refuse is composted one day on each of the six floors and is cured for 30 days in a warehouse; right, receiving bins.*

determined that regrinding usually restored oxygen to values of 14 to 19 per cent for the first 30 minutes or so; values as low as 1.2 to 2.7 per cent were reached in from 3 to 5 hours after regrinding. This gives an indication of the rapidity of the bacterial action and shows why mechanical composting with positive aeration or use of forced air may be more rapid than other methods.

There is a definite relationship between oxygen used, carbon dioxide produced, and water produced and evaporated in aerobic composting; and all three are related to the temperature of the compost. As the temperature increases, so do the other three values—up to a point. The ratio of volume of CO_2 to volume of O_2, called the respiratory quotient, has varied from about 0.85 to 0.95 in the Savannah composting runs.

Temperature

Experiments indicate that the initial or acid stages of decomposition where simple carbohydrates such as sugars and starches break down has an optimum temperature of about 95° F. Artificial heating of the compost above this temperature is inhibitive to rapid digestion. This stage may last from a half to one day in high-rate mechanical composting. With slower windrow decomposition, digestion may last from two to seven days, depending on the degree of control of oxygen, moisture, and temperature.

It is apparent that optimum temperatures for the middle and latter stages of decomposition where protein and other nitrogenous materials break down are about 140° to 150° F. It is only after temperatures go down and the active composting process is complete that actino- mycetes and fungi increase in numbers and play an active role in breaking down the more complex carbohydrates such as cellulose.

Some have advocated heating to speed up the initial phases of com- posting, although tests in Savannah and at Michigan State University indicate this may be detrimental.

Temperatures should be sufficiently high for a long enough time to accomplish three objectives: (1) kill pathogenic organisms, (2) destroy weed and vegetable seeds, and (3) destroy fly eggs and larvae. Most weed seeds and fly eggs and larvae are killed at around 120° F. in a few days and under moist conditions, but 140° F. has been recommended to be safe. Prolonged high temperatures of 158° to 167° F. may inhibit some of the beneficial microbial action and increase nitrogen loss due to vapor- ization of ammonia. The latter occurs mainly at the most alkaline re- actions (pH 8.5 to 9) and at the lower C/N values (30 or less).

There should be little difficulty in maintaining a temperature of 140° F. in all of the composting mass for several hours—even days—in a mechanical unit. But in windrows the outer portions (and if there is no forced air, the bottom and center portions) are usually cooler than the inner portions—the bulk of the material. To be reasonably certain that a maximum portion of the material is subjected to pasteurizing tempera- tures, several mixings may be necessary. Pasteurizing of the entire mass is aided by using a one- to two-inch covering blanket of finished com- post to hold the heat in the pile. One or two temperature cycles of 140° F. or more may not be sufficient to kill all pathogens if the material is not completely turned under during the process or if it is not properly insulated.

Acidity and Alkalinity

The relative intensity of the acidity or alkalinity of a material as measured by pH is a quick and convenient—although indirect—yardstick for measuring digestion. Because pH is an indirect yardstick, it is reliable for any material only after its change pattern has been established for the particular material and the digestion process employed. Raw refuse or raw garbage generally has a pH value of 6 to 7, approaching neutrality (7) when it is fresh, and slight acidity (5 to 6) when it is a day or so old. Ashes in refuse may cause a higher initial pH. Some decomposition starts in the refuse or garbage while it is in the home storage container. Initial aerobic decomposition results in a drop of pH to a range of 4.5 to 5.5 as the acid phase occurs. The pH generally rises after one to four days and is usually followed closely by a rise in temperatures into the thermophilic range. By the time the peak temperature is reached the reaction generally is alkaline (pH 8 to 9). Then the longer the composting process is continued (the rate is much reduced), the nearer the reaction approaches a pH of 7.

It is possible to adjust initial acid conditions with lime but little or no real advantage is to be gained by doing so. Lowering of final pH by the addition of sulfur dust can lessen to some degree the loss of ammonia but the advisability of this practice is also questionable without further study.

Microorganisms

Such wastes as rubbish, garbage, sewage sludge, manure, and mixed vegetable wastes normally contain many types of bacteria, actinomycetes, and fungi. Research indicates that no pure culture of organisms can compare with a mixed culture in the aerobic composting of manures and other organic matter. Many types are believed necessary for composting, and the required microorganisms rapidly multiply if there is the proper environment for them. Temperature, moisture, aeration, pH, and type of food supply must be within a suitable range to provide the best environment for growth. Studies indicate that special "starters" or "inoculants" are unnecessary—if conditions are not right, added organisms will not grow and multiply; if they are right, the organisms already present will grow and multiply. Some experiments have shown that recycling of relatively small amounts of seed (1 to 10 per cent) of actively composting material appreciably shortens lag periods required for large numbers of the right organisms to develop for each stage.

Some materials are difficult to decompose aerobically and require considerable time. Lignins and cellulose are resistant materials and are usually only attacked after the more readily decomposable materials have been used up (sugars, starches, lipids, proteins). Cellulose in the form of paper is a highly resistant material. The actinomycetes and fungi will completely decompose the paper content of refuse in time, however. Complete decomposition of resistant materials such as lignins and cellulose is not necessarily desirable because they are of value to the soil and plant life.

The many microorganisms involved in composting and the role of each are complex, but an extensive knowledge of their characteristics is not necessary for a compost plant operator.

Changes During Composting

Changes in refuse material that may occur during the mechanical composting process are given in Table 37.

In the Savannah research work it was found that sugars usually disappeared by the third day and 75 per cent or more of the starches and lipids were decomposed by the end of the run (average duration was

TABLE 37

SUMMARY OF ANALYSES AND WEIGHT CHANGES IN LABORATORY
COMPOSTING OF REFUSE AT SAVANNAH, GEORGIA, 1958

(Average values based on 13 runs with 32 composting units;
batch time averaged 8.8 days)

Constituent	Per Cent of Dry Wt.		Signif. Diff. (x at 95%)	Weight (lbs.)		Signif. Diff. (x at 95%)	Per Cent Change in Weight
	Raw Refuse*	Com-post		Initial	Final		
Total wet wt.	100.0^Y	100.0^Y		40.47	27.31	Yes(−)	−32.5
Moisture	57.1^Y	56.8^Y	No	24.58	15.85	Yes(−)	−35.5
Total solids (dry wt.)	100.0	100.0		15.89	11.46	Yes(−)	−27.9
Ash (dry wt.-volatile solids)	7.8	12.4	Yes(+)	1.25	1.43	Yes(+)	+14.4
Volatile solids	92.2	87.6	Yes(−)	14.64	10.03	Yes(−)	−31.5
1. Lipids (ether soluble material)	10.1	3.3	Yes(−)	1.62	0.38	Yes(−)	−76.7
2. Crude fiber	35.9	**45.8**	Yes(+)	5.66	5.26	Yes(−)	− 7.0
3. Total sugar	4.9	0.0077^Z	Yes(−)	0.80	0.0008	Yes(−)	−99.9
4. Starch	8.1	1.4	Yes(−)	1.32	0.15	Yes(−)	−88.4
5. Protein (6.25N)	8.2	11.0	Yes(+)	1.29	1.26	No	− 2.7
6. Sum: (1)-(5)	67.2	61.5	Yes(−)	10.69	7.05	Yes(−)	−34.1
7. Volatile solids−(6) (undetermined)	25.0	26.1	No	3.95	2.98	Yes(−)	−24.6
Nitrogen (N)	1.30	1.76	Yes(+)	0.207	0.202	No	− 2.7
Carbon (C)	50.0	47.7	Yes(−)	7.96	5.47	Yes(−)	−31.3
Ratio: C/N	38	27	Yes(−)	38	27	Yes(−)	

*As composted, after sorting and grinding.

x—Significant difference at 95 per cent level (t-test); — indicates decrease; + indicates increase.

Y—Per cent of wet (total) weight.

z—Only one value (0.2%) was above minimum limit of analysis.

8.8 days). Total Kjeldahl nitrogen (excludes nitrite and nitrate-nitrogen, believed to be relatively low) increased percentagewise but showed no significant change on a total weight basis. Carbon was drastically reduced, whereas there was only a 7 per cent loss in weight of crude fiber— probably mostly paper. Of the 25 per cent undetermined portion in the raw material and the 26 per cent in the final compost, the weight reduction of these materials was also significant—about equal to the over-all weight reduction or loss. As a whole, the dry weights and volatile solids were decreased an average of 27.9 per cent and 31.5 per cent respectively. The relation of total bacterial count to composting activity as indicated by the index of oxygen uptake in the Michigan State University experiments are given in Figure 123.

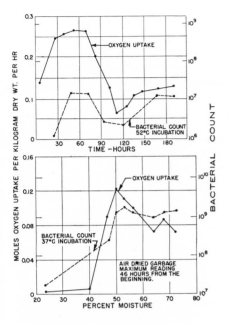

Fig. 123. Typical relationships obtained between oxygen uptake and bacterial count in laboratory digesters at Michigan State University.

Concentration of Volatile Acids

In the aerobic composting process, as in the anaerobic digestion process, the excess concentration of volatile acids can be a serious problem, causing severe inhibition or complete breakdown of the process. In the anaerobic digestion of sewage sludge a slowdown occurs at about 3,000 parts per million (0.2 per cent) volatile acids and a complete stoppage occurs before a concentration of 5,000 ppm (0.5 per cent) is reached. Fortunately, the composting process appears to be much less sensitive to volatile acids, and concentrations of 10,000 ppm (1 per cent) do not seem to cause any serious inhibition.

It might also be assumed that composting is probably incomplete as long as a volatile acid concentration of 4,000 to 5,000 ppm persists.

Public Health Aspects

Pathogenic organisms and their destruction have already been mentioned. Aerobic composting, with continuous or frequent mixing, should render the final compost free of all pathogens as a result of thermal kill alone. Aside from time-temperature, there is probably a biological antagonism (antibiosis) that may render the composting matter free of pathogens at considerably lower temperatures than required for pasteurization. This should not be relied on until more proof is offered, and thermal kill at 140° F. for one hour or more should be used. However, there has not yet been a conclusive study of the survival of pathogenic organisms under normal composting conditions, either in the windrow or enclosed processes.

Control of disease vectors, primarily rats and flies, is an important public health problem in waste disposal. The raw materials for composting usually attract flies and rodents and may offer excellent breeding places if not properly handled. In fact, the raw materials are likely to be infested with fly larvae when they reach the composting plant. Prompt handling of the wastes and plant cleanliness are required, therefore.

Pregrinding offers immediate control and is a preventive step in fly control. While the grinder may destroy some flies in the raw material, it also immediately aerates the mass and practically eliminates odors, even in septic sludge and decomposing garbage. Fly and rat breeding are controlled in mechanical composters. If the best conditions for composting are provided, there should be little trouble with flies and rodents in windrow composting, although several turnings within seven days are

Fig. 124. Modified Earp-Thomas digester used in composting studies at Michigan State University from 1952 to 1955; capacity is five tons a day.

necessary to prevent propagation of flies in cool parts of the windrow. Moisture is particularly important. Both too much and too little should be avoided: flies like wet material for egg-laying and development of larvae, and larvae need relatively dry material for pupation. If a pile or windrow is relatively wet (more than 60 per cent moisture) and is undisturbed for some days so that the outer portion dries to a depth of six or more inches, larvae may migrate from the moist interior to the dryer exterior and flies may hatch.

Windrow composting may be done on a hard, impervious surface, such as a concrete slab or asphalt pavement, which offers no soil or sand for the larvae to migrate to for pupation. A slab is also clean and prevents the compost from becoming excessively contaminated with soil. Soil contamination reduces the value of the compost and interferes with sampling and analytical projects. Chemical control of insects and rodents should be used, if required, in addition to—but not in place of —good operating and housekeeping procedures.

Practical Methods of Composting

There are a number of proprietary composting methods that have been promoted as being the "best" answer to the organic waste disposal problems of municipalities. Although each has merits, none has yet been offered that meets all of the objectives outlined in the previous section, although some meet most of them. The important point is that except for complete conservation of nitrogen, these objectives can be fulfilled by combining the knowledge and experience gained by the various groups that have worked with composting.

Although there are a number of ways to compost refuse, two appear

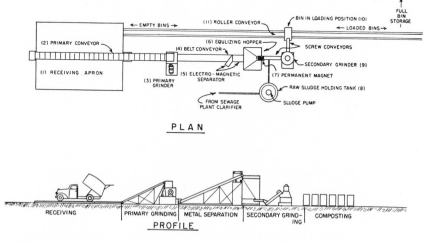

Fig. 125. Schematic layout of demonstration compost plant at Chandler, Arizona, operated by United States Public Health Service.

to be more efficient and economical under usual conditions in the United States. These are the mechanical digestion and the modified windrow or area composting methods.

Mechanical Methods

A number of proprietary mechanical digesters have been developed in recent years. Four are classed as continuous-flow-through-type. Three of these, the Dano, the T. A. Crane, and the Hardy digesters, are horizontal units, and the other, the Earp-Thomas digester, is a vertical unit.

The Dano digester, used to some extent in Europe, was described previously. A 50 to 80-ton modified Dano plant is in operation in Sacramento, California.

The T. A. Crane digester is a three-deck horizontal unit with separate agitating and aeration mechanisms for each level. Provision is made for reseeding on each deck and increased aeration by forced air and blowers. The Earp-Thomas digester is an eight-deck vertical cylinder. Material is agitated and aerated by plows on arms that are turned from a central vertical shaft. A modified 5-ton-a-day model using forced air was used for two years at Michigan State University for research. No full-scale digester—either the Crane or Earp-Thomas design—has been installed for municipal use in the United States, although a modified Crane digester is operating in Kobe, Japan, and Earp-Thomas digesters in Italy and Switzerland.

The Naturizer digester, although a continuous-flow unit, biologically is essentially of the batch-type. It is a six-deck structure with intermittent grinding between the third and fourth decks. Movement in the digester is produced by a slowly moving wooden pan-conveyer and forced air keeps the material aerobic. The shallow pan-conveyer, or receiving hopper, accommodates two trucks at once. A weighted sluice has been designed to control the flow onto a picking belt. The primary grinder consists of a rotating cylinder about 6 feet in diameter and 30 feet long, with several hundred curved swinging saw-toothed hammers, which break up the refuse when they hit it. The secondary grinder is essentially a conventional swing hammer mill. After processing for about three days and dropping several levels, the material is reground and digested another three days in a second three-level digester, followed by the final grinding.

In the late 1950's, a two-ton-per-day plant that composts a mixture of dewatered raw sewage solids, ground municipal garbage, and ground corn cobs was constructed at Williamston, Michigan. Digesters of a special design, with four decks each, are used. Although provision is made to blow air into each deck, difficulty was reported in keeping the material aerobic because the only agitation it receives is when it is dropped from one deck to the next. The Williamston plant is no longer operating.

Modified Windrowing or Area Methods

The process of sorting and shredding refuse and placing it in rows

five or six feet deep for composting is commonly termed "windrowing."
Windrowing, employing preseeding, forced air, and periodic turning
and shredding, and often referred to as "modified windrowing," is much

*Fig. 126. At the Metro Waste Houston plant, the incoming refuse
is conveyed to the sorting platform in background. Baled salvage
(at right in the above photo) awaits shipment to processors. At the
same plant (below), after extraction of all possible salvage, residue,
mostly putrescibles, is ground and conveyed to huge digesting
tanks where it is subject to rigidly controlled thermophilic bacterial action during its 6-day composting process.*

more efficient and requires about half the time of ordinary windrowing, which depends on natural ventilation and occasional turning for aeration. In modified windrowing, material may be piled in long windrows about 4 to 6 feet high and 8 to 12 feet wide. Controlled amounts of air may be blown up through the material in a number of ways.

The term "area composting" is often used interchangeably with "modified windrowing," but they should be distinguished from each other. Area composting requires a third of the space required for windrow composting for the same size plant. In "area composting" ground material is piled to a uniform depth in large, well defined areas. Controlled amounts of air are distributed through ducts under each area and pass up through porous, sandy soil or, preferably, through an especially designed porous floor. Seeding and turning may be employed; when both are used, the process reportedly takes only 10 to 14 days.

Self-propelled machines have been developed that will pick up, shred, and lay down all the material several times during the process. One of these machines was used on refuse that had not been ground before. Doing so greatly reduces the normal capacity of the machine, however. The same thing can be done but less efficiently with a front-end loader and a larger shredder or with some commercial self-propelled loaders.

Capital and Operating Costs

Since there are so few composting plants in operation in the United States that handle refuse for municipalities, capital and operating costs can only be estimated on the basis of experience in pilot operations. There is good reason to believe, however, that costs will approximate those of an incineration plant for a comparable amount of refuse disposal and that net costs will vary widely with the type of plant, degree of mechanization, and amount of revenue there is from the sale of the end product. Capital costs may be as low as $1,500 per ton of daily capacity and as high as $6,000; and the total of fixed and operating costs may vary from $8 to $30 a ton of refuse received at the plant. Revenue from the sale of the end product can reduce the costs.

Experience Outside United States

There are a number of refuse composting plants abroad, several of which were designed and built after considerable study and experimentation.

In Edinburgh, Scotland, separation-composting is done by the Dano process. Refuse is dumped into two 40-ton oscillating bottom hoppers, which in turn dump the refuse on a conveyer belt where it passes over two vibrating perforated steel screens. There ashes, dust, stone, and glass fall into storage hoppers and are carried to a dump. Refuse that does not go through the perforations of the screen is carried forward on rubber conveyer belts, ferrous metal and tin cans are removed by magnetic pulleys, and other salvageable material is taken off by hand. The remaining refuse drops off the end of the belt and without being ground goes into two Dano biostabilizers, which are horizontally rotating cylinders 80 feet long and 11½ feet in diameter. Sewage sludge is added to increase moisture and air is blown into the mass during the digestion period. During the five days of digestion, temperatures range between 120° and 130° F.; the material is reduced in size because the rotation causes friction on the material. After passing through the barrel stabilizers, the material passes through a rotary screen and the fine finish compost is conveyed to a storage bay either for immediate sale or for further maturing. Rejects from the screen are taken to a nearby dump; tin cans and rags are baled and sold for salvage; cullet is stored and sold to a nearby glass works.

At the separation and composting plant at Jersey, Channel Islands, Great Britain, refuse collected in the city is brought to the plant and dumped into a receiving hopper where it is removed by a steel pan-conveyer that carries it to a rotating screen. Material retained on the screen passes over a picking belt, across a magnetic separator, and through a rasping machine. Cinders from the rotating screen and rejects from the picking belt are taken to the dump. Fine dust is stored and remixed with the organic matter after grinding; slaughterhouse wastes and organic farm wastes are ground in a hammer mill and added at the same time; and sludge from a nearby sewage treatment plant is also added.

After thorough mixing the material is elevated by a large clam bucket to the top of a six-deck fermenting cell. Each deck of this specially designed Jersey digester is arranged to discharge the contents to the deck below. Ground material remains in each cell for one day so that retention in the tower is for one week. Afterwards it is matured in sheds for 60 to 70 days or more. The compost is sold to farmers and reportedly is in constant demand. Salvageable material is baled and sold.

In Kobe, Japan, there is a continuous-flow, three-stage horizontal mechanical digester plant in which composting is followed by two days of curing with forced air. The prototype 20-ton a day plant, constructed in late 1956, is adjacent to an old incinerator and night soil transfer station. Domestic refuse is put on a device that feeds it in uniform amounts onto a picking belt. After passing through a vertical swing hammer grinder, the refuse is conveyed to a mixer where about two-thirds of the refuse, by weight, is mixed with about one-third night soil containing 94 per cent moisture. The digester is similar in principle to the T. A. Crane digester. Material is kept aerobic by forced air and continuous slow stirring. After 48 hours in the digester, it is cured and dried for 48 hours in a porous bottom curing bin in which forced air is used. Rags and metal are salvaged. The end product reportedly is much in demand.

Economics of Composting Municipal Refuse. In a study of the economics of composting municipal refuse in Europe and Israel under the various systems in operation at the time, Dr. George J. Kupchik[2] of the American

---

[2] American Public Health Association, *Economics of Composting Municipal Refuse in Europe and Israel* (New York: The Association, 1965).

Public Health Association developed the information shown in Tables 38 and 39, and summarized his findings as follows:

1. Cost and income data were collected from 14 composting plants in Europe and Israel. These plants employed either the Dano Biostabilizer, the Dorr-Oliver Rasp, the ventilated cell, the Buhler-Dano combination, or the van Mannen process.
2. The average cost to process 1 ton of raw refuse was $4.55, of which capital service (amortization, interest, and rent) amounted to $1.76 and operating expense $2.79. Based on comparative cost indices, it is evident that construction and operating costs in the United States would be considerably higher.
3. The weight of compost produced was 46 per cent of raw refuse processed, and the average income from sales amount to $2.73 per ton of compost or 90 cents per ton of raw refuse. Additional income from salvage materials averaged about 20 cents per ton of raw refuse; only in Great Britain was salvage income substantial.
4. None of the plants visited was able to cover its capital service costs and operating expenses through income obtained from salvage and sale of compost. Deficits ranged from 32 cents to $5.32, with an average net cost of $3.38 per ton of refuse processed.
5. Substantial prices for compost were obtainable practically only in Israel. On the basis of the experiences encountered, it is most important that a determination be made that a continuing demand for compost exists before a compost plant is constructed.
6. Pulverization appears to hold promise as a pre-treatment to substantially reduce the volume and alter the character of refuse, prior to either landfill, incineration or composting operations.
7. Additional research and demonstration projects in refuse disposal methods are urgently needed.

PLANT DESIGN AND OPERATION

Experience with composting plants in the United States in which refuse is handled is limited to a few pilot and full-scale projects, but from those and on the basis of experience in Europe and the Far East it is possible to generalize on design and operational factors.

Site Selection

Most new composting plants are fully enclosed, but regardless of whether a plant is open or enclosed considerable care must be given to selection of the site. A 400-ton-a-day area digestion type plant using forced air requires about five acres (including a rail or truck loading area and some open space around it). A fully mechanical 400-ton-a-day plant requires about two acres exclusive of storage and maneuvering space for vehicles. An unenclosed windrow plant of 400-ton-a-day capacity requires 10 to 20 acres or more, depending on the design of the plant.

TABLE 38

COSTS OF PROCESSING RAW REFUSE UTILIZING DIFFERENT COMPOST SYSTEMS

($/U.S. Ton)

Type of System:	Dano	Dorr-Oliver	Ventilated Cells	Bubler-Dano	Van Maanen	Average (unwgtd)
Number of Plants:	5	3	3	2	1	14
Capital Cost:						
Amortization of building & equip.	.78	.68	1.08	2.01	.19	.95
Interest on building & equipment	.74	.55	.65	1.18	.12	.64
Interest on reserve fund	.08	.07	.05	.06	.03	.06
Rental of land	.04	.15	.08	.04	.21	.11
	1.64	1.45	1.86	3.29	.55	1.76
Operating Expense:						
Personnel	1.08	.83	1.92	1.74	.64	1.23
Utilities	.38	.29	.53	.50	.07	.36
Maintenance & Repairs	.33	.64	.25	.73	.46	.49
Disposal of Rejects	.30	.20	.20	.12	.05	.17
Miscellaneous	.36	.31	.37	.18	1.46	.54
	2.45	2.27	3.27	3.27	2.68	2.79
Total Cost	4.09	3.72	5.13	6.56	3.23	4.55
Income:						
Salvage	.42	.08	.17	.02	.13	.16
Sale of Compost	1.18	1.15	1.56	.70	.45	1.01
Total Income	1.60	1.23	1.73	.72	.58	1.17
Net Cost	2.49	2.49	3.40	5.84	2.65	3.38
Cost Indices:						
Interest Rate (%)	7.5	7.5	5.3	4.7	5.0	6.5
Typical Labor Cost/ann.	3000	2300	2300	4000	2500	2800
Date of Construction	1960	1963	1964	1964	1932	1958

TABLE 39

PRODUCTION AND SALE OF COMPOST

System	Plant #	Population Served	Raw Refuse Processed (US. tons)	Compost Produced (US. tons)	Compost Sold (US. tons)	Sales Income ($)	Income ($) per ton of Compost Sold	Income ($) per ton of Refuse Processed
Dano	1	700,000	99,000	66,000	33,000	24,000	0.73	0.24
	2	170,000	46,500	25,800	25,800	171,000	6.63	3.68
	3	80,000	18,800	13,200	9,900	9,900	1.00	0.53
	4	54,000	9,900	4,500	4,400	14,000	3.18	1.41
	5	210,000	32,400	5,300	4,300	2,700	0.63	0.08
		1,214,000	206,600	114,800 (56%)	77,400	221,600	2.86	1.07
Dorr-Oliver	6	700,000	199,000	74,200	37,400	204,000	5.45	1.03
	7	130,000	26,400	18,100	17,600	28,300	1.61	1.07
	8	75,000	17,700	13,200	13,000	24,000	1.85	1.36
		905,000	243,100	105,500 (43%)	68,000	256,300	3.77	1.05
Others	9	27,000	9,300	5,500	5,500	29,000	5.27	3.12
	10	90,000	16,800	10,100	0	0	0.00	0.00
	13	100,000	18,800	8,800	8,800	13,200	1.50	0.70
	14	800,000	162,000	55,000	57,200	72,000	1.26	0.44
		1,017,000	206,900	79,400 (38%)	71,500	114,200	1.60	0.55
TOTAL	(12)	3,136,000	656,600	299,700 (46%)	216,900 (33%)	592,100	2.73	0.90

Materials Handling

There is much to be learned about how to handle raw unground refuse from cities. Probably the best way is to use "live bottom" or vibrating storage bins into which the collection trucks can dump the refuse. Either a sugar cane type pan-conveyer or an oscillating pan may be used for the base of the storage bin. There should be a carefully designed device at the end of the storage bin that feeds the raw refuse evenly onto a picking belt and from there to a grinder. The major problem in the design and operation of these facilities is that the refuse arches, sticks, and goes onto the belt unevenly. Once the refuse has been ground it can be conveyed rapidly by belts or drags. Bucket conveyers should be used with caution with wet material because they have a tendency to stick and clog.

Grinding

Experience in grinding dry or moist refuse for composting is limited. Wet grinding into sewers or sewage treatment plants is better understood and perhaps more efficient but cannot be used in composting because it makes the refuse too moist. Grinding a small amount of refuse is more of a problem than grinding large quantities—several hundred tons a day. Extremely large and rugged grinders are available for big plants. They can grind 100-pound stones and 8-foot logs that are 6 inches in diameter, for instance. They are usually of the horizontal hammer mill type, are built with extra large throat openings and special throat feeding devices, and can grind 30 to 50 tons of refuse an hour. For mixed refuse in typical United States cities the most efficient shredding is believed to be done in two stages: through a primary, or coarse, grind followed by a secondary, or finer, grind. In small plants dual lines of equipment and primary and secondary grinding may not be economical. If the right grinder is used and most large objects are removed, single-stage grinding is efficient. Also the answer may come through the development of a two-stage vertical swing hammer grinder. Grinder wear and replacement or build-up of hammers represent an important part of the cost of composting.

Picking Belts and Salvage Separators

Picking belts, which should be just ahead of the grinder, are an essential part of a composting plant. They facilitate removal of objects harmful to grinders, such as rubber tires, mattresses, large stones, and metal, and they facilitate salvage operations. For example, cotton and wool rags and metal can easily be removed from a picking belt at this point. Tin cans can be removed with a magnetic separator when the refuse is between the primary and secondary grinders. Automatic shredders and bailers are available to salvage paper and cardboard.

Stirring, Aerating

Stirring is necessary only in certain mechanical digesters, but when it is, it is important that it be thorough because composting refuse has a tendency to stick to the sides and bottom of the digester. Aeration by forced air is highly recommended, whether mechanical digesters or modified windrowing, bin, or area composting are the methods used. Air pressure of two to six inches of water should be adequate in most instances but head losses should be properly computed to give even

Fig. 127. In the Amagasaki, Japan, plant (top), refuse is in digesters for two and one-half days, followed by one to two weeks of windrowing; belt conveyer and inlet of digester are shown below.

distribution. Maximum oxygen requirements, measured in the laboratory at Michigan State University, are 0.0244 grams of oxygen per minute per 100 grams of dry-weight material. If even 50 per cent of the air that is furnished is used it is equivalent to 37 cubic feet of air per pound of dry material per day. This rate of oxygen utilization is slightly in excess of that used in a well run activated sludge sewage treatment plant.

Seeding and Reseeding

For mechanical digestion seeding by recycling of actively composting material is readily done and is essential for efficiency. For best results, reseeding should be done at the beginning of each stage of digestion. For modified windrow or bin composting a single seeding or recycling of seed material at the beginning is adequate. A safe approach for a large plant is to manufacture seed material with mechanical digestion units, because they assure a high quality seed material.

Temperature Controls

The most practical way to control temperature in mechanical plants is through the control of the volume of the air used for aeration. Volume can be automatically controlled by thermostats or it can be done manually. In windrow composting it is done by turning the compost material. Composting is most efficient when the optimum temperature is maintained for each stage of digestion. The aeration system and the controls for the various parts of the plant should be taken into consideration when the plant is designed.

Fig. 128. Dorr Oliver composting plant in Tel Aviv, Israel.

Control of pH and Conservation of Nitrogen

Control of pH is unnecessary for most municipal wastes. Normal digestion follows from an acid pH of 5 to a final alkaline pH of 8 to 9. When composting material is high in nitrogen, it is possible that some nitrogen may be lost in the form of ammonia if the pH is allowed to rise too high. The possibility of acidifying the compost by the addition of powdered sulfur has been successful on a small scale. Although there is yet much to be learned about the conservation of nitrogen in the composting process, nitrogen losses are lessened by lowering the temperature and adding oxygen or blowing the exhaust gas through other composting materials while they are still in the acid stage of digestion.

Moisture Control and Final Drying

Since each type of refuse material has an optimum moisture content for rapid composting, it is well to control the moisture by adding wet or dry material during the process. The first obvious time is when the refuse is being ground or just afterward. If mechanical digesters are used, moisture is easily controlled throughout the digester and the wet material is stirred in evenly. With windrows, moisture may be added by special devices as the material is being turned. Wetting the top of the pile or injecting moisture into the pile is rather unsatisfactory, although it is probably better than not adding moisture at all. Toward the end of the composting process it is desirable to reduce the moisture content slowly and dry it as much as possible, using the heat produced in the final stages

Fig. 129. A modified T. A. Crane digester, with 25-ton-a-day capacity, in Kobe, Japan, was built next to an incinerator.

of composting to do it. The drying can be done reasonably well by blowing excess air through the material. A rather large amount of water is produced biologically through the composting process itself and it, as well as the original and added moisture, must be evaporated. One of the problems of composting out of doors is that during heavy rains it is impossible to prevent the piles from becoming too wet. Probably the best solution is to turn the pile as soon as possible after a heavy rain, thus distributing the moisture throughout the pile, which in turn aids in the loss of additional moisture through evaporation, especially during the turning process.

Measuring Degree and Rate of Composting

Those long associated with composting have depended upon appearance, odor, and feel of the end product to determine whether it has been properly composted. More scientific yardsticks are essential. It is not desirable to carry the digestion process too far because less organic material will then be available for enrichment of the soil. However, it is desirable to stabilize the material to the extent that upon being remoistened and piled it will not overheat, lose appreciable nitrogen, become offensive, or create sanitation problems. The exact point during the digestion process at which all of these criteria are fulfilled is difficult to determine for routine work. Because of the wide variation in the nature of materials composted, it is possible that no single criteria or yardstick can be used for all organic wastes.

For example, the change of pH during the normal course of digestion of garbage or animal manure from about pH 5 or 6 to 8 or 9 has proven to be useful. Other wastes with a high initial pH—about 8—may change little so that pH may be of little use as a measure unless its pattern has been predetermined. Currently used yardsticks for measuring the degree of composting are given in Table 40.

Oxygen consumed, ash (100 per cent of total organic solids), and especially total organic solids less crude fiber, are considered the best yardsticks to measure degree of digestion, although pH and transmittance are good, quick, indirect methods after their change pattern has been predetermined for the material and digestion process used. Chemical oxygen demand is a useful yardstick but is more time consuming and causes problems in the laboratory.

Relative stability, BOD, chlorine demand, and iodine demand tests have not yet been developed so that they are dependable.

Other less scientific but commonly used tests are appearance, odor, and generation of heat. During the composting process the material changes from brown to black and from fibrous to friable appearance. The odor of raw garbage varies from rancid to putrid while that of well composted material has a slightly earthy and sometimes musty odor. Generation of heat as a yardstick is unreliable and depends on such factors as the degree of oxygen available, insulation, seeding, per cent of moisture, pH, time, and surrounding temperature. All but very old compost material will reheat to some degree. To carry the digestion process to

TABLE 40

RELIABILITY OF TESTS TO DETERMINE DEGREE OF COMPOSTING
OF GROUND, SEPARATED GARBAGE

Test	Raw Waste	Finished Compost	Reliability
pH	5-6	8-9	Indirectly related; reliable only after change pattern established
Chemical oxygen demand	85% reduction		Good reliability
Oxygen consumed	25% reduction		Fair reliability
Total organic (100%—% ash)	80-90%	60-70%	Reliable but requires large, finely ground sample
Transmittance	70%	10%	Indirectly related; reliable only after change pattern established
Starch	75% reduction		Dependent on degree of digestion of only one constituent

the point where reheating will not occur may be impractical and too costly. Development of a reheating test may prove to give a quantitative answer on the momentary rate of digestion.

Yardsticks for rate of digestion that have proven useful include oxygen utilization and carbon dioxide production. If these yardsticks are used on a pilot project or in a full-scale plant it may be necessary to remove a sample of compost to a laboratory-size digester where standard temperatures can be maintained and adequate, continuous stirring provided. These two yardsticks have been the main methods of measurement used in most of the Michigan State University research. Carbon dioxide produced in these experiments was absorbed by bubbling through caustic before the oxygen utilization was measured directly by reduction in volume. The oxygen measurements are easy to make at frequent intervals, whereas the carbon dioxide production requires titration of the caustic solution and replenishment each time. Unless this is done with the utmost care, inaccurate results may be obtained.

On plant-scale experiments oxygen uptake and carbon dioxide production can be reasonably well estimated by making air flow measurements and also frequent analyses of the exhaust gases. Such a procedure, when practical, is strongly recommended as a control in the operation of full-scale plants.

Quality Control

The aim of composting is to make the highest grade compost possible from the raw materials and do it consistently. This means producing a product as uniform or as near uniform as possible. One of the major aspects of quality control has already been discussed in connection with pH control and conservation of nitrogen. Another important aspect

Fig. 130. Composting plant in Tokyo has two digesters.

is fineness of grind, especially the removal or pulverizing of coarse particles, sharp pieces of glass, and other undesirable objects such as fragments of metal and tin cans. Sometimes plastic objects or even polyethylene bags are objectionable from the point of view of appearance. Quality control is especially important if the material is to be bagged and sold. If it is to be sold in bulk for agricultural purposes, the main thing is to have a uniform end product so that the farmer knows what he is purchasing. If the moisture content varies appreciably, it is well to take this into consideration if the product is sold on a weight basis. It is possible that under some circumstances the producer of large quantities of compost would want to blend the compost material to make fertilizers of different guaranteed qualities. Various elements, including concentrates containing nitrogen, phosphorus, or postassium, might be added.

Bagging

If compost is to be sold in small quantities and at high prices, certain of its qualities must be carefully controlled; it must be dried; and finally it must be attractively packaged. Experience indicates that unlined bags deteriorate rapidly unless the compost is reduced to less than 10 per cent moisture. Even with a low moisture content, bags will deteriorate in 6 to 12 months, especially if they are stored in a damp place, because of the bacterial action of the compost material. One, five, and ten pound sacks are frequently made of polyethylene or plastic lined paper. Compost of 15 to 25 per cent moisture can be used in this type of container and has a better sales appeal than a 10 per cent moisture content compost, which has a tendency to be dusty. Bagging is usually done by a commercial enterprise rather than the municipality. Cans should be removed from the compost if it is to be bagged and sold on the retail market.

Insect and Odor Control

A properly designed and operated compost plant should have few if any problems with insects and odors. Naturally the trucks bringing partially decayed food to a plant will have some odor and may bring flies and larvae with them. Generally, however, chemical sprays will kill flies that come with the refuse; and most of the odor disappears after the refuse is ground the first time. Once the refuse is seeded and starts to heat, most fly larvae are quickly destroyed. If modified windrow or area composting is used all the refuse along the edges will be turned under at the first turning of the pile; in the meantime there should be sufficient biological activity even at the surface of the pile to discourage flies. On occasion the use of chemical sprays is warranted. Outdoor windrowing with aeration by turning requires much vigilance to control flies.

If there are objectionable odors during the composting process, the plant is not functioning correctly; there is probably something wrong with the aeration system because aerobic microorganisms do not produce unpleasant odors. Correction of the aeration system should correct the odor problem.

Labor and Supervision

Safety and cleanliness of employees are particularly important. There are many conveyers and machines and consequently many chances for employees to be injured. Every precaution should be taken to make each operation as safe as possible. Cleanliness of a plant is not only a matter of health but a matter of morale. Strict housekeeping and maintenance standards from the beginning to the end of plant operations pay big dividends. The selection of a plant supervisor should be made with these two points in mind. The technical features of composting can be taught to him, but he must already have the ability to get employees to practice safety and cleanliness.

Laboratory Tests and Controls

As in the operation of a sewage treatment plant, efficient technical operation of a composting plant depends on routine daily laboratory tests and controls. The usual sewage treatment plant laboratory, with the

Fig. 131. Compost was used in the soil from which the bigger of these two vegetables was grown, but not in the soil for the other.

addition of a few pieces of equipment, is satisfactory for most composting plants. Frequent, rapid determinations of pH, temperatures, moisture, and ash are needed. In large plants methods for determining oxygen uptake or carbon dioxide production should be used. Determinations of nitrogen, potassium, phosphorus, crude fiber, volatile solids, carbon dioxide, biochemical oxygen, and chemical oxygen demand are also desirable for medium and large plants or arrangements can be made to have some of these tests run elsewhere as the need arises. In a small plant, routine tests can be made by the supervisor; in a large plant a chemist should be employed. For a relatively new process such as composting it is important that detailed and accurate records be kept and analyzed as the basis for improving plant efficiency. Appendix A tells how to make tests that can be used in analyzing compost.

Marketing Compost

It has been said that under favorable circumstances composting of organic wastes in the United States can be competitive with incineration and sanitary landfill methods of disposal, even if the end product is given away. The real economy of composting comes, however, if the end product can be sold for a fair price. Municipal experience in the sale of sewage sludge is a poor basis for judging how high a price good compost will bring.

Until farmers have personal experience with a product they are likely to be unwilling to pay much for it. It will take time to acquaint potential buyers with compost, determine the value of it in any area, and build up a demand for it. It is unrealistic to think compost can at first be sold at high prices or that all of it can be sold in small quantities to back yard gardeners. Initially a large amount of compost must be sold to farmers at about the cost of production. A realistic economic analysis of a compost plant must be based on this premise, although better markets may develop later.

Retail sale and distribution of compost can probably best be done by private enterprise rather than by a municipality. Bids should be taken on a percentage basis or some other equitable basis or a contract negotiated with a private seller. A long-term contract is probably desirable so that heavy initial promotion costs can be distributed over a long period. An arrangement for selling the compost on a sliding scale basis, with a lower initial cost or percentage, until a demand has been created, has merit.

Ultimately, commercial fertilizer companies will probably be the main distributors of compost. They may sell a wide variety of enriched products that use an organic base rather than an inorganic inert base.

On-Site Composting of Kitchen Wastes

Although many people have back yard compost piles, indiscriminate disposal of kitchen wastes by this method encourages breeding of flies and rats. It is difficult if not impossible to do a good job of home composting without first shredding or grinding the wastes. It is also necessary to mix them with dry porous material if the faster, more efficient aerobic composting method is to be employed.

An anaerobic or semi-anaerobic approach to kitchen waste digestion has been used with varying degrees of success in limited parts of the country in recent years. Essentially it consists of digging a hole about 24 inches in diameter and 20 to 30 inches deep in which a bottomless can with a tight cover to exclude flies is put. If the metal extends 18 to 20 inches below the surface of the ground, rodents are discouraged from burrowing into the decomposing wastes. An installation of this kind works best in dry, porous soil; food wastes shrink and decompose to about one-quarter of their original volume. If food wastes for a family of six are composted, the compost material should be removed every 8 to 14 months. Because it is odorous, it must then be buried or composted elsewhere by mixing with leaves or garden wastes. Rusting of the metal container and the problems of digging and removing the material are the major disadvantages.

This way of disposing of kitchen wastes may be used temporarily in surburban areas but is not recommended as a replacement for refuse collection and disposal by other means nor is it recommended for use in urban areas.

10   SALVAGE AND RECLAMATION

A question often raised that confounds municipal officials responsible for refuse disposal is "Why can't we adopt a method of disposal that produces revenue?" This is usually followed by a quotation from an article in which a new salvage or reclamation method is described or by quoting statistics reported by a city that has found salvage practical because it has a local market for salvage materials.

Salvage and reclamation as a disposal method should be carefully considered and a decision made on the basis of engineering and cost studies. Municipal officials must not lose sight of the primary objective of a disposal program—that it be efficient and nuisance-free for the public. The best revenue producing disposal methods are usually those that are "extra-curricular"—that neither jeopardize nor seriously interfere with the primary disposal methods.

Particularly in large cities, public works officials are justifiably apprehensive of reliance on a disposal method that depends upon fluctuating and sometimes nonexistent markets for salvage or refuse by-products. If the markets collapse, the city may find itself with quantities of refuse and no method of disposal except an emergency landfill a long way from the city. In the past, market prices for salvage have not kept pace with the labor costs involved, and unless there is a reversal of this trend, municipal officials will probably continue to take a dim view of salvage and reclamation as a sound method of disposal. On the other hand, the amount of refuse that must be collected and disposed of by the municipality is influenced by the amount that is salvaged and sold by private interests. When prices for salvage are high, the amount of refuse a city must collect and dispose of can be decreased significantly.

Small cities, where it is not too difficult to get a site for a landfill quickly if the emergency arises, have greater latitude in using revenue producing disposal methods and depending on the market for salvage. In fact, sometimes the city that salvages or reclaims refuse makes a real contribution to the conservation of natural resources.

Changes in salvage practices over the past 50 years are evident from experiences in New York City. At the turn of the century, several large-scale salvage operations were carried on at Barren Island, Rikers Island, and later at Staten Island. Reduction plants processed food wastes, dead animals, and fish for the production of glycerine, oils, fertilizers, and animal hides. Although each of the plants was successful initially, by 1915 all had been abandoned, not only for economic reasons but also because of the uncontrollable nuisances they created.

More recently the city awarded contracts annually to private bidders for salvage and reclamation privileges at some 20 landfill sites, incineration plants, and marine transfer stations. The operations became less and less attractive over the years, however, and interference with normal disposal operations, the nuisances created, and the declining salvage market caused the discontinuance of the operations.

SALVAGEABLE MATERIALS AND THE MARKET

Most salvageable materials are found in rubbish, although garbage and ashes also contain some. Householders are sometimes asked to keep tin cans and bottles, for instance, separate from other rubbish because they have resale value. And during wartime householders have been asked to separate ferrous metals, aluminum, rubber, and tin cans from other refuse.

Of the many items found in rubbish, some have resale value and some have little or none. Those that may have resale value include rags, newspapers, mixed papers, cardboard, books and magazines, bottles, rubber, ferrous metals (including tin cans), nonferrous metals, and glass. Articles with no resale value include leather, enamelware, excelsior, mattresses, matting, linoleum, sawdust, straw, dirt, synthetic fabrics, and plastics.

In combined refuse, materials of value may include garbage, bones, ashes, and cinders. The amount of refuse of this kind has been decreasing for a number of years, however, partly because of the use of gas and electricity for heating, packaging of frozen food, and increased use of home garbage grinders. The results of an analysis of household rubbish in the District of Columbia in 1914 and 1915 are given in Table 41, and

Fig. 132. If some parts of refuse are salvaged, the amount that must be disposed of by municipal agencies is decreased. Metals are frequently salvaged after refuse has been taken to a sanitary landfill site.

TABLE 41

ANALYSIS OF HOUSEHOLD RUBBISH IN THE DISTRICT OF COLUMBIA,
BY SELECTED MONTHS IN 1914 AND 1915
(Per cent by weight)

Material	Nov.	Dec.	Jan.	Mar.	May	June	July	Aug.
Newspaper	10.4	17.8	19.5	16.1	15.6	17.2	17.0	16.0
Manila paper	6.6	12.7	7.0	9.5	8.7	7.3	12.1	13.4
Cardboard	0.8	9.4	11.7	10.5	9.7	6.9	10.9	12.8
Books	4.4	3.0	2.4	2.4	3.3	3.2	1.4	5.6
Mixed paper	16.6	4.4	3.1	5.0	4.6	2.8	2.4	2.6
Rags	5.9	3.7	4.5	5.2	7.2	4.3	5.0	5.7
Wood	1.2	7.4	1.4	2.8	2.6	4.1	3.6	4.1
Leather	1.5	0.2	0.4	0.7	1.2	0.2	1.0	1.1
Rubber	0.3	0.3		0.3	0.5	0.0		
Screenings		4.6	18.5	13.4	10.4	18.6	12.3	11.1
Tinware	10.2	7.3	11.7	13.6	8.8	6.6	5.6	6.4
Enamelware	0.4	0.4	0.1	0.4	0.3	5.0		0.1
Metals	1.8	0.6	0.3	0.8	1.3	1.1	0.8	1.5
Bottles	11.0	8.1	7.7	9.0	7.7	8.3	8.4	7.2
Broken glass	3.8	3.5	4.0	4.7	5.2	4.3	4.8	3.5
Excelsior		0.7	0.3	0.8	0.7	0.1	0.7	
Mattresses	5.2	1.1			0.3	0.0	0.7	0.1
Matting	3.1	0.8	0.1	0.3	1.6	1.5	1.4	
Linoleum	0.7				0.3	0.1		0.1
Straw			0.4			0.1		
Dirt	16.1	14.0	6.9	4.5	10.0	8.4	11.5	8.7
Total	100.0	100.0	100.0	100.0	100.0	100.0	100.0	100.0

the results of analyses of refuse delivered to the city of New Orleans'
Florida Avenue incinerator in 1968 are given in Table 42.

Paper and Paper Products

Paper and paper products make up the largest proportion of salvageable
materials in refuse in the United States and the amount is increasing. Their
market value, however, probably fluctuates more than for any other
salvageable material. At times there is practically no market at all. Many
municipal officials, particularly in large cities, have been faced with the
problem of disposing of baled mixed paper at prices that could not even
pay freight charges to a paper mill.

The *Waste Trade Journal*, reporting prices per 100 pounds for mixed
paper between 1938 and 1957, showed a high of $1.55 in 1951 and a
low of 3¾ cents in 1938. Forty cents per 100 pounds was quoted in
one eastern city in 1970 for bundled newspapers delivered to the local
dealer, and few fund-raising efforts included paper drives. However, salvage of paperboard by private contractors hauling commercial solid

TABLE 42

PHYSICAL COMPOSITION OF REFUSE, CITY OF NEW ORLEANS, JANUARY, 1968[1]
(Averages of 5-day sampling)

Classification of Components	Per Cent Composition Wet Weight Basis	Per Cent Moisture
Combustibles		
Garbage	18.9	39.5
Garden trash	9.2	39.2
Paper products	39.4	10.5
Rags	2.6	4.9
Plastics & miscellaneous	1.5	—
Total combustibles	71.6	21.3
Noncombustibles		
Glass	16.2	—
Miscellaneous metals & cans	12.2	5.9
Total noncombustibles	28.4	3.1[2]
Grand total	100.0	16.2

[1] From "Master Plan for Solid Waste Collection and Disposal—Tri-Parish Metropolitan Area of New Orleans," *Final Report on a Solid Waste Management Demonstration*, 1969, Bureau of Solid Waste Management, U.S. Department of Health, Education, and Welfare. Table V-26, p. V-51. (Samples from well-mixed refuse in the storage pit of the Florida Avenue incinerator.)
[2] Weighted average.

wastes is practiced in many cities and serves as an important source of material to the paper industry.

Tin Cans

Tin cans and scrap metal are among the most important materials that can be salvaged, either before or after incineration. However, in the late 1960's local markets for tin cans from refuse were practically nonexistent.

During World War II many cities requested householders to clean and flatten tin cans, and the city collected them separately and shipped them to detinneries. Both tin and ferrous metal were recovered in this way. Two problems were—and are—the expense of separate collections and the inability to collect enough cans for carload shipments, which are necessary because the cans cannot be baled for this type of processing.

If tin cans are salvaged from incinerator residue after being subjected to temperatures of 1,400° to 2,000° F., sufficient stannic-oxide remains on the cans so that they are not always acceptable at open-hearth steel mills. On the other hand, tin cans that go to steel mills can be baled and shipped more economically than those that go to detinneries.

There was a limited market at much lower prices for baled tin cans to be used for sash weights and other crude metal production in the 1940's and 1950's, but by the 1960's this outlet was also practically nonexistent.

There remains a limited market for tin cans used in copper precipitation processes, but most plants for that process are in the southwestern part of the United States and are far from eastern urban areas. Furthermore, tin cans cannot be baled if they are to be used for this purpose.

A California salvage company, reporting on the market for tin cans for copper precipitation, said:

> Precipitation iron is made from old, discarded tin cans and is sold to the copper mines throughout the Southwest for the precipitation of copper. This material must be well burned, thoroughly cleaned, and shredded in order to be acceptable to the mines. The mining companies generally purchase this material on a long-term contract and shredded cans are not normally handled by the scrap industry. The price of precipitation iron is a matter of negotiation between the buyer and seller and is not affected by the scrap market. It must be understood that precipitation iron is a processed material and that ordinary incinerator cans or burned cans are not acceptable. The material must be completely free of ashes, oxide, scale, etc., and must be properly cleaned and shredded.
>
> Freight charges on "shredded cans" are very high due to the light weight of the material and it is not practical to ship great distances.

The salvage and processing of tin cans for the copper mines have been limited to the southern and western-central areas primarily because of this freight problem.

In the 1960's there apparently was no foreign market for baled tin cans. Furthermore, steel mills ordinarily will not buy bundles of metal that include tin cans. In fact, most mills reject bundles of scrap metal if it is evident they contain any tin coated stock.

Obviously, each city must carefully consider the practicality of salvaging tin cans. If market conditions existing in the late 1960's continue, the resale market for them would soon be glutted if all cities salvaged them and if they continue to be unacceptable for open-hearth use. The use of tin-free steel in the manufacture of "tin" cans in the 1970's could materially change this picture.

Bottles and Rubber

Prices for bottles, cullet (broken glass from glass manufacturers), and rubber also have not kept pace with labor costs, and they require considerable grading if they are to bring a reasonable price. By the end of the 1960's there were few cullet dealers operating in the large urban areas.

In June, 1969, one Baltimore company offered $20 per ton for clean flint cullet and $18 per ton for dirty cullet, delivered at the glass plant; there was no market for colored cullet.

SALVAGE AS A PRINCIPAL DISPOSAL METHOD

Salvage can be a principal means of disposal and all of the refuse in a community can be examined and sorted for salvageable materials, or it can be a "side-line" for another method of disposal.

Few municipalities have attempted "all-out" salvage of either rubbish or combined refuse, and most of those that have tried have abandoned their efforts. However, various types of plants were built for the purpose: those in which salvageable materials in rubbish were removed from moving belts and the unsalvageable materials disposed of at incineration plants or landfills; those in which garbage was reduced to grease and fats; and those in which garbage was composted. (Composting is covered in Chapter 9.)

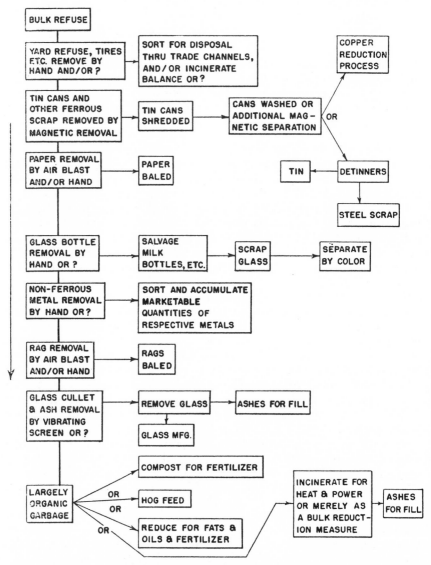

Fig. 133. Flow chart showing processing of refuse for salvage. (Reprinted with permission of Armour Research Foundation.)

Rubbish Salvage

A rubbish salvage plant in Washington, D.C., was operated on a continuous-belt principle. Rags, paper, cardboard, and tin cans were baled; and cullet, bottles, nonferrous metals, and rubber were picked and graded. The plant initially was operated by a private contractor but was taken over by the city and operated by it for about 10 years before it was destroyed by fire and abandoned in 1928.

A more modern salvage plant was built in Detroit in 1945, but it also was abandoned in 1947.

In the late 1960's a composting salvage plant was built by a private company under contract with the City of Houston, Texas. This plant developed with large emphasis on salvage of paperboard and paper, metals recovery, and on-line tested mechanical separation techniques. Plant input quantity can be carefully controlled to allow for market and other fluctuations, since only part of Houston's domestic refuse is handled in this manner.

Garbage Reduction

The method of garbage disposal known as reduction was at one time popular and productive of revenue. Most reduction plants were built before World War I but few continued in operation afterward.

In the reduction process, garbage was cooked with steam in digesters, the grease was extracted by percolating naphtha through the cooked garbage, and the solvents were distilled for further use. If solvents were not used, the cooked garbage was subjected to high pressure in hydraulic or screw presses to extract the grease. The residue, called tankage, was used as feed for livestock, as fertilizers, and as boiler fuel. The grease itself was sold primarily to soap manufacturers.

Odors from the garbage and gases from the cooking made the plants so offensive that they usually had to be located a long way from a city, which increased the costs of getting the garbage to them. The plants were expensive to operate because of high labor costs, rapid deterioration of equipment, and the need for large quantities of steam.

Rochester, New York, and Philadelphia had municipally operated reduction plants, with Philadelphia one of the last to abandon operations (1959). Plants were also closed in Syracuse, New York, in 1956 and in Indianapolis in 1951.

In other cities reduction plants were operated by contractors—in New York, Pittsburgh, Washington, Chicago, and Cincinnati. Some privately operated plants were taken over by the city government when the contractors could not operate them profitably. This happened in New York, Washington, and Chicago.

Why is reduction obsolete as a method of garbage disposal? The national economy and the habits of the people have brought it about. Wages have increased without compensatory automation in reduction plants. Not only has the amount of garbage collected decreased on a per capita basis but the grease content of garbage has also decreased. When reduction plants were profitably operated the grease content of garbage was often in excess of 5 per cent. By 1948 it had gone down to less than 3 per cent.

Furthermore, the market for grease has declined considerably. Soap manufacturers at one time were the principal buyers. Today, however, detergents have taken the place of many soaps and they are made from synthetics or petrochemicals.

Salvage as a principal means of disposal has not in general been found satisfactory and is not acceptable in most United States cities—from aesthetic, sanitary, and economic standpoints.

Partial Salvage

Great quantities of material from rubbish and garbage are salvaged and resold today, in spite of the failure of the so-called all-out salvage plants. Various means are used.

At the Source

Both municipal and private collectors remove saleable materials such as rags, cardboard, and magazines during refuse collection. And although many cities have strict rules against this practice because it delays collections, it has not been entirely eliminated.

In a number of large cities scavengers are permitted to separate salvage materials from other refuse put out for collection or to collect such material put aside for them by householders and businesses.

Many businesses, hotels, and apartment houses also permit or engage in salvage of paper and cardboard. When prices for paper are high the Salvation Army, the Boy Scouts, the public schools, and others sometimes collect newspapers and magazines from householders and sell them to raise money for their activities. In 1969 this approach was used in several cities for the collection of aluminum cans for a bounty of ½ cent per can paid by the container manufacturer. Many public officials responsible for refuse collection and disposal think that voluntary collections are the most practical method of conducting a salvage program. Without voluntary unpaid workers, house-to-house collections would not be economically justified. Indeed, campaigns to salvage metals during the war would not have been "self-supporting" without volunteer workers. Some authorities involved in the wartime campaigns believe that if conservation of metals is the goal—not low-cost disposal—it would be better to separate the materials at the source and collect them in compartmented trucks.

At Incineration Plants

Experiences in New York and Washington and other cities that operate large incinerators indicate that salvage of tin cans and other materials at the incineration plant often interfere with normal operations and in addition cause an unsightly appearance. Materials other than refuse components often can be salvaged at an incineration plant, however.

Residue. Incinerator residue is, roughly, a combination of ferrous metal, glass slag, inert ash, and unburned organic and inorganic matter, the amount depending upon the efficiency of the burning process and the operating procedures. If combustibles and noncombustibles are collected separately so that metal and glass are not included in the refuse taken to the incinerators, the amount of incinerator residue is materially reduced. But metal and glass are never completely eliminated from refuse, and there are two schools of thought about whether year-around separate collections to reduce the amount of noncombustibles taken to incinerators are economical. There is some justification for the belief that tin cans and bottles cause voids in refuse, that the voids accelerate the burning of combustibles, and that metal salvage after incineration is simple and practical.

If there is a good market for low-grade scrap metal, salvage of ferrous metal from incinerator residue has three advantages: it brings in revenue for the city, it does not interfere with the basic refuse disposal operation, and the metal does not take up space in a landfill.

Incinerator residue can also be used to good advantage for land reclamation and for access roads to landfills if there is not a market for it.

Fly Ash. When trapped by dry-type methods, fly ash is another type of incinerator residue. Its potential uses as an additive for concrete and as a base for fertilizer have not been fully explored. The use of steam plant fly ash as a concrete additive, however, was studied by engineers of the Tennessee Valley Authority. Fly ash recovered by mechanical collectors in TVA steam plants replaced 20 per cent of the cement and 10.5 per cent of the sand necessary for the concrete at Wilson Dam Lock. The cement produced had a 28-day compressive strength of 4,500 pounds per square inch.

The TVA report pointed out:

Fly-ash is an artificial pozzolan. A pozzolan is defined as "siliceous or siliceous and aluminous material like volcanic ash, which in itself possesses little or no cementitious value but will, in finely divided form and in the presence of moisture, chemically react with calcium hydroxide at ordinary temperatures to form compounds possessing cementitious properties." Calcium hydroxide is liberated during the hydration of portland cement, and pozzolans combine with this liberated lime to form a hard, durable compound which is mostly insoluble silicates. Natural pozzolans, such as volcanic ash, have been used for over 2,000 years. A mixture of volcanic ash and calcined limestone formed the hydraulic cement used in such enduring Roman structures as the Pantheon in Rome.

The chemical and physical characteristics of a sample of fly ash as determined by analysis by the U.S. Bureau of Mines in 1969 are shown in Table 43.

The use of incinerator fly ash as a pozzolanic base material with pressure hydrated lime and aggregates is acceptable to highway departments. When used in the correct proportions, fly ash, hydrated lime, and aggregate form a concrete-like mass that has proved a superior base material for roads, airport runways, and parking lots.

A mix of 5 parts of lime, 10 parts of incinerator fly ash, and 90 parts of aggregate was tested and found to average a strength of 530 pounds per square inch; and a mix of 5 parts of lime, 15 parts of incinerator fly ash, and 85 parts of aggregate had an average strength of 780 pounds per square inch.

Other uses for incinerator fly ash include:

1. In combination with hydrated lime for mud jacking of concrete slab floors, streets, sidewalks, curbs, and gutters.
2. As an additive and vehicle in the manufacture of commercial fertilizers. Some of the trace elements found in fly ash have been found to be beneficial for agricultural purposes.
3. As a sand blasting material where a highly polished surface is desired, such as turbine rotor blades.

Magnetic oxides have been separated from fly ash to improve them for use in concrete. The iron oxide obtained from the separation is also used as a densifier for concrete, especially in the manufacture of concrete pipes or pipe covering to prevent flotation of lines in marshes and under water.

The satisfactory use of fly ash depends largely upon its quality. If it has a low carbon content (less than 12 per cent) it performs excellently in any of the combinations listed above.

TABLE 43

PHYSICAL AND CHEMICAL ANALYSIS OF INCINERATOR FLY ASH, 1969[1]

Physical		Chemical[2]	
Sieve Mesh	Per Cent by Weight	Element	Per Cent by Weight
+20	4.9	Si	18.64
20 x 40	8.3	Al	10.79
40 x 60	12.5	Fe	2.13
60 x 100	12.8	Ti	2.24
100 x 200	24.4	Ca	4.70
200 x 325	12.8	Mg	0.98
—325	24.3	C	11.62
		Ignition Loss	14.45

[1] Analysis of fly ash from Arlington, Virginia, incinerator by U.S. Bureau of Mines.
[2] Elemental analysis by emission spectrograph; determination of C content by gravimetric technique. Other elements present in small or trace quantities include Na, K, S, Ag, Ba, Cr, Cu, Ga, Hg, Mn, Mo, Ni, Sn, Ta, Zn, Pb.

Waste Heat. Heat from incinerator furnaces is sometimes sold to private businesses and utilities companies or is used in sewage disposal plants and other public facilities. The question of whether to try to use waste heat from incineration plants should be carefully considered. At first glance it appears that there is little justification for wasting the heat generated by the furnaces. But the question usually must be resolved on the basis of local conditions—power rates and the need for the steam by users within a reasonable distance of the plant.

It is usually practical to sell heat only if the buyer is near the incineration plant and is willing to take it on an "as available" basis, however, since the steam is not available in the same quantities at all times. The furnaces must be shut down for repairs and maintenance on weekends and at other times, for fly ash removal, and sometimes simply because it is not economical to operate the incineration plant on weekends and holidays. If steam is sold, it is almost necessary to have auxiliary furnaces to use at such times and to store some refuse to be burned on holidays and weekends.

Incineration plants are successfully used as steam generating plants, however. Examples are those in Atlanta and Miami. And in New York City a heat recovery plant has been successfully operated for more than 20 years at one of the large incineration plants adjoining a sanitation department garage. The new Montreal plant which began operation in 1970 is a steam generating plant. An engineering study in 1968 for a proposed new Washington, D.C., plant termed steam generation as economically questionable because of lack of nearby user sources.

Waste heat from an incineration plant can often be used to advantage if the plant is combined with the sewage disposal plant, however. The hot gases from the incinerator furnaces can be used in the flash sludge dryers in the sewage disposal plant, and the sludge can be returned to the incinerator to be burned if it is not processed for fertilizer. Furthermore, noxious and odorous gases from the sewage disposal plant can be burned in the incineration plant furnaces before they are discharged into the atmosphere.

As discussed more fully in Chapter 5, Central Incineration, water-wall furnaces are coming into use which have certain advantages as incinerators in addition to improving the picture for heat utilization. When these produce their salable energy in the form of electric power, the major problem of proximity to point of usage is removed. With the improvement of equipment and methods, the feasibility of profitable heat recovery offers real hope for this form of salvage.

At Landfill Sites

Landfills themselves are reclamation projects, since refuse is used to fill pits, quarries, marshes, and other land that is unusable unless it is filled.

In addition, refuse materials that are resaleable are often salvaged at the site. At landfill sites, where there is considerable opportunity for partial salvage without interference with fill activities, the appearance of the grounds is often unsightly. The salvage pickers are often slovenly looking, and in some places small children have been permitted to help with the picking. As long ago as 1921 some cities recommended that "no salvaging should be allowed at the dump at any time, except by city employees." Under controlled conditions, however, salvage at landfills may be satisfactory and bring in revenue for the city.

If salvage operations are carried on at landfills, every effort should be made to avoid interference with fill operations. The salvage area should be fenced and monitored to avoid unsightliness caused by windblown paper, and storage of salvage materials should be strictly controlled by the city. An advantage of salvage at landfills is that bulky objects such as oil drums and bedsprings are not put into the fill, which makes the fill more stable.

In San Francisco private refuse collection trucks unload salvageable materials that have been separated during collection at a salvage yard just outside the site of the landfill.

Rendering

The rendering process is somewhat like the reduction process, but it involves animal refuse rather than vegetable refuse. Dead animals, fish, and wastes from slaughter houses and butcher shops are used. Unlike the products of reduction, however, the market for rendered fats has not been lost and the raw materials have not decreased.

Cities do not operate rendering plants but many use them to dispose of dead animals. (Large animals have almost disappeared from big cities, except in zoos and at riding academies, but many cats and dogs die or are killed each year and must be disposed of by the city.)

Not much more than 50 per cent of the weight of cattle on the hoof goes to the meat market so the chances are that there will continue to be a supply of raw material for rendering plants. Large packing houses pride themselves on using the animals to the maximum—and for the most favorable market. (Lips and ears of animals are cured in brine for crab bait!)

Among the many products are fertilizers, glues, oils, glycerine, soaps, and detergents. Although these products are in competition with others produced from different sources, that is not a concern of city officials as long as rendering plants stay in business.

Rendering plants usually must be located far from dwellings. Under zoning ordinance provisions they are in the lowest classification. They are often considered nuisances, but they have their place in the nation's economy.

Dehydration of Garbage

The removal of water from foodstuffs to preserve them has been done commercially more or less successfully for many years, although dehydration of garbage to be fed to pigs has been used as a disposal method only on a limited scale.

Commercial type rotary drum dryers that process garbage were experimented with in the 1950's in Omaha, Nebraska, and jointly in Kansas City, Missouri, and Kansas City, Kansas. Both operations have been abandoned.

There are obvious advantages to businesses in dehydration of foodstuffs but they are not as obvious in garbage processing. In any event, the

TABLE 44

ANALYSIS OF HOUSEHOLD AND RESTAURANT
DEHYDRATED GARBAGE, KANSAS CITY, MISSOURI
(By per cent of sample)

	Household Garbage	Restaurant Garbage
Protein	10.62	11.70
Fat	8.01	16.75
Fiber	9.01	10.10
Ash	27.62	24.96
Moisture	7.26	4.50
Nonfibrous extract (N.F.E.)	39.45	31.99
Carbohydrates (N.F.E. plus fiber)	48.46	42.09

matter of separate garbage collections and the competition from hog farms that use garbage must be considered in determining whether the method is economical and practical.

Automobiles

The problem of final disposal of junked automobiles has become a major one, as anyone may deduce from the number of auto "graveyards" to be seen from our highways. After cars are stripped of salable parts, there is still a great deal of valuable metal which would seem to be well worth salvaging. The U. S. Bureau of Mines states that automobile scrappage has reached a rate that can provide over 9 million tons of ferrous and nonferrous metals annually. But the problem is to separate them from each other and from the glass and combustible materials in a

Fig. 134. A stockpile of shredded auto scrap.

car's construction within the economics of the scrap market. Developments in steel making work against the desirability of "contaminated" ferrous scrap.

As discussed in Chapter 6, incinerators can burn away the combustible parts and some of the nonferrous metals can be removed by manual labor. The remainder can be processed by crushing or shredding to put it into a form acceptable for reprocessing. The machinery required to accomplish this is massive and expensive and the whole enterprise becomes involved in its economics. A large operation is required to support the capital cost, and this means a large source of junked cars available without much transportation expense as well as a close and favorable scrap market. In spite of all these and numerous other problems there are a number of successful plants in operation.

Equipment available for processing the ferrous metals includes baling presses, guillotine shears, and shredders. All of these are designed to reduce the junked car to pieces of acceptable size.

Fig. 135. Vehicle hulks being conveyed into a scrap shredder.

Control of Scavenging

Scavenging causes several problems. It often interferes with disposal operations, delays collections, makes disposal facilities unsightly, can be dangerous to workers at the facilities, and sometimes spreads disease.

A city can, by ordinance, prohibit scavenging entirely or it can control it. If a city permits scavenging but controls it, the city frequently issues permits to scavengers. Those who do not have permits scavenge illegally and can be prosecuted. Fines, imprisonment, or both may be prescribed in the law. If a city has a contract with a private company to collect and dispose of refuse, it can control scavenging through its contract. Administrative regulations are usually sufficient to deter city employees from scavenging.

Scavenging can be prevented at least in some measure if fences are put up around disposal facilities and a uniformed policeman is on duty at the disposal facilities to enforce the ordinances against it.

The Future of Salvage and Reclamation

Perhaps the most serious problems in using salvage and reclamation even as a partial disposal method are the lack of stable markets and reasonable prices for salvageable materials. The availability of salvage materials and their relationship to the costs of salvaging and processing materials for the market plus the prices they bring determine whether salvage is practical. The prodigious waste of everyday materials in the United States assures availability of the source of salvage. The question is whether they can be salvaged economically—and even lucratively.

The record indicates that although paper, cardboard, and rags will continue to find their way to mills, most cities do not find it aesthetically or economically practical to use salvage as a principal means of disposal. The trend is toward partial salvage.

11 REFUSE DISPOSAL MANAGEMENT

Management involves planning, organizing, directing, and controlling the various parts of an undertaking so that all components function correctly and cooperatively. Sound management of refuse disposal activities is essential to achieve an efficient, sanitary, reliable operation that is well accepted by the community.

Basic management principles are the same for cities of all sizes but their application varies from place to place, depending on the extent and complexity of the activities and on the way the function is organized and financed.

The pertinent elements of refuse disposal management discussed in the following pages include organization, personnel, reporting, cost accounting and budgeting, and special administrative considerations such as public relations. Planning of refuse disposal facilities has been covered in preceding chapters.

The Solid Waste Disposal Act of 1965 recognized that the collection and disposal of solid waste are primarily a function of local agencies and encouraged cooperative activities by state and local governments to encourage, where practicable, regional planning for and conduct of disposal programs.

The Waste Management and Control Report (1966) of the National Academy of Sciences–National Research Council, produced for the Federal Council for Science and Technology by the Committee on Pollution, presents the enormous complexities of the environmental problems of air, water, and land on a national basis. Following this study an ad hoc solid waste management committee of the National Research Council was established to advise the Federal Bureau of Solid Waste Management on feasibility priorities and criteria for implementing the broad recommendations on research and development efforts in the solid waste field necessary for implementation of systems concepts. The ad hoc committee's report *Policies for Solid Waste Management* published in 1970 noted: "much of the problem of solid waste management derives from the continued reluctance of those concerned to come to grips with it and apply existing technology, systems, and organizational know-how to its solution—above all, to pay for these services."[1]

There have been a number of specific attempts to apply "Simulation and Analyses of a Refuse Collection System" in an effort to delineate the

---

[1]Ad Hoc Committee on Solid Waste Management, National Research Council, *Policies for Solid Waste Management*, Public Health Service Publication No. 2018 (Washington, D.C.: U.S. Government Printing Office, 1970).

interdependencies of the several significant parameters involved through the use of mathematical simulation. One was reported by Quon, Charnes, and Wersan in the October, 1965 issue of the *Sanitary Engineering Division Journal* of the ASCE. This study was based on conditions in Winnetka, Illinois, and relates the dependency of overall pick-up and haul efficiencies on truck capacity, service density, the variability of daily quantities produced, and the haul distances both on routes and to disposal points. The process was used in Raleigh, North Carolina, to evaluate alternative possibilities for refuse management.

Services applying these principles to computer analysis for any city are now available from consultants. While they are aimed principally at optimizing the collection systems, much information regarding characteristics affecting the disposal operation is also generated.

ORGANIZATION

The basic principles of sound organization that have proved successful in other fields of activity are equally applicable to refuse disposal; yet no single type of organization structure and no standard distribution of responsibilities can be said to be best. The reason is that no two situations are exactly alike and many are widely divergent. Among the many variables found in municipal disposal operations are the methods of disposal, amounts and kinds of refuse, size of the city in population and area, other related operations conducted by the government, use of contractors or private services for collection or disposal, laws or charter provisions, tradition, and even political policy.

Principles of Organization

Organization for refuse disposal in general should be governed by the broad principles that have proved successful in both public and private undertakings. Some of the basic ones are:

1. Lines of authority and responsibility should be clear and definite so that each employee can readily understand his place in the operation, to whom he is accountable, the units or employees under his supervision, and his relationships with other units and employees.
2. Authority and responsibility should flow directly between higher units and those immediately subordinate.
3. Each unit and employee should be given authority commensurate with assigned responsibility.
4. Responsibility should be distributed to units and employees to avoid overlapping, duplication, and dual accountability.
5. Division of responsibility among organizational units according to area, purpose, time, or process should be on the basis of comprehensive consideration of the basic functions of the whole operation.
6. The number of subordinates reporting to a superior should not be greater than he can supervise competently.

Disposal in Municipal Government

The refuse disposal function is ordinarily grouped with other municipal sanitation or public works functions in a major department of the government. The purpose of this arrangement is twofold: first, the chief executive or chief administrator of a city can deal successfully with only a limited number of departments or agency heads; and second, this is the best means by which most municipalities can afford to obtain the necessary high quality professional, technical, and management leadership for public works functions. Linking refuse disposal to other sanitation and public works activities permits easier direction, planning, and co-ordination by utilizing the specialized engineering, environmental sanitation, and public works skills of organizational unit heads.

A review of practices throughout the United States shows that the refuse collection and disposal functions are included in public works or public service departments in about 60 per cent of the cities, in sanitation departments in about 20 per cent, in street or street and sanitation departments in about 5 per cent, in engineering departments in about 5 per cent, and in various other departments in about 10 per cent.

A great variety of grouping patterns exists within departments. Patterns depend largely on such factors as the size of the municipality, traditional arrangements, and area. In a public works department, a common practice is to include refuse disposal with refuse collection and other functions in a bureau or division of sanitation (occasionally called by a different name, such as refuse collection and disposal, waste disposal, or street sanitation). The other functions may be street cleaning, snow removal, sewer maintenance, sewage disposal, or catch basin cleaning. Occasionally, however, refuse operations are grouped with street maintenance in various arrangements.

A typical large sanitation department would properly include refuse collection and disposal functions in addition to street cleaning and snow removal. Sewage disposal, a major municipal operation in itself; catch basin cleaning; and other related activities might logically be in-cluded as sanitary functions. Some large municipalities have separate divisions of collection and disposal.

The internal organization of a refuse disposal unit may be divided according to area, kind of disposal method, or disposal locations. In a small municipality the head of each disposal operation may report directly to the refuse disposal supervisor, or in very small places to the head of the sanitation or similar unit that includes both refuse collection and disposal. Large cities that have various types of disposal facilities may have an incinerator section and a sanitary fill section, for example. District organization, however, may be more important if relatively large areas are involved; in this type of organization all disposal facilities in a portion of the city may be brought together under a district supervisor.

A few municipalities have provided for division of responsibility on an area basis at the top level of a sanitation or similar unit. In such cases, a district supervisor has charge of all refuse collection, refuse disposal, and possibly other functions in his assigned area. Within a district functional divisions are normally established for collection, disposal, and other assigned work.

If either refuse collection or refuse disposal is done by contractors, the organization pattern may be somewhat different from what it is for operation by city forces. If only disposal is done by contract the responsibility for supervising contract work should be with the head of the collection agency or in an echelon immediately above it. If refuse is collected by contract, the city supervisor for this activity may be in the refuse disposal unit, but more frequently he is assigned to the head of a sanitation bureau or division or to a department of public works of which the refuse disposal unit is part.

Staff and Auxiliary Services

Staff and auxiliary services must be provided for a refuse disposal unit regardless of its size or kind. Such services may be furnished partially or completely by the disposal unit itself, for an entire sanitation division or bureau, for an entire department, or for the entire city.

Staff activities as adjuncts to management are carried on in some degree at each level of supervision, performed by a special unit attached to the operation, by a combination unit serving several operations, or by a line officer or his assistant. Staff activities relating to refuse disposal include, among others, planning, research, technical advice and assistance, standardization of procedures and methods, budget preparation and control, employee relations, personnel, public relations, legal counsel, and financing. The organization for some of these activities is described in the paragraphs immediately following and for others in major sections below.

Several staff activities are almost always furnished on a city-wide or department-wide basis, but even in these cases some residual responsibilities may be important enough to justify organizational attention at lower levels. Planning is an example. Overall planning for refuse disposal may be done by the city planning agency, but the most important immediate aspects of the planning must be done much closer to the function itself—within the disposal unit, in a more comprehensive sanitation unit, or in a still larger department unit. Administrative and operations planning for collection and disposal may also be provided at the department level, but more often at the bureau or division level for collection and disposal. Some planning, of course, is done at all levels, but a separate operations planning unit is seldom justifiable for a refuse disposal unit alone, although one may be created to serve both collection and disposal and possibly other functions. Responsibility for operations planning may also be assigned to the unit that is responsible for research and operation analysis. If planning is not provided in a staff unit it must be performed by line officials in addition to their operating duties.

Technical assistance may be provided by a special technical unit in a bureau or department. Often it is provided by engineering units outside the bureau or even outside the department. Engineers also frequently consult on the design of incinerators and occasionally in connection with other disposal problems. Selection of consultants is usually done by negotiation, since experienced engineering firms will not submit competitive bids. Engineering fees for such services have been fairly well standardized through action of the engineering societies. Choice of a firm to supply technical assistance in refuse disposal problems, therefore, can be made largely on the basis of comparisons of experience records.

Service activities for refuse disposal also may include equipment maintenance and servicing, accounting, preparation of statistical reports, purchasing, stores, and property and plant maintenance. Here again, services may be provided for the entire city government, for an entire department, for a bureau or division, or for the refuse disposal unit alone. Patterns vary greatly, depending upon the size of the city, the number of disposal sites, and many other factors. However, in general few staff or service units are established for refuse disposal organizations alone. Exceptions are plant maintenance, research, and technical assistance in very large refuse disposal agencies.

Cities sometimes use outside maintenance or shop services either on a continuing contractual basis or for individual jobs. Private consultants are also retained when qualified engineering or specialist services are not available from the city itself.

Various ways of organizing to provide for staff and service functions may be noted in Figure 136, which shows possible staff or service units attached to successive units in the command line from the city's chief executive through a department head and a bureau to a division of

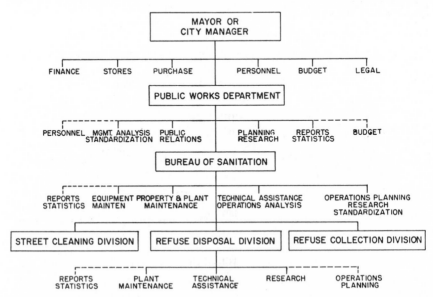

Fig. 136. Organization chart showing alternative arrangements of staff and service units for refuse collection and disposal agencies within municipal government.

refuse disposal. The decision on whether to create a staff unit, to combine two or more staff activities in one unit, or to assign the duties to a line officer depends largely on the amount of responsibility and work involved. If the work load is small enough so that the line officer can perform staff functions himself, no staff units are created, since staff activities are performed solely to aid the line officer.

Technical assistance may be provided within a refuse disposal unit if a city has a sufficient number of incinerators or sanitary fills to make adequate use of specialists' knowledge. In a small city or one with few disposal locations, technical assistance may be provided by a unit that serves an entire sanitation bureau or division, or again, it may be provided by a unit that also has certain other staff assignments.

Cities that have incinerators or other disposal plants must consider the appropriate allocations of maintenance and rehabilitation activities. Often the plant supervisor has the maintenance responsibility. Sometimes only routine repairs are so assigned and major maintenance is provided as a bureau or departmental service to all installations. Thus, in cities that have more than one incineration plant or other facility a maintenance unit may be created in the sanitation bureau or division to serve the disposal unit, as well as others.

Coordination of Collection and Disposal

The necessity for coordinating refuse collection and disposal operations for ease and effectiveness of management has been pointed out in preceding chapters. Although coordination may be achieved largely through physical and operations planning, good organization also promotes harmonious operations. Coordination is most easily effected when refuse collection and disposal units are located in the same bureau, division, or department.

Disposal facilities should be provided and operations planned so that all refuse can be received promptly and efficiently when it reaches the disposal facility. Disposal units and storage capacity should be flexible enough to meet daily and seasonal variations and all except the most unusual emergencies. Collection activities, in turn, should be planned to provide a reasonably continuous flow of refuse to the disposal facilities.

Coordination is much more difficult when one function is performed by a contractor and the other by the municipality or by another contractor. If only one function is performed by a contractor, smooth operation can be most easily attained by placing responsibility for contract supervision in the municipal agency that is responsible for the other function or in the echelon immediately higher. If both services are performed by contract, the same municipal agency should supervise both. The official or unit responsible for contract supervision should be specifically designated in the contract. Neither the city council nor a committee of the council should supervise such contracts for a number of obvious reasons. The responsibility should be centered in one qualified sanitation or public works employee.

Avoidance of Dual Supervision and Accountability

Refuse disposal operations are not particularly susceptible to awkward interrelationships among municipal services because, in general, the installations are isolated or easily separable and interference is negligible Nevertheless there are times when the principles of establishing clear lines of authority and avoiding overlapping responsibility and dual accountability have been violated.

The usual interrelationships with collection forces in routing trucks and designating unloading locations at disposal sites or with garages in storing or servicing vehicles, however, cannot be classed as dual responsibility. The collection truck drivers do not come under the authority of the disposal agency any more than they come under the authority of traffic officials when they obey the directions of a traffic policeman or abide by traffic regulations. Normally, the refuse collection unit issues regulations to its drivers to follow the instructions of attendants at disposal locations or at garages. The refuse disposal unit should not, and usually does not, hold itself accountable for collection employees or equipment.

In large cities, instances of dual accountability may occur when greater emphasis is given to equipment care and maintenance than to effective operation. For example, an undesirable, complex, dual supervision situation, which can result from such emphasis, occurred in a large eastern city where the purchase of all automotive and mobile construction equipment is the responsibility of the department of public property. The equipment used for refuse disposal is operated by the automotive section of the sanitation division of the streets department under the direction of the refuse disposal section. In this case a tractor operator who is digging, compacting, and covering refuse in a sanitary landfill operation is responsible both to the automotive section and to the refuse disposal section of the sanitation division. Maintenance of the tractor also is the responsibility of two agencies—the sanitation automotive section for first and second echelon maintenance and the department of public property for major maintenance. Such organization tends to produce conflicts.

There is no real justification for dual accountability even when the purchase and maintenance of equipment is the responsibility of one agency and the operation of it is the responsibility of another. The equipment operators and the equipment should be under the exclusive control of the functional agency once operators and equipment have been assigned to it, subject only to regulations of the equipment agency on the care and handling of the equipment. Most cities have found it more satisfactory to have equipment operators be employees of the functional agency than the equipment agency. The interests of the equipment agency can be adequately protected through the development of regulations that have the full force of orders when issued by line officials of the functional agency.

Examples of Disposal Organization

Typical organizational principals are illustrated by the arrangements in use in municipalities such as Los Angeles; Cincinnati; Winnetka, Illinois; and New York.

The arrangement in Los Angeles is representative of the allocation of

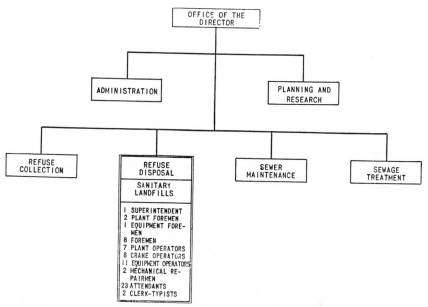

Fig. 137. Organization chart, Bureau of Sanitation, Department of Public Works, Los Angeles.

refuse disposal to a public works department in a large city, as shown in Figure 137. The function is included in a bureau of sanitation along with refuse collection, sewer maintenance, and sewage treatment. Each of these four functions is carried on by a division of the bureau of sanitation. The refuse disposal division is divided generally on the basis of the two types of disposal methods. Some staff activities, including planning and research, are provided at the bureau level, whereas others, such as personnel and legal services, are provided either at the department level or for the city as a whole. Administrative services are provided at the bureau level, but equipment maintenance is in the division.

Cincinnati uses a similar top organization structure, but has some interesting differences, as shown in Figure 138. Refuse disposal is allocated to the division of waste collection in the department of public works. In each of three geographical areas, the responsibility for dumps and for refuse collection is under an area supervisor. Four incinerators are operated under a supervisor of incinerators as a separate operating unit of the division. No formal provisions for staff services are made at the division level. Those not peformed by line officials are performed at the depart-

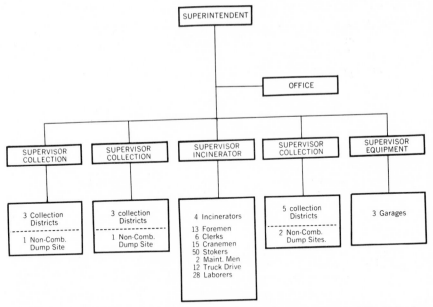

Fig. 138. Division of Waste Collection, Department of Public Works, Cincinnati, Ohio, 1967.

ment level or for the entire city. Equipment maintenance and servicing are provided within the division but most staff services are provided at the department level.

In the Village of Winnetka, Illinois, refuse disposal is one of three operations supervised by a public works foreman, as shown in Figure 139. Central services are provided at the village level except for equipment maintenance, which is a departmental responsibility.

The organization chart for New York (Figure 140) illustrates the allocation of the disposal function to a department of sanitation, a top administrative division of the city government. Other functions of the department are refuse collection, snow removal, and street cleaning. All operations, including plant maintenance and equipment services, are in a main operating unit made up of four bureaus, one of which is the bureau of waste disposal. This bureau in turn is divided by kinds of disposal method used into three divisions: incineration, landfill, and marine operations. Although some staff services are provided within the bureau of waste disposal, some units serve the whole operating unit. Engineering and other staff services are provided at the departmental level.

Disposal Authorities

A special government agency—an authority—is sometimes formed to handle refuse disposal responsibilities, particularly if several adjacent municipalities want to combine forces in a single disposal agency. The Southeastern Oakland County Garbage and Rubbish Authority, which

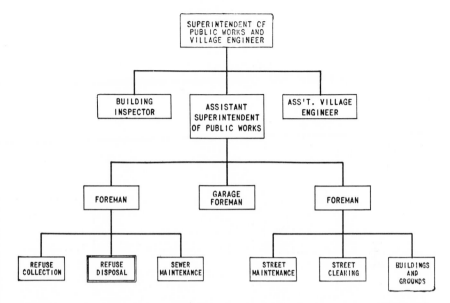

Fig. 139. Organization chart, Public Works Department, Winnetka, Illinois.

operates an incinerator that serves 12 Detroit suburbs, and a Delaware County, Pennsylvania, authority, which services several Philadelphia suburbs, are examples.

The organization for an authority must be self-sufficient. It must include a governing body and provide staff services that in a department type organization are often furnished by municipal departments other than the sanitation or public works agency.

Personnel Administration

Sound personnel administration is important to the success of refuse disposal operations. Recruiting and keeping qualified, loyal workers and supervisors depend on fair dealings, adequate compensation, competent management, and good working conditions.

Since most cities have brought their personnel activities into a central administrative unit, the routine personnel activities of recruitment, classification, compensation, and retirement are not the direct and immediate concern of the management of refuse disposal operations. Therefore, this discussion deals mainly with those aspects of personnel administration that are of special importance to the disposal service and with the activities in which refuse disposal supervisors and employees participate.

Municipalities that have not centralized personnel administration place a much bigger burden on the operating units by requiring that they select and hire their employees and fix their compensation. This may be entirely satisfactory unless there is political involvement; but whenever personnel policies and decisions are subject to political pressures, the chance of having competent and efficient workers is greatly reduced.

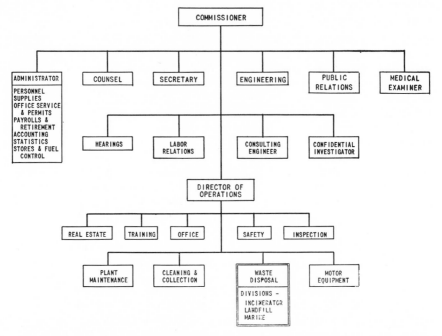

Fig. 140. Organization chart, Department of Sanitation, City of New York.

Basic Standards

Good personnel administration requires the application of basic standards that will result in:

1. Attracting qualified persons to the refuse disposal service through a reputation for fair dealings, career opportunities, able management, and as favorable working conditions as are possible.
2. Providing remuneration that is equal at least to pay for similar work in private industry, taking into account the fact that work must sometimes be performed under unfavorable physical conditions.
3. Encouraging long service on a career basis through dependable, stable employment with opportunities for advancement and eventual retirement.
4. Guaranteeing equal opportunities for all qualified persons to compete for entrance and promotion under impartial and high standard examination procedures.
5. Training employees to do their work better and easier as a means to advancement.
6. Protecting employees from arbitrary separation from the service for trivial or personal reasons, but providing means of discharging incompetent and other undesirable employees for cause.

Routine Activities

All disposal agencies will have some personnel duties to perform. If the city has a central personnel department, the disposal division, bureau, or section is normally limited in its personnel functions to interviewing and accepting employees after they have been centrally certified, checking on competence during the probationary period, promoting morale, and keeping certain records. The operating department, however, often assists the central personnel agency in recruiting (particularly for technical positions), evaluating for promotions, and training. The central agency should establish personnel policies and standards and assist the operating agency in applying them. The operating agency's responsibility should normally be limited to applying the general policies and standards and making them effective. Good standards will be meaningless, however, if personnel policies are subject to political pressures; and if politics is a major factor the administrator should at least insist upon the right to discharge incompetent employees.

If a central personnel agency develops classification plans for employees of the refuse disposal service, disposal supervisors should be consulted in the process. Enough classes of positions should be provided to fit all of the kinds of work performed by the service, but the plan should provide some flexibility in utilizing employees on related work, particularly in preparation for advancement. Some municipalities put all incinerator personnel in one class to permit them to develop versatility in their operations. This, it is claimed, reduces the requirements for stand-by or relief personnel. However, the establishment of several classes makes it possible to utilize personnel in lower classifications as relief for higher classified personnel, thus providing an incentive for improvement and advancement and at the same time establishing an excellent in-service training opportunity.

Compensation elsewhere in the municipal service is normally higher than in the refuse disposal agency, but unusual conditions of the disposal service should be brought to the attention of the officials responsible for the compensation plan. For example, overtime work is not infrequent in some disposal operations and holiday employment may be common. Compensatory leave may be the answer, but usually an overtime pay provision should be incorporated in the pay plan. Furthermore, consideration must be given in the classification and compensation system to work under adverse conditions—dust, odor, and heat.

The personnel in charge of incinerators, landfills, and other facilities are key employees, and special attention should be given to their selection and training. These supervisors are responsible in large part for the efficiency of operations and their success depends upon technical, administrative, and leadership abilities.

Plant supervisors, in turn, should be allowed all possible latitude in selecting new employees for their operations. At the very least, they should interview eligible candidates and make recommendations on appointment to their supervisors or to the personnel agency.

In retirement plans, particular attention should be given to limitations on the useful span of service because of the kinds of tasks and the conditions of work involved.

Civil Service

Civil service systems are becoming increasingly common in municipal government because they offer advantages to both employees and employers. And more and more cities are including laborers' jobs (of which there are many in refuse disposal facilities) in the civil service system, although the trend is more pronounced in cities of more than 100,000 population than it is in smaller ones.

Civil service provides security to good employees by establishing rules of employment and eliminating for the most part the political influence in the appointment and retention of employees that adversely affects the quality of government. A merit system of appointment and promotion provides for selection of employees on the basis of competitive examinations, which take into account training and experience. A positive program of personnel management also provides for equal pay for equal work through a classification and pay plan that includes pay ranges and pay increases for each job. Employees are usually rated by supervisors and are promoted or given pay increases on the bases of the rating and examinations. Most civil service systems provide for paid sick and annual leave and many include a retirement plan. These features make it easier for government agencies to recruit and retain well qualified employees than it was under the old political spoils system.

There are some disadvantages in the civil service systems of many municipalities that limit their usefulness, however. For example, when the system makes it difficult to discharge an incompetent, disloyal, or unproductive civil service employee, the quality of public service is lowered; also, some employees produce less than they would if unsatisfactory work was a cause for dismissal. The disadvantages of civil service may be reduced significantly, however, by recruiting as well qualified employees as possible and by dismissing unsatisfactory recruits during the initial probation period.

Training

Employee training has become an integral part of the personnel system of most cities. It is frequently provided by the sanitation or public works department with assistance from the central personnel department. It may take the form of on-the-job instruction, formal class work within the city service, special concentrated short courses, or classes in colleges or universities.

A good training program is rewarding not only to the employee but also to the city. The time spent by any employee in learning new procedures, methods, or techniques is usually more than compensated for by improved performance. The training of new employees before they actually start work is essential and may prevent costly blunders and wasted time.

Visits by both supervisory and operating personnel to other operating incinerators and sanitary landfills can be helpful in broadening the viewpoint and understanding beyond the employee's own immediate operation. He may pick up tips on operating details that can improve his own performance.

Full use should be made of the training programs available through agencies such as the American Public Works Association and the U. S. Public Health Service, both of which offer courses thoroughly covering both incineration and sanitary landfill. The APWA courses may be arranged for on a city or regional basis. Equipment manufacturers likewise can provide valuable training courses for users of their products. The benefits to the operating agency of knowledgeable and efficient use of equipment provided in connection with refuse disposal are so evident and so important that it would seem remiss on the part of management to fail to take advantage of these training opportunities.

At the level of management there are also many courses offered by universities, the American Public Works Association, the U. S. Public Health Service and others.

In-service training is one of the most rewarding means of promoting morale and efficiency. This type of training can be conducted in sessions provided for particular groups or for individuals. At lower organizational levels, sessions are usually conducted during regular work hours without loss of pay to employees. For higher levels it may be advisable to conduct sessions in whole or in part outside of working hours. In-service training provides a means whereby labor and management can work together for the good of both the employees and the municipal service. In unionized operations it also makes for a better working relationship between unions and municipal governments.

Employee-Management Relations; Working Conditions

Good relations between the city administration, including the sanitation and refuse disposal supervisors, and the disposal employee require a thorough understanding on the part of both of the work that is involved, the conditions under which it is performed, and any special problems. Important among the many factors making for satisfactory employee-management relations are work incentives, employee facilities at disposal sites, employee suggestion systems, employee organization, recreation and social functions, and uniforms.

Work Incentives. Incentives in a refuse disposal operation are designed to raise the stature of the employment and to foster pride in membership in a merit organization. Morale also is built in the course of routine personnel activities through fair dealing in compensation, advancement, training, and career employment, including paid vacations, sick leave, and other fringe benefits. Good working conditions and employee participation in the improvement of disposal methods, procedures, and equipment also raise the level of operations. *Esprit de corps* can be developed by creating friendly competition among the crews of various facilities.

Emphasis on the public health aspects of refuse disposal also has proved a useful work incentive. Workers need to understand the difference between good and poor or inefficient disposal methods and the public benefit that results from sanitary operations. They can experience an intense satisfaction from simple improvements in procedures or methods if they are translated into terms of better public service and better health for the community.

An increasing number of public and private agencies are using incentive devices to maintain the interest of workers and to improve their performance. Among the incentives for outstanding service are:

1. Assignment to preferential shifts.
2. Assignment to preferential routing.
3. Provision of preferred equipment.
4. Letters of commendation from an administrative or elected official.
5. Money or other awards.
6. Safe driving emblems, cumulative by years.
7. Posting of photographs, other personal publicity.
8. Special time off, vacations, or leaves.
9. Dinners and banquets.

Employee Facilities at Disposal Sites. Improvements in the level of the refuse disposal service and in the caliber of refuse disposal employees have generated parallel improvements in working conditions, including facilities for personal sanitation and comfort. This advance is similar to that in industrial plants brought about through state labor laws, activities of employee organizations, and greater employer awareness of the importance of the health and well-being of workers to the quality of their performance.

Certain minimum facilities should be provided at any disposal site to which employees are regularly assigned: sanitary toilets, a supply of safe drinking water, and shelter for eating lunch and changing clothes.

New incinerators should and usually do have modern, sanitary, well maintained toilet rooms, washrooms, showers, lunchrooms, locker rooms, and water coolers. Present-day standards call for two lockers or a double locker for each employee, one for work clothes and the other for street clothes. Other facilities should be adequate for the maximum number of employees on a shift and for equipment operators, truck drivers, and laborers on operations attached to the plant. Incineration plants that do not include appropriate facilities for personnel should be modernized.

Facilities for personnel at sanitary fill and dump sites are a special problem because of the temporary nature of the operations. Minimum facilities should be equivalent to those furnished on large construction projects, but permanent service buildings are possible only at the largest operations. At other sites, portable sheds or specially built trailers can be made to serve effectively for locker rooms, lunchrooms, and toilets.

Suggestion Systems. One of the most fruitful means of securing worker participation in the improvement of refuse disposal services is through employee suggestion programs. An employee gets a genuine sense of belonging and of accomplishment from the adoption of his suggestions and public recognition of them.

A suggestion plan should encourage workers to submit ideas by making the submission as easy and free from embarrassment as possible. Each suggestion should be reviewed and evaluated and when judged valuable should be put into effect. Awards must be made carefully and publicized upon presentation.

Normally workers must be encouraged and even cajoled into making suggestions; the prospect of financial reward helps to overcome their reluctance. Usually a great deal of publicity is necessary to initiate such a program and to keep it alive, and announcements about it should be made at every opportunity in meetings and publications.

Suggestions must be made in writing, but this chore can be eased by the use of forms that indicate what information is required and provide places to enter it. Locked suggestion boxes should be placed at convenient locations, with a supply of suggestion forms nearby. Foremen and other supervisors should offer encouragement and should give assistance when asked. Some systems require that an idea be tried out and savings or benefits proved before the suggestion is put into writing for submission. Such restrictions eliminate many worthless ideas but may also prevent good ideas from being tried at all.

The review and evaluation of suggestions must be made impartially on the basis of careful analysis of potential benefits. Usually a committee of municipal officers and supervisors makes evaluations and recommends awards. The review must be thorough enough to identify suggestions that merit trial or testing, as well as to appraise those of proven merit. Specialists in refuse disposal should be on the committee or available as advisers. Sometimes anonymity is secured by detaching the name of the suggestor as the first step in the review process and identifying the suggestion by number until a decision is made on its usefulness.

Refuse disposal supervisors should give all possible assistance to suggestors to try out their ideas before submission. The awards committee should also have authority to accept untried suggestions that in its discretion seem promising either for trial or for award without trial. In these decisions, the committee should have the full support and assistance of management.

An award can be cash, savings bonds, certificates of merit, or other recognition; its value should be consistent with the value of the suggestion. Sometimes cash is given in proportion to the probable savings, but obviously savings cannot be the sole basis of judgment. Awards consist of 10 per cent of one year's savings in Philadelphia, New York, and San Diego County. The District of Columbia established an incentive awards program in 1955 based on authority contained in the Government Employees' Incentive Awards Act of 1954 (see Section 14C of the District personnel manual).

Perhaps the most important part of a suggestion system is the acclaim given to award winners. Often awards are presented personally by the mayor or a department head at special functions or at regular assemblies of employees. The widest publicity should be given to such presentations.

Although many excellent ideas for improvement come from refuse disposal forces, the suggestion system cannot be considered a moneymaker and should not be expected to be even self-supporting. Most programs cost much more than the value of the direct benefits of the suggestions. The real value comes from improved worker morale and the development of teamwork.

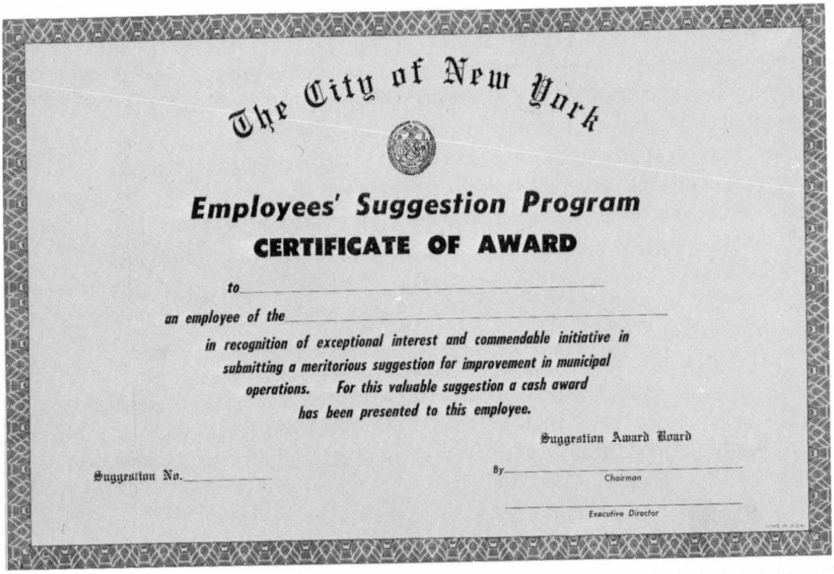

The City of New York

Employees' Suggestion Program

CERTIFICATE OF AWARD

to ______

an employee of the ______

in recognition of exceptional interest and commendable initiative in submitting a meritorious suggestion for improvement in municipal operations. For this valuable suggestion a cash award has been presented to this employee.

Suggestion Award Board

Suggestion No. ______

By ______ Chairman

______ Executive Director

Fig. 141. Certificate issued by New York City to employee who makes an acceptable suggestion. The certificate is given at the same time that the employee is given a cash award.

Organization of Employees. The right of employees of public jurisdictions to organize and bargain collectively is now generally recognized. Public works or sanitation employees may be affiliated with a national or local union. Their organizations may be formed on an industry basis and include all skills and services in a city department or they may include only a single craft.

A 1968 survey, conducted by the International City Management Association, showed that slightly more than half of the public works employees in the 1,474 reporting cities over 10,000 population belonged to a union or employees association. The percentage of reporting cities which had one or more such organizations of public works employees ranged from 30 per cent in cities between 10,000-25,000 to 90 per cent in those over 500,000 population.[2]

[2] The International City Management Association, *The Municipal Year Book 1969* (Washington, D. C.: The Association, 1969), pp. 31-39.

THE CITY OF NEW YORK

EMPLOYEES SUGGESTION PROGRAM

DEPARTMENT OF PERSONNEL
299 Broadway, New York 7, New York

SUGGESTION FORM		FOR OFFICE USE ONLY
Date received		Suggestion No. _____

Please print or type and submit in duplicate either by mail or in person to above address.

Be concise, complete, clear. If necessary attach drawings or charts.

If you need information or assistance in preparing your suggestion, see your departmental coordinator or your supervisor. You may also visit the Suggestion Program office at the above address.

Use separate blank for each distinct subject or suggestion.

The Suggestion Program is CONTINUOUS. There is no time limit. Your suggestions ARE WELCOME AT ANY TIME.

SUBJECT_____DATE_____

Department in which applicable _____

I SUGGEST:

This is the present practice

This is what my suggestion will accomplish

I BELIEVE THIS SUGGESTION WILL

☐ SAVE TIME   ☐ SAVE MATERIAL   ☐ SAVE SPACE   ☐ IMPROVE METHODS   ☐ IMPROVE SAFETY   ☐ SIMPLIFY WORK   ☐ SAVE MONEY

OR (give other reason, if any)

IF MORE SPACE IS NEEDED ATTACH ADDITIONAL SHEETS

(This portion of form will be detached by secretary before department suggestion committee considers your idea.)

SUBJECT_____

I hereby grant to the City of New York and any agency thereof an irrevocable right to use the within suggestion or any modification thereof, whether or not I receive an award therefor, and I hereby agree that the use thereof by the City of New York or by any of its agencies shall not give rise to any claim of any nature whatsoever against the City of New York or any of its agencies, on the part of myself, my heirs or my assigns.

Suggestion No. _____

FOR OFFICE USE ONLY

PRINT Suggester's Name_____

Home Address _____

X _____
SUGGESTER'S SIGNATURE

TITLE_____

DEPT._____

BUREAU_____

MAIL POSTPAID OR DELIVER TO EMPLOYEES SUGGESTION PROGRAM AT ADDRESS SHOWN ABOVE

HP 218 (ESPI)-30M-601054(59)

Fig. 142. Form used by New York City to encourage submission of suggestions by employees. Anonymity of employee can be achieved by removing the perforated stub at the bottom before the filled-in form is sent for evaluation to the agency affected by the suggestion.

Formerly there was a traditional distinction between labor organizations of public employees and those engaged in private enterprise. Strikes against governments were discouraged by public opinion because of the threats they presented to essential public health and safety. Employees felt a need for collective action in the field of grievances more than for compensation increases. With progressive personnel practices and alert, prompt responses as circumstances developed calling for wage scale or other adjustments, most public administrators were able to maintain a degree of confidence and harmony and to avoid confrontations or at least to resolve them without strikes.

This situation no longer holds. Because of spiraling inflation, increased tax load, changes in attitudes toward loyalty and responsibility, and many other influences there are numerous instances where public employees no longer have compunctions about actions crippling essential services. Serious situations resulting from strikes to enforce wage and other demands by police, fire-fighters, teachers, sanitation workers, and even hospital employees are commonplace.

Under these circumstances there still seems to be no better solution for the administrator of refuse disposal services, as well as others, than alert and intelligent use of the best in personnel practices. As a representative of the public's interests, he obviously cannot surrender to every demand presented. His freedom of action is properly limited by the requirement of the approval of an elected city council. Still his best asset in personnel negotiations will be the confidence of his employees in his honesty, fairness, sympathy, sensitivity, impartiality, and helpful intent. Any sense of *esprit de corps* and responsibility that can be engendered will be of fundamental help, not only in personnel relations but also in the quality and efficiency of the service activity.

Properly established and operated grievance procedures are a valuable aid to effective management. City administrators and public works and sanitation officials should support the grievance procedure adopted sincerely and vigorously, doing their utmost to make it work and thus insuring employee confidence in it. Care also must be exercised to prevent undermining the authority of government officials to carry out their duties. Grievance policies and procedures must be based on the principle that management is the final arbiter of grievances, except in those cases where grievances reach the courts.

Grievances are seldom heard by refuse disposal agencies. Grievance procedures are usually administered by the department of public works or sanitation or on a city-wide basis. Refuse disposal officials and supervisors must do their part in developing and maintaining good employee-management relations; adjusting operations, conditions, and policies as needed; and helping management generate trust and confidence by hearing complaints before they become grievances and making reasonable corrections.

Recreation and Social Functions. It is a good policy to encourage occasional social functions for employees such as dinners and picnics and to develop athletic competitions such as bowling and softball. Some of these functions may be limited to refuse disposal personnel, while others such as athletic competitions may be on a department or city-wide basis. It is important to keep athletic activities within bounds in order to avoid interference with the efficiency of the operation, a condition that often occurs when "professionalism" develops.

Uniforms. A requirement that refuse disposal employees wear uniforms is generally recognized as aiding morale. A smart, practical uniform promotes neatness and cleanliness; it also results in savings for the employees in work clothes expense.

Uniforms may be furnished free or they may be purchased by the municipality and sold at cost to employees. Cities may launder the uniforms without charge whether they are provided by the city or by the workers, or they may require the employees to keep the uniforms clean. A usual requirement is two clean uniforms a week.

Accident Prevention

One of the fundamental rules of humanity is "to live and let live." It is also a generally accepted principle that no one shall injure or destroy life or property in the performance of his duties. Thus the basic motivations for an accident prevention program are humanitarian but economic considerations also are important.

It is generally conceded that accidents are a form of economic waste. The amount of money spent to settle claims for injuries or damages incurred in an accident is only one measure of economic loss. Other costs that must be borne by management overshadow direct accident settlement costs; they include repairs to vehicles or machines or the acquisition of new ones, interruptions of service, loss of the workers' services, loss of public good will, and costs of accident investigations, lawsuits, and court appearances.

Safety training for public employees has proved fruitful; accidents have been reduced impressively in a number of cities. Truck driver, charger in an incinerator plant, and equipment operator are among the many occupations that can be made safer through training.

A safety program must be formalized to be effective. It requires:

1. The cooperation and full support of key personnel.
2. A competent staff of trained specialists for implementation of the program.
3. Complete analysis of accidents and accident records, and a systematic prevention plan emphasizing major causes first.
4. Meetings of operating heads.
5. Supervisor and employee education in accident prevention.
6. Maintaining interest through meetings and awards.
7. Development of safe-practice manuals for each major area of activity.

Records. The efficient management of any enterprise depends on proper control of men and materials; control in part depends on the use of records of personnel, equipment, and costs. Accident records are important in determining responsibility; they also provide data needed in

CITY OF NEW YORK — ACCIDENT CONTROL PROGRAM

MONTHLY RECAP OF CAUSES

DEPARTMENT_____

MONTH - YEAR
MANHOURS WORKED
MONTH_____
TO DATE_____

DAYS CHARGED
MONTH_____
TO DATE_____

	FREQUENCY				SEVERITY			
	THIS MONTH	CALENDAR YEAR TO DATE			THIS MONTH	CALENDAR YEAR TO DATE		
		19	19	19		19	19	19

UNSAFE ACT OR UNSAFE CONDITION — UNIT OR SECTION — DISABLING INJURIES (THIS MONTH / YEAR TO DATE)

A 1 OPERATING WITHOUT AUTHORITY
A 2 OPERATING UNSAFE SPEED
A 3 MAKING SAFETY DEVICES INOPERATIVE
A 4 USING UNSAFE EQUIPMENT
A 5 UNSAFE LOADING, ETC.
A 6 TAKING UNSAFE POSITION
A 7 WORKING ON DANGEROUS EQUIPT.
A 8 DISTRACTING, TEASING, ETC.
A 9 FAILURE TO USE PROTECTIVE DEVICES
C 1 INADEQUATELY GUARDED
C 2 UNGUARDED
C 3 DEFECTIVE CONDITION
C 4 UNSAFE DESIGN OR CONSTR.
C 5 HAZARDOUS ARRANGEMENT
C 6 UNSAFE ILLUMINATION
C 7 UNSAFE VENTILATION
C 8 UNSAFE DRESS

TOTAL MONTH

PART OF BODY

TRUNK
HANDS OR ARMS
EYES OR HEAD
LEGS OR FEET
HERNIA
OTHER

NOTE SEE REVERSE SIDE FOR INSTRUCTIONS.

Fig. 143. Form used in New York City for monthly report on accidents. Such reports pinpoint unusual conditions that alert management to the need for corrective steps.

disposal of claims and for supervision and control of workers. They are helpful in securing appropriations for prevention programs.

Accident records in themselves will not prevent accidents. They are valuable in prevention only if used to identify and determine conditions and practices that cause accidents, to maintain the interest of executives in accident prevention through appropriate reports, as a basis for a sound accident prevention program, and for the evaluation of rate and type of progress. Accident records must be accurate and comprehensive. They must reveal unsafe practices by workers and unsafe conditions of plants and facilities and suggest ways in which these practices and conditions can be corrected.

Program Activity. Activities directed to insuring maximum safety may include supervisor and employee meetings on accident prevention, supervisor and employee participation in safety committee work, and the showing of films or slides covering appropriate subject matter. A series of educational talks on accident prevention keyed to prime accident causes, limited to approximately 15 minutes, and given by competent accident prevention specialists, arouses and maintains supervisor and employee interest, brings the accident prevention message to the men directly concerned, and develops employee interest in further investigation, thus creating a pool of "on the spot" safety advocates.

Safety Manuals. It is accepted throughout industry that an employee should be provided with printed matter in easily understood language that describes how he should perform his work efficiently and safely. A manual outlining safety practices should be developed as a part of the accident prevention program in refuse disposal operations so that the men will have definite guides for safe operating practices.

Protective Clothing and Equipment. Protective clothing and equipment should be provided for comfort and must be provided for the safety of refuse disposal employees. Federal labor laws and some state laws set safety standards for certain workers, but they are usually minimal and meet only a part of the needs.

Incinerator employees who are subjected to dust, heat, and smoke must have goggles, shields, or masks, as required; maintenance workers should wear helmets; and charging floor attendants must have safety belts if

TABLE 45

EQUIPMENT USED TO PROTECT EMPLOYEES AT REFUSE DISPOSAL FACILITIES

Head (including hair and ears)	Skull guard (hard hat)
Face and eyes	Hood
	Goggles
	Face shield
	Welding helmet
Respiratory system	Oxygen breathing apparatus
	Air respirator
	Canister and cartridge respirator
	Filter respirator
Hands and feet	Gloves and hand leathers
	Safety shoes
	Foot guards
Body	Chemical resistant clothing
	Heat resistant clothing
	Cold resistant clothing
	Water resistant clothing
	Radioactive resistant clothing
	Special purpose equipment:
	Life line
	Life ring
	Reflector belt

operating conditions warrant. Personal safety equipment is usually provided by the city without charge to employees.

Employees at sanitary fills, dumps, or other outside disposal facilities who work in all kinds of weather should be protected from rain, snow, cold, and heat to the degree possible. Sometimes cities provide raincoats, boots, and rain hats to make sure that workers have them when needed.

In addition to protective clothing, protective equipment and devices must be provided for the safety of employees. Basic precautions must be taken to protect men who operate machines and prime mover and power transmission devices. Safety equipment includes mechanical feeding devices, remote control operating mechanisms, and dust and fume controls. Processes and procedures should be reviewed to insure that as many hazards as possible are eliminated before installing personal protective equipment (summarized in Table 45).

Studies of accident data have led to the development of personal safety equipment specifically designed to protect against known hazards. Workers required to wear such equipment must understand its uses and limitations. The ease and comfort with which it can be worn and its noninterference with normal work procedures are prime considerations in selecting such equipment.

Wages and Hours

Compensation for employees at refuse disposal facilities is usually equivalent to that paid in private industry for work of similar skills and hazards. Some municipalities have a standard work week with standard pay for it for such employees, and time worked beyond the standard week is usually paid for as overtime. Most cities pay workers in refuse disposal facilities on an annual salary basis and give paid vacations and sick leave. Others, however, pay workers on an hourly basis. Employees who work other than day shifts at disposal facilities are paid higher rates than those on the day shift to compensate for the less favorable working hours.

A survey of compensation to incineration plant personnel of 11 major cities, made in 1969 by the American Public Works Association, is summarized in Table 46. The range in annual pay for selected positions is:

	From	To
Superintendent	$8,085	$18,538
Foreman	6,318	11,121
Fireman	5,394	9,256
Crane operator	5,929	14,900
Truck driver	5,170	9,401
Laborer	4,650	8,424

All cities reported overtime payments, usually at 1½ times the regular rate, and ranging up to as high as 25 per cent of normal wages. One city allowed compensatory time off for overtime work.

ANNUAL SALARIES FOR EMPLOYEES AT MUNICIPAL INCINERATION PLANTS
IN 11 CITIES, 1968-69, BY POSITION

	Year	Superintendent	Foreman	Fireman	Crane Operator	Truck Driver	Laborer	Notes
Buffalo	1969	$ 8,085–10,005	$ 6,730–8,430	$5,480–6,840	$ 6,730–8,430	$5,170–6,450	$4,650–5,830	Overtime average 25%. Fringe benefit equivalent to 30% additional.
Chicago	1969	15,318	—	9,256	—	8,944	8,424	
Cincinnati	1968	8,541– 9,206	6,879–7,545	5,394–5,724	6,219–6,549	5,559–5,889	5,070–5,394	Overtime 1½ & 2. Fringe benefits = $0.80/hr overtime at 1½ x.
Detroit	1968	17,332–18,538	8,375–8,911	3,375–3,425/hr	3.60/hr	3.41–3.46/hr	3.045–3.145/hr	
District of Columbia	1969	9,320–12,119	8,050–9,838	6,594–7,134	6,843–7,426	6,843–7,426	5,678–6,136	$0.15/hr night shift premium.
Houston	1969	10,296	6,318	—	7,228	5,278–5,538	4,498–5,070	
Milwaukee	1969	11,934–14,227	9,434–11,121	7,021–8,070	7,517–8,743	6,792–7,785	6,363–7,263	Overtime at 1½ x (averages 100 hrs/yr/man).
Minneapolis	1969	—	10,548	8,016	8,856	8,016	8,016	Overtime at 1 x, 1½ x, 2 x.
New York	1969	12,390	10,060–10,800	9,100	14,900	9,401	—	Overtime in compensatory time off, except truck drivers and all employees Sun. & holidays at 1½ x.
Philadelphia	1969	9,468–10,663	7,496–9,552	*6,018–6,990	7,496–8,411	6,257–6,990	5,410–6,031	Overtime about 10%. *Classification "plant helper."
St. Louis	1969	11,025	7,800–9,412	5,642–6,786	5,929–7,124	5,642–6,786	5,174–6,188	Overtime at 1 x.

Fiscal Management of Disposal Operations

Reporting and analyzing information on refuse disposal operations are important to good management. Many of the major decisions in planning, providing new facilities or additions to old ones, scheduling activities, staffing, and financing depend in large measure on regular, complete, and accurate data on performance and costs. Meaningful budgeting depends on reliable forecasts, specific work programs, and accurate information on costs.

Fortunately, refuse disposal operations lend themselves readily to quantity determinations, simple reporting, and analysis. The processes involve measuring performance and costs, reporting on operations, summarizing and analyzing the data regularly, and making the results known promptly to supervisors and management.

Measurement of Performance

Unit cost and performance determinations require basic measurements of work accomplished. The usual measures are volume (cubic yards) or weight (tons) of the refuse received for disposal.

Most municipalities have used volumetric measurements in the past and for the most part these measurements have been unreliable and misleading. Determinations of volume should be made while the refuse is on the collection truck and each truckload should be examined to determine the degree of compaction, general nature of the material, and percentage of the truck body volume that is occupied. In practice these refinements are seldom incorporated into the volume recorded. Partial loads are often indiscriminately reported as full loads and approximations are used that result in inaccurate reporting.

Volumetric information is necessary, however, for making certain decisions. Since the life of a landfill site is determined by its volumetric capacity, it is important to keep volume records and utilize accurate compaction computations to determine it. This information is essential to sound planning. Periodic surveys of actual fill volume will provide not only firsthand information on future capacity but also an accurate means of checking truck volume records. If refuse is measured by weight, sample loads should be analyzed to determine volume as well. A density factor for converting tons to cubic yards is necessary for this purpose.

Weight measurement provides much more realistic and accurate refuse disposal data and is the only measure of quantity that is sufficiently exact for performance reporting. A ton is the normal unit used for measuring refuse. Scales must be provided to weigh all refuse if this measure is adopted. Inasmuch as scales are almost always provided at incineration and other plants, and even at large landfills, weight determinations are no problem at such places. Most cities do not provide scales at small fills or at dumps, however, because of the expense of installation and operation. Some recent developments, including portable scales and others that although not actually portable can be moved easily from one location to another, give promise of overcoming the most serious objections to weighing at landfills.

The trend is toward weight measurement of all refuse and some cities have already achieved this goal. New York, for instance, is now weighing all of the refuse taken to all of its disposal facilities (incinerators, marine transfer stations, and landfills). Weighing is done semi-automatically on 25 electronic scales that print net payloads and nine other items of information. The use of self-printing truck scales provides a continuous record of production, including the weight of each truck load by truck number and time of delivery. The recording mechanism can be located some distance from the scale platform.

Truck scales are expensive to purchase, install, and operate, and the self-printing type costs more initially and requires slightly more maintenance than the manual or indicating type. Weight records, to be useful, must be kept continuously, which requires rapid repairs or the provision of stand-by scales in case of breakdown. Consequently, a reasonable number of spare parts should be kept on hand. The type of scales and the number needed should be determined on the basis of records of breakdowns and the availability of parts. It may be desirable to contract for scale maintenance.

Maintenance of scales is important; the cost of neglect is high. Normal maintenance requirements of modern scales are low unless the scales are tampered with or abused. Maximum protection against tampering should be provided for all installations.

Field Reporting

Field reports of refuse disposal operations constitute the initial and most important phase of the performance and cost analysis process. Management analyses and reports can be no more complete and accurate than the field data prepared by disposal workers and supervisors on which they are based.

The amount of refuse received and disposed of and other needed information is reported automatically if self-printing scales are used; if manual scales are used, care must be used to record gross, tare, and net weight, truck number, and time. If scales are not used, the volume must be estimated as accurately as possible. Complete records should be prepared at each refuse disposal facility.

Incinerator operating reports should show all pertinent data for each shift of personnel on duty, hours of work, furnaces operated, fuel used, breakdowns, maintenance work, and quantities of refuse received and ash removed. Reports on sanitary landfills may be simpler, but should include information as to location, personnel on duty, hours of work, weather, and amount of refuse and cover material placed.

All field reports should be made daily and forwarded to superiors at the end of the day or the beginning of the following day.

Performance Records

Refuse disposal supervisors depend more and more on performance records and analyses in operational control. The analyses require only simple calculations, so the supervisor of a disposal facility should have complete performance data promptly.

Performance units for refuse disposal usually are man-hours per ton of refuse disposed of or tons per hour of operation. Cubic yards instead of tons must be used at facilities without scales. All the data needed for performance records, such as man-hours, amount of refuse, and operating hours, must be included in the daily reports, which should be summarized for district, area, division, bureau, and department officials. Reports also should be summarized weekly, monthly, and annually to give a continuous appraisal of operations and to provide the means of discovering weak points in the operation.

In summary, the establishment of performance measures as a means of controlling operations depends on:

1. A reporting system that includes all personnel, materials, and equipment used.
2. Report forms that are simple but comprehensive.
3. Prompt and accurate reporting.
4. Prompt and accurate analysis and evaluation of data.
5. The presentation of data and evaluations in a simple, easily understood, and useful manner.

The use of charts, graphs, tables, and figures can aid in the presentation of much of the information.

Cost Accounting

Unit costs have been the principal basis of refuse disposal control for many years. Reliable cost data, carefully interpreted and used, are still important to management—second only to performance measurement. One difficulty with using unit costs to measure performance effectiveness, however, is that the information is usually available so late that it is valueless for day-to-day or week-to-week control. Unit cost reports are usually prepared monthly and are not available until about 10 days after the close of a month's business and often much later.

Another shortcoming of unit costs as a measure of efficiency is the lack of agreement among cities on what elements of cost should be included. For example, most cities report incineration costs that reflect only direct operating costs—labor, materials, and utilities such as electricity and gas. Occasionally water is included if it is used in large quantities. Fixed capital costs of the plant are usually ignored. Sometimes an item is included for amortization of that portion of a new facility that was financed by a long-term loan. Final disposal of incinerator residue is often not reported at all. Equipment expense is sometimes omitted. Office and other kinds of overhead are another variable that is sometimes included to show a portion of the cost of direct administration and supervision up through the bureau head, but more often overhead is ignored. Because of these variations, valid comparisons of unit costs among cities are usually impossible; comparisons of dissimilar data are seriously misleading.

Within a single jurisdiction in which the same cost elements are included in each statement, unit costs can be useful in operational control and management. If adequately reported, such costs constitute an over-all measure of the amounts spent for manpower, equipment, materials, utilities, and overhead. The total cost per ton disposed of is a useful and reliable measure of long-term efficiency, and each refuse disposal agency should develop and use unit costs for continuing analysis of operating efficiency.

A standard reporting system for refuse disposal operations that includes fixed and final costs is desirable. The following elements of cost can be standardized:

1. Amortization of capital investment, including equipment replacement and major alterations and repairs.
2. Direct operations (personnel).
3. Tools, supplies, and utilities.
4. Routine maintenance and repairs.
5. Administration and overhead.
6. Reclamation and salvage revenues (credit).

In working out the amortization of plant and major equipment costs, the basis should be the tonnage that can be processed in a 24-hour-day operation and the amortization should be spread over periods from 15 to 40 years, depending on the parts of the plant involved. On a 25-year life basis, assuming a unit costing $1,000 per ton per day of estimated or rated capacity, 4 per cent interest, 80 per cent use of capacity (a conservative figure for a 25-year life), and 24-hour operation for 250 days a year, the amortized cost of a plant on a tonnage processed basis (using straight line depreciation) would be 30 cents a ton. The amortized cost per ton of a plant that costs $5,000 a ton to construct would be five times 30 cents, or $1.50 per ton of refuse processed. If experience indicates a change in the number of tons of refuse processed from that estimated, corrections are required in the amortization computation.

Operating Personnel. Costs for operating personnel should include those for all personnel involved: (1) all clerical help used in keeping plant records; (2) personnel used in the weighing, tipping, and furnace charging areas; (3) men used to charge, operate, stoke, fire, and tend the furnaces; (4) personnel used for loading and transporting incinerator residue to a final disposal site; (5) plant cleaning and first echelon maintenance personnel, including all persons involved in plant sanitation, the cleaning of bins, furnaces, flues, and so forth, and those who perform daily and weekly maintenance operations, such as partial replacement of grates and links, small areas of refractory surfaces, stoking tools, and piping; and (6) all plant supervisory personnel.

If the plant is equipped with devices such as waste heat boilers and fly ash eliminators that require employees not covered in the categories above, their costs of operating should be added. To these direct costs should also be added overhead, including insurance, vacations, sick leave, pensions, and all other employee fringe benefits. In the absence of exact data on the cost of fringe benefits, an allowance of 15 to 20 per cent of direct labor costs is usually adequate.

The breakdown of personnel operating costs described may be difficult to compute in small plants where employees frequently perform several of the functions noted. In such instances, it may be simpler and equally satisfactory to consolidate some of these costs, provided that the consolidation is clearly recognized.

Tools, Supplies, and Utilities. Costs for tools, supplies and utilities include everything used in operating the plant—among others, light bulbs, weight tickets, refractory patching material, stoking tools, brooms, crane parts, fuel, power, and water. The costs involved in purchasing supplies should be included under administration and overhead and should include an allowance for warehousing and transporting materials.

Routine Maintenance and Repairs. Costs for maintenance and repairs should be included in the expense budget and should be dealt with in the same way as personnel and other expenses. However, major alterations, plant rehabilitation, and equipment replacement items that require amortization should be included in the capital budget. Included in the capital budget category are reconstruction of furnaces, flues, and combustion chambers; structural changes to the building; extensive chimney repairs.

Administration and Overhead. Costs for administration and overhead, which include all those for employees outside of the plant operation

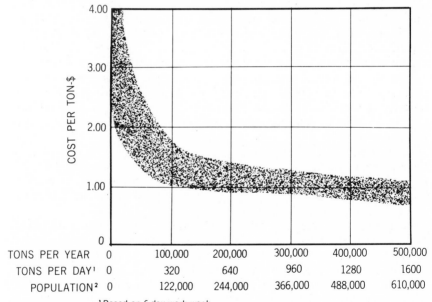

TONS PER YEAR	0	100,000	200,000	300,000	400,000	500,000
TONS PER DAY[1]	0	320	640	960	1280	1600
POPULATION[2]	0	122,000	244,000	366,000	488,000	610,000

[1] Based on 6-day work week.
[2] Based on national average of 4 5 lbs per person per calendar day.

Fig. 144. Sanitary landfill operating costs are taken from "Sanitary Landfill Facts," U. S. Department of Health, Education, and Welfare, Public Health Service, Solid Waste Program, 1968.

(engineers, analysts, secretaries, clerks) and for rent and insurance, for instance, should be prorated to the various operations.

Revenue received from the sale of steam from waste heat or salvage should be considered as a credit. Charges for administrative and operating costs related to salvage or reclamation should be taken into account in computing net revenue.

Factors used in determining incineration costs also are used, with appropriate modifications, to determine sanitary landfill operating costs. Amortization of capital costs, for example, is applied to site preparation and automotive equipment costs. The costs of land acquisition must also be taken into account, but they may be a net credit because of the appreciating value of the property as a result of the filling operation.

Sanitary Landfill Costs. The costs of operating a sanitary landfill were reported to be as shown in Figure 144 by the U.S. Public Health Service in 1968. The influence of size of operation on unit costs is demonstrated.

Budget Control

Modern budget control is another essential tool of mangement. The purposes of budgeting are to assure that suitable plans for development and operation are made, that adopted policies are carried out, and that spending is held within the amount budgeted for the various purposes.

The first step in budget preparation is forecasting the amount of each kind of work to be done during the coming budget year. Forecasts should be based on long- and short-range plans for development of facilities, on plans of operation, and on past operating records. Plans for expanded activities and new operations must be given special attention.

The second step of budget preparation is the development of work programs. The forecasted amount of work is translated into dollars by correlating work standards and unit costs. A work program should indicate by months or quarters what work is to be accomplished and how much it will cost.

After the budget is adopted, the work program must be revised to fit the amount of money available. The revised program becomes the year's plan of operation, both as to spending and as to the amount of work to be done for the amount budgeted. Budget appropriations are frequently allotted on a quarterly basis for control purposes.

Inasmuch as the budget is the official plan of control, regular statements of cost and performance should be based on it. Sometimes current spending and performance are compared with those forecast for a year ahead to show the status of the programs. If budgets do not include amortization of capital expenditures and major plant maintenance, the budgetary control statements should not include such expenses. Budget statements that omit amortization figures may be adequate for operational analysis and control, since the costs represent valid amounts for internal comparisons among plants, crews, methods, and for most other operating purposes. The omission from such statements of amortization costs should not be overlooked, however, in making comparisons among various methods or with other jurisidictions. The unit amortization cost of capital outlays should be recorded for use when total unit costs are needed.

Purchasing

Refuse disposal does not require extensive use of materials, so purchasing is not a major management problem. Equipment, parts, supplies, fuel, and lubricants are usually procured through a central services office or agency for the city. Large municipal refuse disposal agencies may have the authority to make direct purchases under certain conditions and in accordance with prescribed procedures, however.

Under a central purchasing arrangement, the head of the disposal agency and his authorized representatives usually issue requisitions for the supplies and equipment required. Items that are in stock are issued to the refuse disposal agency and charged to the appropriate accounts; items that are not in stock are procured by the purchasing agent.

Good practice requires that the city finance office review purchase orders for encumbrance of appropriations or allotments in order to keep budgetary control. Blanket and emergency purchases must be controlled if the budget is not to be exceeded.

Analysis of Performance and Costs

Accurate records and analysis of performance data are important in a refuse disposal operation, whether it is large or small. If it is large, a detailed system and the use of mechanical aids are essential; if it is small, the analysis can be simple. The collecting, sorting, and summarizing of data can be simplified if well designed forms and well planned reports are used. A form for reporting operations at an incineration plant in

PLANT OPERATING REPORT

Period from ______ to ______ incl.

MATERIAL RECEIVED - TONS							
GARBAGE			RUBBISH			TANKAGE TOTAL	TOTAL MATERIAL
CITY	INDUSTRIAL	TOTAL	CITY	INDUSTRIAL	TOTAL		

RESIDUE						
CLASS	FURNACE ASH	FLUE ASH	FLY ASH	METAL	TANKAGE	GREASE POUNDS
TONS - WET WEIGHT						
CU. YDS. EST. VOLUME						X
TONS - EST. DRY WEIGHT						X
FURNACE NUMBER	1	2	3	4	5	6
BURNING HOURS						
DOWN TIME HOURS						

COST OF OPERATION	
ITEM	AMOUNT
OPERATING	
PERSONNEL	
EQUIP. & SUPPL.	
POWER	
OTHER	
Total Operating	
MAINTENANCE	
PERSONNEL	
EQUIP. & SUPPL.	
OTHER	
Total Maintenance	
Total Operation	
INCOME	
Net Cost of Oper.	
Water Used - Gal.	

REMARKS

SIGNED

(Continue remarks on other side)

77-132

Fig. 145. Form used in Philadelphia for reporting bi-weekly on incineration plant operations.

THE CITY OF EDMONTON — ENGINEERING DEPARTMENT
MONTHLY SUMMARY OF INCINERATOR OPERATION _____ 19___

	LOADS AND TONS RECEIVED									NUMBER OF CHARGES				FURNACE HOURS				ASHES CU. YDS.	FLY ASH REM'D CU. YDS.	PAYROLL	
Days	City Trucks		Hired Trucks		Private Trucks		TOTAL		CU. YDS.	No. 1	No. 2	No. 3	TOTAL	No. 1	No. 2	No. 3	TOTAL				AVERAGE TONS PER FURNACE HOUR
	L	T	L	T	L	T	L	T													

(Days rows 1 through 31, and Totals)

Right-side summary entries:
No. 1
No. 2
No. 3
TOTAL
% Ash By Volume
POWER READINGS K.W.H.
31st
1st
TOTAL K.W.H.
WATER READINGS Cu. Ft.
31st
1st
TOTAL Cu. Ft.
GAS READINGS M.C.F.
31st
1st
TOTAL M.C.F.
Total Utilities
Payroll
Total Cost
Cost Per Ton
Animals Burned _____
Signed

Fig. 146. Form used in Edmonton, Alberta, Canada, for reporting monthly on incineration plant operations.

Plant	(A) Rated Design Capacity in Tons per Day	Total Refuse Received		(2) Tons of Residue Produced, (Dry)	Refuse Destroyed		Plant Performance				(8)* Operating Man-Days per Ton Burned		(9)** Total Man-Days per Ton Burned	
		Truck Loads	(1) Tons		(3) Quantity in Tons	(4) Per Cent of Tons Received	(5) Per Cent of Design Capacity	(6) Per Cent Furnace Up-time	(7) Per Cent Furnace Per-formance		This Period	Per Cent Change from Last Year	This Period	Per Cent Change from Last Year
					③÷①	①÷Ⓐ			⑤÷⑥					
No. 1														
No. 2														
No. 3														

*Total plant manpower, including residue hauling.
**Total of column 8 plus plant supervisory, housekeeping and security manpower.

Fig. 147. Form for reporting performance and manpower utilization for incinerator operations (exclusive of fixed administrative overhead). This type of report gives management comparative information on performances in several incineration plants and on a weekly, monthly, or annual basis. With modifications the form can be used to report performance at landfills.

COUNTY SANITATION DISTRICTS
REFUSE DISPOSAL CREDIT CARD

771-5   4.25
STEED BROS BLDG CNTR
714 DATE AVE.
ALHAMBRA, CALIF.

Fig. 148. Charge-a-plate issued by the Los Angeles County Sanitation Districts to private contractors who use the districts' refuse disposal facilities and pay a fee for the use of them.

Philadelphia is shown in Figure 145. Figure 146 is a similar form used in Edmonton, Alberta, Canada, for monthly reports. A performance record and man-hour correlation recording and computation form is shown in Figure 147.

Another aid to keeping accurate records and accounts is a charge-a-plate (Figure 148) issued to private refuse collectors who must pay to dispose of refuse at city facilities. Another is a receipt form for refuse received from a private collector (Figure 149), which can be forwarded to the accounting office where the information is punched on cards to facilitate billing.

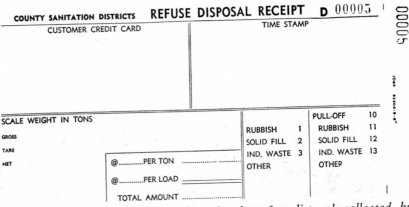

COUNTY SANITATION DISTRICTS	REFUSE DISPOSAL RECEIPT	D 00005
CUSTOMER CREDIT CARD	TIME STAMP	

SCALE WEIGHT IN TONS		PULL-OFF 10
GROSS	RUBBISH 1	RUBBISH 11
TARE	SOLID FILL 2	SOLID FILL 12
NET	IND. WASTE 3	IND. WASTE 13
	OTHER	OTHER
@............PER TON		
@............PER LOAD		
TOTAL AMOUNT		

Fig. 149. Form showing receipt of refuse for disposal collected by private contractors who use Los Angeles County Sanitation Districts' disposal facilities.

In any event, tabulating and reporting data on refuse disposal operations are useless unless the information is properly analyzed; and analysis of tabulated data and physical operations is useless unless action is taken to change operations if change is desirable. When performance data are properly used, operations can be improved and costs reduced.

Financing Disposal Operations

About 70 per cent of the cities in the United States finance disposal operations out of general tax revenues; the balance charge fees to finance operations. It is customary in most cases to charge private collectors, industries, and businesses for disposal of all waste delivered to the public agency regardless of tax support, although the comparatively reasonable rates formerly charged reflected some credit for tax support.

A check made by the American Public Works Association in 1969, as shown in Table 47, disclosed that most cities have revised upwards their charges for disposal of solid wastes delivered by private haulers, industries, and businesses since a previous similar survey in 1959. Current rates charged usually reflect more realistically the actual disposal costs involved in most cases, with those for incineration ranging from $4.00 to $9.00 per ton. The bases for the charges differ, however, usually to reflect peculiarities of local practices. In some cases, particularly in smaller places, only a nominal charge or none at all is made to residents for household refuse self-hauled to a landfill, presumably on the theory that public expense of operating a collection system can thus be minimized, avoided, or postponed.

SPECIAL ADMINISTRATIVE CONSIDERATIONS

Administrative considerations of special interest to refuse disposal planners, officials, and supervisors include (1) selection and maintenance of the correct equipment to insure dependable operations; (2) provision and management of stand-by facilities and capacity; (3) prevention of nuisances and hazards; (4) provision of services to rural and semirural areas; (5) establishment of a good public relations program; (6) development of suitable work standards; and (7) control of private users of facilities.

Selection and Maintenance of Equipment

Trouble-free operation of refuse disposal facilities requires that equipment be selected carefully and maintained properly. It must be sufficiently rugged to withstand the wear and tear to which it is subjected. It is foolhardy to think that purchasing equipment on the basis of low initial cost will necessarily save money. Equipment should be simple and practical. Both plant and equipment should be designed for dependable operation under the most extreme loads to which they are likely to be subjected.

Justification for the purchase of adequate equipment takes into account amortization and operating and maintenance costs. It also takes into account the public acceptance and good will that are generated by uninterrupted and adequate services. Overtime work and disrupted operations

TABLE 47

CHARGES TO PRIVATE USERS OF MUNICIPAL DISPOSAL FACILITIES, 1969

City	Rate	Remarks
Buffalo, New York	$5.00/T	Rate is $1.00/500 lbs plus $1.00/load. This is $5.00/T for first ton and $1.00 for each additional ton. Incinerated.
Chicago, Illinois	6.00/T	Refuse not accepted from private sources in general. Rate applies to material incinerated, hauled by private truckers from foreign vessels in port.
Evanston, Illinois	5.00/T	Incinerated. $5.00 minimum charge.
Houston, Texas	0.25/load under 1T 0.50/load over 1T	Land-filled only.
Milwaukee, Wisconsin	8.00/T	Incinerated. $2.00/500 lbs or fraction thereof.
Minneapolis, Minnesota	4.00–9.00/T	Incinerated. $4.00 rate applies to dry material. $9.00 rate applies to wet material.
New York, New York	1.55–2.15/cu. yd.	Incinerated or land-filled at same rate. Compacted or baled refuse $2.15/cu. yd.; non-compacted $1.55/cu. yd. Construction wastes $3.90/load veh. wt. 5T or less; $9.75 over 5T; $19.50 tractor-trailer.
Philadelphia, Pennsylvania	6.00/T	Incinerated.
Sandusky, Ohio	2.80–3.80/T	Land-filled. 14¢/100 lbs to resident; 19¢/100 lbs to nonresident. Minimum charge 50¢ to resident; $1.00 to nonresident.
Tacoma, Washington	0.50/load 4T GVW 1.00/load 4–10/T GVW 1.25/load over 10T GVW	Land-filled only. Cars and pickups from residences free. 50% higher to nonresidents.

resulting from mechanical failures may be much more expensive than the cost of high quality equipment to begin with.

A sound maintenance program is needed to keep disposal equipment in top operating condition. The most important element in such a program is advance planning—knowing enough about each item of equipment to be able to determine the best time to withdraw it from operation for examination, testing, and any needed rehabilitation. Orderly replacement of equipment should be done routinely. That it is a mistake to operate equipment until it fails is a well established fact; nevertheless, penurious budget authorities and legislatures often do not permit the establishment of proper preventive maintenance programs through lack of understanding.

Planned maintenance involves three operations. The first two are preventive, calling for routine inspections on a daily and a monthly basis and the making of necessary minor repairs. The third is a complete periodic overhaul. Through proper scheduling of inspections, repairs, and overhauls, incipient defects that might lead to operating difficulties are discovered in time to permit routine corrections and thus avoid some major repairs and replacements.

For preventive maintenance to be fully effective, backlogs of work must be avoided. Often this is difficult to achieve, but a course of action that initiates preventive maintenance as each new facility is completed and put into operation helps to this end.

Stand-By Facilities

Stand-by capacity to take care of peak loads, heavy seasonal loads, and breakdowns is necessary to avoid nuisances and unsanitary conditions. The possibility of multiple simultaneous breakdowns should be anticipated and reasonable care taken so that the effects of such occurrences are not disastrous. Since refuse disposal is to a great extent a materials handling process, and, since some types of material cause rapid deterioration of equipment, a disposal operation should make adequate provision for emergencies and extended down-time. These provisions may include stand-by or alternative equipment or facilities, oversize storage bins, or arrangements with neighboring municipalities for use of their facilities. If sufficient stand-by arrangements have not been made, other less satisfactory methods must be used or refuse must be allowed to accumulate. Either of these courses of action is likely to result in nuisances and potential health and fire hazards.

In spite of shortcomings, it is well to investigate the possibilities of using at least for short periods less desirable though adequate alternatives to take care of excess amounts of refuse during peak periods—or even all the refuse if a plant breaks down. For example, all refuse can be deposited in a landfill that is normally used only for disposing of incinerator residue and other noncombustibles. It should be recognized, however, that hauling refuse to a landfill may be more expensive than providing proper stand-by facilities.

Prevention of Nuisances and Hazards

Good administration of a disposal operation involves providing for as many safeguards against the possibility of nuisances and hazards as can be justified economically in light of their probable frequency and degree. Many safeguards, such as a fire extinguisher, a hose and pump connected to a small water storage tank, or a shallow well or hydrant as protection against fire at a landfill site, are relatively inexpensive.

The number of spare parts that should be kept on hand for an overhead crane used at an incineration plant, for instance, has to be determined by realistically forecasting the frequency of breakdowns in relation to the time required to get the parts from the manufacturer or his distributor.

When a poor disposal facility such as a burning dump is shut down, the municipality should take steps to prevent rodent and insect migration. A concerted rat-baiting and insect-spraying program, following good pest control practices, will protect the neighboring area from a potentially dangerous situation.

Services to Rural and Semirural Areas

Refuse disposal problems in rural and semirural areas relate to, among others, farms; strip developments along highways, rural roads, and streams; fringe areas of towns; and unincorporated communities.

These refuse disposal problems involve special management considerations. Most problems pertain to health but there are also problems relating to the jurisdiction that provides disposal services. These latter involve such matters as storage, transportation, disposal, funds available, regulations, and enforcement.

Farms usually present no serious problems; farm animals and poultry provide easy disposal for most garbage. Combustible rubbish is disposed of by burning and noncombustible rubbish is allowed to accumulate until there is enough to justify hauling it away or burying it.

Strip development areas are usually without their own local government or facilities to carry on refuse disposal as a public undertaking. In such instances, where the volume of work justifies, it may be practical for the county to provide collection and disposal services through scavengers or private collectors that it licenses. If a scavenger disposes of garbage by feeding it to pigs, he must conform to state and local health regulations.

In fringe areas and in unincorporated communities, cooperation of adjoining cities in providing collection and disposal services is desirable. The cost of such services may be met by fees charged to the householder or business or the county government may reimburse the city. When this arrangement is not practical or acceptable it may be advisable to have the service carried out by licensed scavengers, as in strip developments. There are also instances where refuse disposal service is provided to such areas through sanitation or garbage districts.

The operating personnel engaged in providing services to unincorporated towns, villages, and other small places should have a variety of skills. A bulldozer operator, for instance, may be used part-time as a truck driver, or his services may be divided between the street department and the department of sanitation. Such divisions of time are not a disadvantage provided competent personnel can be employed. If employees do not have sufficient technical knowledge to guide disposal operations, state health agencies usually will assist in training them.

Responsibility for sanitary refuse disposal rests with government officials, no matter what the form or size of government. There should be a basic willingness on the part of the governing body to meet sanitation standards and it should make a sincere effort to convince the public of the need for such standards and of the need for funds to provide adequate services. When officials are unwilling to take the initiative, interested citizens and citizen groups can work to bring about community consciousness of need and to secure the necessary action.

Local conditions and the size of the disposal operation help to determine the most satisfactory operating procedure—that is, whether public employees, licensed scavengers, or contract services should be used. More important than procedure is the matter of suitably trained employees and adequate supervision. Periodic inspections of sanitary conditions by state health authorities can be helpful; and often supervision is necessary to prevent regression of standards of sanitation.

Public Relations Program

Securing public approval and engendering confidence in refuse disposal operations are the objectives of public relations programs. The success of operations depends to a large extent on public understanding of the disposal function—its problems and the steps taken to overcome them—and public knowledge that a real effort is being made to give good service. Success also depends on awareness on the part of the responsible officials of public desires for service and of the social changes that are taking place in the city.

It has become increasingly evident that the most serious obstacle to be overcome in the establishment of a new disposal facility is the matter of obtaining public acceptance and permission for the operation at the desired locality. Zoning and other official permits must be obtained, usually after public hearings. Objections of surrounding property owners can be extreme and even violent. Unfortunately there are still so many examples of poor disposal operations that the courts and other official bodies can be persuaded to look with suspicion on any proposal, despite assurances of its proponents that it will be well conducted and free of nuisances and health hazards.

Refuse disposal deals with obnoxious materials that have long been synonymous in the public mind with obnoxious disposal methods. Many residents associate the evils of open burning dumps and completely obsolete and inadequate incinerators with any new proposal. It is to the discredit of many disposal agencies that such conditions are still allowed to exist, sometimes under the label of "sanitary landfills". Such practices make it extremely difficult to get permission to establish even the most modern, nuisance-free facilities. The public can hardly be criticized for suspicion of the conditions that will arise from a new disposal project.

In such cases a great deal of preliminary public education is called for. The most convincing argument that can be produced is the example of a well-conceived and well-conducted project that can be pointed to as a demonstration of what the proposed operation will be. This must be accompanied by publicity on technical and operational advances aimed at eliminating hazards and nuisances, as well as education along the lines that refuse disposal is a very necessary public activity to take care of a problem to which everyone contributes and has a responsibility. Somehow there must also be engendered a public confidence that the promises made will be meticulously carried out.

Much attention and emphasis should be given to the positive angle of neighborhood improvement. Incinerators that are attractive architecturally, on well-landscaped grounds, are more appealing than run-down, out-moded industrial or slum eyesores. The prospect of creating a park area by filling a tract which is currently wasteland can be an attractive incentive.

Employees in direct contact with the public who are well trained in and practice courtesy and cooperation contribute substantially to good public relations. Although normally only a minority of refuse disposal employees have direct contact with the public, one rude, uncooperative employee can destroy a disproportionately large amount of public good will.

Suitable Work Standards

It is important to good administration to develop and adhere to suitable standards of work. Quantity standards for work production are necessary to budgeting in determining manpower and equipment requirements; they are also necessary in evaluating the performance of individual employees and machines. Quality standards are necessary in meeting public health requirements consistently. Unfortunately, quality standards have not been established for all facets of disposal—incinerator residue, for example. Although there are air pollution regulations in many cities in which an attempt has been made to set acceptable standards for stack emissions, for instance, such standards are not usually applicable to incineration of refuse because they do not recognize local and seasonal tolerances and climatic conditions. These and other standards for incineration, for landfills, and for the other disposal methods are discussed elsewhere in this manual.

It is the responsibility of management to work for the improvement of standards. Management should also insure that established standards are met, first by communicating them to all operating personnel involved and then by providing a reporting, recording, and inspection system that permits management constantly to control performance.

Control of Private Use of Facilities

The private use of municipally owned disposal facilities must be carefully controlled. Methods include (1) licensing of commercial users; (2)

establishment of standard fees for users; (3) development of a practical method for billing or for advanced sale of dump tickets; (4) establishment and strict enforcement of regulations; and (5) keeping of records of those who do not comply with regulations and denying use of the facilities to those who repeatedly violate the regulations.

In Conclusion

The tremendous growth of urban areas is continually reducing the amount of space available, suitable, and close enough for disposal of refuse in landfills. The feasibility of using more distant sites through economical transportation is not yet fully accepted although studies indicate some promise. Meanwhile there is increased demand for disposal methods that do not utilize as much space but are economical, sanitary, and nuisance-free.

The demand has led to greater use of incineration to reduce the volume of the combustible materials which constitute such a large part of the total solid wastes. There is a trend in large metropolitan areas toward highly mechanized plants which reduce man-hour requirements and operating nuisances. Recognizing this trend, management should work consistently to recruit or train highly skilled personnel and to improve systems. Electronic data processing machines are needed in large operations for computing and record keeping. Employee unions are growing in importance, and management should foster good working relationships with them. The administrator should lead and cooperate in improving working conditions, safety practices, in-service training, and other services and practices that will contribute to an efficient and effective disposal system.

Refuse disposal is already big business in many cities and it is growing bigger year by year. Municipalities must recognize this growth and provide, through enlightened management, for continuing improvement in techniques and standards so that ever more effective refuse disposal will be assured.

APPENDIXES

Appendix A

TENTATIVE METHODS OF ANALYSIS OF REFUSE AND COMPOST

Initial Sampling
General Instructions
Tests for Moisture (Water)
   Oven Drying Method
   Infrared Method
   Toluene Distillation Method
Test for Volatile Solids and Ash
Test for Lipids (Ether Extract)
Test for Liquids
Test for Crude Fiber
Test for Sugars
Tests for Starch
   Anthrone-Sulfuric Acid Method
   Direct Acid Hydrolysis Method
Test for Carbon
Test for Nitrogen (Organic and Ammoniacal)
   Kjeldahl-Wilfarth-Gunning Method
Test for Protein
Test for Carbon-Nitrogen Ratio
Test for Phosphorus (Phosphate)
Tests for Potassium (Potash)
   Flame Photometric Method
   Sodium Tetraphenyl Borate Method
Test for Hydrogen-Ion Concentration (pH)
Test for Gross Calorific Value
Test for Net Calorific Value
Test for Sulfur
Test for Hydrogen and Carbon

This appendix is the first compilation of proposed methods for the examination of solid and semi-solid wastes—particularly domestic refuse. The tests described were selected because of practical experience with them in several comprehensive municipal studies. Several of the methods of testing were developed or adapted for use by the Technical Development Laboratory Communicable Disease Center of the United States Public Health Service in Savannah, Georgia.[1]

---

[1] John Wiley and Janet T. Spillane, *Methods for Examination of Raw and Composted Organic Wastes*, Chemical Memorandum No. 4, U. S. Public Health Service, Communicable Disease Center, Technical Development Laboratories (Savannah, Ga.: U. S. Public Health Service, 1956), 24 pp. (mimeo.).
Assay of Carbon-14 Labeled Materials and Determination of Total Carbon in Organic Materials by Induction Furnace Combustion Technique, Chemical Memorandum No. 5, U. S. Public Health Service, Communicable Disease Center, Technical Development Laboratories (Savannah, Ga.: U. S. Public Health Service, 1958), 9 pp. (mimeo.).

It is hoped that careful use and evaluation of the tests will lead to the adoption of more uniform and efficient methods of solid waste analysis. The tests may also be of value in analyzing agricultural, industrial, and commercial solid wastes and products of their decomposition.

Analysis of refuse is helpful—and even necessary in many cases—in planning and designing refuse disposal systems and facilities, in operation of the facilities, in evaluation and grading of facilities by operators and by regulatory agencies, and in pilot studies and research on methods of disposal and treatment. They are especially useful in planning and designing incineration and composting plants and in determining whether salvage is worthwhile. Various types of chemical tests made of the refuse used in composting are valuable in regulating the production cycle and controlling the quality of the end product.

Standard analysis methods also make possible standard reporting, which is necessary if the results of tests from different cities are to be accurately compared. It is also important to keep records of refuse components by the 10 categories listed below over a number of years to ascertain trends in refuse production. Little or no time is saved if records are kept by fewer categories.

Most solid wastes consist of refuse, as defined in Chapter 1 and classified in Table 3. Sampling and analyses are usually made on the basis of how refuse is collected in a city: combined or mixed, rubbish, combustible refuse with or without garbage, and garbage. Less important kinds of refuse also analyzed on the basis of how they are collected are ashes, street refuse, yard rubbish (if collected separately), and sewage solids (if they are disposed of with refuse or some of its components). Of minor importance in chemical analytical studies are noncombustible refuse, dead animals, abandoned automobiles, and construction and demolition refuse. Some kinds of refuse, such as explosives, pathological and radioactive wastes, and some industrial wastes, may require special analytical methods not discussed here.

Since accurate and reproducible chemical analysis requires small and finely ground samples of refuse, it is necessary to separate all components that cannot be finely ground and that can be analyzed by estimating rather than by laboratory methods. Separation categories vary with the investigator. Ten are listed below.

1. Cans
2. Bottles
3. Ferrous metals
4. Nonferrous metals
5. Rags
6. Paper
7. Plastics, leather, rubber
8. Wood, limbs, sawdust
9. Food wastes, grass clippings, leaves
10. Bricks, stones, dirt, ashes

Refuse quantities are best measured by weight and reported in terms of pounds per capita per year or per day. By taking the weight and preferably the volume of the refuse components in each of the 10 categories, it is possible to reconstruct on paper the composition of the refuse samples. Some authorities believe that this procedure gives more accurate results than if a refuse sample that had not been separated into its components had been ground and analyzed.

The composition of commercial and industrial refuse usually varies so much that accurate weights and analyses are not practical. Information about such refuse can be gotten by stationing men at disposal points who can estimate volumes and weights and the percentage of refuse in each of the major categories.

INITIAL SAMPLING

Relatively large initial samples of most mixed refuse materials are required because of the extreme heterogeneity and particle size range. It is suggested that a quarter of a truckload, or not less than 500 pounds, of such materials as mixed refuse or rubbish be taken for the initial sample. Unless samples are to be taken in many sections of the city, the refuse should be collected from an area in which conditions are average and from a number of premises.

Sampling and sample preparation should be done rapidly to avoid excessive change in moisture content. The sample should be ground in a small grinder or shredder immediately after it is brought in. Gloves and safety goggles should be worn by the operators and a respirator should also be worn if the grinding creates dusty conditions. The material should be ground so that no particle exceeds 1½ inches. A grating with 6-square-inch openings or a roller screen with about 1½-inch spacing should be used. If the grating or screen clogs frequently it may save time to double grind: first coarse and then finer.

The ground sample should be mixed rapidly on a smooth, clean, impervious floor or slab with a shovel; the materials should be cut in quarters; and a shovelful extracted from each quarter. The four shovelfuls are combined and mixed rapidly as before and again are quartered. Again four samples are collected, one from each quadrant, as explained under the section, "Tests for Moisture, Oven Drying Method." Because all subsequent analyses are conducted with oven-dried material, this method of obtaining moisture is recommended. It is the first step in preparation of samples for other analyses. In addition to providing four replicates for the moisture determination, the four samples provide sufficient dried materials for all subsequent analyses that may be required. If less accuracy is desired or less dried material is required for additional analyses, the number of replicates may be reduced to two.

GENERAL INSTRUCTIONS

All samples analyzed by the following methods, with the exception of moisture and pH determinations, should be dried to constant weight at 75° C., ground to pass a 1 millimeter sieve, and stored in widemouth, screw top jars. They should be from 50 to 100 grams (wet weight) or larger to insure representative samples, and analyzed in triplicate. Larger samples require excessive drying periods but may be needed if the material sampled is coarse. A sufficient number of replicates are required to provide sufficient dry material for all subsequent analyses.

Before the analyses are made, the samples or aliquots should be redried at 75° C. for at least two hours to eliminate moisture picked up during grinding or transferring of the samples. The dry weight of the sample may be obtained by difference (i.e., carefully transferring redried material from light sample containers) or directly by placing the approximate amount of sample in the tared dry flask or crucible, redrying, and weighing.

Covered containers with small tare weights are required for accurate results. Samples from drying ovens or muffle furnaces should be cooled to room temperature in desiccator jars or cabinets containing desiccant. Dry weights are most accurately obtained by rapid weighing in glass encased laboratory balances provided with desiccant. All results, except for moisture and liquid content and pH, are reported on a per cent dry weight basis. Moisture and liquid are reported on a wet (total) weight basis. No attempt should be made to preserve or transport fresh (moist) samples, but dried samples may be stored or shipped. All water used in analysis should be distilled.

TESTS FOR MOISTURE (WATER)

There are three methods of making moisture tests: (1) oven drying; (2) infrared; and (3) toluene distillation. The oven drying method is the one of choice because it is more accurate than the others and is a step in the preparation of samples for subsequent analyses. It should always be used in preference to the other tests unless it is necessary to get an answer rapidly and it is not necessary to have complete accuracy.

Oven Drying Method

Equipment: Drying oven, preferably with forced air circulation; large desiccator jar or cabinet and desiccant; sample containers (covered aluminum cans about 3½ inches in diameter and 2 inches deep have proven satisfactory); triple beam balance graduated to 0.1 grams (an analytical balance is satisfactory if it has a capacity of 200 grams).

Procedure: Duplicate samples of 50 to 100 grams of fresh ground refuse, compost, or other organic wastes are taken in tared sample containers and immediately covered. Inorganic materials such as glass, metal, and ceramics a ½-inch or larger are discarded. Material should not be packed down. Samples should be weighed to the nearest decigram within an hour and dried to a constant weight in drying oven at 75° C. with lids cocked or off. With samples of less than 60 per cent moisture content, drying for 24 hours in a forced air oven may be sufficient; 48 hours are preferred. Drying at 75° C. is preferable to drying at 103° C. because it permits retention of more of the volatile constituents other than water (particularly ammonia-N and lipids). With materials containing free liquid (70 to 75 per cent or more water) such as raw garbage or sewage sludge, most of the water may be evaporated first on a steam bath, with final drying in the oven. The sample is then cooled in a desiccator jar or cabinet with lids on, and it is weighed.

$$\text{Calculation: } \frac{100 \ (\text{loss in weight})}{(\text{net wet weight})} = \% \text{ moisture (wet basis)}$$

The value is approximately equal to per cent water by weight and should not be confused with per cent liquid.

Infrared Method

The infrared method provides a rough approximation of moisture content in a much shorter time than the oven drying method does. It is suitable, for instance, if it is necessary to know rapidly the amount of moisture in refuse for control of an incineration or composting plant. It is not suitable as a means of drying samples for subsequent analyses because it may volatilize substances other than water.

Equipment: Moisture balance of infrared type with 25-gram sample pan.

Procedure: Directions supplied with the instrument should be followed. Most moisture balances read directly in per cent moisture for the size of the sample specified. Care must be taken to insure clean sample pans, accurate centering and balancing, and sufficiently low setting of powerstat dial to insure against charring or burning the sample. The infrared lamp should be operated with the lid closed to avoid charring or burning the refuse sample.

Toluene Distillation Method[2]

The toluene method is based on the distillation of water from a refuse sample that has been immersed in toluene at boiling temperature—110.8° C. Toluene and water vapors condense in the trap, but they are immiscible so the toluene, being lighter, fills the upper part of the trap, the excess spilling back through the distilling tube to the flask, and the water collects in the graduated part of the trap. The method is more rapid but less accurate than oven drying and is recommended primarily for plant control.

Equipment: Water determination apparatus consisting of a 250 to 300-milliliter Pyrex Florence or Erlenmeyer distilling flask connected by a distilling tube receiver and trap calibrated from 0 to 20 milliliter in 0.1 milliliter divisions; and a 20-inch sealed-in straight-tube Liebig condenser, preferably with ground glass connections (see Figure A-1). (Some laboratory supply houses have the complete apparatus made up; if that is the case, the 20-milliliter trap should be specified because 5 to 10-milliliter traps are more common.)

Reagents: Toluene, purified.

Procedure: The apparatus must be clean and dry; the trap and condenser should be cleaned with dichromate cleaning solution, thoroughly rinsed with water and with acetone or alcohol, and dried in the oven. Weigh into the flask to the nearest 0.1 grams the amount of fresh refuse sample that can be expected to have between 15 to 20 milliliters of water (i.e., a sample thought to contain about 60 per cent moisture should be approximately 30 grams in fresh weight). Add sufficient toluene—about 75 milliliters—to cover the sample completely. Connect the apparatus, turn on the cooling water, and fill the trap with toluene to the level of the distilling (overflow) tube by pouring through the top of the condenser.

Bring to a boil on a hot plate and distill at about 2 drops per second until most of the water passes over, and then increase the rate to about 4 drops per second. When all the water apparently is over, wash down the condenser tube by pipetting 5 to 10 milliliters of toluene into the top. Continue distilling a short time to ascertain whether any more water will distill over. If it does, repeat the washing process. If drops of moisture remain in the condenser, remove them by brushing down with the tube brush attached to a copper wire and saturated with toluene, washing down condenser at the same time. The entire process usually requires 30 to 40 minutes. Allow the receiving trap to come to room temperature. Read volume of water and calculate to per cent moisture (wet weight basis).

Test for Volatile Solids and Ash

Equipment: Drying oven; analytical balance; desiccator jar; porcelain crucibles, high form No. 1, 1A, or 2; muffle furnace with indicating pyrometer and rheostat temperature control.

---

[2]Association of Official Agricultural Chemists, *Official Methods of Analysis,* 8th ed. (Washington, D. C.: The Association, 1955), p. 367.

Procedure: Transfer 3 to 6 grams of dried and ground sample to a previously ignited and tared crucible. Redry for 2 hours at 75° C. and obtain sample weight directly to nearest centigram. Place the crucibles in a cold muffle furnace and gradually bring the temperature to 600° to 650° C., with the door raised about ½-inch. Muffle at this temperature for 2 hours; cool in desiccator and weigh.

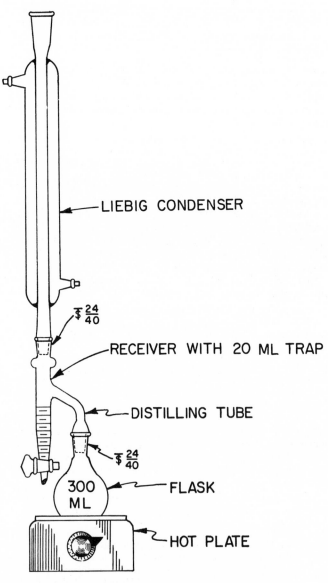

LIEBIG CONDENSER

RECEIVER WITH 20 ML TRAP

DISTILLING TUBE

FLASK

HOT PLATE

300 ML

Fig. A-1. Toluene distillation apparatus for moisture determination.

$$Calculation: \frac{100 \ (\text{loss in weight})}{(\text{net dry weight})} = \% \text{ volatile solids}$$

This value approximates the per cent organic matter of the material. The value for per cent ash is 100 minus per cent volatile solids.

TEST FOR LIPIDS (ETHER EXTRACT)[3]

Lipids (oils, greases, fats, and waxes) have a heat equivalent (calorific) value of about 16,700 B.T.U. per pound, or more than twice that of other common combustible constituents of refuse. They are liquids at thermophilic composting temperatures.

Equipment: Soxhlet extractor with 125-milliliter flask; water bath or low-temperature heater; extraction thimbles (Whatman, 22 by 80-millimeter, fat extracted); steam bath in exhaust hood; drying oven; analytical balance; desiccator jar; sample containers (covered aluminum cans about 2 inches in diameter by ⅞-inch deep).

Reagent: Ether, c. p. anhydrous (ethyl).

Procedure: Redry a portion of the ground sample refuse in an aluminum can at 75° C.; cover, cool in desiccator, and weigh. Transfer about 5 grams of redried and ground sample to an extraction thimble, obtaining sample weight indirectly to nearest milligram; obtain dry tare weight of extraction flask. Add about 80 milliliter of ether to the extraction flask, place thimble in extraction tube, and extract continuously in Soxhlet extractor for 16 to 18 hours on the water bath. Extraction temperature should be regulated so that extraction tube discharges every 5 to 10 minutes. Make up ether loss if necessary. Cooling condenser with ice water instead of tap water will conserve ether better. Evaporate ether from flask under hood over a steam bath and continue drying in oven for 1 hour at 75° C. Cool flask in desiccator and weigh. Redry to constant weight.

$$Calculation: \frac{100 \ (\text{weight of ether extract})}{(\text{net dry weight})} = \% \text{ lipids (ether extract)}$$

While the value obtained is for ether extractable matter and includes all substances soluble in ether, it represents essentially the lipids content.

TEST FOR LIQUIDS[4]

The liquid content of wastes to be aerobically composted may be more meaningful than the moisture content of some wastes, particularly those with high lipids content, high ash content, or both. The reason that liquid content may be important is that while a certain degree of water is required for microorganism metabolism, too much liquid in any form hinders aeration.

Lipids addd to the moisture content may take up excessive pore space, retarding aeration. Ash content (i.e., metal, glass, ceramics, and dirt), while

[3]John S. Wiley, "Composting Studies, II, Progress Report on High-Rate Composting Studies," *Proceedings, 12th Industrial Waste Conference*, May 13-15, 1957, Purdue University Engineering Bulletin, Series 94 (Lafayette, Ind., 1957), pp. 596-603.

[4] John S. Wiley, "Liquid Content of Garbage and Refuse," American Society of Civil Engineers, Proceedings Paper 1411, Sanitary Engineering Division 83, SA5 (New York, 1957), pp. 1-8.

it absorbs moisture, acts much like ballast. Increasing the amount of ash decreases the per cent of moisture but it does not increase air spaces. Thus with various materials, optimum moisture content for composting has a wide range. Computing the liquid content takes into account two additional important variables and narrows the range of values for optimum composting conditions. These are the lipids and the ash contents.

Procedure: The liquid content is computed from the moisture, lipids, and ash contents, all values expressed as per cent of wet (total) weight. The formula is:

$$\% \text{ liquid} = \frac{100 \ (\% \text{ moisture} + \% \text{ lipids})}{(100 - \% \text{ ash})}$$

Convert lipids and ash contents from dry to wet basis before use in the above formula as follows:

$$\% \text{ lipids (WW)} = \frac{[\% \text{ lipids (DW)}] \ [100 - \% \text{ moisture}]}{100}$$

Example: Moisture $= 60\%$ (WW); lipids $= 12\%$ (DW); ash $= 8\%$ (DW)

$$\text{Lipids (WW)} = \frac{12 \ (100 - 60)}{100} = 4.8\%$$

$$\text{Ash (WW)} = \frac{8 \ (100 - 60)}{100} = 3.2\%$$

$$\text{Liquid} = \frac{100 \ (60 + 4.8)}{(100 - 3.2)} = 66.9\%$$

Optimum *moisture* contents for composting three quite different wastes ranged from 52.5 to 62.5 per cent, but for the same wastes the optimum *liquid* content had a range of only 67.5 to 70.1 per cent.

Test for Crude Fiber[5]

Equipment: Cold finger condenser, reflux, with 24/40 $T_{/s}$ joint; digestion flasks, 1 l. (liter) Erlenmeyer, with 24/40 $T_{/s}$ joint, marked at 200 milliliter; Pyrex filtering funnel, 100 millimeter diameter; No. 40 filtering cloth (National Filter Cloth and Weaving Co.) cut into 6½-inch squares; Alundum crucibles, 25-milliliter, medium porosity; drying oven; muffle furnace; desiccator jar; analytical balance; aluminum sample containers (2-inch diameter by ⅞-inch).

Reagents: 0.255N sulfuric acid (14.28 milliliter concentrate $H_2SO_4/2$ 1.); 0.313N sodium hydroxide (1.25 grams NaOH/100 milliliter, free from Na_2CO_3). Concentration of these solutions must be accurately checked by titration.

Procedure: Dry residue that has been extracted with ether (see procedure for lipids) in oven at 100° C. for several hours in aluminum sample container; cover; cool in desiccator; and weigh. Transfer about 2 grams of material to an Erlenmeyer flask, obtaining weight indirectly to nearest milligram. Add 200 milliliters of boiling H_2SO_4 solution, connect flask to condenser, and

---

[5] Association of Official Agricultural Chemists, *op. cit.*, p. 372.

heat immediately. It is essential that the contents of the flask come to the boiling point within 1 minute and continue boiling briskly for exactly 30 minutes. (A little testing will show what height of flame must be used and the burner can be marked for subsequent determinations. An Atlantic high temperature burner has proved to be efficient, and asbestos gauze should be used to prevent undue bumping.) Rotate the flask to keep the sample thoroughly wet. Take care during boiling to keep the material on the sides of the flask in contact with the solution. (A piece of rubber tubing connected to a rubber bulb can be used to introduce a blast of air at intervals to reduce foaming.) At the end of 30 minutes remove flask and immediately filter onto No. 40 filtering cloth through a filtering funnel and wash with boiling distilled water until washings are no longer acid to litmus paper.

Bring a quantity of NaOH solution to the boiling point in a Pyrex wash bottle, using a funnel in the neck as a condenser. Wash material on filtering cloth into 1 l. flask using 200 milliliters of boiling NaOH. Connect flask with reflux condenser and boil for exactly 30 minutes. A constant watch must be kept so that the solution does not foam through the condenser and into the side arm. An air blast should be applied in the manner described for acid digestion; on some samples it will have to be applied about once a minute. Bumping can be reduced by swirling the flask occasionally. At the end of 30 minutes, remove the flask and immediately filter through No. 40 filtering cloth. Thoroughly wash the residue with boiling distilled water to remove all NaOH and transfer to an Alundum crucible. (It is convenient to transfer the bulk of the residue to the crucible with a spatula and wash the remainder from the filter cloth into a flask from which it is easily transferred to the crucible. Filtering the NaOH solution directly into a prepared Gooch crucible has been tried but the fine particles clog the asbestos filter.) Once the residue is in the Alundum crucible, wash with several portions of boiling distilled water and test washes for NaOH with litmus paper. Rinse with 15 milliliters of 95 per cent ETOH and dry crucible to constant weight in oven at 100° C. Cool in desiccator and weigh. Incinerate contents of crucible in muffle furnace at 600 to 650° C. for 30 minutes. Cool in desiccator and weigh.

$$Calculation: \frac{\text{(net loss on ignition) } (100 - \% \text{ ether extract})}{\text{(dry weight ether extracted material)}} = \% \text{ crude fiber}$$

The formula given above corrects for ether extracted material so that the crude fiber is expressed as per cent of the total dry weight of the original sample.

TEST FOR SUGARS[6]

Reagents:

Ethyl alcohol, 50 per cent and 95 per cent.
Saturated lead acetate, $Pb(C_2H_3O_2)_2 \cdot 3H_2O$ (neutral, not basic lead acetate).
Potassium oxalate, $K_2C_2O_4 \cdot H_2O$.
Sodium carbonate, Na_2CO_3.
Calcium carbonate, $CaCO_3$.
Hydrochloric acid, HCl, concentrated.
4N sulfuric acid.
Asbestos (prepared according to the Association of Official Agricultural

---

[6] *Ibid.,* pp. 545-47, 550, 896-900.

Chemists, *Official Methods of Analysis*, 10th ed., 1965, p. 435 [Munson-Walker method for determination of sugar]).

Copper sulfate solution: 34.639 grams of $CuSO_4 \cdot 5H_2O$ in distilled water, diluted to 500 milliliters and filtered through prepared asbestos.

Alkaline tartrate solution: dissolve 173 grams of sodium potassium tartrate and 50 grams of NaOH in distilled water and dilute to 500 milliliters. Let stand for two days and filter through prepared asbestos.

Ferric sulfate solution: dissolve 135 grams of $FeNH_4(SO_4)_2 \cdot 12H_2O$, or 55 grams anhydrous $Fe_2(SO_4)_3$, or 77.33 grams $Fe_2(SO_4)_3 \cdot n\ H_2O$ and dilute to 1 liter with water.

Ferrous phenanthroline indicator: dissolve 0.7425 grams of orthphenanthroline monohydrate in 25 milliliters of $0.025M$ $FeSO_4$ solution (6.95 grams of $FeSO_4 \cdot 7H_2O$ per liter).

Potassium permanganate solution: approximately $0.1573N$ and containing 4.98 grams per liter; after several days of aging, filter through asbestos or sintered glass. Standardize by one of the classic methods.

Standard invert sugar solution: to a solution of 9.5 grams of pure sucrose (table sugar is sufficiently pure) add 5 milliliters of concentrated HCl and dilute with distilled water to about 100 milliliters; let stand three days at room temperature, then dilute to 1 liter. (This constitutes an acidified 1 per cent invert sugar solution, which is very stable.) Neutralize with NaOH and dilute to desired concentration immediately before use.

Preparation of Sample: Weigh 20 grams of redried sample into a tared beaker and transfer to a 1 liter Erlenmeyer flask. Add 350 milliliters of 50 per cent ETOH, using some of the alcohol to transfer small particles adhering to the beaker and transfer funnel. If the material is acid to litmus paper, add 1 to 3 grams of $CaCO_3$. (The material must be neutral or slightly alkaline to prevent hydrolysis of the sugars during boiling.) Boil for one hour on steam bath with a small funnel in the neck of the flask as a condenser. Allow samples to stand for 2 to 3 days.

Using a filtrator such as Fisher's High Form, Catalogue No. 9-789, and rapid filter paper, filter the sample into a 500-milliliter volumetric flask. (A little experimenting may be needed to determine the best filter paper to use. If the particles rapidly clog filter paper, a linen cloth on top of a clean paper may permit more rapid filtering. Rinse the residue only with 50 per cent alcohol.) Make up to volume with 95 per cent ethyl alcohol. Depending on the amount of sugar present, an aliquot (300 milliliters have been found to be convenient) is transferred to a 600-milliliter beaker and evaporated to about 50 milliliters on a steam bath. Transfer the residue with hot distilled water to a 200-milliliter volumetric flask and rinse the beaker thoroughly with hot distilled water, adding the rinsings to the contents of the flask. Add 5 milliliters of saturated lead acetate, shake the flask, and allow the contents to stand for 15 minutes, or until cool. Then make up the sample to volume with distilled water, mix thoroughly, and filter through No. 52 and No. 42 filter papers together in a filtering funnel into a 400-milliliter beaker. Add sufficient potassium oxalate to precipitate all the lead. Using filter papers Nos. 52, 40, and 42, placed together in the funnel of the filtrator, filter the sample directly into a 200-milliliter beaker or flask. Additional dilution of the filtrate is not required before removing aliquots for the determination of the reducing and total sugars.

Reducing Sugars: Usually the term sugars refers to total sugars. Sugars are rapidly decomposed, being essentially all decomposed or converted to simpler compounds by about the third day of aerobic mechanical composting. It may be unnecessary to determine reducing sugars, but many of the steps given below are required for the total sugars determination that follows.

A 50-milliliter aliquot of the prepared solution is pipetted into a 400-milliliter beaker. (Larger amounts cannot be used; if a smaller aliquot is used add distilled water to total 50 milliliters.) Add exactly 25 milliliters of $CuSO_4$ and 25 milliliters of alkaline tartrate solution. Heat the beaker on an asbestos gauze over a Bunsen burner with the flame regulated so that boiling begins in *exactly 4 minutes* and continue boiling for *exactly 2 minutes*. Keep beaker covered with a watch glass during heating. Filter hot solution at once through an asbestos mat in a porcelain Gooch crucible. Wash precipitate thoroughly with hot distilled water (60° C.), testing final rinse with litmus paper. When the precipitate is thoroughly washed, transfer the asbestos mat from the crucible to the beaker with a glass rod. Add 50 milliliters of ferric sulfate solution. (It is usually necessary to rinse the crucible with the ferric sulfate solution as a fine film of Cu_2O is generally present on the sides.) Stir the solution vigorously until the Cu_2O is completely dissolved. To examine for complete solution, hold the beaker above eye level. The Cu_2O takes some time to dissolve and it is quite often necessary to break up the precipitate with a glass rod. Add 20 milliliters of $4N$ H_2SO_4 and titrate with standard $KMnO_4$ to a faint pink color that persists for 30 seconds or longer. Obtain the weight of reducing sugar equivalent to the weight of copper from the Hammond table in *Official Methods of Analysis*, 10th ed., 1965, pp. 840-844, using values for invert sugar. A blank, consisting of 50 milliliters of distilled water, should be carried through the procedure for reducing sugars with each set of samples, as the alkaline tartrate deteriorates on standing and the quantity of Cu_2O obtained in the blank increases. The method may be checked using the standard invert sugar solution in which the standard solution should analyze 1 per cent invert sugar.

Calculations:

(1) 63.57 (ml $KMnO_4$ soln − ml blank) norm. $KMnO_4$ = mg copper as Cu
(2)   mg copper = mg invert sugar (from Hammond table)
(3)   (mg invert sugar) (ml 1st tot. vol.) (ml 2nd tot. vol.)

$$\frac{\text{(mg invert sugar) (ml 1st tot. vol.) (ml 2nd tot. vol.)}}{10 \text{ (init. dry sample wt., g) (ml 1st aliquot) (ml 2nd aliquot)}} = \% \text{ reducing sugars}$$

The factor 63.57 is the milli-equivalent weight of copper (milligrams).

Total Sugars: A 100-milliliter aliquot of the prepared solution is pipetted into a 200-milliliter volumetric flask and 40 milliliters of distilled water are added. While rotating the flask, slowly add 20 milliliters of HCl (S.G. 1.1029 at 20/4°). Place the flask in a carefully controlled 60° C. waterbath, agitate continuously for 3 minutes, and leave in bath for *exactly 7 minutes longer*. Immediately plunge flask into water at 20°C. When the contents of the flask have cooled, neutralize with Na_2CO_3 and dilute to 200 milliliters with water. Filter if necessary and determine reducing sugars in 50 milliliters of the solution as described above. (A larger sample may be taken and reduced on the steam bath to 50 milliliters if necessary.) A blank should be carried through the procedure for reducing sugars with each set of samples.

Calculate the per cent total sugars on a dry sample weight basis using equations (1) and (2) above and (4) below.

(4) (mg invert sugar) (ml 1st tot. vol.) (ml 2nd tot. vol.) (ml 3d tot. vol.)

10(init. dry sample wt., g) (ml 1st aliquot) (ml 2nd aliquot) (ml 3rd aliquot)
= % total sugars

TESTS FOR STARCH

There are two methods of testing for starch: (1) the anthrone-sulfuric acid method and (2) the direct acid hydrolysis method.

Anthrone-Sulfuric Acid Method[7]

Equipment: Centrifuge, equipped with 50-milliliter head and tubes with pouring lips, adjustable speed to 1,200 rpm; magnetic stirrer and stirring fleas; metal disc holder, 8-place, for 22 by 175-millimeter test tubes to fit a 2-l. beaker; spectrophotometer; timer.

Reagents: Standard glucose solution. Stock solution: dissolve 100 milligrams of C.P. dextrose (anhydrous in 100 milliliters of water) and preserve with 100 milligrams of sodium benzoate. Standard solution: dilute stock solution 1:100 (10 micrograms per milliliter) and use 5-milliliter portion for the standardization. Prepare standard solution daily.

Anthrone-sulfuric acid reagent: dissolve 500 milligrams of anthrone in 250 milliliters of cold 95 per cent sulfuric acid. Store at 0° C. and allow to stand at least 4 hours before use. Prepare fresh every 2 days; the reagent is unstable and gives high blanks and variable results when too old.

Ethyl alcohol, 80 per cent: dilute 1,680 milliliters of 95 per cent ethyl alcohol to 2 l. with water.

Perchloric acid, 52 per cent: add 217 milliliters of 60 per cent perchloric acid to 33 milliliters of water; store in a glass stoppered bottle.

Procedure: Weigh to fourth place approximately 200 milligrams of redried sample (indirectly from aluminum sample container) into a 50-milliliter centrifuge tube. Add a few drops of 80 per cent alcohol to wet the sample and prevent clumping. Add 5 milliliters of water and a stirring flea; stir thoroughly with magnetic stirrer. Add 25 milliliters of hot 80 per cent alcohol, stir thoroughly and after 5 minutes standing centrifuge at 1,200 rpm for 10 minutes. Aspirate and discard the alcoholic solution, taking care not to disturb the settled solids. Add 30 milliliters of hot 80 per cent alcohol, stir, centrifuge, and aspirate as before. Repeat this washing treatment until the alcohol solution gives a negative test for sugar with anthrone. Six or seven washings are usually necessary.

Add 5 milliliters of water to the residue after final centrifugation and stir on magnetic stirrer while adding 6.5 milliliters of 52 per cent perchloric acid. Stir for about 5 minutes and occasionally during the next 15 minutes. Add 20 milliliters of water and centrifuge. Pour the aqueous starch solution into a 100-milliliter volumetric flask. Add 5 milliliters of water and stir while adding 6.5 milliliters of 52 per cent perchloric acid. Solubilize as before for 30 minutes with occasional stirring and wash the entire contents of the tube into the 100-milliliter flask containing the first extract. Dilute the suspension to 100 milliliters and filter, using Whatman No. 1 paper, discarding the first 5 milliliters of solution.

Dilute 5 to 10 milliliters of the filtered starch solution with water to 100 milliliters or to contain 25 to 100 micrograms of starch per 5 milliliters of

---

[7] Adapted from *Analytical Chemistry,* Vol. 22 (September, 1950), p. 1,156.

solution. Pipette 5 milliliters of the diluted solution into a 22 by 175 millimeter test tube, cool in ice water bath, and add 10 milliliters of chilled anthrone reagent down the sides of the tube. Swirl to mix the contents of each tube thoroughly while in the ice water bath and then transfer to a hot water bath and heat them together for 7.5 minutes at 100° C. (Suspending the tubes from an 8-place metal disc holder that fits a 2-l. beaker has proved to be satisfactory for mixing, heating, and cooling the solutions.) Cool the tubes rapidly to 25° C. in a water bath and determine the optical densities, using a spectrophotometer at 625 millimicrons. It is desirable to cover the tubes with aluminum foil after removing them from the cooling bath to prevent a turbidity, probably caused by moisture in the air. While the color is reputed to be stable up to 2 hours, prompt reading of the samples in the spectrophotometer seems desirable.

Prepare a daily standard curve using 0, 50, and 100 micrograms of glucose containing the same amounts of perchloric acid as that in the starch aliquots; use this calibration to obtain the yield of glucose from starch.

Calculation:

$$\frac{0.90 \; (\text{microg. glucose 2}^{\text{nd}} \text{ aliquot})}{10 \; (\text{mg init. dry sample wt.})} \; \frac{100}{(\text{ml 1st aliquot})} \; \frac{(\text{ml 2}^{\text{nd}} \text{ tot. vol.})}{5} = \% \text{ starch}$$

The factor 0.90 converts weight of glucose determined to weight of starch desired. The values 100 and 5 are milliliters in first total volume and in second aliquot, respectively.

Direct Acid Hydrolysis Method[8]

Equipment: Reflux condenser and 500-milliliter Erlenmeyer flask with $T_{/s}$ joint; magnetic stirrer and stirring bars.

Reagents: Hydrochloric acid, sp. gr. 1.125; ether (ethyl), C.P.: 18N sodium hydroxide.

Procedure: Weigh to nearest milligram approximately 4 grams of redried sample (indirectly from aluminum sample container) into a No. 1 filter paper in a funnel and rinse with five 10-milliliter portions of ether. Let ether evaporate and transfer residue to a 250-milliliter beaker. (Washing with ether is unnecessary if fat is not present.) Add 50 milliliters of cold water and stir for 1 hour with magnetic stirrer. Filter through No. 1 filter paper with suction, and rinse residue with about 250 milliliters of cold water. Transfer residue to a 500-milliliter $T_{/s}$ flask with 200 milliliters of water and add 20 milliliters of HCl. Fit flask with a cold finger condenser and reflux for 2.5 hours. (It is convenient to calibrate the flask at 200 and 250 milliliters.) Cool, nearly neutralize with NaOH and dilute to 250-milliliter volume with water. Filter through No. 52 and No. 42 filter papers together in filtering funnel. Take a suitable aliquot and determine dextrose as directed in the method for reducing sugars.

Calculation: (See calculations for per cent reducing sugars)

$$0.90 \; [\% \text{ reducing sugars (dextrose)}] = \% \text{ starch}$$

Analysis by this method includes as starch the pentosans and other carbohydrates that undergo hydrolysis and are converted to reducing sugars on boiling with HCl.

---

[8]Association of Official Agricultural Chemists, *op. cit.*, p. 374.

Test for Carbon

Determination of total carbon by any micro method is presently unreliable. Procedures for collection and preparation of samples must be refined before it will be applicable.

The induction furnace combustion method is a semi-micro method of estimating total carbon and has been found to be superior to the semi-micro wet combustion method. The samples are put in platinum crucibles and covered with alundum, and the crucibles and contents are placed in the field of a high frequency coil. The resistance of the crucible and contents to the rapidly changing magnetic field causes a rapid rise in temperature to more than 2,000° F. A jet of oxygen directed onto the sample insures immediate and complete oxidation; and the gases, carbon monoxide, and carbon dioxide pass through a catalyst furnace for conversion of the former gas to carbon dioxide. The gas stream is then passed into an absorption tube containing sodium hydroxide. The carbon dioxide is precipitated as barium carbonate, and this is collected on a Gooch crucible or filter paper.

Equipment (including company catalog number): Induction furnace, Leco 1-H-10; oxygen valve, Leco 77-250; purifying train with rotometer, Leco 1150; dust trap, Leco 501-10; sulfur trap, Leco 6013; absorbent for sulfur trap, Leco 501-C, platinum crucibles, 10-15 milliliters, Fisher; gas absorption tube (see Figure A-2); Gooch crucibles; oxygen cylinder(standard commercial); pressure regulator (standard commercial).

Reagents: Alundum (granular 90 mesh), Fisher No. 7-689; sodium hydroxide 0.4N carbon dioxide free; ammonium hydroxide 0.4N carbon dioxide free; barium chloride 0.8N carbon dioxide free; filter paper (Whatman No. 52).

Procedure: Weigh 25 to 50 milligrams of redried sample directly into a 10- or 15-milliliter platinum crucible. (The sample weight should be great enough

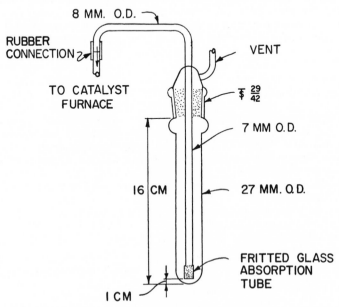

Fig. A-2. Gas absorption assembly.

to yield 62.5 milligrams or more of $BaCO_3$ precipitate. Most organic materials sampled will yield 150 to 300 milligrams of $BaCO_3$.) Cover the sample with 90-mesh granular alundum, filling the crucible to within about ¼-inch of the top.

Before running the first sample, turn on the filament switch of the Leco induction furnace and allow the instrument to warm up for 15 minutes, then blank the train by placing an empty platinum crucible in the combustion chamber, and ignite for 15 minutes in a stream of oxygen flowing at 500 milliliters per minute. The instrument is now ready for the first sample.

Place the crucible on the ceramic pedestal of the induction furnace, and raise the crucible into the combustion chamber. The pedestal should be adjusted so that the crucible comes to rest in the center of the induction coil. Open the oxygen valve and adjust the flow rate to 500 milliliters per minute. Immediately measure 20 milliliters of $0.4N$ NaOH (CO_2-free) into the CO_2 absorption tube and connect it to the apparatus so that the gases from the furnace bubble into the solution through the fritted glass gas dispersion tube (Figure A-2). Set the grid tap switch at its highest setting and turn on the plate current. The crucible will reach its maximum temperature within 1 minute. After 15 minutes, remove the absorption tube, rinse the gas dispersion tube several times with distilled water, collecting the rinses in the absorption tube, and then transfer the contents into a 125-milliliter g.s. bottle; rinse several times with distilled water. (Always remove the absorption tube before turning off the oxygen to prevent the solution from backing up into the fritted glass tube.) Turn off the power and oxygen and remove the crucible. Crucibles may be cleaned with a small, stiff brush.

Precipitate the sample by adding 25 milliliters of $BaCl_2$-NH_4Cl solution (prepared by mixing 1 volume of $0.8N$ $BaCl_2$ and 4 volumes of $0.4N$ NH_4Cl) to the NaOH solution in the 125-milliliter g.s. bottle. Mix well and allow to digest at room temperature for 2 hours. Shake occasionally during this 2-hour period. The $BaCO_3$ is quantitatively filtered off in a tared Gooch or other suitable gravimetric filtering crucible using boiled distilled water as transfer and washing medium. Wash the precipitate with acetone, dry in an oven at 100° C. for 1 hour, cool in desiccator and weigh.

Calculation:

$$\frac{6.08 \text{ (net wt. } BaCO_3 \text{ ppt)}}{\text{(net dry weight)}} = \% \text{ carbon}$$

The accuracy of this procedure for total carbon is highly dependent on maintaining consistently low blanks. Using weighed amounts of alundum is helpful and care to avoid contamination with atmospheric CO_2 during analysis is essential for accurate results. Reproducibility is well within 15 per cent with reasonable care.

While this method of total carbon assay is preferred to the wet combustion method, the cost of the induction furnace may prevent its use in many laboratories. The main disadvantage of the wet combustion method is that some materials are not completely oxidized and this is not always apparent, especially when dealing with biological materials.

Test for Nitrogen (Organic and Ammoniacal)

Kjeldahl-Wilfarth-Gunning Method

Equipment: Kjeldahl flasks for digestion and distillation, 800-milliliter;

exhaust hood and special stack to outside for venting acid fumes during digestion; Kjeldahl connecting bulbs (use bulbs 5 to 6 centimeters in diameter, fit lower end with rubber stopper, and connect upper end to a condenser with rubber tubing); Erlenmeyer flasks, 500-milliliter.

Reagents:

Standard sulfuric acid, 0.1N: standardize by any official method.

Standard sodium hydroxide, 0.1N: standardize by titration against standard acid.

Sulfuric acid, 93 to 96 per cent H_2SO_4, free from nitrates and $(NH_4)_2SO_4$.

Mercuric oxide, reagent grade, free from nitrogen.

Sodium hydroxide-thiosulfate solution: dissolve 450 grams of NaOH, free from nitrates, in water and allow to cool; add 80 grams of $Na_2S_2O_3 \cdot 5H_2O$, keeping solution cool, and make to 1 l. with water.

Methyl red indicator: dissolve 1 gram of methyl red in 200 milliliters of 95 per cent ethyl alcohol.

Potassium sulfate, K_2SO_4.

Granulated zinc.

Procedure: Weigh to fourth place 0.7 to 2.5 grams of redried sample (indirectly from aluminum sample container) into a piece of Whatman No. 1 filter paper (9 centimeters). Fold paper and introduce into digestion flask. Add 15 to 18 grams of K_2SO_4, about 0.7 gram of mercuric oxide, and 25 milliliters of concentrated H_2SO_4. Heat gently until frothing ceases, then boil briskly, continuing digestion for a time after the mixture is colorless or nearly so—about 2 hours. Cool, add 200 milliliters of water, and dissolve cake. Add 1 gram of granulated zinc to prevent bumping and 75 milliliters of alkali-thiosulfate solution, pouring down the side of the flask so that it does not mix at once with the acid solution. Connect flask immediately to the condenser by means of the Kjeldahl connecting bulb, taking care that the tip of the condenser extends below the surface of the standard acid in the 500-milliliter flask, which acts as a receiver. Mix the contents by shaking and distill until all of the NH_3 has passed over into a measured quantity (usually 50 milliliters) of the standard acid. The first 150 milliliters of distillate usually contains all the NH_3. (It is helpful to mark the receiving flasks at about 200 milliliters and distill to the mark.) Titrate with standard alkali solution, using methyl red indicator.

A blank determination should be run with approximately 500 milligrams of cane sugar and with the same amount of standard acid to determine the nitrates that might be present in the reagents and reduced during digestion. A new blank value should be established when new reagents are used.

Calculations:

(1) Blank: (ml acid)-(ml base) $\dfrac{\text{(norm. base)}}{\text{(norm. acid)}}$ = ml equiv. acid in blank

(2) Sample: (ml acid)-(ml base) $\dfrac{\text{(norm. base)}}{\text{(norm. acid)}}$ =

　　　　　　　　　　　　　　　　　ml equiv. acid in sample + blank

(3) Sample corrected for blank: (2) — (1) = ml equiv. acid in sample

$$(4) \quad \frac{(\text{ml equiv. acid in sample}) \; (\text{norm. acid}) \; (14 \text{ mg})}{10 \; (\text{g init. dry sample wt.})} = \% \text{ nitrogen}$$

The nitrogen measured is organic and ammoniacal and does not include the nitrite and nitrate nitrogen because the latter are not reduced to ammoniacal form during the analytical procedure. However, it is doubtful that many, if any, nitrites or nitrates would be formed in aerobic composting unless the stabilization period is greatly prolonged.

The following simplified calculation may be applied when the amounts of standard H_2SO_4 used for both blank and sample are exactly the same:

$$\frac{[(\text{ml base blank}) - (\text{ml base sample})] \; (\text{norm. base}) \; (14)}{10 \; (\text{g init. dry sample wt.})} = \% \text{ nitrogen}$$

Test for Protein

The protein content may be roughly estimated by multiplying the nitrogen (organic and ammoniacal) content by 6.25.

Calculation:

6.25 (% nitrogen) = % protein (approx.)

Test for Carbon-Nitrogen Ratio

The carbon-nitrogen ratio (C/N) is of interest in composting and in composts, sludges, and other humus containing materials applied to the soil.

Calculation:

$$\frac{\% \text{ carbon}}{\% \text{ nitrogen}} = \text{carbon-nitrogen ratio}$$

In the United States, total carbon and nitrogen contents—the latter approximated by the organic and ammoniacal nitrogen analysis—are usually used in computing C/N. In Europe, the trend is to use only the available carbon and nitrogen contents. These are generally determined as water-soluble C and N, which eliminates much of the organic C and N in such materials as wood, coal and coke, paper, stalks, and leaves. However, in time decomposition in the soil will gradually make much of the organic C and N available to plants, and this refinement in C/N calculation is debatable.

Test for Phosphorus (Phosphate)

Equipment: Kjeldahl flasks for digestion, 800-milliliter; fume wood; volumetric flasks, 200-milliliter; aluminum sample containers (2-inch diameter by ⅞-inch); spectrophotometer, photoelectric colorimeter (equipped with a light filter with maximum transmittance near 625 to 675 millimicrons, or visual colorimeter; drying oven, desiccator, analytical balance, and columetric pipettes.

Reagents:

Sulfuric acid, 93 to 96 per cent H_2SO_4.
Sodium hydroxide, 10N (40 per cent).
Ammonium molybdate solution: dissolve 5 grams of $(NH_4)_2$ Mo 04 in 1 l. of 0.75N HCl.

Elon solution: dissolve 10 grams of elon in 1 l. of 3 per cent $NaHSO_3$.

Standard potassium dihydrogen phosphate solution: dissolve 1.917 grams of pure dry KH_2PO_4 in water and dilute to 1 l. One milliliter of this solution is equivalent to 1 milligram of P_2O_5.

Procedure: Weigh about 3 grams of redried sample in previously dried and tared sample container. (It is best to do the redrying at 75° C. for two hours after transfer into the sample container.) Transfer the sample to a Kjeldahl flask and add about 25 milliliters of concentrated H_2SO_4 and a few boiling beads. Digest under fume hood until the liquor becomes straw colored, indicating that the organic matter is destroyed. Cool, rinse into a 200-milliliter volumetric flask (except for the beads), and add about 80 milliliters of water. Make alkaline with the NaOH solution, using phenolphthalein indicator until the solution just turns pink. Make up to the mark with water and mix thoroughly. Filter, discarding the first portion of the filtrate, retaining the solution for determination of both phosphate and potash. (Basic sample solution volume is 200 milliliters.)

Pipette 10 milliliters of the above solution into a 100-milliliter beaker, add 30 milliliters of ammonium molybdate solution and 10 milliliters of elon solution (50 milliliters total volume). At the same time, pipette measured portions of standard phosphate solution into 50-milliliter volumetric flasks, add the same amounts of ammonium molybdate and elon solutions, and dilute to the mark with water. Mix sample and standards thoroughly and allow to stand 30 minutes. (It is suggested that standards of 1, 2, 4, 6, 8, and 10 milligrams of P_2O_5 in 50 milliliters be used for comparison or to prepare calibration curve for spectrophotometer or photoelectric colorimeter.) Read or compare sample immediately in colorimeter.

Calculation:

$$\frac{\text{mg of } P_2O_5 \text{ (colorimetric determination)} \times 2}{\text{g net dry weight}} = \% \ P_2O_5$$

(This calculation is for an aliquot of 10 milliliters from the 200-milliliter prepared sample solution and must be adjusted if amounts are varied.)

TESTS FOR POTASSIUM (POTASH)

There are two methods of testing for potassium: (1) the flame photometric method and (2) the sodium tetraphenyl borate method.

Flame Photometric Method[9]

Equipment: Spectrophotometer with flame photometer attachment.

Reagents: Standard potassium chloride solution: dissolve 1.584 grams of dry reagent grade KCl in H_2O and dilute to 1:1. One milliliter of this solution is equivalent to 1 milligram of K_2O.

Procedure: Prepare a series of standards ranging from 10 to 100 parts per million K_2O (1 to 10 milliliters KCl solution diluted to 100 milliliters).

The solution prepared for the phosphorus determination is used for the determination of potassium by means of the spectrophotometer. Operate the instrument in accordance with the instructions of the manufacturer. Allow

---

[9] J. M. Spain and J. L. White, "Procedure for the Determination of Phosphorus and Potassium in Soil Samples," Special Bulletin, Soils Testing Laboratory (Lafayette, Ind.: Purdue University, March, 1960).

instrument to reach operating equilibrium before use. Atomize portions of the standards toward the end of the warm-up period until reproducible readings for the series are obtained.

Run standards, covering the K_2O range of the samples involved at frequent intervals during atomization of series of sample solutions. Repeat this operation with both standard and sample solutions a sufficient number of times, depending on the precision desired, to result in reliable average readings for each sample solution.

Prepare a standardization curve of concentration (ppm) of potassium as K_2O versus optical density from the KCl standards.

Determine concentration of K_2O in sample solutions from the standardization curve.

Calculation:

$$\frac{\text{ppm of } K_2O \text{ in sample solution}}{50 \times (\text{g net dry weight})} = \% K_2O$$

(If sample solution is above the range of the standards, dilute a portion of the solution so that it will be within the range and adjust the calculation. The formula above is for a basic sample solution volume of 200 milliliters and must be adjusted if volume is varied.)

Sodium Tetraphenyl Borate Method[10, 11]

Equipment: Fritted glass crucible; drying oven; desiccator; analytical balance.

Reagents:

Sodium tetraphenyl boron solution: dissolve 23 grams of $(C_6H_5)_4BNa$ in about 800 milliliters of water. Add 20 to 25 grams of reagent grade $Al(OH)_3$, stir for 10 minutes and filter, collecting the first 100 milliliters of filtrate separately for refiltration. Dilute the clear filtrate to 1 l.

Ethylene diamine tetra acetic acid (EDTA) solution: dissolve 40 grams of the disodium salt of the above acid in distilled water and make up to 1 l.

Sodium hydroxide solution, 40 per cent NaOH.

Wash solution: add 0.10 grams of $(C_6H_5)_4BNa$ to 900 milliliters of water. Stir occasionally for 30 minutes; add 5 grams of $Al(OH)_3$, stir for 5 minutes and filter; dilute filtrate to 1 l.

Ammonium carbonate $(NH_4)_2CO_3$.

Formaldehyde, 36 per cent.

Procedure: Transfer 25 to 50 milliliters aliquot of sample solution as prepared under procedure for phosphorus to a 250-milliliter beaker. Make slightly alkaline with $(NH_4)_2CO_3$. Filter if necessary. Add 10 to 25 milliliters of EDTA solution, 5 to 10 milliliters of 36 per cent formaldehyde, 2 to 5 milliliters of 40 per cent NaOH, and 100 milliliters of water. Slowly, while stirring, add 1 milliliter of sodium tetraphenyl boron solution for each 2 milligrams of K_2O expected in the sample, plus an additional 10 milliliters to provide an excess. Let stand for 5 to 10 minutes and filter through a previously dried and tared fritted glass crucible. Wash final traces of precipitate with 5-milliliter portions of wash solution in transferring from beaker

---

[10] *Ibid.*

[11] Purdue University, "Determination of Potassium in Fertilizer by the Sodium-Tetra-Phenyl-Borate Method," Special Bulletin, Department of Agriculture (Lafayette, Ind.: Purdue University, 1957).

to crucible. Wash bulk of the precipitate in the crucible using a total of 50 milliliters of wash solution. Wash the precipitate with 5 milliliters of distilled water, dry at 110° C., cool in desiccator, and weigh.

Dissolve precipitate in acetone, rinse the crucible with distilled water, dry, cool in desiccator, and reweigh. Run a blank on reagents.

Calculation:

$$\frac{(\text{wt. of ppt.-wt. blank}) \times 13.143}{\text{wt. of sample, g}} \times \frac{200}{(\text{ml aliquot})} = \% \, K_2O$$

Test for Hydrogen-Ion Concentration (pH)

Equipment: Potentiometer (pH meter) with glass-calomel electrode system.

Reagents:

CO_2-free distilled water: boil distilled water, pour while boiling into Pyrex carboy or siphon bottle and immediately insert stopper through which siphon and air inlet tube protrude; immediately connect a CO_2-absorbing tube to air inlet tube, the absorber containing soda lime (4-8 mesh), ascarite, or similar CO_2 absorber.

Buffer solution, concentrated, pH7: dilute as directed on label and use to standardize potentiometer for each series of determinations.

Procedure: Use fresh sample collected immediately after preliminary grinding, preferably at the same time and from the same materials as samples collected for moisture determination. For partially decomposed materials (in piles, bins or cells, pits, or windrows) the pH may vary greatly with depth, so samples should be related to it. To indicate over-all pH value for the mass, samples should be taken immediately after thorough mixing, grinding, or regrinding. Size of individual samples and number of replicates are dependent on particle size and uniformity of materials. For materials prepared as recommended under "Initial Sampling" use of a 100-milliliter beaker ⅓ to ½ full of loose sample should be adequate.

If sample is semifluid or fluid, stir and determine pH directly. If not, add an equal weight of CO_2-free distilled water and stir (a glass rod fitted with rubber or neoprene policeman is recommended). Determine pH according to instructions by the manufacturer of the potentiometer used. Avoid contact between electrodes and glass beaker. Check pH meter before and after use against diluted buffer solution. Rinse both electrodes and stirrer with CO_2-free water (a polyethylene washing bottle is recommended) and wipe with disposable cleaning tissue after each determination and standardization check. Report pH to nearest 0.1.

Test for Gross Calorific Value

Equipment: Parr oxygen bomb calorimeter, Series 1300 (isothermal jacket); Parr oxygen filling connection, Series 1823; oxygen cylinder (standard commercial); trip balance, net capacity 3,000 to 5,000 grams; pressure regulator (standard commercial); drying oven; desiccator; analytical balance.

Reagents:

Distilled water.

Sodium carbonate solution, 0.0725N.: dissolve 3.84 grams of NA_2CO_3 in distilled water and dilute to 1 liter; sodium hydroxide or potassium hydroxide solutions of the same normality are acceptable.

Methyl orange or methyl red indicator.

Procedure: Attach a single length of 10 centimeters of standard fuse wire between the electrodes of the oxygen bomb head.

Weigh 0.8 to 1.2 grams of the redried sample directly into a metal combustion capsule. (Limit the sample size to insure that the total heat liberated in any test does not exceed 8,000 calories.) Place the capsule in the loop holder on the bomb head. Bend the center of the fuse wire down so that it is set slightly above the surface of the material in the capsule.

Put 1 milliliter of water in the bomb from a pipette; put the bomb head into the cylinder; place contact ring above the sealing gasket; screw the cap down firmly by hand.

Attach the filling connection to the bomb inlet valve and slowly admit oxygen to 30 atmospheres gauge pressure at room temperature. (If too much oxygen should accidentally be introduced, do not proceed with the combustion; exhaust the bomb.)

Fill the calorimeter bucket with 2,000 grams (plus or minus 0.5 gram) of distilled water, which may be measured volumetrically instead of by weighing if it is always done at the same temperature. The temperature of the water should be 3° to 4° F. below that of the room.

Set the filled bucket in the calorimeter jacket; grasp the bomb valve between the thumb and the forefinger, and lower the bomb into the water, taking care to avoid jarring or disturbing the contents. Attach the thrust terminal to the bomb electrode and shake back into the bucket all drops of water adhering to the fingers.

Place the cover on the jacket with the thermometer toward the operator. Lower the cover into position, using care to avoid striking the thermometer against anything. Put on the rubber drive belt and start the motor. The stirrer will turn at the proper speed if the electric supply to the motor corresponds to that stamped on the Parr motor nameplate. If any other drive motor is used, adjust the stirrer to 150 clockwise revolutions per minute.

Run the motor for 5 minutes to attain thermal equilibrium, but do not record temperatures during this period. Adjust the thermometer reading lens and be prepared to take temperature readings as soon as equilibrium is indicated by a slow, uniform rise.

Read and record the calorimeter temperature to the nearest 0.005° F. at 1-minute intervals for exactly 5 minutes. Then press the button on the ignition unit to fire the charge at the start of the sixth minute, recording the exact time and temperature at the firing point.

Record temperature readings (taken without magnifier) at 45, 60, 75, 90, and 105 seconds after firing. After the period of rapid rise (about 4 or 5 minutes after firing) adjust the reading lens and record temperatures to the nearest 0.005°F. at 1-minute intervals until the difference between successive readings has been constant for 5 minutes. Usually the temperature will reach a maximum, then drop slowly.

The net rise is equal to the difference between the initial temperature at the time of firing and the final maximum temperature developed in the calorimeter. Take 60 per cent of this net rise and add it to the observed temperature at the firing point. By interpolation, calculate the time at which the thermometer had reached this temperature.

After completing the readings, stop the motor, remove the belt, and lift the cover from the jacket; wipe the thermometer bulb with a clean cloth to remove any water, and set the cover on the support stand; disconnect the firing connection from the bomb terminal, and lift the bucket and bomb out of the jacket.

Lift the bomb out of the bucket and relieve all residual pressure.

After all pressure has been relieved, remove the screw cap, lift out the bomb head, and place it on the support stand. Examine the interior of the bomb for soot or other evidence of incomplete combustion, and discard the test if any is found.

Wash all interior surfaces of the bomb with a jet of distilled water and quantitatively collect the washings in a beaker. Titrate with $0.075N$ alkali solution, using methyl orange or methyl red. Save the solution remaining after titration for determining the sulfur content of the sample.

Carefully remove all unburned pieces of fuse wire from the bomb electrodes, straighten them, and measure their combined length in centimeters. Subtract this length from the initial 10 centimeters, and enter this value on the data sheet as the net amount of wire burned.

Calculations: The following data should be available at the completion of a test in the plain calorimeter:

a = time of firing.

b = time (nearest 0.1 minute) when the temperature reaches 60 per cent of the net rise.

c = time at beginning of period (after the temperature rise) in which the rate of temperature change has become constant.

t_a = temperature at time of firing.

t_c = temperature at time.

r_1 = rate at which temperature was rising during the 5-minute period before firing (degrees F. per minute).

r_2 = rate at which the temperature was falling during the 5-minute period after time c (degrees F. per minute). If the temperature was rising instead of falling after time c, subtract the quantity r_2 (c-b) instead of adding it when computing the corrected temperature rise.

c_1 = milliliters of $0.0725N$ alkali solution used in the acid titration.

c_2 = percentage of sulfur in the sample.

c_3 = centimeters of fuse wire consumed in firing.

W = energy equivalent of the calorimeter in calories per degree Fahrenheit. (Each analyst must determine his own W factor experimentally.)

m = mass of sample in grams.

$t = t_c - t_a - r_1(b\text{-}a) + r_2(c\text{-}b)$.

$e_1 = c_1$ if $0.0725N$ alkali was used for titration.

$e_2 = (14)\ (c_2)\ (m)$.

$e_3 = (2.3)\ (c_3)$ when using Parr 45C10 nickel-chromium fuse wire, or
     $= (2.7)\ (c_3)$ when using No. 34 B&S gauge iron fuse wire.

H_g = gross calorific value

$$H_g = \frac{tW - e_1 - e_2 - e_3}{m}, \text{ calories per gram}$$

Calories per gram (1.8) = B.T.U. per pound

TEST FOR NET CALORIFIC VALUE

Net calorific value is calculated from the gross calorific value by making a deduction of 1,030 B.T.U. per pound of water derived from a unit quantity of the material, including both the water originally present as moisture and that formed by combustion.

Calculations:

$$H_n = \text{net calorific value}$$
$$H_n = H_g - 10.30 \ (H \times 9), \text{ B.T.U. per pound}$$
$$\text{where,}$$
$$H_g = \text{gross calorific value, B.T.U. per lb.}$$
$$H = \text{total \% hydrogen in the material, \%.}$$

Test for Sulfur[12]

Equipment: Parr oxygen bomb calorimeter, Series 1300; or Parr oxygen bomb sulfur apparatus, Series 1900; oxygen cylinder (standard commercial); pressure regulator (standard commercial); steam bath or hot plate; crucible; muffle furnace (600° to 900° C.); drying oven; desiccator; analytical balance; beakers, filter paper (ashless); watch glass; and volumetric pipettes.

Reagents: Wash water, 1 milliliter saturated solution of methyl orange indicator per liter of distilled water; ammonium hydroxide, concentrated; hydrochloric acid, concentrated; bromine solution, saturated; barium chloride solution (10 per cent).

Procedure: Collect the bomb washings following the combustion of a sample weighing not more than 1 gram. If this sample has not been used for a calorimetric test, allow the bomb to stand in the water bath at least 10 minutes after firing.

Release the residual gases slowly and at an even rate so that the pressure is reduced to atmospheric in not less than 1 minute.

Open the bomb and wash all parts of its interior, including the combustion capsule, valve passages, and electrodes, with a fine jet of wash water. Wash until no acid reaction is observed, collecting the washings in a beaker. Be sure to transfer any precipitate from the bomb or capsule to the beaker.

If a calorimetric test has been made, titrate the washings with standard sodium carbonate solution to determine the acid correction. After neutralizing the solution, add 1 milliliter of ammonium hydroxide, heat the solution to boiling, and filter through a rapid filter paper. Wash the residue and filter paper with hot distilled water and add sufficient water to bring the total volume of solution to approximately 250 milliliters. Neutralize with concentrated hydrochloric acid and add 2 milliliters in excess.

Add 10 milliliters of saturated bromine water and evaporate to approximately 200 milliliters on a hot plate or other source of heat. Adjust to a slow boil and stir constantly while adding 10 milliliters of a 10 per cent barium chloride solution from a pipette.

Continue stirring for 2 minutes, cover with a fluted watch glass and keep just below boiling on a steam bath or hot plate until the volume is reduced to 75 milliliters, then allow the precipitate to settle for another hour while cooling; filter through an ashless filter paper, and wash with warm water until free from chlorides.

Transfer the paper and precipitate to a weighed crucible, dry at low heat, char the paper without flaming, then raise the temperature to a good red heat (approximately 800° C.) and heat to constant weight.

---

[12]Parr Instrument Co., "Oxygen Bomb Calorimetry and Combustion Methods," Technical Manual No. 130 (Moline, Ill.: The Company, 1960).

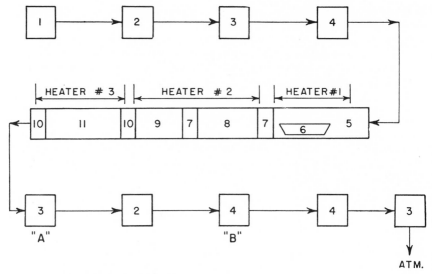

1 — OXYGEN CYLINDER

2 — GAS WASHER WITH CONCENTRATED SULFURIC ACID

3 — DRYING TUBE WITH MAGNESIUM PERCHLORATE

4 — DRYING TUBE WITH ASCARITE

5 — COMBUSTION TUBE

6 — COMBUSTION BOAT

7 — ASBESTOS FIBER PLUG

8 — LEAD CHROMATE

9 — CUPRIC OXIDE

10 — SILVER WIRE (TWISTED INTO A MAT)

11 — LEAD PEROXIDE (MAINTAINED AT 190 °C)

Fig. A-3. Combustion train assembly.

After ignition is complete, allow the crucible to cool to room temperature (final cooling in a desiccator) and weigh.

Calculation: Determine the exact weight of the barium sulfate precipitate and calculate the percentage of sulfur in the sample as follows:

$$\text{Sulfur, } \% = \frac{\text{wt. BaSO}_4 \times 13.734}{\text{sample wt.}}$$

TEST FOR HYDROGEN AND CARBON

Equipment: Electrically heated organic combustion tube furnace; combustion boats and covers; drying tubes, U-shaped, with side tubes, I.D. 16 milliliters, height 150 millimeters; Fisher-Milligan gas washers; analytical balance; drying oven, desiccator; tygon tubing; oxygen cylinder (extra dry oxygen, prepared from liquid air).

Reagents: Sulfuric acid, concentrated; cupric oxide, granular (ignite at 900°C. for 1 hour before using); lead chromate, granular; lead peroxide, granular; magnesium perchlorate; ascarite, 8-20 mesh; silver wire, 3-4 B & S gauge, pure grade; asbestos filter.

Procedure: Assemble combustion train as indicated in Figure A-3. Item 10 of the train is used to help conduct the heat from the center of the combustion tube to the exit so that no moisture collects in this part of the tube. The lead peroxide (item 11) should be maintained at 190° C. throughout the entire test. Obtain initial weight of items "A" and "B." Weigh 0.5 to 1 gram of the redried sample directly into a combustion boat. Place the cover on the boat and put it into the end of the combustion tube. Turn on heaters No. 1 and No. 2 and gradually increase the temperature to approximately 800° to 900° C. Regulate the flow of oxygen through the combustion train at approximately 500 milliliters per minute. Allow the sample to combust for at least 30 minutes, and then allow enough time to insure that all of the water formed during combustion has been driven (carried by the oxygen flow) into the drying tube containing the magnesium perchlorate.

Obtain final weight of items "A" and "B."

Calculations:

$$\% \text{ hydrogen} = \frac{\text{increase in weight of "A"} \times 11.19}{\text{sample weight}}$$

$$\% \text{ carbon} = \frac{\text{increase in weight of "B"} \times 27.29}{\text{sample weight}}$$

References — Appendix A

American Public Health Association. *Standard Methods for the Examination of Water, Sewage, and Industrial Wastes.* 10th ed. New York: The Association, 1955. 497 pp.

American Society for Testing Materials. *Book of A.S.T.M. Standards, Part 5.* Philadelphia: The Society, 1952.

Steyermark, Al. *Quantitative Organic Microanalysis.* Philadelphia: Blakiston Co., 1951. 389 pp.

Theroux, Eldridge F., and Mallmann, W. L. *Laboratory Manual for Chemical and Bacterial Analysis of Water and Sewage.* 3rd ed. New York: McGraw-Hill Book Co., 1943. 274 pp.

Appendix B

ORDINANCE PROVISIONS FOR REFUSE DISPOSAL[1]

Typical provisions in municipal ordinances for regulating the disposal of refuse are presented here as a guide to local officials in developing a new ordinance or revising an old one. Ordinances are not reproduced in their entirety because it is most improbable that any two cities are confronted with all of the same local conditions and therefore need all of the same provisions.

The ordinance provisions quoted have proved satisfactory in the city in which they are in force. They are not necessarily the best ones possible, and changing local conditions sometimes require changes in what once were satisfactory provisions.

The subjects ordinarily covered by disposal provisions of a refuse removal ordinance can be grouped under the following headings:

1. Definitions
2. Responsibility for refuse disposal
3. Management of disposal facilities
   A. Designation of authorized sites and facilities
   B. Who may use disposal sites
   C. Responsibility of site users
   D. Salvage
4. Control of kinds of refuse disposed of at municipal facilities
   A. Separation of refuse
   B. Hazardous refuse
   C. Dead animals
5. Control of private disposal sites
6. On-site disposal
7. Air pollution controls
8. Financing
9. Penalties for violations; severability

DEFINITIONS

The terms used to designate different kinds and classes of refuse and technicalities should be defined in the ordinance. Standard definitions should be used in the ordinance, and in all published rules, notices, instructions, and publicity material. Definitions are given in Chapter 1.

The application of definitions to local needs is illustrated in the refuse collection and disposal ordinance for Rochester, New York:

11.1-2. Definitions. For the purpose of this ordinance, the following terms shall have the meanings ascribed to them in this section unless different meanings are clearly indicated by the context.

(a) Department shall mean the Department of Public Works of the City of Rochester.

---

[1]The following ordinances are included solely as examples of types of provisions various cities have used. They do not reflect what is in current use for any individual jurisdiction as specific provisions cited may have been changed or eliminated since their publication in this appendix.

(b) Commissioner shall mean the Commissioner of Public Works of the City of Rochester.

.   .   .   .   .

(h) Garbage shall mean all putrescible animal or vegetable wastes resulting from the handling, preparation, cooking and consumption of food in any private dwelling house, multiple dwelling, hotel, restaurant, building, or institution.

(i) Rubbish shall mean all cardboard, plastic, metal, or glass food containers, waste paper, rags, sweepings, small pieces of wood, excelsior, rubber, leather, and similar waste materials that ordinarily accumulate around a home, business or industry. It shall not include garbage, ashes, bulk refuse, dead animals, hazardous refuse, industrial waste or building waste resulting from the operations of a contractor.

(j) Mixed refuse shall mean garbage and rubbish placed and stored together in a standard refuse container or in a substitute refuse container as required by this ordinance.

(k) Ashes shall mean the residue of the combustion of solid fuels.

(l) Bulk refuse shall mean discarded household furniture, beddings and mattresses, leaves, lawn cuttings, tree trimmings and hedge trimmings.

(m) Dead animals shall mean animals that have died naturally or have been accidentally killed. Animals or parts of animals from slaughter houses are not included in this category.

(n) Hazardous refuse shall mean any refuse the handling or disposal of which, in the opinion of the commissioner, would constitute a danger to city employees or to city property.

(o) Household waste shall mean mixed refuse, ashes and bulk refuse originating in and around private dwellings, multiple dwellings, fraternity houses, living quarters or dining facilities located in schools, colleges or universities.

(p) Institutional waste shall mean mixed refuse and ashes originating in and around tax exempt hospitals and public, charitable, philanthropic or religious institutions conducted for the benefit of the public or a recognized section of the public. Institutions not covered by the foregoing definition shall be considered commercial establishments.

(q) Commercial waste shall mean rubbish, mixed refuse, and ashes originating in and around commercial establishments, industrial establishments, hotels, restaurants, cafeterias and nonpublic institutions.

(r) Industrial waste shall mean any and all residue resulting directly from industrial or manufacturing operations. It shall not include waste originating from commercial operations of an industrial establishment, nor shall it include waste resulting from the commercial operations of persons, firms or corporations engaged in the construction of buildings, the repairing of streets and buildings, demolition or excavation. Residue or waste resulting from tree or landscaping services shall also be excluded.

(s) Building waste shall mean any and all refuse or residue resulting directly from building construction, reconstruction, repair, or demolition; from grading, shrubbing, or other incidental work in connection with any premises; or from replacement of building equipment or appliances.

(t) A licensed waste collector shall mean any person, firm, or corporation who obtains a license from the Commissioner of Public Works to collect or transport public or private household waste, institutional waste, industrial or commercial wastes, regardless of the place of origin, over the streets of the city.

(u) Building debris shall mean any refuse or residue resulting from minor noncommercial repairs to a private dwelling made by the owner or occupant himself.

Where feeding garbage to hogs is a method of disposal the term swill is often defined the way Sacramento County, California, has done it:

Section 3(e) "Swill" shall mean that particular garbage which is wholly or nearly . . . edible and salable as food and having food value for animals or fowl, accumulating from animal, vegetable, or other waste material from clubs, hospitals, hotels, restaurants, homes and other dwelling places, and from public eating places.

In some cities where refuse is incinerated, combustible and noncombustible refuse are specifically defined. The Hartford, Connecticut, ordinance designates these types of refuse as follows:

Sec. 18-1 (a-2) The term "incinerator refuse" as used in this chapter shall mean plastic, metal and glass food containers, dust, sweepings, waste paper, rags, wood, excelsior, bedding, rubber, leather, rubbish, leaves, brush, small dead animals and birds and similar waste materials that ordinarily accumulate in and around a home or business, except building materials and portions of trees greater than six inches in diameter.

(b-1) The term "non-combustible" refuse as used in this chapter shall mean ashes, cans, bottles (other than food containers), earth, wire, glass, heavy metal, automobile parts, broken kitchen ware, mattresses and other materials of like nature.

RESPONSIBILITY FOR REFUSE DISPOSAL

It is customary to designate in the refuse disposal ordinance the officer, department, or agency responsible for carrying out the provisions. Frequently the authority is clearly set forth in administrative codes or in separate ordinances but if there is any question as to the allocation of authority, powers, and duties, it should be spelled out. In Eugene, Oregon, supervision of disposal is the responsibility of the city manager and a garbage board:

Section 2. The regulation of the disposal and hauling of garbage in the City of Eugene shall be under the supervision of the City Manager; provided, however, the City Manager may appoint a Garbage Board consisting of three (3) members residing in the City of Eugene, and designating its powers and duties for the administration of this Ordinance. Said powers and duties shall not be inconsistent with the provisions of this Ordinance and shall include, but not be limited to, authority to conduct periodic inspections to insure full compliance with the terms and provisions of this Ordinance. . . .

The Board of Public Works is responsible for disposal of refuse in Waterbury, Connecticut:

I. Responsibility. The Board of Public Works of the City of Waterbury shall have power and is hereby empowered to take such measures as they shall deem effectual for the removal and disposal of refuse from the City of Waterbury or any portion thereof; under the following rules and regulations. . . .

The city council issues permits for refuse disposal in Somerset, Kentucky:

Section III, I. Permits.— No person, firm or corporation shall collect, transport, or dispose of garbage or refuse within the city limits who does not possess a permit, said permit shall be issued only by the City Council and approved by the Mayor or his designated representative, and only upon the payment of any annual permit fee which is to be set by the City Council and only after the Mayor has satisfied himself that the licensee is capable of complying with the requirements of this code. The permit may be revoked when deemed necessary to the public welfare by the Mayor or upon recommendation of the City Council.

Specific powers to regulate and direct users of the Albert Lea, Minnesota, sanitary landfill are included in that city's ordinance:

Section 6, 6.1. All garbage and other refuse shall be delivered and deposited for disposal on the sanitary landfill area in accord with the directions and orders of the city's representative in charge of operations.

Enforcement of the Manitowoc, Wisconsin, refuse ordinance is the responsibility of the city health commissioner with the assistance of the police and street commissioners:

13.06 (7) City Health Commissioner to Enforce Provisions of This Section. Duty of Police and Street Commissioners. It shall be the duty of the City Health Commissioner to strictly enforce the provisions of this Section and to see that any and all violations thereof are promptly abated and the violators prosecuted, and it shall be the special duty of the Chief of Police, Street Commissioner, and all policemen to give attention throughout the city to any and every case of violation of this Section and to promptly report to the City Health Commissioner, in writing, every such violation which shall come to their knowledge.

MANAGEMENT OF DISPOSAL FACILITIES

Designation of Authorized Disposal Sites and Facilities

The elimination of unauthorized and promiscuous disposal of refuse is basic to an effective sanitation program. It is customary, therefore, to restrict disposal as it is in Omaha, Nebraska:

Section 19-4A.7—III Disposal of Refuse. No person shall throw, drop, or deposit, or cause to be thrown, dropped, or deposited on any premises or vacant property in the City any waste (including, but not limited to, garbage, ashes, rubbish, building rubbish, dead animals, putrescible matter, and anything injurious to health), provided, however, that the prohibition contained in this paragraph shall not apply to the deposit of wastes not injurious to health on a public site where permission to make such a deposit is granted by the Sanitation Commission of the City of Omaha, nor to the filling in or grading of property with earth, mud, ashes, and similar materials. . . .

The Salt Lake City, Utah, ordinance is similar, but it also refers to the control of farms on which hogs are fed garbage and to trade wastes:

Sec. 18-3-6—Disposition of garbage and waste. It shall be unlawful for any person to deposit or cause or permit to be deposited any garbage, market waste, stove waste, trade waste, or any other similar refuse in or upon any street or alley, or upon any premises in Salt Lake City without express permission from the board of health. The board of health may give permit for the feeding of garbage or swill upon premises properly equipped and maintained so as to prevent the creation of a nuisance, or for the depositing of ashes and other dry material for filling purposes, or for health [purposes] may designate and under such restriction as said board may impose, or for the assorting, baling, and marketing of trade waste upon premises properly equipped and maintained.

Deposit of refuse in or around bodies of water is specifically prohibited in Knoxville, Tennessee:

Section 14: [from code supplement]. Depositing in streams, ponds, etc. It shall be unlawful for any person to throw, discard, deposit, dispose of, or allow any trash, garbage waste, scraps of food, vegetables, fruits, meat, industrial or processed waste, or the like into, about, around, or near any stream or body of water, regardless of size, within the confines of the city.

This section shall not be construed to prohibit people from feeding ducks, swans, fish, and like aquatic creatures within reasonable bounds as the need may require.

Who May Use Disposal Sites

Restriction of the use of disposal sites or facilities to designated individuals or establishments located within certain governmental boundaries is common practice. In Rochester, New York, refuse disposed of at the municipal incinerator or landfill is restricted to that originating within the city; and certification of this fact is required:

11.1-16. Disposal of Refuse. Acceptable rubbish and mixed refuse and household or commercial ashes and unburnables originating within the city and transported to a designated city-operated incinerator or city-operated landfill by any person shall be accepted by the department for disposal during designated hours of operation. All persons offering such acceptable rubbish and mixed refuse or household or commercial ashes and unburnables for disposal, shall, in each instance, submit proof of the origin of the said rubbish and mixed refuse, in the form of a certificate certifying ownership that the said material originated within the city and requesting disposal.

Provision is made in the Rochester, New York, ordinance, however, for contracts for disposal of wastes from cities within the county and from industrial establishments:

11.1-17. Contracts for Disposal of Wastes. Contracts between the City of Rochester and a town or other municipality within the County of Monroe for the disposal of wastes originating within the town or municipality, as authorized by 11.1-1 hereof, shall be limited to the disposal in city-owned and operated incinerator plants of garbage and mixed refuse as defined in this chapter. Use of city landfill areas for such disposal is expressly prohibited.

Contracts between the City of Rochester and an industrial establishment for the disposal of acceptable industrial wastes originating within the city, as authorized by 11.1-1 hereof, may provide for such disposal in city landfill areas or in city-owned and operated incinerators of acceptable industrial wastes, as defined in this chapter.

A contractor who collects refuse in Santa Clara, California, may be authorized by the board of trustees to use the municipal disposal site:

Section 12. For the collection, removal and disposal of the refuse, garbage and waste matter in the City of Santa Clara in the manner in this ordinance provided, a contract for a period not to exceed five (5) years may be entered into by the City of Santa Clara, in accordance with, and subject to the terms of this ordinance.

Said contract may or may not provide that the said Scavenger may have the use of the municipal dump for the dumping of garbage, waste matter or refuse, and further that the City may or may not upon reasonable notice terminate the right to such use of said municipal dump, and require all garbage, waste matter and refuse to be disposed of elsewhere than said dump. Said contract shall provide further that the Scavenger, while being allowed the use of said dump, shall keep the same in good order and condition, and to the satisfaction of the Health Officer, or other officer which the Board of Trustees of said City may from time to time designate, and that said Scavenger shall incinerate any matter required to be incinerated, to the satisfaction of the Health Officer. Said contract may or may not provide that any matter collected outside of the City of Santa Clara shall be disposed of in said municipal dump.

In Washington, D. C., no charge is made for disposal at city incinerators and landfills, but no refuse from outside the district can be disposed of at them:

Sec. 29. The incinerators and landfills operated and maintained by the Division of Sanitation of the government of the District of Columbia shall be for the disposal of refuse produced within the boundaries of the District of Columbia. No person, firm or corporation shall be permitted to deposit at any such incinerator or landfill any refuse which has been produced outside of the District of Columbia, and any person delivering refuse produced outside the District to same, or, in the event such refuse may have been unloaded at such incinerator or landfill, such person shall be required to remove such refuse immediately.

Responsibility of Site Users

Many cities control the actions of users of refuse disposal facilities and spell out their responsibilities in regulations.

The Patchogue, New York, ordinance empowers the village superintendent of public works to set up pertinent rules and regulations:

Section 17—Refuse Disposal. . . . Refuse shall be disposed of at the Village incinerator only during the times designated by the Superintendent of Public Works and in accordance with the rules and regulations established by the Superintendent of Public Works.

Norwich, Connecticut, has a similar ordinance provision governing use of the city dump:

Section 15. Public dumping grounds owned by the city shall be under the control and jurisdiction of the director of public works. He shall establish rules and regulations as to the time and conditions of use of such dumping grounds. It shall be unlawful for any person to use any such dumping ground except in compliance with such rules and regulations.

To use the city disposal grounds or incinerator in Rochester, New York, a general release must be signed by persons entering into contract disposal arrangements:

> Section 11.1. . . . All such persons, excepting those who are required to have filed with the comptroller a liability insurance policy as provided in 11.1-15, shall sign and file with the Department a general release in the form satisfactory to the corporation counsel, which shall absolve the city and its officers and employees from responsibility for any accident to said person or persons or their employees or for any damage to trucks or other property owned or operated by them, when such accident or such damage occurs in a city-operated incinerator or city-operated landfill, or on the grounds thereof. Such release shall be signed and filed as required upon each entry to the said premises.

Most cities find it desirable to restrict use of disposal facilities to designated times. The times that disposal sites can be used are set forth in the Manitowoc, Wisconsin, ordinance:

> 13.06 (3) Regulating the Public Dumps. Penalty. No person shall deposit, throw or place any rubbish, garbage, or other matter in or at the public dump or dumps maintained by the City of Manitowoc, between the hours of nine o'clock P.M. and six o'clock A.M. of the following day from the 1st of April to the 30th of September, and from eight o'clock P.M. to six o'clock A.M. of the following day from the 1st of October to the 31st of March of any year, or at any time on Sundays and legal holidays.

Sanitary landfill users in Knoxville, Tennessee, are specifically prohibited from burning refuse on the site:

> Section 13: Burning on city's dumping grounds. It shall be unlawful for any person to set fire to, or burn any papers, trash or garbage deposited within the city limits upon the dumping grounds used by the city for the depositing or dumping of such trash or garbage collected by the city trash carts, or trash wagons, without the permission of the superintendent of streets authorizing and directing such burning.

Salvage

Salvage or reclamation of re-usable components of refuse some times pays some of the costs of refuse disposal. If salvage by individuals or contractors is permitted at refuse disposal facilities, close regulation is essential.

The Albert Lea, Minnesota, ordinance specifies that all refuse delivered to the sanitary landfill is the property of the city and prohibits salvage unless authorized by the city manager or his representative:

> 6.2. All materials delivered and deposited for disposal on the Sanitary Landfill Area are the property of the City. No person shall separate, collect, carry off or dispose of such materials unless authorized to do so by the City Manager or his representative.

At Doylestown, Pennsylvania, scavenging at a landfill is prohibited:

> Article VII Section 2. It shall be unlawful for any person to enter the landfill area except when the attendant is present and at the hours

prescribed by Borough Council. It shall be unlawful for any person to scavenge or remove any article from the landfill area.

In Philadelphia salvage of refuse on private disposal sites is permitted provided the operation is carried out as prescribed in the board of health's regulations:

8. Salvage Operations—(a) No person operating a private dump or landfill shall, or permit anyone else to, salvage or reclaim any food or food products, whether or not in a container, which may be delivered to the site for disposal. Such food or food products shall be promptly unloaded, spread and compacted to firmness, and covered to a depth of at least twenty-four (24) inches with other refuse material, or with cover material.

(b) Salvaging or reclamation of materials (except food or food products) is permitted, provided all salvaged materials are removed to a location at such distance from the active surface as not to interfere with unloading, spreading, compacting or covering operations.

CONTROL OF KINDS OF REFUSE DISPOSED OF AT MUNICIPAL FACILITIES

Separation of Refuse

Whether all refuse is collected together or separated into components depends on the method of disposal.

Garden City, New York, requires that refuse delivered to the village incinerator and dump be separated into combustibles and noncombustibles and prohibits disposal of swill, slops, and offal:

Section 11: Use of Disposal Facilities—The facilities of the municipal incinerator and dump will be available for the disposal of refuse herein designated . . . except swill, slops and offal. Such refuse shall be segregated as to combustible and non-combustible, shall be delivered during work hours only, and shall be unloaded or dumped at such locations and in such manner as may be directed. The Superintendent of Public Works shall have the right, however, to further regulate, restrict or prohibit the use of the municipal incinerator or dump as may be necessary in the public interest or due to operating conditions thereat or for repeated violation of regulations.

If sanitary landfills are used for disposal, usually all ordinary refuse is accepted without separation. Some items are considered extraordinary, however, and are not accepted for disposal.

The Albert Lea, Minnesota, ordinance sets out the items not acceptable at the landfill:

Section 3. Refuse Not Acceptable for Disposal.

The City of Albert Lea will operate a Sanitary Landfill for the disposal of combined garbage and refuse. The following refuse shall be considered not acceptable for disposal in the City operated Sanitary Landfill:

3.1 Dangerous materials or substances such as poisons, acids, caustics, infected materials and explosives.

3.2 Any materials of any kind or nature, including ashes, that contain any hot live coals or fire.

3.3 Unusual quantities of materials resulting from the construction or wrecking of buildings and structures or that may result from manufacturing, industrial or agricultural processes.

3.4 All large and bulky materials such as auto car bodies that may require special preparation and processing for disposal.

Garbage, combustible refuse, and ashes are disposed of separately in the District of Columbia. Requirements for combustible commercial refuse received at the district's incinerators are given in police regulations, as follows:

Sec. 26. . . . (d) The District of Columbia reserves the right to reject or further restrict deliveries of combustible commercial refuse at any time.

Sec. 27. Combustible commercial refuse to be disposed of at the District of Columbia incinerators specified in Section 26 (a) of this Article shall conform with the following requirements:

(a) Such refuse shall be readily combustible and shall not contain explosives, materials which may be toxic when burned, ashes, garbage, dirt, rock, or rubble.

(b) No refuse subject to absorption of moisture, such as leaves, paper, and other materials capable of absorbing moisture, shall be delivered to the said incinerators in large quantities unless such refuse be dry or readily combustible. When the moisture content of such materials is high, the amounts received will be limited at the discretion of the Superintendent of Incineration or the Superintendent of Landfills.

(c) No piece of combustible commercial refuse delivered to the above-specified incinerators for disposal shall be greater in size than 24 inches by 24 inches by 4 feet in length and larger articles, such as, for example, packing cases or furniture constructed of wood, cardboard, or other combustible material, shall be broken into pieces not larger in size than 24 inches by 24 inches by 4 feet.

Hazardous Refuse

Hazardous refuse as defined in the Hartford, Connecticut, ordinance includes:

. . . cleaning fluids, crank case oils, cutting oils, paints, plastics, explosives, acids, caustics, poisons, drugs, radioactive materials, fine powdery earth used to filter cleaning fluid and refuse of similar nature.

Usually hazardous material is not accepted for the regular collection service and must be disposed of in a special manner as prescribed by regulations.

This is also stipulated in the Hartford ordinance, which places the responsibility for supervising disposal of radioactive materials and other hazardous substances upon the director of health:

Sec. 18-10. Hazardous refuse.

(a) No hazardous refuse will be collected by the department of public works but shall be transported by the owner, responsible person or agent to the municipal disposal area and disposed of as prescribed by the director of public works.

(b) Radioactive materials, drugs, poisons and like substances shall be disposed of under the supervision of the director of health.

Dead Animals

The disposal of large dead animals is usually considered the responsibility of the owner. Large dead animals are usually disposed of at rendering plants if there is one within reasonable hauling distance. Some municipal incinerators can burn large animals such as horses and cows. Small animals may be incinerated or put in sanitary landfills.

In Detroit, Michigan, small dead animals are collected and disposed of by the department of public works upon proper notification, but large animals are handled separately:

Sec. 306. All small dead animals, if kept separate from garbage and rubbish, will be collected without charge upon notice to the Department; provided that a charge will be made by the Department for all such animals collected from animal hospitals, kennels and the like. Owners of large dead animals shall be responsible for their removal and disposal.

Regulations of the Davidson County, Tennessee, health department specify method, time within which disposal must take place, and procedure for handling animals known to have or suspected of having a communicable disease:

G. Disposal . . . 4. Dead animals shall be disposed of by burial or in an approved rendering or incineration plant. The owner of the animal, or if said owner cannot be found, then the person in charge of the property on which the dead animal is located is responsible for disposal within twenty-four hours by burying and covering with at least eighteen inches of earth or by arrangements for delivery to an approved disposal site or to a rendering or incineration plant as specified above. Dead animals will be accepted for disposal at County operated disposal sites provided they are delivered at a pre-arranged time at which they can be buried promptly as a part of the regular operation of the particular disposal site. In case an animal is known or suspected to have died of a communicable disease, the handling and disposal of the carcass must conform with laws and regulations of the State Department of Agriculture for the control of diseases of animals.

A schedule of fees for the removal and disposal of dead animals in included in the bylaws of Edmonton, Alberta, Canada:

By-Law No. 283–23. Arrangements may be made with the Engineer's Department to remove the dead animals and the cost of such collection shall be charged as per the following schedule:

(a) Pigs, Sheep and Calves—
Pick-up, haul and cremate at Incinerator . . . .$5.00 each
(b) Cattle—Pick-up, haul and cremate at Incinerator. . . . . . 6.50 each
(c) Horses—Pick-up, haul and cremate at Incinerator. . . . . . 7.50 each
(d) Dogs—Pick-up, haul and cremate at Incinerator. . . . . . . 1.00 each
(e) Cremating animals that are hauled to the incinerator by private parties, 25¢ per 100 lbs. or portion thereof.

CONTROL OF PRIVATE DISPOSAL SITES

In some cities all refuse disposed of within the corporate limits must be disposed of at municipally operated refuse disposal facilities. Most cities, however, permit private refuse disposal operations but control the activities at them.

In Louisville, Kentucky, a permit is required before noncombustible waste can be deposited:

Section 19. Control of Dumps. It shall be unlawful for any person, firm or corporation to deposit or permit to be deposited any noncombustible waste on any land owned or controlled by such person, firm, or corporation without having first obtained a permit from the Director of Works to do so. Application for a permit to operate a private dump shall be made to the Director of Works, who shall issue such a permit if he is satisfied that the applicant is responsible and is willing to comply with the rules and regulations of the Director of Works concerning the operation of private dumps. Such permits shall be valid until revoked.

The Fresno, California, ordinance makes it unlawful for any person other than enfranchised garbage collectors to dispose of garbage:

Section 9. It shall be unlawful for any person, within the City of Fresno, other than garbage collectors enfranchised by the City or duly authorized by the Fresno City Waste Disposal Department, to gather, collect, transport, burn, bury or dispose of any garbage or mixed garbage from any place where the same is placed by any occupant or other person described in Section 1 hereof, or to remove the contents of any garbage or mixed garbage receptacle.

Los Angeles issues permits for the operation of garbage disposal facilities, including incineration and reduction plants and ranches on which hogs are fed garbage. (The latter are controlled by state regulation in practically all states; particularly the cooking of the garbage.)

Sec. 66.06. Garbage Disposal—Permits.

(a) Any person disposing of garbage within the City by the methods of incineration or reduction, or disposing of garbage obtained by a duly authorized contractor from this City by such methods, shall make application agreeing to such rules and regulations as may be promulgated by the City for the construction and maintenance of any such incinerator or reduction plant in a sanitary manner and the disposal of any waste materials therefrom in a manner which shall not create a menace to human or animal health or a public nuisance, and shall thereafter receive a permit which shall be revocable at any time for cause.

(b) Any person feeding garbage to hogs from any source other than the household or ranch on which the hogs are maintained must first make application agreeing to the rules and regulations embodying the principles set forth in Section 66.07 and Sections 34.06 to 34.08, inclusive, and shall thereafter receive a permit which is revocable at any time for cause.

The Davidson County, Tennessee, health department requires that the location and the equipment and methods used in feeding garbage to animals be subject to the approval of the director of health:

5. In cases where garbage is collected and used as food for hogs, cattle, or other animals within the county, such feeding must be done either at locations sufficiently removed from habitations, public places, or human activities to avoid the creation of nuisances or by means of such special equipment and methods as may be necessary for the prevention of nuisances. In all cases the location, equipment, and methods of feeding garbage to animals shall be subject to the approval of the Director of Health.

Hartford, Connecticut, requires that all dumping grounds be licensed and that owners keep them orderly:

Sec. 18-15. Licenses for dumping grounds. The bureau of licenses and permits shall, with the approval of the director of health and at his discretion, issue and revoke licenses authorizing the dumping of ashes, rubbish and waste material, except garbage, and other offensive material on premises in the city, subject to the rules and regulations of the department of health as to the time and conditions of use, the materials that may be deposited in a particular location, and the placing and maintaining of signs indicating permitted uses.

Sec. 18-16. Maintenance of dumps. It shall be the duty of the owner of any dumping ground to keep the same in an orderly condition, and when ordered by the director of health, to erect and maintain suitable fences to prevent the use of such place by unauthorized persons, or at times other than those specified in his permit.

The disposal method used by private collectors in the Borough of State College, Pennsylvania, must be approved by the board of health:

Article No. 8–Disposal by the Collector. Section No. 1–The method used for the disposal of garbage shall be approved by the Boards of Health having jurisdiction. It shall be conducted and maintained so as not to create a public nuisance, permit fly breeding or be in any way a menace to the public health.

South Orange, New Jersey, requires as a license prerequisite proof that the scavenger has adequate disposal facilities and equipment and that the governing body of the area in which the site is located has given permission to use the site for refuse disposal:

Section 4, 2. The applicant shall submit satisfactory evidence that:

(a) He has a place for the disposal of ashes, garbage, rubbish and other collected material;

(b) The said uses of such disposal site are assured for the period of the license;

(c) The said place for disposal of ashes, garbage, rubbish and other collected material is located outside the limits of the Village of South Orange; that the use of such site for disposal is guaranteed for the period of the license; that the governing body of the municipality in which the said site for disposal is located has established a dump by ordinance and the applicant shall submit a duly authenticated copy of such ordinance; that the said governing body by resolution or other appropriate proceeding has selected and specified the site of said dump for the purpose of depositing ashes, garbage, rubbish and other materials, and the applicant shall submit a duly authenticated copy of such resolution or other proceeding; that a permit has been granted to the applicant for dumping purposes on said site by the Board of Health or other duly constituted authority of such municipality.

3. The applicant shall furnish an itemized list of all machinery and equipment owned by the applicant or available for use by the applicant in accordance with the provisions of this Ordinance. The applicant shall make the said equipment available for inspection by the Village Engineer, at reasonable times, during a period of ten (10) days prior to the hearing hereinafter provided for.

Sacramento County, California, requires that application for a permit to operate a refuse disposal area be approved by the board of health and the county planning commission and specifies "fill and cover method" and incineration:

Section 19. The application for a permit to operate a refuse disposal area shall be made in writing to the Health Department on forms provided by the Health Department. If the Department finds from the facts that applicant is capable of complying with the provisions of this ordinance and the rules and regulations of the Health Department, said department shall issue a revocable permit for the conduct of the refuse disposal area. Such permit shall be issued for a period of two years and shall not be transferable. Renewal of permits shall be applied for and acted upon in the same manner as the original application. Before any permit shall be issued for a refuse disposal area, the proposed site shall be referred to the County Planning Commision to determine whether or not said disposal site is in a proper zone.

Section 21. Except as herein provided, the refuse and rubbish disposal at all refuse disposal areas shall be by the fill and cover method, or by burning in properly designed and properly operated incinerators approved by the Health Department.

The Philadelphia department of public health has developed a comprehensive set of regulations governing private dumps and landfills:

Section 9-604. Refuse Collection—(7) Private Dumps and Landfills.

(a) No person shall operate or permit the operation of a private dump or landfill unless he has obtained a license from the Department of Licenses and Inspections.

(b) No license to operate a private dump or landfill shall be issued unless:

(.1) the applicant furnishes proof satisfactory to the Department of Licenses and Inspections of ownership of, or permission from the owner to use, the land on which the dump or landfill is located;

(.2) the applicant furnishes a plan of the area of the private dump or landfill indicating the boundary lines, approximate elevations, established grade elevations, and approximate total cubic yards required to fill the area to established grades;

(.3) the plan has been approved by the Department of Public Health;

(.4) the applicant pays an annual license fee of $100, except that when an application is filed after the first six months of a license year the fee for that year shall be $50.

(c) All licenses shall be conditioned upon compliance with S9-605 (7)(b) and with the regulations issued by the Board of Health and the Air Pollution Control Board with regard to the location and operation of private dumps.

(d) No person shall deposit or permit the depositing of any refuse coming from a source outside the City on any private dump or landfill within the City.

(e) When the Department of Public Health finds that a licensed private dump has been filled to the established grade levels, it shall so certify to the Department of Licenses and Inspections which shall cancel the license for the dump and refund to the licensee a pro rata amount of the license fee.

(f) In addition to any fine or other sanction, the Department of Licenses and Inspections may suspend or revoke the license of a private dump or landfill operator who violates any provision of this Section or any condition of a license.

1. Definitions—(a) Private dump or landfill. Real property in or upon which refuse is deposited, other than when operated by the City.

2. Scope of Regulations—These regulations shall apply to all private dumps or landfills, except the receipt or storage of cover material and the disposal by a householder of his own household refuse on the property where he lives.

3. Supervision—A person in responsible charge of operations shall be on duty at private dumps or landfills continuously during the hours of active operation.

4. Trespassing—Effective measures shall be taken to prevent trespassing or dumping at private dumps or landfills by unauthorized persons, and to prevent trespassing and dumping when unattended.

5. Receipt of Dangerous Materials—Where the operator of a private dump or landfill has knowledge of, or reason to know of, the inclusion of dangerous materials in refuse delivered to the private dump or landfill, he shall receive, handle, and dispose of such materials in accordance with procedures established by or in a manner approved by the Department of Public Health.

6. Operation—(a) All private dumps and landfills within the City of Philadelphia shall be operated as sanitary landfills. . . .

7. Surface Elevations ....
8. Salvage Operations ....
9. Access Roads ....
10. Water Supply ....
11. Drainage and Water Pollution ....
12. Rodent and Arthropod Control ....
13. Fencing ....

14. Disasters or Emergencies—When, in the opinion of the Health Commissioner, a period of disaster or emergency exists involving Public Health, he may waive any of the provisions of these regulations for a period not to exceed thirty (30) days.

15. Approval of Application for License for Private Dumps or Landfills—Plans for private dumps or landfills submitted to the Department of Public Health for approval shall be accompanied by such information as the Department of Public Health may request to show how the proposed operation of the private dump or landfill will comply with these regulations and with Sections 9-604(7) and 6-214 (1)(g) of The Philadelphia Code.

16. Inspection—Authorized representatives of the Department of Public Health shall be permitted to enter private dumps or landfills at any time for the purpose of determining compliance with these regulations or with Section 9-604(7) and Section 6-214(1)(g) of The Philadelphia Code, and the owner, operator, or person in charge shall give such representatives free and unhindered access for inspection purposes.

ON-SITE DISPOSAL

On-site, or on-premises, disposal is said to be the most widely used means of refuse disposal in the United States. Since on-site disposal is usually interpreted to mean the use of garbage grinders and burning (not necessarily incineration), the term disposal is used loosely. Actually, final disposal of much of the refuse is done off the premises. It is important, therefore, to regulate on-site disposal to prevent nuisances and health hazards.

The City of Detroit has promoted the use of food waste grinders; and has set up standards and controls governing their installation and the use of domestic burning equipment:

1.11a—Domestic refuse burning equipment: any refuse-burning equipment or incinerator having a firebox or charging compartment of not more than 5 cubic feet in capacity.

.   .   .   .

2.6a—It shall be unlawful for any person, firm, corporation or their agents to import, sell, offer for sale, expose for sale, exchange, deliver or install for use in the City of Detroit:

(1) Any make, model, or type of domestic refuse burning equipment which has not been approved by the bureau.

(2) Any make, model, or type of approved domestic refuse burning equipment for the burning of any type of refuse other than the types for which the refuse burning equipment has been approved by the bureau.

(3) Provided that the importation, delivery or transportation of such domestic refuse burning equipment by railroad companies and other common carriers in the course of their common carrier business, shall not be deemed to be a violation of the provisions of this section.

2.6b—Prior to approval, each make, model or type of domestic refuse burning equipment shall be submitted to the bureau and be subjected to such tests as may be deemed necessary to establish the performance efficiency, durability, minimum installation requirements, air pollution potential and fire hazard potential under ordinary operation. For fire hazard potential and efficiency determination, nationally recognized standards such as those of the American Gas Association and the Underwriters Laboratories may be employed.

(1) The bureau shall list each make, model or type of domestic refuse burning equipment which it has approved, and shall designate the approval as being limited to one of the following four categories:

Type A. Outdoor burning equipment for ordinary paper or similar material only.

Type B. Indoor burning equipment for ordinary paper or similar material only.

Type C. Rubbish incinerator for burning ordinary paper, rags, floor sweepings or similar material only.

Type D. Domestic incinerator for burning rubbish and garbage.

(2) Any approved domestic refuse burning equipment, except Type A, that is imported, sold, offered for sale, exposed for sale, exchanged, delivered or installed for use in the City of Detroit shall bear a plate or tag in accordance with the regulations of the department which identifies the equipment and the category for which it is approved.

(3) Any person, firm, or corporation whose domestic refuse burning equipment is submitted to tests by the bureau must pay all expenses necessary to the attendant tests, and the bureau shall furnish the submittor a copy of the results of such tests. . . .

.   .   .   .

2.11—Plans and specifications so filed with the Department shall show the type of installation, the amount of work and the amount of heating to be done by such fuel or refuse-burning equipment and all appurtenances thereto, including all provisions made for the purpose of securing complete combustion of the fuel or refuse to be used and the manner in which it is to be burned for the purpose of preventing smoke and other air pollution as provided by this Ordinance.

(a) Such plans and specifications shall also contain a statement of the rate of burning and kind of fuel or refuse proposed to be used and the manner in which it is to be burned.

(b) Such plans shall further show the dimensions of the room in which such fuel or refuse-burning equipment is to be located, the location and dimensions of all stacks used in connection with or as a part of said fuel or refuse-burning equipment.

(c) The Bureau may require such additional data as is deemed necessary for the purpose of issuing a permit for the operation of such fuel or refuse burning devices. . . .

Although few if any cities require food waste grinders in all dwellings, a number of cities require them in new construction.

The Detroit ordinance includes such a requirement:

Section 3. Structures erected in the City after January 1, 1956, designed, arranged or intended to be used for purposes which cause, result in, produce or develop food wastes, and all structures converted or altered for such purposes, shall provide approved food waste disposal equipment for such purposes within the premises thereof. It shall be unlawful for any person to use, permit or cause to be used any such structure that does not conform to the provisions of this section.

Section 4. The Department of Buildings and Safety Engineering, through its officers, inspectors, or employees, shall enforce the provisions of this Ordinance.

Section 4.1. The installation, operation, and maintenance of any equipment or method to be used for on-the-site disposal of food wastes, shall comply with the applicable provisions and regulations of the building, housing, plumbing, electrical, smoke abatement, air pollution, safety engineering, health, sanitation, and fire ordinances of the City.

Section 5. The Commissioner shall have on file in the Department, a list of approved food waste disposal equipment.

A Lombard, Illinois, ordinance specifies that dead leaves and similar wastes may be burned on the premises under certain conditions and permits the installation of incinerators and grinders under certain conditions:

Section 9. Disposal Other than Collection:

(a) Dead leaves and other wastes from plants may be burned upon a lot or plot of ground upon which such waste has accumulated, if proper precautions are taken to prevent the spread of fire, and provided further that no nuisance is created by such fire.

(b) Garbage and other combustible wastes may be disposed of within the building where it accumulates or within a closed building accessory thereto situated on the same premises by complete incineration of such garbage or wastes in such a manner as to create no noxious odors, fire hazard, smoke or other nuisance, by grinding or shredding it finely and disposing of it through pipes leading to a public sanitary sewer, provided that all garbage or combustible matter so disposed of in such pipes shall have been ground or shredded to such a degree that all particles are carried freely under the flow conditions normally prevailing in the sewers into which such is deposited, with no particle greater than one-half inch in any dimension and further provided that all incinerators or grinders used for such disposal of wastes must be approved by the Health Officer and the Village Manager or their respective representatives.

The Davidson County, Tennessee, health department requires that if on-site disposal is used, refuse must be stored in the same way it would be if the refuse were stored for collection:

6. Persons who propose to dispose of refuse on their individual premises must observe the same conditions of storage as would be required if the refuse were stored for collection, as specified in D above. Garbage may be disposed of by adequate burial and covering with earth but garbage and refuse containing garbage shall not be burned except in a high temperature furnace. Refuse that does not contain garbage, dead animals, night soil, or manure may be disposed of in any manner that will not cause nuisance from appearance or odor or provide harborage for rats or a breeding place for flies and other insects. When it appears that the methods employed for disposal of refuse on individual premises is causing or may cause a nuisance, collection, removal, and disposal in accordance with the foregoing regulations may be required by the Director of Health.

AIR POLLUTION CONTROLS

During the 1950's the serious air pollution problems in many urban areas received increased attention. Among the first air pollution nuisances studied were smoke and odors from improperly disposed of wastes. Back yard burning of combustible refuse and open burning of refuse on dumps were found to be significant contributors to atmospheric pollution in such metropolitan areas as Los Angeles and Philadelphia. Incinerators in apartment houses and similar places were also often found to be heavy contributors.

As a result, many municipalities in recent years have passed ordinances to control disposal practices. Probably the first and most popular step was to limit or outlaw open burning.

The Newark, New Jersey, health and sanitation ordinance, adopted in 1951, requires that a permit be obtained for burning, restricts the hours of burning, and limits the location of dumps in which burning is permitted:

Sec. 15.654. Burning certain waste matter—Permit required. It shall be unlawful to set fire to, or burn, any of the items specified in section 15.651 of this Revision, on any dump licensed as herein provided, without first obtaining a permit from the inspector of combustibles and fire risks of the city. (8-22-51, S3.)

Sec. 15.655. Same—Hours permitted; water facilities. The controlled burning of combustible rubbish, paper, cardboard, wood and trade wastes will be permitted only during the daylight hours from 9:00 A.M. to 5:00 P.M. of each day, exclusive of Sundays, or holidays. Adequate water facilities must be available for the control of these fires and to deal with all other fires such as are caused by spontaneous combustion. (8-21-51, S4.)

Sec. 15.656. Location in accordance with zoning regulations. Any and all dumps licensed under the provisions of this division shall be located only in such place or places as is permitted by the zoning ordinances of the city. (8-22-51, S6.)

Salt Lake City sanitary regulations prohibit burning of refuse in furnaces and stoves, as well as outdoor burning:

Sec. 18-3-16. Burning of refuse. It shall be unlawful for any person to burn garbage, market waste, manure, or other offensive refuse in the open air, or in any furnace or stove within the city limits; provided however, that trade waste and other similar refuse may be burned at the city incinerating plant, or other places designated by the board of health.

The Rapid City, South Dakota, ordinance prohibits outside burning of garbage but permits burning of refuse such as newspapers:

6.0606. Burning Garbage. No garbage or other matter from which offensive or noisome odors emanate during combustion shall be burned outside of any building.

Burning on the city dump by the public is prohibited in Traverse City, Michigan:

502.5. No person shall set fire to or burn any matter of any kind on the refuse ground of the City in Garfield Township, Grand Traverse County, except the attendant at the refuse ground.

In Omaha, Nebraska, regular burning of refuse is prohibited but certain types of burning are permissible with the special permission of the fire department:

18-6.4 (a) It shall be unlawful to conduct open or unconfined burning within the limits of the City of Omaha either on public or private property except at the discretion of the Chief of the Fire Department and then only upon the receipt of special permission of said Fire Chief or his authorized agents and specifying the time and location at which said authorized burning will take place. Such burning when authorized shall not be carried on closer than 25 feet from any permanent structure unless said permission specifically allows it, nor shall any burning permitted under this section be carried on without one or more persons in direct attendance and as may be specified by the Fire Chief or his agents.

(b) All regular burning of waste material and combustibles of every type, including wood, paper, cardboard, rakings, leaves, grass, weeds, litter, sweepings, and all waste within the confines of the City of Omaha must be conducted within a properly designed and constructed incinerator or closure which is up to the minimum safety standard specified in this ordinance and conforming further with ordinances of the City with respect to the structural standards and smoke emission.

(c) It shall be unlawful to conduct open burning of waste materials, wood, paper, cardboard, rakings, leaves, grass, weeds, litter, sweepings, and all waste in public paved streets, alleys, or public areas.

The burning of garbage is prohibited in Albuquerque, New Mexico, but dry combustible refuse may be burned between sunup and sundown under specified conditions.

Section 1—No garbage shall be burned in the open air within the City of Albuquerque provided however that dry combustible waste paper, trash, weeds and leaves may be burned between the time of sunrise and sundown and any day when burned no closer than twenty five (25) feet from any dwelling and guarded by a person over the age of fourteen years, and such fire shall be extinguished at sundown in such a manner as to prevent smoke and smudging.

Standards of incineration of refuse are prescribed by air pollution control authorities in such cities as New York, Philadelphia, Detroit, Chicago, and Los Angeles. Although regulations vary according to local needs, the Philadelphia controls are considered more or less typical of requirements in large cities:

Section 4A—Limits and Measurements

(a) No person may cause, suffer or allow to be discharged into the open air dust, fume, gas, mist, odor, smoke, vapor, or any combination thereof, from any single point, vent, stack or source which constitutes air pollution or an air pollution nuisance or which is of a shade in excess of No. 2 on the Ringelmann chart or its equivalent for a period of more than two (2) minutes in any fifteen (15) minutes; or for more than three such two (2) minute periods in any one day;

(a-1) except when building a new fire, when adjusting new equipment, when a breakdown of equipment occurs, or in the operation of mobile equipment, and prompt notice of such exceptions is given to the Department of Public Health, Air Pollution Control Division, one initial startup allowance of ten (10) minutes in sixty (60) minutes shall be permitted when dust, fume, gas, mist, odor, smoke, vapor or any combination thereof, not to exceed No. 3 on the Ringelmann chart or its equivalent may be emitted:

(a-2) except that when soot blowing, with a resultant emission of dust, fume, gas, mist, odor, smoke, vapor, or any combination thereof, in a shade in excess of No. 2 on the Ringelmann chart or its equivalent may be permitted for not more than a reasonable scheduled time agreed to by the Air Pollution Control Division prior to any such emissions:

(a-3) In the case of an emission having a color other than black, an equivalent density as shown by any equivalent density scale approved by the Air Pollution Control Board may be used.

(a-4) All references to the Ringelmann chart mean the "Standards and Instructions" published by the United States Bureau of Mines (Circular 6888, dated 1936, revised April 1941) to determine the density of smoke.

(b) Dust, fume or smoke discharged into the open air, or passing any convenient measuring point, from any fuel fired combustion process, shall not: (1) exceed 0.85 pounds per 1,000 pounds of gases adjusted to 12 per cent CO_2 (carbon dioxide) content; or (2) create air pollution or an air pollution nuisance at any time or place.

(c) When applicable, the Air Pollution Control Division, in attempting to evaluate the environmental extent of and effects of toxic contaminants in the atmosphere, may be guided by the limits set forth in "Table of Threshold Values" adopted by the American Conference of Governmental Industrial Hygienists in April 1952, or by any of the limits relating to this subject published by the American Standards

Association, the American Petroleum Institute, the Manufacturing Chemists Association, the National Safety Council, or any other recognized authority that the Air Pollution Control Board deems advisable. It is recognized that in some cases such limits are partially based on animal experimentation as related to a normal person being exposed for a forty-hour week. Adjustment for other exposures and conditions and for a reasonable range of deviation from normal will be made.

(d) The measurement or evaluation of the amounts of matter, or concentration of pollutants, may be by the observation of trained observers or by such other methods and procedures as may be approved by the Air Pollution Control Board either in these Regulations or at meetings of the Board.

(e) After due consideration of specific technical data assembled by the Board or submitted by any person which shows that limits in the Regulations in a particular area can be modified without prejudice to the public interest or should be strengthened in the public interest, the Air Pollution Control Board may approve special changes of limits for specific areas for a reasonable trial period of not more than six (6) months. After such trial period, the Air Pollution Control Board may set for each such area suitable limits based on such experience and their best judgment in the light of the provisions and purposes of the Ordinance.

FINANCING

Charges for disposing of refuse at municipally operated or regulated landfills or incineration plants are levied in many cities, but practices vary considerably. Some cities (Washington, D.C., for example) levy no charge for the disposal of ordinary residential and commercial refuse from within the city; disposal costs are paid out of general tax funds. On the other hand, many cities charge householders for both collection and disposal.

If refuse is weighed, rates are almost always based on weight; if not, the basis is load, kind of vehicle, or volume.

Rates for a number of cities are:

Tacoma, Washington

Code Section 5.20.180—Use of Dumps—No person shall use or be permitted to use any dump or dumps, sanitary fill or fills or other place of disposal established and used by the Public Works Department, Utility Services Division, except with the approval of the Public Works Department and in accordance with all of its rules and regulations and the following schedule of rates:

Up to 7,999 lbs. gross vehicle weight..........................$ .50
8,000-19,999 lbs. gross vehicle weight........................ 1.00
Over 20,000 lbs. gross vehicle weight......................... 1.25
For refuse brought in a private car,
with or without a trailer, or pickup
truck from the driver's residence,
no charge.

Provided, however, every person with refuse requiring special handling shall pay such additional charge as will fairly compensate the Public Works Department for the expense of properly disposing of such refuse.

The foregoing rates shall be inapplicable to persons engaged in the business of collecting and hauling garbage and refuse in areas outside of the City of Tacoma; as to such persons, the charge shall be $0.25 per cubic yard of garbage and refuse.

Sandusky, Ohio

Section 2. That the following schedule of rates shall be charged for the disposal of refuse, rubbish and/or garbage at the Sanitary Landfill operated by the City of Sandusky in Perkins Township, Erie County, Ohio:

(1) For all refuse, rubbish and/or garbage hauled in an automobile $0.50

(2) For all refuse, rubbish and/or garbage, except that hauled in an automobile: $0.14½ for each 100 pounds or part thereof, except there shall be a minimum charge of $0.50.

(3) For all refuse, rubbish and/or garbage, except that hauled in an automobile, a non-resident of the City of Sandusky who is permitted to use the landfill shall pay a charge of $0.19 for each 100 pounds or part thereof, except that there shall be a minimum charge of $1.00.

Wichita, Kansas

The following rates are to be charged by the City of Wichita, Kansas, for refuse disposal, as provided in Sec. 7.08.280, Chapter 708, of The Code of the City of Wichita:

Type of Vehicle	Rate Per Load
Automobiles	.50
Pickups—no sides	1.00
Pickups—with built-up sides	1.50
Two-Wheel Trailers	1.50
Four-Wheel Trailers	2.50
Single-Axle Dump Truck	3.00
Tandem-Axle Dump Truck	3.50
Commercial & Other Stake Trucks	3.00
Rubbish Collectors Stake Trucks	3.00
Tree Haulers	3.00
Packer Trucks 9-14 cu. yds.	3.00
Packer Trucks 15-17 cu. yds.	3.50
Packer Trucks 18-20 cu. yds.	4.00
Packer Trucks 21-25 cu. yds.	5.00
Packer Trucks 26-30 cu. yds.	7.00
Stake Semi-Trailers	7.00
Compaction Semi-Trailers	14.00

Morgantown, West Virginia

Article III—Section 1—(f) Minimum Charges for Refuse Delivered to the Location of Disposal without Expense to the City:
Horses, cattle or other large animals $25.00
Cats or dogs ....$ 1.25
Raw garbage (as defined), at the rate of $4.50 per ton or any fraction

thereof, with a minimum charge of $1.25.

Trash (as defined), at the rate of $4.50 per ton or any fraction thereof with a minimum charge of $1.00.

Other materials at rates set by Superintendent after inspection and examination of load. All such charges shall be collected upon delivery to the disposal location.

Pendleton, Oregon

Section 17. . . . Any collectors using the city refuse disposal site to deposit garbage and rubbish collected outside the city shall be charged a fee of 25% of the gross receipts derived from fees charged their customers outside the city limits of the City of Pendleton for the collection and removal of garbage and rubbish. Such garbage collector shall keep proper books and records concerning his garbage collection and removal operations, which books and records shall always be open to the inspection of the City of Pendleton.

Section 19. There is hereby created a "Sanitation Department Regulatory Board" which board shall be composed of one member of the City Council and two residents of the City of Pendleton appointed annually by the Council. The Regulatory Board will act as arbitrators in all matters referred to them concerning garbage rates, service, and policy, but decisions of the board shall be reported to the City Council which will approve or disapprove of the same. The determination of the Council shall be final.

In Richmond, California, a contractor is authorized to operate the disposal site provided by the city and to charge within specified limits:

Section 12.1: Said contractor may charge all persons, firms or corporations using said premises for the purposes of depositing garbage and/or rubbish thereon at rates not exceeding those hereafter specified as follows:

For use of said premises by commercial houses and industries having their places of business or plants within said city: Automobiles, trailers and pick-ups not exceeding ½ ton each, 50c; trucks not exceeding 1½ tons each, 75c; clean fill, no charge; trucks hauling rubbish and garbage mixed with dirt, any size truck each, $1.00; semi-trailer, any size each, $2.00; when material to be disposed of is either highly combustible or inflammable or of such nature that special supervision is required to be supplied by the contractor to dispose of it properly, any size load in any vehicle each, $4.00.

For use of said premises by persons, commercial houses or industries living or having their places of business or plants without said city: Household garbage and rubbish per can of garbage or load of rubbish, 25c; automobiles; trailers and pick-ups not exceeding ½ ton each, 75c; trucks not exceeding 1 ton each, 75c; clean fill, no charge; trucks between 2 and 3 tons each, $1.75; trucks 3 tons and over each, $2.25; semi-trailer, any size each, $3.00; when material to be disposed of is either highly combustible or inflammable or of such nature that special supervision is required to be supplied by the contractor to dispose of it properly, any size load in any vehicle each, $5.00.

The Doylestown, Pennsylvania, ordinance sets fees for use of the borough's landfill and provides for monthly billing of licensed collectors:

Article IX—Fees for use of landfill—Section 1. The attendant on duty at the Borough landfill shall keep a daily record of all refuse deposited by licensed collectors or others from whom fees are due. At the end of each day he shall transmit said record to the Secretary who shall, at least monthly, bill the collector or other persons from whom fees are due as hereinafter set forth.

Section 2. Each licensed collector, each contractor transporting building rubble and each owner of commercial property transporting refuse therefrom shall pay to the Borough a fee for the privilege of depositing refuse in the landfill, as follows:

(a) Each load or part thereof from a "Load Packer" or similar vehicle $1.00

(b) Each load or part thereof from all other vehicles except "Load Packers" or similar vehicles $0.50

Cincinnati charges for incinerating refuse from beyond the limits of the city:

Sec. 707-31a. Charge for Incinerating Combustible Waste and Garbage. A service charge of five dollars ($5.00) per ton shall be made for the incineration of combustible waste and garbage delivered at public incinerators and originating from sources beyond the limits of the city.

Rates for disposal of refuse delivered to the municipal incinerator at Edmonton, Alberta, Canada, are specified in the by-laws:

By-Law No. 1283, 23. . . . Other waste delivered to the Incinerator will be burned at the following rates:

Loose refuse such as shavings and papers, 15c per 100 lbs.

Other waste, excepting animals (as above), 20c per 100 lbs.

Private collectors of refuse are licensed by the Department of Sanitation in New York City. Each permit holder has the privilege of disposing of refuse at the sanitation department's disposal facilities upon payment of the charge fixed by the Board of Estimate and in compliance with rules and regulations. A ticket system of payment, as prescribed in the rules and regulations of the department, is used:

Section 4—Payments:

a—Payment shall be made in advance by the purchase of books of tickets from the Chief Clerk of the Department of Sanitation at his office, Room 725, 125 Worth Street, Manhattan, New York 13, N. Y.

b—The office of the Chief Clerk will be open for the sale of books of tickets only at these times: Mondays to Fridays, inclusive, 9 A.M. to 4 P.M.

c—Each prospective purchaser shall identify by the D.S. waste conveyance truck permit number, the vehicle for which it is desired to purchase tickets.

d—Only cash, U. S. postal money order or note, or certified check drawn on a State or National Bank located in the City of New York, or officer's check of such a bank will be received and accepted in payment for tickets. All such checks shall be drawn to the order of "Department of Sanitation," as payee.

e—Tickets will be sold in books of twenty-five (25) tickets, each separate ticket being in payment for one load at the cubic capacity calculated and determined by the Commissioner of Sanitation for the

body of the particular vehicle for which the ticket is sold and purchased.

f—Tickets will be sold only for a vehicle for which a D.S. waste
conveyance truck permit has been issued under Sections 755(2)-6.1
and 755(2)-6.2, Administrative Code.

g—One ticket shall be delivered by the method prescribed in the
next paragraph to the Commissioner's representative at the Department
location where material is offered for each load or partial load, in
advance of dumping and as a condition to receipt and acceptance
thereof.

h—When offering a load for disposal, the permit holder or his employee shall deliver to the Commissioner's representative the embossed
metal plate issued by the Department with the permit listing permit
number, cubic yard capacity of vehicle body, and name and address
of permittee, and the current ticket book in use for the vehicle.
Tickets shall not be detached and offered separately. The Commissioner's representative will detach and retain the next unused ticket
from the book in numerical order and, after complying with Department instructions as to recording, return the embossed plate and book
of remaining tickets to permittee or his employee, instructing him
where and how to dump the load. When the last ticket in a book is
used for a load, the Commissioner's representative will retain the book
cover and forward it in accordance with Department instructions.

i—The Commissioner of Sanitation is without power to make to,
or secure for purchasers, refunds for unused tickets. Unused tickets
should be delivered (or sent by registered mail) to the Comptroller's
Bureau of Law and Adjustment, Municipal Building, Manhattan, New
York 7, N. Y., together with a written demand for refund, giving
purchaser's name and address, permit plate number, vehicle registered
capacity, and book and ticket numbers surrendered.

j—Requirements for prepayment shall not apply to purchase contracts or purchase orders of U. S. Government agencies.

Provisions for calculating the volume of refuse delivered to New York
disposal facilities are included in Section 3. These are applicable if weighing
facilities are not available.

e—To calculate the load charge for the volume of material that
may be carried in the body of a particular vehicle, the Commissioner's
representative will measure the body of the vehicle.

f—In determining body capacities for purposes of payment, calculations will be made to the hundredth of a cubic yard. When the calculated capacity contains a fraction not exceeding fifty one-hundredths
(50/100's) of a cubic yard, capacity will be fixed at the whole number
of cubic yards less the fraction. When the fraction exceeds fifty one-
hundredths of a cubic yard, capacity will be fixed at the next higher
whole number of cubic yards.

g—The manufacturer's rated cubic body capacity for a totally
enclosed body may be accepted, or such body may be measured and
capacity calculated.

h—Some dangerous materials may be accepted but only after special
arrangements have been made through the Bureau of Waste Disposal

at the Department's Main Office, 125 Worth Street, Manhattan, New York 13, N. Y.

PENALTIES FOR VIOLATIONS; SEVERABILITY

Provisions for penalties for violations of all or part of refuse collection and disposal ordinances and a severability clause are common.

The provisions in the Temple, Texas, ordinance are typical:

Penalty:

Any person or persons, firm or corporation who violates any of the provisions of this ordinance shall be deemed guilty of a misdemeanor and upon conviction shall be fined not less than Five Dollars ($5.00) nor more than Two Hundred Dollars ($200.00) for each offense, and each violation hereof shall be deemed a separate offense and each day's continuance or failure to comply herewith shall constitute a separate and distinct offense for each of said days and shall be punishable as such.

Severability:

Should any Section, Paragraph, Sentence, Clause or Phrase of this ordinance be declared unconstitutional or invalid for any reason, the remainder of said ordinance shall not be affected thereby.

Appendix C

SPECIFICATIONS, PROPOSAL, AND CONTRACT FOR REFUSE DISPOSAL, SEATTLE, WASHINGTON, 1964[1]

THE CITY OF SEATTLE, DEPARTMENT OF PUBLIC WORKS

INSTRUCTIONS TO BIDDERS, PROPOSAL, SPECIFICATIONS AND CONTRACT FOR GARBAGE AND RUBBISH DISPOSAL FOR THE CITY OF SEATTLE

As authorized by Ordinance No. _____

Prepared by the City Engineer

ROY W. MORSE
City Engineer

PHILIP M. BUSWELL
Principal Assistant City Engineer

Examined and approved by the Board of Public Works December 11, 1963

Attest:

E. G. HENRY
Secretary

JOHN M. NELSON
Vice-Chairman

INSTRUCTIONS TO BIDDERS

Sealed proposals for this work will be received by the Board of Public Works of the City of Seattle until 2:00 o'clock p.m., Wednesday, June 3, 1964, in Room 404 Seattle Municipal Building.

Bidders shall make proposals for carrying on the disposal operation set forth in the specifications attached hereto. All bids shall be accompanied by a certified check payable to the order of the City Comptroller, or by a bid bond approved as to form by the Corporation Counsel in writing prior to the time and date set for the bid opening, for a sum of SEVENTY FIVE THOUSAND AND NO/100 DOLLARS ($75,000.00) and no bid shall be considered unless accompanied by such check or bid bond. If the contract is let, all checks shall be returned to the bidders except that of the successful bidder, which shall be retained until a contract is entered into between the bidder and the City, in accordance with such bid. If the said bidder fails to enter into such contract in accordance with his bid within ten days from the date at which he is notified that he is the successful bidder, the said check and the amount thereof shall be forfeited to the City, or, if a bid bond accompanied

---

[1] Although the system presented in this appendix is no longer in operation in Seattle, the documents are cited here as an example of good practice where such a system is to be used.

the bid, the necessary legal steps will be taken by the City to recover the penalty of the bond.

Before such contract between the successful bidder and the City shall be valid or binding against the City, the contractor shall enter into a joint and several bond with the City of Seattle as provided in the specifications attached hereto.

All payments for the work done under the specifications attached hereto shall be made by warrants drawn on THE GARBAGE COLLECTION AND DISPOSAL FUND, and not otherwise.

The work embraced in the following Proposal and Contract shall be under the jurisdiction of the City Engineer. It shall begin on July 1, 1965 and shall run for a period of seven and one-half years to December 31, 1972. Bidder's attention is called to the extension option in Section 5.0 of the specifications attached hereto.

Permission will not be given for the withdrawal or modification of any bid or proposal.

Bids for this contract shall be made upon the printed blanks provided therefor by the City Engineer, without modification, interlineation, or amendment, or the bid will not be considered.

Bids will not be considered if detached from the form of contract with which they are bound, nor shall any of the accompanying papers be detached therefrom, but the entire package must be unbroken, in good order and enclosed in a sealed envelope, endorsed with the name of the bidder and the name of the work.

For the purpose of comparing bids only, the quantity of 504,500 tons per year of garbage and rubbish will be used. This is the estimated quantity that will be generated within the City of Seattle during the year of 1965. In determining the lowest and best bid, the appraised value of the transfer station sites, as determined by the City Engineer, shall be considered in determining the total amount of bid.

Before the City will accept any bids on this contract, the Board of Public Works shall be provided with copies of agreements, permits or approvals from all agencies, federal, state and local, that have jurisdiction over and/or an interest in the operation of the proposed landfill sites as specified in Section 21.0 of the specifications attached hereto.

Bidders are notified to examine thoroughly these instructions, the proposal, the specifications, and the form of contract. If there be any doubt or obscurity as to meaning of the same, or any doubt as to the adequacy of proposed facilities or sites, intending bidders shall ask the City Engineer for an explanation before submitting their proposal.

The Board of Public Works may award a contract to the lowest and best bidder and reserves the right to reject any or all bids.

After the bids are opened, the Board of Public Works may require bidders to submit satisfactory evidence that they are financially responsible and have sufficient resources to perform all the work required under this contract. As evidence of the foregoing the Board of Public Works may require the following:

1. Names and addresses of all interested parties in the bidder, including the names and addresses of all principal stockholders and the amount of stock held, if a corporation; names and addresses of all partners and their interest, if a partnership or joint venture; name and address of owner, if a sole proprietorship.

2. Detailed financial statements for the past five years. If a new corporation, provide pro forma statements of the corporation and the principal stockholders. Such statements to include profit and loss statements, balance sheets and earnings records.

3. A cash forecast and detailed operating budget, showing projections of income and expense for the next five years.

4. A detailed outline of all financing arrangements for equipment and facilities. Such detail shall include the names of owners or other persons holding a security interest in the equipment and facilities, a statement fully indicating the rights of the owner or security interest holder in such equipment and facilities, and the amounts secured.

5. A detailed list of all outstanding loans of the bidder, their term, amount, and interest rate.

6. Such further statements, including pending or threatened litigation, as may be necessary to clearly indicate the present financial condition and proposed financial plan of the bidder.

Should the apparent low bidder fail to provide such information within five days after request by the Board of Public Works or should the evidence fail to satisfy the Board of Public Works that the apparent low bidder is financially capable of performing the contract, then the Board of Public Works may reject his bid.

PROPOSAL

Seattle, Washington _____

TO THE BOARD OF PUBLIC WORKS OF THE CITY OF SEATTLE:

The undersigned hereby certifies as follows:

That_____ ha___ personally and carefully examined the instructions to bidders, the specifications, and form of contract for the work to be done in GARBAGE AND RUBBISH DISPOSAL FOR THE CITY OF SEATTLE as authorized by Ordinance No. _____.

That _____ ha___ made examination of the type and amount of material to be disposed of and fully understand___ the character of the work to be done and the manner in which payment is to be made:

That having made the necessary examinations, the undersigned hereby propose___ to furnish all materials, vehicles, plant, equipment, sites and facilities, and to perform all labor which may be required to do said work during the period fixed and upon the terms and conditions provided in the said instructions, specifications, and contract, at the following prices, to wit:

Certified Check Enclosed $_____

Bid Bond Enclosed $_____

(NOTE: Unit prices for all items, all extensions and total amount of bid must be shown. Show unit prices in both words and figures and where conflict occurs the written or typed words shall prevail.)

Item No.	Approx. Quantity	Item With Unit Price Bid (Unit prices to be written in words)	Unit Price		Total Amount	
			Dollars	Cents	Dollars	Cents
1a	100,000 Tons in Six Months	Complete Disposal of the first 100,000 Tons of Garbage and Rubbish for the period July 1, 1965, thru December 31, 1965 Per Ton				
1b	152,200 Tons in Six Months	Complete Disposal of all Garbage and Rubbish in excess of the first 100,000 Tons for the period July 1, 1965, thru December 31, 1965. Per Ton				
2a	200,000 Tons Per Year	Complete Disposal of the first 200,000 Tons of Garbage and Rubbish for the calendar year of 1966 Per Ton				

Item No.	Approx. Quantity	Item With Unit Price Bid (Unit prices to be written in words)	Unit Price		Total Amount	
			Dollars	Cents	Dollars	Cents
2b	304,500 Tons Per Year	Complete Disposal of all Garbage and Rubbish in excess of the first 200,000 Tons for the calendar year of 1966 Per Ton				
3a	200,000 Tons Per Year	Complete Disposal of the first 200,000 Tons of Garbage and Rubbish for the calendar year of 1967 Per Ton				
3b	304,500 Tons Per Year	Complete Disposal of all Garbage and Rubbish in excess of the first 200,000 Tons for the calendar year of 1967 Per Ton				
4a	200,000 Tons Per Year	Complete Disposal of the first 200,000 Tons of Garbage and Rubbish for the calendar year of 1968 Per Ton				
4b	304,500 Tons Per Year	Complete Disposal of all Garbage and Rubbish in excess of the first 200,000 Tons for the calendar year of 1968 Per Ton				
5a	200,000 Tons Per Year	Complete Disposal of the first 200,000 Tons of Garbage and Rubbish for the calendar year of 1969 Per Ton				

Item No.	Approx. Quantity	Item With Unit Price Bid (Unit prices to be written in words)	Unit Price Dollars	Cents	Total Amount Dollars	Cents
5b	304,500 Tons Per Year	Complete Disposal of all Garbage and Rubbish in excess of the first 200,000 Tons for the calendar year of 1969 Per Ton				
6a	200,000 Tons Per Year	Complete Disposal of the first 200,000 Tons of Garbage and Rubbish for the calendar year of 1970 Per Ton				
6b	304,500 Tons Per Year	Complete Disposal of all Garbage and Rubbish in excess of the first 200,000 Tons for the calendar year of 1970 Per Ton				
7a	200,000 Tons Per Year	Complete Disposal of the first 200,000 Tons of Garbage and Rubbish for the calendar year of 1971 Per Ton				
7b	304,500 Tons Per Year	Complete Disposal of all Garbage and Rubbish in excess of the first 200,000 Tons for the calendar year of 1971 Per Ton				
8a	200,000 Tons Per Year	Complete Disposal of the first 200,000 Tons of Garbage and Rubbish for the calendar year of 1972 Per Ton				

Item No.	Approx. Quantity	Item With Unit Price Bid (Unit prices to be written in words)	Unit Price		Total Amount	
			Dollars	Cents	Dollars	Cents
8b	304,500 Tons Per Year	Complete Disposal of all Garbage and Rubbish in excess of the first 200,000 Tons for the calendar year of 1972				
		Per Ton				

Total Amount of Bid $_____

Address _____

Contractor _____

Tel. No. _____

By _____

SPECIFICATIONS
FOR
GARBAGE AND RUBBISH DISPOSAL
FOR THE
CITY OF SEATTLE

Ordinance No._____

1.0 GENERAL DESCRIPTION:

The work to be done consists of the construction, operation and maintenance of two garbage and rubbish transfer stations on property of the City; the transportation of all garbage and rubbish delivered to such transfer stations to a sanitary landfill site or sites; and the disposal of all garbage and rubbish in such landfill sites.

The landfill sites, transfer station structures and facilities, and transportation equipment are to be supplied, maintained and operated by the Contractor as provided herein.

2.0 QUANTITIES FURNISHED TO BIDDERS:

The quantities listed on the proposal sheet and in the instructions to bidders are for the purpose of comparing bids only. They may be increased or decreased and do not constitute a warranty or guarantee by the City as to the actual quantity disposed of, as determined by the City Engineer.

3.0 DISAGREEMENTS:

To prevent all disputes or litigation, it is understood that all questions arising as to the proper performance and the amount of work to be paid for under this contract shall be subject to the decision of the City Engineer, subject to the right of the Contractor to appeal to the Board of Public Works, whose decision shall be final.

4.0 CONTRACTOR TO MAKE EXAMINATION:

The Contractor shall make his own examination, investigation and research regarding the proper method of doing the work, all conditions affecting the work to be done, the labor, equipment, sites, facilities and materials needed thereon, and the quantity of the work to be performed. The Contractor agrees that he has satisfied himself by his own investigation and research regarding all of such conditions, and that his conclusion to enter into the proposed contract is based upon such investigation and research, and that he shall make no claim against the City because any of the estimates, statements or interpretations made by an officer or agent of the City may prove to be in any respect erroneous.

The Contractor assumes the risk of all conditions foreseen or unforeseen and agrees to continue the work without additional compensation under whatever circumstances which may develop other than as herein provided.

5.0 TERM OF CONTRACT:

This contract shall run for a period of 7½ years, from July 1, 1965, until December 31, 1972, provided that the City, at its option, may extend the term an additional 10 years at a price to be negotiated by January 1, 1970.

6.0 MEANING OF TERMS:

The meaning of terms and words used herein, unless clearly indicated otherwise by context, shall be as follows:

A. "Board of Public Works" means the Board of Public Works of The City of Seattle.

B. "City" means the City of Seattle.

C. "City Engineer" means the City Engineer of the City of Seattle and authorized employees.

D. "Contractor" means the one contracting with the City to dispose of garbage and rubbish as herein described, his sub-contractors, or the authorized representatives of such contractors.

E. "Garbage" means all discarded putrescible waste matter, except sewage or human or animal excrement.

F. "Rubbish" means all discarded non-putrescible waste matter.

7.0 COMPANY NAME:

The Contractor shall not use a firm name containing the words "Seattle," "City," or any other words implying municipal ownership.

8.0 CONTRACTOR'S OFFICE:

The Contractor shall be required to maintain an office provided with telephones and such attendants as may be necessary during normal business hours to take care of complaints, orders for special service and instructions from the City Engineer.

9.0 MATERIAL TO BE ACCEPTED:

At the transfer stations, the Contractor shall accept for disposal all garbage and rubbish generated in the City of Seattle, whether delivered by automobile, trailer or truck, except sewage, oil, or animal or human excrement, and all material whatever collected under the City's garbage and rubbish collection contract; provided that the City reserves the right to require the Contractor to dispose of garbage and rubbish delivered to the transfer stations that is generated outside the city limits of Seattle from either incorporated or unincorporated areas within King County.

The City Engineer shall be sole judge as to what material shall be accepted for disposal at the transfer stations.

10.0 TRANSFER STATIONS—LAND:

The bidders shall recommend sites for the transfer stations and the amount of property required for each. Upon awarding a contract, the City will, by ordinance, acquire the recommended sites or other comparable sites within the areas indicated in the following paragraph and lease them at no cost to the Contractor for the term of the Contract.

One of these transfer stations shall be within an area designated as Zone A and described as that area between Mercer Street and the north

City limits. One other transfer station shall be within an area designated as Zone B and described as that area between Holgate Street and the south City limits. All transfer stations shall be in zones permitted by the Zoning Ordinance and shall be three hunred feet or more from any lot in a residential zone.

11.0 TRANSFER STATIONS:

The Contractor shall construct, operate and maintain two transfer stations as provided in Section 10.0 for the disposal of garbage and rubbish.

All primary transferring operations shall be conducted within totally covered buildings. These facilities shall provide space for the simultaneous dumping of at least twelve trucks or twenty-five passenger vehicles. Auxiliary dumping facilities for an additional twenty-five passenger cars shall be provided on the transfer station site.

The transfer station sites shall be landscaped and fenced to effectively screen their operations from adjoining property.

The Contractor shall provide hard surfaced access roads from city streets to the transfer stations. Such access roads shall be designed to provide vehicle storage during peak traffic hours at the sites and to eliminate traffic congestion. Driveway entrances shall be installed by the Contractor only at locations approved by the City Engineer.

On each site the Contractor shall provide sufficient area for the City to construct and operate a weighing station.

At least 30 days prior to the opening of bids, bidders shall submit architectural renderings and layouts of the proposed transfer stations to the City Engineer for approval. Such plans shall include details of site development, landscaping and fencing, traffic control, access, and of the area provided for the City's weighing station.

Upon completion of this contract, the Contractor shall remove all buildings, structures and facilities from the transfer station sites, as directed by the City Engineer.

12.0 TRANSFER STATIONS—OPERATION & MAINTENANCE:

The Contractor shall assign sufficient personnel to work at the transfer stations to adequately direct the public, control dumping and to perform all necessary duties.

The south transfer station shall be open to the public and operated 24 hours each day, seven days per week, including holidays. The north transfer station shall be open to the public and operated between the hours of 6:00 a.m. and 10:00 p.m. each day, seven days per week, including holidays.

The Contractor shall take adequate measures to control odors, flies and other nuisances at the transfer stations. Such measures shall include chemical sprays when directed by the City Engineer.

The transfer stations sites shall be kept in a clean and sanitary condition at all times and, in addition, all equipment and facilities which come in contact with garbage and rubbish in the transferring operations shall be steam-cleaned not less often than twice each week.

13.0 TRANSPORTATION EQUIPMENT:

All equipment used by the Contractor in the transportion of garbage and rubbish shall be maintained in good operating condition, shall conform to all applicable weight, size and safety regulations, and shall be approved as to its suitability by all applicable regulatory agencies and by the City Engineer. This shall apply equally to marine, rail or automotive equipment.

All such equipment shall be completely covered during transit to prevent blowing material. In addition, where automotive equipment is used, the bodies thereof shall be watertight.

14.0 LOADING OF TRANSPORTATION EQUIPMENT:

Extra care shall be taken in the loading and transportation of garbage and rubbish so that material is not scattered or spilled either onto private property or onto streets or highways. If the Contractor fails to clean up any scattered or spilled material within two hours after notice from the City Engineer, the City Engineer may cause such work to be done and deduct the cost thereof from the special fund created in Section 40.0 notwithstanding the provision in Section 40.0 relative to twenty-four hours notice.

15.0 OWNERSHIP OF EQUIPMENT:

All vehicles and equipment used in the performance of this contract, except marine or railroad equipment shall be wholly owned by the Contractor; provided, leasing or rental agreements may be allowed where approved by the Board of Public Works prior to submission of bids; and conditional sale contracts, mortgages, or other contractual agreements for financing the purchase of such equipment may be allowed if the Board of Public Works is satisfied, prior to execution of this contract, as to the City's right to take possession of the equipment in the event of forfeiture. All such leasing or rental agreements shall provide that in the event of default of this contract, or of such leasing or rental agreement, the City, at its option, shall have the right to take possession of and operate vehicles and equipment covered by such leasing or rental agreement for the unexpired term of this contract. Any such conditional sales contract, mortgage, or other contractual arrangements for financing purchase of such equipment shall provide that in the event of default of this contract or of such conditional sales contract, mortgage, or other contractual arrangement, the right to the possession and use of such vehicles, equipment and facilities may be taken by the City for the unexpired term of this contract. No further encumbrance shall be placed upon any of such equipment without the approval of the Board of Public Works, save that the Contractor may, without such consent, mortgage or otherwise encumber said vehicles, equipment and facilities for the purpose of enabling the Contractor to replace the same or add thereto.

16.0 CLEANING AND PAINTING OF TRANSPORTATION EQUIPMENT:

All transportation equipment used by the Contractor shall be kept in a clean and sanitary condition and shall be flushed or swept out after each load. Such flushing or sweeping shall be conducted so that none of the material from the vehicles is deposited in other than a sump or pit on the landfill.

All trucks shall be painted white and numbered consecutively from one upward, and shall have the Contractor's name and the number of the vehicle painted in letters of a contrasting color, at least four inches high, on each side of each vehicle, and the number painted on the rear. No advertising on trucks shall be permitted other than the name of the Contractor. All trucks shall be steam cleaned, inside and out, at least once each week, and shall be repainted not less often than every 2½ years.

17.0 PARKING OF VEHICLES:

The Contractor shall not use property in or within 100 feet of property zoned for or occupied by residential uses for the parking, standing, washing, cleaning, or storing of his trucks or equipment and shall otherwise comply with the Zoning Ordinance in such connection.

Areas used by the Contractor for the parking, standing, washing, cleaning or storing of vehicles shall be kept in a clean and orderly condition.

18.0 METHOD OF DISPOSAL:

The Contractor shall use the sanitary landfill disposal method. For the purpose of this specification, sanitary landfill shall mean that method of disposing of garbage and rubbish on land without creating nuisances or unnecessary hazards to the public health or safety, by confining the garbage or rubbish to the smallest practical area, compacting it to the smallest practical volume by employing bulldozing and/or mechanical compacting equipment and covering with a layer of suitable cover material as provided in Section 24.0 hereof at the conclusion of each day's operation or oftener as may be necessary.

19.0 LANDFILL SITES:

The landfill sites used in the performance of this contract shall be wholly owned by the Contractor; provided, leasing or rental agreements may be allowed where approved by the Board of Public Works prior to submission of bids. All such leasing or rental agreements shall provide that in the event of default of this contract, or of such leasing or rental agreement, the City, at its option, shall have the right to take possession of and operate the landfill sites covered by such leasing or rental agreement for the unexpired term of this contract.

The Contractor shall furnish the City Engineer with detailed property descriptions of the landfill sites; detailed maps showing ownership and topography; and plans delineating the method and order of filling, proposed intermediate and final grades and methods to be used to control natural drainage, water courses, or tidal erosion. Any changes in such descriptions, ownership, method, grades or control shall also be furnished to the City Engineer.

These landfill sites shall be of sufficient size and capacity to permit the disposal of all garbage and rubbish generated within the City of Seattle during the term of this contract.

The Contractor shall also furnish maps showing the routes to be taken by his transportation vehicles between the transfer stations and the landfill sites.

20.0 AUXILIARY LANDFILL SITE:

The Contractor shall provide an auxiliary fill site available and ready for use during periods when his primary site is unavailable for use for any reason whatever. This auxiliary fill site shall be of sufficient size and capacity to permit the disposal of all garbage and rubbish generated within the City of Seattle for a period of three years.

The transportation method used to transport garbage and rubbish to the auxiliary landfill site shall be the same as that used to transport garbage and rubbish to the primary site or sites.

21.0 GOVERNMENTAL APPROVALS:

Before the City will accept any bid on this contract, the Board of Public Works shall be provided with copies of agreements, permits, or approvals from all federal, state and local governmental bodies having jurisdiction over and/or an interest in the operation of the Contractor's landfill, including the necessary transportation routes. Such agreements or permits shall specifically state that the operation of such a landfill site as proposed by the bidder is allowed and approved under applicable laws, rules and policies and shall be dated no earlier than one month prior to bid opening.

The Contractor shall comply with all lawful police, health, sanitary and other regulations imposed by public bodies having jurisdiction during the term of this contract.

22.0 LANDFILL EQUIPMENT:

At each landfill site, the Contractor shall employ sufficient equipment to place, compact and cover all material brought to the disposal site each day. The City Engineer shall be final judge as to the sufficiency of such equipment. Sufficient auxiliary equipment shall be maintained on the site or shall be shown to be otherwise available to perform continued operation in case of equipment failure.

23.0 PERSONNEL-LANDFILL:

The Contractor shall employ such persons on each landfill site as are necessary to operate the equipment, direct vehicles, keep the area free of litter, cover the garbage and rubbish and perform other necessary work.

24.0 COVERING:

Each day's accumulation of garbage and rubbish received at the landfill site is to be covered on all sides and on the top at the end of each day's operation. The minimum cover depth shall be no less than six inches (uncompacted).

25.0 COVER MATERIAL:

All material used to cover the landfill shall be clean earth, or dredged sand, free of roots, stumps, chunks of earth or clay, concrete or other foreign materials, and shall contain not more than 50 per cent clay. Inert materials, such as ashes, cinders or gravel may be used if, before placing on the fill, they are effectively mixed with at least 50 per cent loam, clay or sand. All cover material shall be subject to inspection by the City Engineer and material not meeting the above specifications may be rejected by the City Engineer.

26.0 DRAINAGE:

Adequate provision shall be made to control natural drainage and storm water crossing the landfill site and to prevent ground water contamination.

No fill shall be placed in streambeds or other areas where streams would be obstructed or where erosion by the stream would remove cover material. There shall be no seepage or drainage of any material from the fill of such a nature as would constitute an odor nuisance, health hazard, or pollute any body of water.

No fill shall be placed in tidal areas unless an adequate sea wall is constructed that will prevent the erosion and spreading of the material away from the landfill site.

27.0 ACCESS ROADS-LANDFILL:

The Contractor shall provide an access to the dumping site at the landfill site that is useable during all types of weather conditions.

28.0 FIRES:

Burning of any materials deposited on the landfill sites is prohibited.

The Contractor shall immediately and diligently extinguish any fires occurring on the landfill or transfer stations. Adequate fire-fighting equipment shall be available at all times at the landfill and transfer station sites, or, in lieu of such equipment, the Contractor shall furnish the City Engineer with a copy of a fire-fighting agreement between the Contractor and the local fire district or department.

29.0 FENCING:

The immediate dumping area of the sanitary landfill shall be adequately fenced to intercept any windblown material. This fence is to be moved from time to time as the dumping area moves.

30.0 SALVAGE:

The Contractor shall not be allowed to conduct salvage operations.

31.0 MAINTENANCE OF LANDFILL SITES:

The landfill sites shall be controlled to prevent blowing material, and all material blown or deposited away from the active face shall be removed.

The Contractor shall maintain and keep free of litter and other foreign material all completed lifts and access routes at the landfill and shall pick up all paper blown from the active lift.

The Contractor shall take adequate measures to control odors, dust, rats, flies and other nuisances at the landfill sites. Such measures shall include chemical sprays as needed.

32.0 CONFLICTS:

If any provision of these specifications at any time during the term of this contract is or becomes in conflict with any provision of any zoning, building, safety or health ordinance, regulation, or law the provision which establishes a higher standard for the promotion and protection of the health and safety of the public shall prevail.

33.0 PERFORMANCE BOND:

Before the contract between the successful bidder and the City shall be valid or binding against the City of Seattle, the Contractor shall provide a joint and several performance bond to the City of Seattle to protect said City, and also to protect anyone who may perform or cause to be performed any work or labor, or furnish or cause to be furnished any skill, labor, equipment or material in the execution of such contract, which bond shall be signed by the Contractor and two or more good and sufficient sureties or with a surety company as surety, and shall be in the amount of Five Hundred Thousand and 00/100 Dollars ($500,000.00), which bond shall at all times be kept in full force and effect.

The condition of which bond shall be that the Contractor shall fully and faithfully perform all provisions of the contract and these specifications and shall pay all laborers, mechanics and sub-contractors and material men, and all persons who shall supply such person or persons, or sub-contractors with provisions and supplies for the performance of the contract; provided that the bond shall not be security for money loaned or advanced to the Contractor, a sub-contractor or other person in the performance of the contract.

34.0 LIABILITY INSURANCE:

The Contractor shall obtain and keep in force during the term of the contract, public liability and property damage insurance in companies and in form to be approved by the City Engineer. Said insurance shall provide coverage to the Contractor, any sub-contractor performing work provided by this contract, and the City. The City shall be named as an additional insured on said policy insofar as the work and obligations performed under the contract are concerned. The coverage so provided shall insure against claims for bodily injuries, or death, as well as claims for property damages which may be made for any occurrence arising out of the performance of the work covered by the contract.

The minimum policy limits of such insurance shall be as follows:

Bodily injury liability coverage: $100,000 for bodily injury, including death to any one person, and $300,000 for each occurrence; and for property damage, $100,000 for each occurrence.

A copy of the insurance policy or policies together with a copy of the endorsement naming the City as an additional insured, shall be provided to the City within a reasonable time after receiving notice of award of contract.

Such policy shall provide for ten days' notices to the City of any change, cancellation, or lapse of such policy.

The Contractor shall further save harmless and indemnify the City from any and all loss, damage, claims, suits, judgments and recoveries which may be asserted, made or arise or be had, brought or recovered against the City by reason of any such claims; and he shall immediately appear and defend the same at his own cost and expense.

35.0 METHOD OF DETERMINING PAYMENT:

Payment for the complete disposal of garbage and rubbish shall be based on the applicable bid unit price and the number of tons actually disposed of as weighed by the City Engineer at the transfer stations. For the purposes of determining payment, it shall be conclusively presumed that the load of each passenger car weighs 125 pounds.

For each of the first 100,000 tons of garbage and rubbish actually disposed of during the period July 1, 1965, through December 31, 1965, the contractor will be paid the sum bid on Item 1a of the proposal. For each ton of garbage and rubbish over 100,000 tons disposed of during the period July 1, 1965, through December 31, 1965, the Contractor will be paid the sum bid on Item 1b of the proposal.

For each of the first 200,000 tons of garbage and rubbish actually disposed of during the calendar years 1966, 1967, 1968, 1969, 1970, 1971, and 1972, the Contractor will be paid the sum bid on Item 2a, 3a, 4a, 5a, 6a, 7a, or 8a, respectively, of the proposal. For each ton of garbage and rubbish over 200,000 tons disposed of during the calendar years 1966, 1967, 1968, 1969, 1970, 1971 and 1972, the Contractor will be paid the sum bid on Item 2b, 3b, 4b, 5b, 6b, 7b, or 8b, respectively, of the proposal.

Except for payment for Extra Work in Section 43.0 hereof, no other payment shall be due the Contractor under this contract.

36.0 ESTIMATES AND PAYMENTS:

During the life of this contract the City Engineer shall, on or about the second Wednesday of each month, issue an itemized statement of the sum due the Contractor for the previous month's work. Said itemized statement shall state the amount due the Contractor for the disposal of garbage and rubbish and, in addition, shall include items of amounts due, if any, for extra work.

After the issuance of said statement, the City Comptroller shall, on or about the fourth Wednesday of the month, deliver to the Contractor warrants of an amount equal to such statements, less any sums retained to cover any verified claims filed with the City Comptroller, due to or arising out of this contract; and also less any sums that may have been expended in accordance with Section 40.0 and Section 51.0.

37.0 WORKMEN:

All workmen employed shall be competent and skilled in the performance of the work to which they may be assigned. Failure or delay in the performance of this contract due to the Contractor's inability to obtain workmen of the number and skill required shall constitute a default of the contract.

Whenever the Contractor is not present on the work, orders may be given by the City Engineer to the superintendent or foreman who may have immediate charge thereof.

If any person employed on the work shall refuse or neglect to obey the direction of the City Engineer, or in the opinion of said City Engineer shall be incompetent, unfaithful, disorderly, or otherwise unsatisfactory, he shall, upon the order of the City Engineer, be at once discharged and not again employed upon any part of the work. Any person so discharged shall, however, have the right to appeal to the Board of Public Works, whose decision shall be final and conclusive.

38.0 PAYMENT FOR LABOR AND MATERIALS:

The Contractor shall perform this contract according to the terms, conditions and stipulations herein, and shall pay as they become due, all just claims for all work and labor performed on or about said work, and all skill or labor and materials and equipment purchased for or furnished in the execution of the contract; and further, shall comply with all the provisions of State laws and with all the requirements of the charter and ordinances of the City and the amendments thereto. Any person furnishing supplies, equipment or materials, or performing any work or labor on this contract who is not paid when his claim is due, may file with the City Comptroller a verified claim for such amount. The City Comptroller shall withhold such amount from payments due the Contractor under this contract and such claims shall be foreclosed in the manner and within the time limits prescribed for the foreclosure of labor and material liens on public works in R.C.W. 60.28.

If, at any time during the progress of the work, it shall appear to the City Comptroller that time checks or other evidences of indebtedness have been issued for labor by such Contractor, then the City Comptroller, upon presentation to him of such time checks or other evidence of indebtedness, shall issue to such labor claimants a warrant or warrants therefor upon the Special Fund created by the cash deposit hereinafter mentioned. The City Comptroller shall charge the amount of all warrants so issued against the account of the Contractor for this work and shall deduct the amount thereof, together with a penalty of ten per cent thereon, from the next or succeeding payment to be made to said Contractor.

39.0 PREVAILING WAGES:

Pursuant to Chapter 63, Laws of Washington 1945, the Contractor awarded this contract shall pay his employees on such work not less than the prevailing hourly scale of wages for the same trade or occupation in the City of Seattle.

In the event any dispute arises as to whether the rates paid are the prevailing rates for this locality, and the dispute cannot be adjusted by the parties involved, the matter shall be referred for arbitration to the Director of the Department of Labor and Industries of the State of Washington and his decision therein shall be final and conclusive and binding on all parties involved in the dispute.

40.0 SPECIAL FUND:

Within ten days of the execution of this contract, the Contractor shall be required to make a cash deposit of Ten Thousand Dollars to guarantee the immediate compliance with the requirements of this contract and compliance within a period of twenty-four hours with any written order of the City Engineer in respect thereto. Said cash shall be deposited in the City Treasury in a special fund. Upon failure of the Contractor to take the necessary action on said written order, the City Engineer may cause the work to be done and payment therefor to be made by warrants drawn upon such fund.

The City Engineer shall deduct the amount of any such sums spent in any month from payments due the Contractor and deposit the same in the special fund to the end that said fund shall be constantly maintained at its original sum.

Thirty days after the expiration of the contract, the cash deposit shall be returned to the contractor as provided in Section 54.0.

41.0 INDUSTRIAL INSURANCE AND MEDICAL AID:

The Contractor shall pay into the City Treasury or to the Department of Labor and Industries of the State of Washington, in cash, the amounts required to be paid to the State of Washington in connection with the Workmen's Compensation Act, or any other payments due the State of Washington in the form of taxes or fees as required by law on account of this contract before payment is made to him by the City on any monthly statement of amount due, and final payment shall not be made until the Contractor shall have complied with the provisions of this section.

42.0 CONTRACTOR TO SUBMIT BOOKS:

At any and all times during the life of this contract, should the Contractor request any compensation other than that provided herein, the Contractor shall submit his books and accounts to the Board of Public Works and the City Comptroller for complete examination.

43.0 EXTRA WORK:

If the City Engineer orders in writing the performance of any work not covered by these specifications and for which no item is provided in the contract, then such extra work shall be done and be paid for at a price to be agreed upon between the City and the Contractor before such extra work begins.

44.0 DEFAULT OF CONTRACT:

Should the Contractor abandon, delay unnecessarily in the performance of, or in any manner refuse or fail to comply with any of the terms of the contract, or neglect or refuse to comply with the instructions of the City Engineer relative thereto, the City Engineer shall notify the Contractor in writing of such abandonment, delay, refusal, failure, or neglect and direct him to comply with the applicable provisions of the contract. A copy of such written notice shall be mailed to the surety on the performance bond and delivered to the Board of Public Works. The Board of Public Works shall hear the matter at open session within ten days after receipt of such written notice from the City Engineer and shall, not less than five days prior to the date of such hearing, notify the Contractor and the surety on the performance bond of the date and place thereof. The Contractor agrees to be present at such hearing and show cause why he has abandoned, delayed, refused, failed or neglected to comply with the terms of the contract.

Should the Contractor fail to appear or fail to show cause why he has abandoned, delayed, refused, failed or neglected to comply with the terms of the contract, satisfactory to the Board of Public Works, such Board may, with the consent of the City Council by resolution, declare a default of the contract and notify the Contractor and the surety on the performance bond of such declaration of default, or the Board of Public Works may take such other action as it may deem advisable.

Upon receipt by the Contractor of such declaration of default, the Contractor agrees that he will discontinue the work, whereupon the surety on the performance bond may, at its option to be exercised within ten days of such declaration of default, assume the work that the Board of Public Works has ordered discontinued, and proceed to perform the same at its own cost and expense.

Upon such declaration of default, all payments due the Contractor shall be retained by the City and applied to the completion of the contract and to damages suffered and expense incurred by the City by reason of such default, unless the surety on the performance bond shall assume the contract, in which event all payments remaining due the Contractor at the time of default, less amounts due the City from the Contractor and less all sums due the City for damages suffered and expense incurred by reason of such default shall be due and payable to such surety. Thereafter, such surety shall receive monthly payments equal to those that would have been paid the Contractor had such Contractor continued to perform the contract.

If such surety fails to exercise such option, the Board of Public Works may complete the contract or any part thereof, either by day labor or by re-letting a contract for the same, and the City shall have the right to take possession of and use any or all of the vehicles, materials, equipment, facilities and property of every kind provided by the Contractor for the performance of this contract, and to procure other vehicles, equipment and facilities necessary for the completion of same, and to charge the cost of same to the Contractor, together with the cost incident thereto. In such event, however, the Contractor shall be entitled to receive reasonable compensation for the City's use of his vehicles, equipment and facilities and reasonable compensation for his material and property so taken.

In the event the Board of Public Works completes the contract at a lesser cost than would have been payable to the Contractor under such contract if the same had been fulfilled by said Contractor, then the City shall retain such difference. Should such cost to the City be greater, the Contractor shall be liable for and pay the amount of such excess to the City.

Should the Contractor fail at any time to perform all or any part of the contract for a period of more than 72 hours, for whatever cause or reason, the Board of Public Works may at such time or any time thereafter, with the consent of the City Council, take possession of all the Contractor's equipment, vehicles, and facilities, and employ such force as it may deem advisable to continue the work; and the cost of all labor, materials and equipment necessary for such work shall be paid by the City of Seattle out of moneys then due or to become due the Contractor under and by virtue of the contract for the work herein specified.

45.0 PERMITS AND LICENSES:

The Contractor shall procure all necessary permits, pay for the same and obtain all official licenses for the performance of the contract.

46.0 FEDERAL, STATE AND LOCAL LAWS:

All federal, state, and local laws, ordinances and regulations now or hereafter enacted shall become a part of the contract and be complied with in the performance of all portions of the work.

The Contractor is assumed to be familiar with all such laws, ordinances and regulations which in any manner affect those engaged or employed in the work, or the materials, facilities or equipment used in the proposed work or which in any way affect the conduct of the work, and no plea of misunderstanding will be considered on account of ignorance thereof.

If the Contractor, shall discover any provision in the specifications or contract which is contrary to or inconsistent with any law, ordinance or regulation, he shall forthwith report it to the City Engineer in writing.

47.0 CONTRACTOR RESPONSIBLE FOR WORK DONE:

The Contractor shall furnish for the prices bid all skill, labor, equipment, sites, structures and materials required for the complete performance of the contract, and shall fully perform the work in accordance with these specifications. The presence of a representative of the City Engineer during the progress of any work shall not relieve the Contractor from responsibility for defects discovered after the completion thereof.

48.0 ASSIGNMENT OF MONEYS BY THE CONTRACTOR:

No assignment or pledge of the moneys to become due under this contract shall be made without the written approval of the surety on the performance bond and the consent of the Board of Public Works being first obtained and endorsed thereon. Such assignment or pledge, however, shall not release the Contractor or his sureties from any obligations or liabilities arising under or because of this contract.

49.0 ASSIGNMENT OR SUBLETTING OF CONTRACT:

No assignment or subletting of the operation of the landfill or transfer stations shall be permitted. The Contractor, at his option, may sublet the transportation of the garbage and rubbish from the transfer station to the landfill.

Any person or persons or any firm or corporation, entering into a subcontract or other agreement with the Contractor to furnish labor, equipment or material for or upon this contract, shall be deemed an employee of the Contractor; and any such person or persons, or the employees of any such firm or corporation when employed directly upon such contract, shall be subject to all the provisions respecting workmen, orders, rates and payment of wages, hours of labor, and all other provisions regarding employees herein specified. The Contractor and his surety alone shall be held responsible for the full and faithful performance of this contract.

50.0 UTILITY CHARGES:

All sewerage, water, electric light or power or other utility charges incurred by the Contractor in the performance of the contract shall be paid for by the Contractor.

51.0 BILLS OF CITY DEPARTMENTS—HOW PAID:

The Contractor shall pay all lawful bills rendered against him by any

City Department. If the Contractor shall fail to pay any such bill within thirty days, the City Engineer may pay such bill and deduct the amount thereof from moneys in the special fund created in Section 40.0 or from any monthly payment due the Contractor.

52.0 PAYROLL REPORTS:

The Contractor shall keep complete and accurate payrolls, upon which shall appear the following information with respect to each person employed upon or in connection with this contract:

1. Name and residence address;
2. Classification of work;
3. Number of hours employed each day;
4. Total number of hours employed each payroll period;
5. Rate of wages;
6. Total amount earned;
7. All deductions;
8. Net amount paid;
9. Whether a citizen of the United States;
10. Whether a head of a family;

Said payrolls are to be at all times accessible and open to inspection by the Board of Public Works, and copies thereof duly signed by the Contractor or his authorized agent, and verified before a Notary Public, are to be filed with the Secretary of said Board not later than seventy-two hours after each regular payroll period.

All employees shall be paid in full not less often than twice monthly and in lawful money of the United States, in the full amount accrued to each employee at the time of closing the payroll, which shall not be more than three days prior to the date of payment.

Work performed at the straight time rate shall be shown on one line of the payroll for each day, and any overtime worked or other additional compensation shall be shown on a separate line for each day and extended at the premium rate.

Payroll reports shall be signed by the Contractor or his authorized agent.

An authorization for an agent, in substantially the following form, shall be submitted with the first payroll report. If the agent is changed, a new authorization shall be required.

I, _____, hereby certify that
(Affiant)

_____, _____, pays or
(Agent)   (Title)

supervises the paying of the employees of _____
(Contractor)

on the Garbage and Rubbish Disposal Contract, for the City of Seattle, and is in a position to have full knowledge of the facts set forth in the affidavit respecting the payment of wages of employees working on the contract herein mentioned.

_____
(Affiant)

Sworn to before me this _____ day of _____, 19_____.

_____
Notary Public in and for the State of

Washington, residing at _____

An affidavit shall accompany each payroll report and shall be in substantially the following form:

I, _____, _____
(Name of Affiant)   (Title)

hereby certify that I pay or supervise the payment of the persons employed by

_____ on the Garbage and Rubbish Disposal
(Contractor)

contract for the City of Seattle.

That the attached payroll sets out accurately and completely the name, occupation, hourly wage rate, total number of hours worked and the full weekly wages earned, of each person employed on the above project for

the weekly payroll period from the _____ day of _____, 19_____,

to the _____ day of _____, 19_____.

That no laborer, workman or mechanic employed on the above project has been paid less than the prevailing rate of wage.

That no rebates have been made either directly or indirectly to or on behalf of said Contractor from the full weekly wages earned as set out on the attached payroll and that the full amount due has been paid.

_____
(Signature of Affiant)

Sworn to before me this _____ day of _____, 19__.

_____
Notary Public in and for the State of

Washington, residing at _____

The City Comptroller shall withhold payment on all estimates for work performed by the Contractor under this contract until all payroll reports of said Contractor for work performed have been filed with the Secretary of the Board of Public Works.

53.0 FINAL CLEANUP:

Upon completion of this contract and before final payment is made, the Contractor shall remove from the transfer stations, parking, washing, cleaning or repair areas, and adjoining property all discarded materials, rubbish, temporary structures, construction equipment and debris for which he is responsible and which may have accumulated during the life of this contract.

54.0 FINAL PAYMENT:

Thirty days after the expiration of this contract, all moneys due the Contractor held by the City in excess of a sufficient sum retained to cover any claims, verified or otherwise, filed with the city Comptroller due to or arising out of this contract; a sufficient sum to meet and discharge the claims of material, equipment and supply men, laborers and costs of action and sufficient sum to pay any bills due the City of Seattle, shall be paid to the said Contractor.

CONTRACT

THIS CONTRACT, made this _____ day of _____, by and between the City of Seattle, a municipal corporation of the State of Washington, hereinafter referred to as the "City", and _____, hereinafter referred to as the "Contractor":

WITNESSETH:

Section 1. The Contractor agrees, for the consideration hereinafter stated to dispose of all garbage and rubbish generated in the City of Seattle and all such other garbage and rubbish generated outside the City as shall be ordered disposed by the City Engineer in accordance with this contract and the proposal and specifications therefore, which are by express reference thereto hereby made a part of this contract and are attached hereto.

Section 2. Performance of the disposal provisions of this contract shall begin on July 1, 1965 and continue for a period of seven and one-half years, to and including December 31, 1972, provided that the City at its option may extend such contract an additional ten years.

Section 3. The City agrees to pay the Contractor the unit price of: _____ dollars per ton for the complete disposal of the first 100,000 tons of Garbage and Rubbish for the period July 1, 1965 through December 31, 1965, _____ dollars per ton for the complete disposal of all Garbage and Rubbish in excess of 100,000 tons for the period July 1, 1965 through December 31, 1965, _____ dollars per ton for the complete disposal of the first 200,000 tons of Garbage and Rubbish for the calendar year 1966, _____ dollars per ton for the complete disposal of all Garbage and Rubbish in excess of the first 200,000 tons for the calendar year 1966, _____ dollars per ton for the complete disposal of the first 200,000 tons of Garbage and Rubbish for the calendar year 1967, _____ dollars per ton for the complete disposal of all Garbage and Rubbish in excess of the first 200,000 tons for the calendar year 1967, _____ dollars per ton for the complete disposal of the first 200,000 tons of Garbage and Rubbish for the calendar year 1968, _____ dollars per ton for the complete disposal of all Garbage and Rubbish in excess of the first 200,000 tons for the calendar year 1968, _____ dollars per ton for the complete disposal of the first 200,000 tons of Garbage and Rubbish for the calendar year 1969, _____ dollars per ton for the complete disposal of all Garbage and Rubbish in excess of the first 200,000 tons for the calendar year 1969, _____ dollars per ton for the complete disposal of the first 200,000 tons of Garbage and Rubbish for the calendar year 1970, _____ dollars per ton for the complete disposal of all Garbage and Rubbish in excess of the first 200,000 tons for the calendar year 1970, _____ dollars per ton for the complete disposal of the first 200,000 tons of Garbage and Rubbish for the calendar year 1971, _____ dollars per ton for the complete disposal of all Garbage and Rubbish in excess of the first 200,000 tons for the calendar year 1971, _____ dollars per ton for the complete disposal of the first 200,000 tons of Garbage and Rubbish for the calendar year 1972, _____ dollars per ton for the complete disposal of all Garbage and Rubbish in excess of the first 200,000 tons for the calendar year 1972.

Section 4. As contemplated by Chapter 63, Laws of Washington 1945, the said Contractor hereby covenants, stipulates and agrees:

That he will pay or cause to be paid to the employees on or in connection with this work or under this contract not less than the prevailing rate of wages for the class of labor performed.

That he will not enter directly or indirectly into any agreement with any person or persons for labor or employment at any less wage.

That he will neither make nor permit any assignment or transfer of this contract, or of any of the work to be performed hereunder, nor sublet said work or any part thereof except as provided in the specifications, in any manner or by any scheme, device or subterfuge which will permit or secure the performance of labor upon or in connection with this work or under this contract, at a rate of wage less than herein specified.

That every scheme or device by which employees employed upon or in connection with this work or under this contract shall sublet or sub-contract the same, or take any transfer or assignment of this contract or of any work herein provided for, as a co-partnership or other association, whereby in lieu of receiving the minimum rate of wages hereinabove specified they shall receive a less sum in cash and become sharers in the profits or losses under this contract in compensation for their labor, shall be deemed a subterfuge, device or scheme to evade the provisions of this contract, and shall be null and void and shall render this contract subject to default.

That the above covenants are made for the benefit of the individual employee of the Contractor, and that any employee performing work or labor under this contract shall have a cause of action against the Contractor for the difference between the wages herein specified and the amount actually paid to such employees.

Section 5. This contract shall not take effect until approval of the Contractor's bond by the Mayor and the City Comptroller, as to sufficiency, and of the Corporation Counsel as to form, and such bond shall be filed with the City Comptroller by the Secretary of the Board of Public Works with the original copy of this contract.

Section 6. In the event of violation of any of these covenants or any provision thereof, payment due from the City of Seattle on any work done under this contract may be withheld until full compliance therewith; and the work may be stopped or, at the discretion of said Board of Public Works, with the consent of the City Council, this contract may be defaulted, all in accordance with the specifications.

IN WITNESS WHEREOF, said City has, by Ordinance No.＿＿＿＿＿＿＿＿ authorized this contract to be executed in its behalf in duplicate original by the Chairman of the Board of Public Works and attested by the Secretary of said Board; and the Contractor has hereunto set his hand the day and year first above written.

THE CITY OF SEATTLE

By ＿＿＿＿＿＿＿＿＿＿＿＿＿＿＿＿＿＿＿＿＿
Chairman of Board of Public Works

＿＿＿＿＿＿＿＿＿＿＿＿＿＿＿＿＿＿＿(Seal)
Secretary of Board of Public Works

＿＿＿＿＿＿＿＿＿＿＿＿＿＿＿＿＿＿＿(Seal)

＿＿＿＿＿＿＿＿＿＿＿＿＿＿＿＿＿＿＿(Seal)

ST. LOUIS COUNTY, MISSOURI, REFUSE DISPOSAL ORDINANCE

AN ORDINANCE
(No. 308)

To regulate and control the disposal and dumping of garbage, refuse and other trash in that part of St. Louis County outside the incorporated cities; providing penalties for the violation of this ordinance; and repealing St. Louis County Council Ordinance No. 202, 1952, enacted on July 16, 1952, relating to dumps; and declaring an emergency. (As amended by Ordinance No. 337, adopted July 29, 1953.)

BE IT ORDAINED BY THE COUNTY COUNCIL OF ST. LOUIS COUNTY, MISSOURI, AS FOLLOWS:

Section 1. The following Sections shall become a part of the Administrative Code of St. Louis County:

Section 28.01. The County Council of St. Louis County finds, determines and declares that it is necessary and conducive for the protection of the public health, safety and welfare of the people of St. Louis County to provide regulations for the dumping and disposal of garbage, refuse and other trash within St. Louis County. The purpose of this Ordinance is to regulate and control the dumping and disposal of garbage and refuse in those parts of St. Louis County outside the incorporated cities, to the end that the public health, safety and welfare of the people of St. Louis County will be protected and enhanced and to prevent and prohibit the indiscriminate and uncontrolled use of property for dumping purposes in violation of zoning and health regulations and recognized public health standards; to prevent and prohibit open dumping on land in St. Louis County and to require that disposal and dumping of garbage and refuse be authorized and permitted only in County licensed and approved County dumps and sanitary landfills. It is not the purpose of this Ordinance to prohibit any person owning or operating a farm from disposing of garbage from his own household to swine upon said farm, or from collecting and disposing of garbage for the feeding of swine upon said farm, where such disposal shall not violate the health regulations of St. Louis County, and shall be authorized by the laws of the State of Missouri, including House Bill No. 60, as amended, adopted by the Sixty-Seventh General Assembly of Missouri, approved on the 1st day of May, 1953.

Section 28.02. The provisions of this Ordinance shall be in effect in all parts of St. Louis County outside incorporated cities. This Ordinance is enacted pursuant to the St. Louis County Charter and the Constitution of the State of Missouri, which grants to St. Louis County the authority to exercise legislative power on matters pertaining to public health, planning and zoning and police in that part of St. Louis County outside incorporated cities.

Section 28.03. For the purpose of this ordinance certain words and terms are defined as follows:

(a) COUNTY shall mean that portion of St. Louis County outside incorporated cities.
(b) PERSON includes an individual, a corporation or other legal entity, a partnership, and any unincorporated association, and includes the plural.
(c) PRIVATE DUMP shall mean all land or parcels of land on which non-putrescible refuse is accepted for deposit or permitted to be deposited regardless of whether a charge is made therefor.
(d) GARBAGE shall mean all animal and vegetable waste and all putrescible matter.
(e) REFUSE shall mean all waste substances including garbage as well as combustible and noncombustible wastes.
(f) COMBUSTIBLE WASTE shall mean all waste substances capable of incineration or burning, but excluding explosive or highly inflammable material.
(g) NON-COMBUSTIBLE WASTE shall mean all other waste substance not capable of incineration or burning, including ashes, glass, metal, earthenware and the like.
(h) SANITARY LANDFILL shall mean a type of operation in which refuse is deposited by plan on a specified portion of open land, is compacted by force applied by mechanical equipment, and then is covered by a layer of earth, ashes or suitable covering material to a depth of at least two (2) feet.
(i) ENFORCEMENT OFFICER shall mean the Health Commissioner of St. Louis County.

Section 28.04. It shall be unlawful for any person, firm, association, or corporation, or any combination or combinations of the same, to use any land, premises or property within the County for the dumping or disposal of any garbage, refuse or other waste materials of any kind, without first making application for and securing a license so to do. The issuance of such license shall be subject to and governed by the following provisions:

(1) The application for a license to operate a private dump or sanitary landfill shall be filed with the Health Commissioner and shall contain a description and plat of the land on which the disposal of refuse is proposed, a description of the sequence and plan of operation, availability of and equipment for water supply, type and capacity of equipment to be used for operations, plans for fire, nuisance and vermin control, existing and proposed roadways and easements, existing topography and water courses, together with a diagram and written statement explaining the proposed location and extent of earthwork and fill operations, proposed equipment and estimated daily or weekly volume of garbage and refuse, facts which show that public convenience and necessity and the public health and general welfare of the people of the County require the granting of a license to the applicant, and such other information as may be required by the Council. Copies of the application shall be forwarded by the Health Commissioner to the Planning Commission for its study and recommendation.

The Health Commissioner shall examine the premises to determine whether public convenience and necessity require the granting of the permit to the applicant and whether the granting of the permit to the applicant is to the best interest of St. Louis County and whether the granting of the permit to the applicant would or would not violate the health regulations of St. Louis County or would, in any way, create a hazard or menace to the public health or would, in any way, create a nuisance to the people of St. Louis County, and shall make a report giving his recommendations to the County Council and shall submit a copy of his report to the Planning Commission.

The Planning Commission shall make a report to the County Council as to whether or not the granting of the permit in the location described in the application would be a violation of the zoning regulations of St. Louis County and shall submit a copy of this report to the Health Commissioner. The Planning Commission shall also report to the County Council as to the effect of such proposed use upon the character of the neighborhood, the traffic conditions, public utility facilities and other matters pertaining to the general welfare, and shall advise the County Council as to whether public convenience and necessity require the granting of a permit to the applicant.

In determining whether public convenience and necessity require the issuance of a permit to the applicant, both the Health Commissioner and the Planning Commission shall consider such matters as:

(1) The number of dumps and sanitary landfills necessary for the entire County.
(2) The locations best suited to serve the entire County.
(3) The length of time that a proposed location can be expected to be used as a dump or sanitary landfill for the best interests of the people of St. Louis County.
(4) The possible effect on the area in the vicinity of the proposed dump or sanitary landfill.

The report to the County Council by the Planning Commission shall be made in accordance with the provision of Section 7 of Article XVII of the zoning ordinance in St. Louis County.

Before submitting their reports to the County Council, the Planning Commission and the Health Commissioner shall notify in writing all persons heretofore licensed under this ordinance and, if requested in writing by any such person within seven days from the date of the mailing of the notice to the last known address of the licensee or licensees, shall hold a joint public hearing on the question of whether public convenience and necessity and the public health and general welfare of the people of St. Louis County require the issuance of a permit to the applicant. The entire proceeding and testimony offered at such joint public hearing shall be transcribed by a reporter and the transcription thereof shall be transmitted to the County Council.

Thereafter, the Health Commissioner and the Planning Commission shall submit their reports and recommendations to the County Council, including the above-mentioned transcript, stating their reasons why they recommend that the application be granted or denied and shall send a copy thereof to the applicant and to any person who has requested in writing a hearing on the application as hereinabove set forth. The County Council shall then consider the reports and recommendations so transmitted by the Health Commissioner and the Planning Commission and if the County Council finds that public convenience and necessity, as well as the public health and general welfare of the people of St. Louis County, require, shall issue a permit to the applicant; otherwise, the application for a permit shall be denied and the St. Louis County Clerk shall be instructed to notify the applicant. Such permit shall be issued by the County Council upon the payment of annual fee of Two Hundred Dollars ($200.00) payable to the Treasurer of St. Louis County, and to be deposited by him in the Health Center Maintenance Fund, and upon delivery to St. Louis County of a cash or corporate bond in the amount of $1,000.00; said cash or corporate bond shall run to St. Louis County, Missouri, and shall be conditioned as follows:

a) That the permittee, his agents and servants, will comply with all of the terms, conditions, provisions, requirements and specifications contained in this Ordinance.

b) That the permittee, his agents and servants, will faithfully operate the dump or landfill for which the permit is issued in accordance with the provisions of this Ordinance.

c) That the permittee, his agents and servants, will save harmless St. Louis County from any expense incurred through the failure of the permittee, his agents and servants, to operate and maintain the dump or landfill as required by this Ordinance including any expense the County may be put to for correcting any condition or violation of this Ordinance by the County's own labor and equipment, whenever the Health Commissioner determines it is necessary for the County to correct any unhealthy condition or conditions violative of this Ordinance or from any damages growing out of the negligence of the permittee or his agents or servants.

d) Before acceptance all bonds shall be approved by the County Council. If a corporate bond is offered, it shall be executed by a surety or guaranty company qualified to transact business in the State of Missouri. If a cash bond is offered, it shall be deposited with the St. Louis County Clerk, who shall give his official receipt therefor, reciting that said cash has been deposited in compliance with and subject to the provisions of this Ordinance.

Section 28.05. No person shall permit the disposing of any refuse in any quarry in St. Louis County unless the same is operated as a licensed dump or sanitary landfill in accordance with this Ordinance. Quarries operated as dumps may accept for deposit only non-combustible refuse having no putrescible material therein, and the dumping of garbage and combustible refuse in quarries is hereby prohibited, unless said quarries apply for and receive a permit to operate a sanitary landfill.

Section 28.06. The dumping of garbage and combustible material on private dumps is prohibited unless operated as a sanitary landfill in accordance with this Ordinance.

Section 28.07. The following regulations shall be observed by any person, firm or corporation to whom a permit is issued by the St. Louis County Council for the operation of a sanitary landfill. These regulations shall govern the operation of all St. Louis County approved sanitary landfills, and any failure to observe these regulations shall be sufficient grounds for the revocation of the permit by the Council.

(A) All garbage and other refuse accepted by the permit holder shall be thoroughly compacted by equipment of a size and weight capable of producing a downward or ground pressure of at least _____ pounds[1] per square inch. Such equipment shall have sufficient weight and capacity to carry out all necessary operations to the satisfaction of the enforcement officer. Sufficient auxiliary equipment shall be maintained on the site or otherwise available to permit operation in case of a breakdown.

(B) Mixed refuse material shall be spread out on the working face of the landfill so that the depth does not exceed a maximum depth of two (2) feet prior to its compaction.

---

[1]Five pounds are recommended by the American Public Works Association's Committee on Refuse Disposal.

(C) The areas shall be continually policed to prevent fire and the blowing of papers; shall be neat and sanitary at all times, and shall be covered at the end of each day's operation, as well as when wind conditions warrant it through the day, with sufficient material to prevent blowing papers and unsightly conditions. The size of the active face on which refuse is being currently deposited shall be kept to a minimum.

(D) Cover material will consist of earth, loam, clay, sand, etc., or a mixture of at least 50 percent earth and other inert materials, such as ashes, cinders or gravel. A minimum depth of 12 inches of compacted cover and final spread cover material shall be kept on all inactive faces of the landfill at all times. The active faces of the landfills should be covered at the end of each day's operation, or as otherwise directed by the Health Commissioner, with at least 6 inches (before compaction) of cover material.

(E) When the fill has been brought up to two (2) feet below the desired finished grade, it shall be covered with at least _____ inches[2] of compacted cover material graded and seeded in such a manner as to prevent erosion.

(F) Where the "trench system" of sanitary landfill is used, successive parallel trenches must be at least two (2) feet apart.

(G) All garbage and refuse material existing on the site at the time the permit is issued either in the form of an open dump or any other form, shall be collected, compacted, and covered with cover material at least one (1) foot in depth if below the desired finished grade, or with inert material at least two (2) feet in depth at the finished grade. This cover operation shall be completed within fifteen (15) working days after the issuance of a special permit for the sanitary landfill.

(H) The permittee or operator shall erect such temporary or permanent fences or take other measures as may be necessary to reasonably control blowing of paper and other materials from the landfill.

(I) Any materials salvaged from the fill must be handled and stored in such a manner as to prevent rat harborage and permit proper operation of the landfill. Such salvaged material must be removed to a location at least two-hundred (200) feet from the working surface so as not to interfere with the compacting and covering. All salvaged material must be completely removed from the landfill site every twenty-four (24) hours unless provision is made for temporary storage within an enclosed, roofed and rat-proof structure approved by the Enforcement Officer.

(J) Burning of any materials deposited in a dump or landfill is expressly prohibited, except that when the dump or landfill is located in a "J" or "K" Industrial District. In the latter districts tree limbs, wooden crates, or similar combustible material, which will burn readily without smouldering or producing offensive odors, may be burned in a separate place at least two hundred (200) feet away from the area where refuse is being compacted and covered, provided precautions are taken to confine the fire, and the burning is done in such a manner as not to create a nuisance condition. All burning shall be restricted to the hours between 8:00 A.M. and 12:00 Noon.

(K) Adequate fire-fighting equipment shall be available at all times on the site or the operator of the landfill shall furnish the Enforcement Officer with proof of a fire-fighting agreement between the operator and the local fire district.

---

[2]At least 24 inches are required under Section 28.03 (h) and are recommended by the American Public Works Association's Committee on Refuse Disposal.

(L) No fill shall be placed in streambeds or other areas where streams would be obstructed or where erosion by the stream would remove cover material. There shall be no seepage or drainage of any material from the fill of such a nature as would constitute an odor nuisance, or health hazard, or pollute any water course.

(M) The permit holder shall provide an access road, approved by the Enforcement Officer, that is passable in all types of weather conditions to the dumping site.

(N) The license holder shall also provide an auxiliary fill site available and ready for use during periods of heavy rain or snowfall, and when the area being filled and covered may not be reached because of said weather conditions. The permit holder shall also take precautions to eliminate excess dust in dry weather.

(O) Insects and rodents on the landfill site shall be controlled and exterminated as directed by the Enforcement Officer.

(P) For good and sufficient reasons the Enforcement Officer may grant exceptions to the above operating procedures and standards or may impose additional requirements subject to specific site conditions. The Enforcement Officer shall advise the County Council of the exceptions or additional requirements granted at the next regular council meeting after the exceptions or additional requirements are granted.

Section 28.08. No person, including those persons hauling or disposing of garbage or refuse, trash or other rubbish for a fee, shall deposit or dispose of any garbage, trash or other refuse on any property in St. Louis County not operated under a permit issued by the St. Louis County Council. Each sanitary landfill shall display a prominent sign containing the word "Approved Sanitary Landfill operated under Permit No._____ issued by the St. Louis County Council;" provided, however, that nothing in this Ordinance shall be deemed to prohibit or prevent the owner or operator of a farm engaged in the raising and feeding of swine from disposing of garbage for the feeding of his own swine so long as such disposal shall not constitute a nuisance nor a health hazard to the people of St. Louis County or be contrary to the Health Regulations of St. Louis County, and subject to the laws of the State of Missouri, including House Bill No. 60, as amended, adopted by the Sixty-Seventh General Assembly of Missouri, and approved on the 1st day of May, 1953.

Section 28.09. The officer responsible for the enforcement of the provisions of this ordinance shall be the Health Commissioner. He shall provide adequate and frequent inspections of the sanitary landfill sites and to this end shall be authorized to call upon the Planning Commission for assistance in making inspections. He shall notify any permit holder who is violating the provisions of this Ordinance of the specific manner in which the Ordinance is being violated. Unless said violation is corrected within twenty-four (24) hours after notice in writing to the permit holder by the Enforcement Officer, the Enforcement Officer shall notify the County Council of any violation of the provisions of this Ordinance and the County Council may, after a public hearing to which the violator shall have been invited, suspend or revoke any permit for non-compliance or violation of any of the provisions of this Ordinance or when satisfied that the landfill constitutes a real menace and nuisance to the health, safety and welfare of the immediate residents in the neighborhood in which it is located. In the event the permit holder refuses to correct the violation within twenty-four (24) hours after notice in writing by the Enforcement Officer, the Enforcement Officer may, if he deems it necessary in the interest of public health, enter upon the premises of the dump or landfill and, either with the equipment and employees of the license holder, or with County owned or leased equipment and County employees, do such work as is necessary to correct any condition violative of this Ordinance, and which in his opinion if left uncorrected may be hazardous to the public health. The cost to the County of correcting such conditions in privately owned dumps or landfills shall be assessed against the permit holder who shall be required to pay all costs and expenses of the County in correcting said conditions.

Section 28.10. Any permit or license granted hereunder may be revoked or suspended at any time for any failure to pay the license fee or the cost of correcting hazardous conditions, as hereinbefore set forth, or whenever in the opinion of the Health Commissioner the continuance of the landfill or other means of final disposal of refuse would endanger the health, welfare or safety of the public; provided that no such permit or license shall be revoked or suspended except for failure to pay the fee, or the cost of correcting hazardous conditions as herein provided except after public hearing before the St. Louis County Council after the notice of said hearing and the purpose thereof shall have been sent to the permit holder at least ten (10) days prior to the date of said hearing, at which hearing any person interested in said landfill shall have the right to be heard.

Section 28.11. St. Louis County Council Ordinance No. 202, 1952 enacted on the 16th day of July, 1952, relating to dumps, is hereby repealed, and all Ordinances or parts of Ordinances in conflict herewith are to the extent of such conflict hereby repealed. Any person who violates or causes to be violated any provisions of this Ordinance, shall upon conviction thereof, be fined not less than Twenty-five ($25.00) Dollars nor more than Five Hundred ($500.00) Dollars and each day of such violation shall constitute a separate offense.

Section 28.12. The passage of this ordinance being deemed necessary for the immediate preservation of the public health, safety and welfare of the people of St. Louis County, an emergency is hereby declared to exist and this Ordinance shall be in full force and effect immediately upon its passage, and approval by the County Supervisor.

ADOPTED THIS 24TH DAY OF JUNE, 1953

Frank L. Martini
ACTING CHAIRMAN, COUNTY COUNCIL

APPROVED THIS 24TH DAY OF JUNE, 1953

Luman F. Matthews
COUNTY SUPERVISOR

ATTEST:

Leo E. Sievers
COUNTY CLERK

EXCERPTS OF INTERIM GUIDE OF GOOD PRACTICE
FOR INCINERATION AT FEDERAL FACILITIES[1]

1 INTRODUCTION

Section 111 (a) of the Clean Air Act as amended requires any Federal department or agency having jurisdiction over any building, installation, or other property to cooperate with the Department of Health, Education, and Welfare in preventing and controlling air pollution. In furtherance of this purpose, Presidential Executive Order 11282 requires establishments of the Executive Branch of the Government to provide leadership in the nation-wide effort to improve the quality of our air by, among other measures, keeping the emissions of fly ash and other particulate matter to a minimum. Acting upon Executive Order 11282 the Secretary of Health, Education, and Welfare has prescribed standards for implementing these goals and has requested that guides to good practice be issued for specific operations to aid Federal departments, agencies, and establishments in the selection of equipment and methods for meeting the standards. This document is the first such Guide to be issued.

Standards issued as a result of this Executive Order appear as Part 76 in Subchapter F of Title 42, Code of Federal Regulations. As these Standards apply to incinerators, they are detailed in Sections 1.3 and 1.4 of this Guide.

Requests for guides of good practice, technical material, or consultation should be directed either to the Chief, Federal Facilities Branch, Division of Abatement, National Air Pollution Control Administration, Public Health Service, Department of Health, Education, and Welfare, 5600 Fishers Lane, Rockville, Md. 20852, or to the appropriate Regional Director of the Public Health Service at Department of Health, Education, and Welfare Regional Offices. (See Table 1-1 for addresses of Regional Directors.)

1.1 PURPOSE OF INTERIM GUIDE OF GOOD PRACTICE

This Interim Guide of Good Practice is to be used by Federal agencies to select incinerators for burning Types 0, 1, 2, and 4 wastes as defined in Section 3. The information in this Guide applies to incinerators having a burning capacity of 2000 pounds per hour or less of general refuse and up to 200 pounds per hour of pathological waste. Advice on burning other types of waste may be obtained from the Federal Facilities Branch.

The designs recommended herein are believed to be such as to produce incinerators that will operate in compliance with the Code of Federal Regulations. It is not the intent of this Guide to inhibit progress and ingenuity in the development of other incinerator designs or methods of waste disposal.

In addition, the entire Guide has been designated as an "Interim" Guide until studies presently being conducted show whether incinerators of other designs, suitably controlled, can comply with Federal emission standards. When additional designs have been proven capable of meeting Federal

---

[1] Reprinted with permission of the National Air Pollution Control Administration, Publication No. HP-46, November, 1969.

471

emission standards, they may be included in a subsequent Guide of Good Practice for Incineration at Federal Facilities.

1.2 Applicability of Federal Regulations to Incinerators

The provisions of this Guide apply to Federal Facilities in the 50 states, the District of Columbia, the Commonwealth of Puerto Rico, the Virgin Islands, Guam, and American Samoa. However, if state or local emission standards applicable to incinerators are more strict than those given herein, then the Chief, Federal Facilities Branch, should be consulted prior to installation of an incinerator of the designs described in this Guide.

1.2.1 *Existing Incinerators*

All existing incinerators must comply with the standards set forth in the Code of Federal Regulations under Title 42, Chapter 1, Subchapter F, Part 76, Section 76.8, as amended. (See Sections 1.3 and 1.4 of this Guide.) Compliance may be achieved by one or more of the following actions.

1.2.1.1 MODIFICATION OF INCINERATOR—Usually, modification will be practicable only if the changes are relatively minor, such as the addition of bricks to the flame port, the addition of a secondary burner, or the installation of a barometric damper. If extensive changes in the brickwork are required, the cost and results usually justify installation of a new incinerator.

1.2.1.2. ADDITION OF AIR POLLUTION CONTROL DEVICE—The most commonly employed air pollution control device is the low-pressure-drop scrubber. Design specifications for such a control device that would be suitable for use with incinerator designs described herein are given in Section 8. When a scrubber is used to upgrade an existing incinerator, however, it would probably be desirable to use a more efficient scrubber than that described herein, inasmuch as the incinerators described in this Guide will emit less particulate matter than incinerators in need of upgrading.

1.2.1.3. REPLACEMENT OF INCINERATOR—See Section 6 of this Guide for recommendations for new incinerators.

1.2.1.4. ALTERNATIVE METHOD OF REFUSE DISPOSAL—In considering alternatives, assistance may be sought from the Bureau of Solid Waste Management, Division of Technical Operations, 5600 Fishers Lane, Rockville, Maryland 20852.

1.2.2 *New Incinerators*

All new incinerators must comply with the standards set forth in the Code of Federal Regulations under Title 42, Chapter 1, Subchapter F, Part 76, Section 76.8, as amended. These standards are given in Sections 1.3 and 1.4 of this Guide.

1.3 Standards for Particulate Emissions

Particulate emissions shall be measured by the test procedures described in "Specifications for Incinerator Testing at Federal Facilities" (PHS publication, October 1967) and any amendments or revisions thereof.

1.3.1 *Incinerators of Over 200 Pounds per Hour Capacity*

Incinerators having burning rates of more than 200 pounds per hour shall not emit more than 0.2 grain of particulate matter per standard cubic foot

Table 1-1
ADDRESSES OF REGIONAL DIRECTORS[1]

Regions	States and Addresses
I	Connecticut, Maine, Massachusetts, New Hampshire, Rhode Island, and Vermont DHEW, J. F. Kennedy Federal Building, Boston, Massachusetts 02203
II	Delaware, New Jersey, New York, and Pennsylvania DHEW-PHS, Federal Office Building, 26 Federal Plaza (Foley Square), New York, N.Y. 10007
III	District of Columbia, Kentucky, Maryland, North Carolina, Virginia, West Virginia, Puerto Rico, and Virgin Islands DHEW, 220 Seventh Street, N.E., Charlottesville, Virginia 22901
IV	Alabama, Florida, Georgia, Mississippi, South Carolina, and Tennessee DHEW, Room 404, 50 Seventh Street, N.E., Atlanta, Georgia 30323
V	Illinois, Indiana, Michigan, Ohio, and Wisconsin DHEW, Room 712, New Post Office Building, 433 W. Van Buren St., Chicago, Illinois 60607
VI	Iowa, Kansas, Minnesota, Missouri, Nebraska, North Dakota, and South Dakota DHEW, 601 E. 12th Street, Kansas City, Missouri 64106
VII	Arkansas, Louisiana, New Mexico, Oklahoma, and Texas DHEW, 1114 Commerce Street, Dallas, Texas 75202
VIII	Colorado, Idaho, Montana, Utah, and Wyoming DHEW, Room 8026, Federal Office Building, 19th and Stout Street, Denver, Colorado 80202
IX	Alaska, Arizona, California, Hawaii, Nevada, Oregon, Washington, Guam, and American Samoa DHEW, 50 Fulton Street, Federal Office Building, San Francisco, California 94102

[1] Correspondence should be addressed to the Regional Air Pollution Control Director, National Air Pollution Control Administration, at the appropriate address given above.

of dry flue gas corrected to 12 percent carbon dioxide (without the contribution of carbon dioxide from auxiliary fuel).

1.3.2 *Incinerators of 200 Pounds per Hour Capacity and Less*
Incinerators having burning rates of 200 pounds per hour or less shall not emit more than 0.3 grain of particulate matter per standard cubic foot of dry flue gas corrected to 12 percent carbon dioxide (without the contribution of carbon dioxide from auxiliary fuel).

1.4 STANDARDS FOR VISIBLE EMISSIONS

1.4.1 *Incinerators Acquired On or After June 3, 1966*
For incinerators acquired on or after June 3, 1966, the density of any

emission to the atmosphere shall not exceed number 1 on the Ringelmann Scale or the Smoke Inspection Guide for a period or periods aggregating more than 3 minutes in any 1 hour, or be of such opacity as to obscure an observer's view to an equivalent degree.

The Ringelmann chart should be used in accordance with the Procedures in the Bureau of Mines Information Circular No. 8333. The Smoke Inspection Guide should be used in accordance with procedures in Title 42, Chapter 1, Subchapter F, Section 75.2 of the Code of Federal Regulations.

1.4.2 *Incinerators Acquired Prior to June 3, 1966*

For incinerators acquired prior to June 3, 1966, the density of any emission to the atmosphere shall not exceed number 2 on the Ringelmann Scale or the Smoke Inspection Guide for a period or periods aggregating more than 3 minutes in any 1 hour or be of such opacity as to obscure an observer's view to an equivalent degree.

1.5 CONSIDERATIONS FOR GOOD PLANNING OTHER THAN INCINERATOR DESIGN

In addition to the design of the incinerator itself, careful consideration must be given to the following items when installation of an incinerator is being planned:

1. Collection and method of charging the refuse.
2. Ample areas around the incinerator for charging, stoking, ash handling and general maintenance.
3. Adequate air supply to the incinerator room at the stoking and charging levels.
4. Effect of air conditioning and ventilating equipment on the air supply or the draft available from the draft-producing equipment.
5. Adequate draft (negative pressure) to handle all theoretical and excess air required to assure safe operation and complete combustion at reasonable temperatures.
6. Location of the top of the chimney or stack with respect to ventilation intakes, penthouse, or other obstructions.

2 DEFINITIONS OF INCINERATOR TERMS

AIR SUPPLY

All air supplied to the incinerator equipment for combustion, ventilation, and cooling. Standard air is air at standard temperature and pressure, namely, 70° F and 29.92 inches of mercury.

1. Air Jets—Streams of high-velocity air issuing from nozzles in the incinerator enclosure to provide turbulence. The air jets, depending on their location, may be used to provide excess, primary, secondary, or overfire air.
2. Excess Air—The air remaining after a fuel has been completely burned, or the air supplied in addition to the theoretical quantity.
3. Overfire Air—Any air, controlled with respect to quantity and direction, supplied beyond the fuel bed, as through ports in the walls of the primary combustion chamber, for the purpose of completing combustion of combustible materials in the gases from the fuel bed or reducing operating temperatures within the incinerator.
4. Primary Air—Any air, controlled with respect to quantity and direction,

forced or induced, supplied through or adjacent to the fuel bed, to promote combustion of the combustible materials in the fuel bed.

5. Secondary Air—Any air, controlled with respect to quantity and direction, supplied beyond the fuel bed, as through ports in the walls or bridge wall of the primary combustion chamber (overfire air), or the secondary combustion chamber, to complete combustion of combustible materials in the gases from the fuel bed or to reduce operating temperature within the incinerator.

6. Theoretical Air—The stoichiometric amount of air required for complete combustion of a given quantity of a specific fuel.

7. Underfire Air—Any air, controlled with respect to quantity and direction, forced or induced, supplied beneath the grate, that passes through the fuel bed.

AUXILIARY-FUEL FIRING EQUIPMENT

Equipment to supply additional heat, by the combustion of an auxiliary fuel, for the purpose of attaining temperatures sufficiently high (1) to dry and ignite the waste material; (2) to maintain ignition thereof; and (3) to effect complete combustion of combustible solids, vapors, and gases.

BAFFLE

Any refractory construction intended to change the direction of flow of the products of combustion.

BREECHING OR FLUE CONNECTION

The connection between the incinerator and auxiliary equipment, between the incinerator and stack or chimney, or between auxiliary equipment and stack or chimney.

BRIDGE WALL

A partition wall between chambers over which products of combustion pass.

BRITISH THERMAL UNIT

The quantity of heat required to raise 1 pound of water 1° Fahrenheit, abbreviated Btu and B. T. U.

BURNER

A device for the introduction of a flame by delivering fuel and its combustion air, at desired velocities and turbulence, to establish and maintain proper ignition and combustion of the fuel.

1. Afterburner—A burner installed in the secondary combustion chamber or in chambers separated from the incinerator proper (also referred to as a secondary burner).

2. Primary Burner—A burner installed in the primary combustion chamber to dry out and ignite the material to be burned.

3. Secondary Burner—A burner installed in the secondary combustion

chamber to maintain temperature and complete the combustion process (also referred to as an afterburner).

BURNING AREA

The horizontal projected area of the grate, hearth, or combination thereof on which burning takes place.

BURNING RATE

The amount of waste incinerated per unit of time, usually expressed in pounds per hour.

BYPASS

An arrangement of breechings or flue connections and dampers to permit the alternate use of two or more pieces of equipment by directing or diverting the flow of the products of combustion.

CAPACITY

The amount of waste stipulated as the incineration rate for specific types of refuse, expressed in pounds per hour.

CHARGING CHUTE

A passage through which waste materials are conveyed from above to the primary combustion chamber.

CHARGING DOOR

A closure for the primary chamber loading entrance.

CHECKERWORK

A pattern of multiple openings in refractory structures through which the products of combustion pass to promote turbulent mixing of the gases.

CHIMNEY, STACK, FLUE

A passage for conducting products of combustion to the atmosphere.

CLINKER

Hard sintered or fused material, formed in the fire by the agglomeration of residual ash, metals, glass, and ceramic material.

COMBUSTION CHAMBER, EXPANSION CHAMBER, SETTLING CHAMBER

Any chamber designed to reduce the velocity of the products of combustion to promote the settling of fly ash from the gas stream and to allow space and time to complete combustion.

CURTAIN WALL

A partition wall between chambers, which serves to deflect gases in a downward direction (also referred to as a drop arch).

DAMPER

A manually or automatically controlled device to regulate draft or the rate of flow of air or combustion gases.

1. Barometric Damper—A hinged or pivoted valve placed and adjusted by counterbalancing so as to admit air to the breeching, flue connection, or stack to maintain automatically the required draft in the incinerator.
2. Butterfly Damper—A throttling disk or valve that rotates on its hinged axis to control airflow in a duct, breeching, flue connection, or stack.
3. Guillotine Damper—An adjustable, counterbalanced blade installed in a breeching or flue connection and arranged to move vertically across the breeching or flue connection.
4. Sliding Damper—An adjustable blade installed in a duct, breeching, flue connection, or stack and arranged to move horizontally across the duct, breeching, flue connection or stack.

DOWN PASS

Chamber or passage between two chambers that carries the products of combustion in a downward direction.

DRAFT

The pressure difference between the incinerator or any component part and the atmosphere, that causes a continuous flow of air and products of combustion through the gas passage of the incinerator to the atmosphere.

1. Forced Draft—The pressure difference created by the action of a fan, blower, or ejector to supply primary combustion air greater than atmospheric pressure.
2. Induced Draft—The pressure difference created by the action of a fan, blower, or ejector installed between the incinerator and the stack, or at the stack exit.
3. Natural Draft—The pressure difference created by stack or chimney because of its height and the temperature difference between the flue gases and the atmosphere.

DUST LOADING

The amount of fly ash carried in the products of combustion, usually expressed in grains per standard cubic foot at 12 percent carbon dioxide, without the contribution of carbon dioxide from the burning of auxiliary fuel.

EFFLUENT

The flue gas or products of combustion that reach the atmosphere from the burning process.

EXPANSION CHAMBER, COMBUSTION CHAMBER, SETTLING CHAMBER

See definition under Combustion Chamber, Expansion Chamber, Settling Chamber.

FLAME PORT

A small port in the parting wall through which the flames and products of combustion from the burning refuse must pass.

FLUE GAS

All gases leaving the incinerator by way of the flue, including gaseous products of combustion, water vapor, excess air, and nitrogen.

FLY ASH

Suspended ash particles, charred paper, dust, soot, and other partially incinerated matter carried in the products of combustion (also referred to as particulate matter or pollutant).

FLY ASH COLLECTOR

Auxiliary equipment designed to remove fly ash in dry form from the products of combustion.

GAS WASHER OR SCRUBBER

Equipment for removing fly ash and other objectionable materials from the products of combustion by means of water sprays or wetted baffles.

GRATE

Surface that supports waste material, but with suitable openings to permit passage of air through the burning waste. It is usually located in the primary combustion chamber and is designed to permit removal of ash and unburned residue. Grates may be horizontal or inclined, stationary or movable.

HEARTH

A solid surface on which waste material with high moisture content, or waste material that may turn to liquid before burning, is placed for drying or burning.

1. Cold Hearth—A surface on which waste material is dried and/or burned by the action of hot combustion gases that pass only over the waste material.
2. Hot Hearth—A heated surface on which waste material is dried and/or burned by the action of hot combustion gases that pass first over the waste materials and then under the hearth.

HEATING VALUE

The heat released by combustion of a unit quantity of waste or fuel, measured in British Thermal Units (Btu). In this Guide heating value is on an as-fired basis for refuse and on the higher or gross heating value for fuel.

HEAT RELEASE RATE

The amount of heat liberated during the process of complete combustion and expressed in Btu per hour per cubic foot of the internal furnace volume in which such combustion takes place.

IGNITION CHAMBER, PRIMARY CHAMBER

The chamber of the incinerator in which refuse is burned.

INCINERATION

The process of igniting and burning solid, semisolid, liquid, or gaseous combustible waste to carbon dioxide and water vapor.

INCINERATOR

An engineered apparatus capable of withstanding heat and designed to efficiently reduce solid, semisolid, liquid, or gaseous waste by combustion at specified rates, to residues containing little or no combustible material. As used herein, a general-refuse incinerator is a multiple-chamber incinerator designed primarily for burning waste of Types 0, 1, and 2 at rates of from 50 to 2000 pounds per hour. A pathological incinerator is a multiple-chamber incinerator designed to burn 200 pounds per hour or less of Type 4 waste.

MIXING CHAMBER

A chamber usually placed between the primary combustion chamber and an expansion chamber wherein thorough mixing of the products of combustion is accomplished by turbulence created by increased velocities of gases, checkerwork, and/or changes in direction of the gas flow.

MULTIPLE-CHAMBER INCINERATOR

A multiple-chamber incinerator is any article, machine, equipment, contrivance, structure, or part of a structure consisting of three or more refractory-lined combustion chambers in series, physically separated by refractory walls and interconnected by gas passage ports or ducts that is used to dispose of waste material by burning.

PARTICULATES OR PARTICULATE MATTER

Suspended ash particles, charred paper, dust, soot, and other partially incinerated matter carried in the products of combustion (also referred to as fly ash). For the purposes of determining compliance with Section 76.8, Title 42 of the Code of Federal Regulations, particulate matter is defined as any material, except uncombined water, which is suspended in a gas stream as a liquid or solid at standard conditions.

PARTING WALL

In retort incinerators, the parting wall separates the primary chamber from both a secondary chamber and an expansion chamber.

PRIMARY CHAMBER, IGNITION CHAMBER

See definition under Ignition Chamber, Primary Chamber.

SETTLING CHAMBER, EXPANSION CHAMBER, COMBUSTION CHAMBER

See definition under Combustion Chamber, Expansion Chamber, Settling Chamber.

SIDE CHAMBER

A small chamber used for burning pathological waste that is built into the side of a general-refuse burner.

SPARK ARRESTER

A screen-like device that prevents sparks, embers, and other ignited materials larger than a given size from being expelled to the atmosphere.

STANDARD CONDITIONS

Standard conditions are a gas temperature of 70° Fahrenheit and a gas pressure of 14.7 pounds per square inch, absolute. Results of all analyses and tests should be calculated or reported at this gas temperature and pressure.

3 WASTE CLASSIFICATIONS

TYPE 0

A mixture of highly combustible waste such as paper, cardboard cartons, wood boxes, and floor sweepings from commercial and industrial activities. The mixture contains up to 10 percent by weight of plastic bags, coated paper, laminated paper, treated corrugated cardboard, oily rags, and plastic or rubber scraps.

This type of waste contains 10 percent moisture and 5 percent noncombustible solids, and has a heating value of 8,500 Btu per pound as fired. (See Table 3-1.)

TYPE 1

A mixture of combustible waste such as paper, cardboard cartons, wood scrap, foliage, and floor sweepings from domestic, commercial, and industrial activities. The mixture contains up to 20 percent by weight of restaurant waste, but contains little or no treated paper, plastic, or rubber wastes.

This type of waste contains 25 percent moisture and 10 percent incombustible solids, and has a heating value of 6,500 Btu per pound as fired.

TYPE 2

An approximately even mixture of rubbish and garbage by weight.

This type of waste, common to apartment and residential occupancy, consists of up to 50 percent moisture and 7 percent incombustible solids, and has a heating value of 4,300 Btu per pound as fired.

TYPE 3

Garbage such as animal and vegetable wastes from restaurants, hotels, hospitals, markets, and similar installations.

This type of waste contains up to 70 percent moisture and up to 5 percent

Table 3-1

CHEMICAL PROPERTIES AND COMBUSTION DATA FOR PAPER, WOOD, AND GARBAGE

	Sulfite paper[1]	Average wood[2]	Douglas fir[3]	Garbage[4]
Analysis, %				
Carbon	44.34	49.56	52.30	52.78
Hydrogen	6.27	6.11	6.30	6.27
Nitrogen		0.07	0.10	
Oxygen	48.39	43.83	40.50	39.95
Ash	1.00	0.42	0.80	1.00
Gross heating value (dry basis), Btu/lb	7590	8517	9050	8820

Constituent (based on 1 lb)	Sulfite paper[1] Cubic feet	Pounds	Average wood[2] Cubic feet	Pounds	Douglas fir[3] Cubic feet	Pounds	Garbage[4] Cubic feet	Pounds
Theoretical air	67.58	5.165	77.30	5.909	84.16	6.433	85.12	6.507
Theoretical air 40% sat. @ 60°F	68.05	5.188	77.84	5.935	84.75	6.461	85.72	6.536
Flue gas with theor. air — CO_2	13.993	1.625	15.641	1.816	16.51	1.917	16.668	1.935
N_2	53.401	3.947	61.104	4.517	66.53	4.918	67.234	4.976
H_2O formed	11.787	0.560	11.487	0.546	11.84	0.563	11.880	0.564
H_2O (air)	0.471	0.023	0.539	0.026	0.587	0.028	0.593	0.029
Total	79.652	6.155	88.771	6.905	95.467	7.426	96.375	7.495
Flue gas with % excess air as indicated — 0	79.65	6.16	88.77	6.91	95.47	7.43	96.38	7.50
50.0	113.44	8.74	127.42	9.86	137.55	10.64	139.24	10.77
100.0	147.23	11.32	166.07	12.81	179.63	13.86	182.00	14.04
150.0	181.26	13.91	204.99	15.79	222.01	17.09	224.86	17.21
200.0	215.28	16.51	243.91	18.75	264.38	20.12	267.72	20.58
300.0	283.33	21.70	321.75	24.68	349.13	26.58	353.44	27.12

[1] Sulfite paper constituents: Cellulose $C_6H_{10}O_5$; Hemicellulose $C_5H_{10}O_5$; Lignin $C_6H_{10}O_5$.

Average wood constituents: Cellulose $C_6H_{10}O_5$ 84%; Hemicellulose $C_6H_{10}O_5$ 8; Lignin $C_6H_{10}O_5$ 6; Resin $C_{20}H_{30}O_2$ 2%; Ash 1.

[2] R. T. Kent, *Mechanical Engineer's Handbook*, 11th ed. (New York: John Wiley and Sons, 1936), pp. 6-104.

[3] *Ibid.*, 12th ed., 1961, pp. 2-40.

[4] Estimated on dry basis.

incombustible solids, and has a heating value of 2,500 Btu per pound as fired.

TYPE 4

Human and animal remains, such as organs, carcasses, and solid organic wastes from hospitals, laboratories, slaughterhouses, animal pounds, and similar sources, consisting of up to 85 percent moisture and 5 percent incombustible solids, and having a heating value as low as 1,000 Btu per pound as fired.

TYPE 5

Gaseous, liquid, or semiliquid by-product waste, such as tar, paint, solvent, sludge, and fumes from industrial operations. Btu values must be determined by the individual materials to be destroyed.

TYPE 6

Solid by-product waste, such as rubber, plastic, and wood waste from industrial operations. Btu values must be determined by the individual materials to be destroyed.

6 DESIGN RECOMMENDATIONS FOR GENERAL-REFUSE INCINERATORS

6.1 BASIS FOR DESIGN RECOMMENDATIONS

Tests on incinerators designed according to these recommended standards have shown that when properly operated, the incinerators can meet, without the use of scrubbers, the applicable Federal emission standards for incinerators with rated burning capacity of 200 pounds per hour or less. At capacities of more than 200 pounds per hour, incinerators should be equipped with scrubbers to ensure that applicable Federal emission limits are met.

6.2 TYPES OF GENERAL-REFUSE INCINERATORS

Multiple-chamber incinerators are of two general types. Figure 6-1 illustrates the retort type, named for the return flow of gases through the "U" arrangement of the component chambers; and Figure 6-2 shows the in-line type, so called because the three chambers follow one another in a line.

6.2.1 Multiple-Chamber Retort Incinerators

The following guidelines are recommended:

1. That general-refuse retort incinerators installed in Federal facilities have the configuration shown in Figure 6-3.
2. That retort incinerators with rated capacities of over 1,000 pounds per hour not be built.
3. That incinerators of over 200 pounds per hour rated capacity be equipped with gas washers as specified in Section 8 of this Guide, or equivalent gas washers as determined by the Federal Facilities Section.

6.2.2 Multiple-Chamber In-Line Incinerators

The following guidelines are recommended:

1. That all in-line incinerators installed in Federal facilities for the purpose

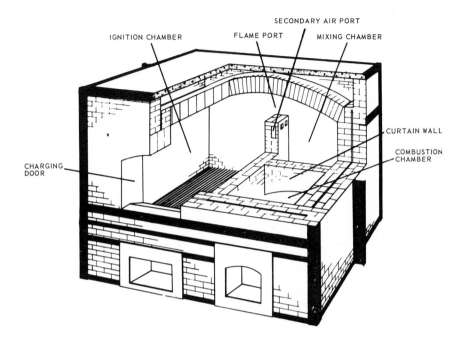

Fig. 6-1. Cutaway drawing of multiple-chamber retort incinerator.

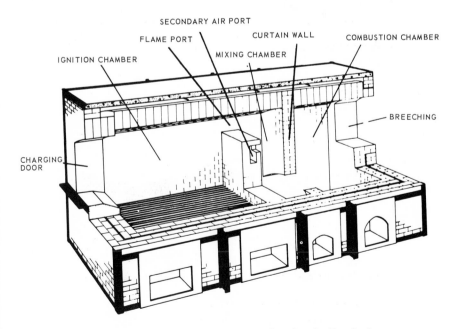

Fig. 6-2. Cutaway drawing of multiple-chamber in-line incinerator.

of burning wastes of Types 0, 1, or 2 have the configuration shown in Figure 6-4.

2. That in-line incinerators with a rated burning capacity of less than 750 pounds per hour not be built.

3. That all in-line incinerators be equipped with gas washers as specified in Section 8 of this Guide, or equivalent gas washers, as determined by the Federal Facilities Branch.

4. That the actual dimensions of incinerators shown in Figures 6-2 and 6-4 be established by using the design considerations of this Guide.

6.3 RECOMMENDATIONS FOR AUXILIARY GAS BURNERS

6.3.1 *Incinerators Requiring Burners*

Secondary burners alone need be installed on incinerators that are to be used solely to burn Type 0 waste. If the incinerator is to burn wastes of Types 1, 2, 3, or 4, both primary and secondary burners should be installed. The need for burners in incinerating other types of waste is dictated by the nature of the waste itself.

6.3.2 *Types of Natural Gas Burners Recommended*

Incinerators having a capacity of less than 200 pounds per hour that use

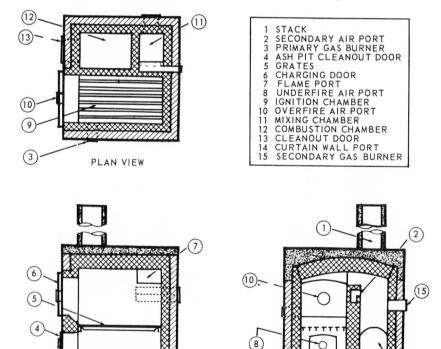

```
PLAN VIEW

 1  STACK
 2  SECONDARY AIR PORT
 3  PRIMARY GAS BURNER
 4  ASH PIT CLEANOUT DOOR
 5  GRATES
 6  CHARGING DOOR
 7  FLAME PORT
 8  UNDERFIRE AIR PORT
 9  IGNITION CHAMBER
10  OVERFIRE AIR PORT
11  MIXING CHAMBER
12  COMBUSTION CHAMBER
13  CLEANOUT DOOR
14  CURTAIN WALL PORT
15  SECONDARY GAS BURNER

SIDE ELEVATION        END ELEVATION
```

Fig. 6-3. Recommended plan for multiple-chamber retort incinerators.

burners rated at less than 400,000 Btu per hour may be of either the atmospheric or power-burner type. In either case, a continuously or intermittently burning stable pilot adequate to ensure safe, reliable ignition should be installed. A flame safeguard should be used so that no gas can flow to the main burner unless satisfactory ignition is assured. The response time of this flame safeguard to de-energize the gas shutoff device on flame failure should not exceed 180 seconds.

Auxiliary burners on incinerators with ratings of 200 pounds per hour or more, i.e., those equipped with a fan and scrubber, should be of the power-burner type, because this type of burner usually retains its flame better when a fan is used to induce draft. For burners with ratings of more than 400,000 Btu per hour input, the burner equipment shall be of the power type that utilizes a forced-draft blower to supply air needed for combustion under controlled conditions. A continuously or intermittently burning pilot should be used to ensure safe and reliable ignition. Automatic spark ignition should be used on pilots for burners with input of more than 1,000,000 Btu per

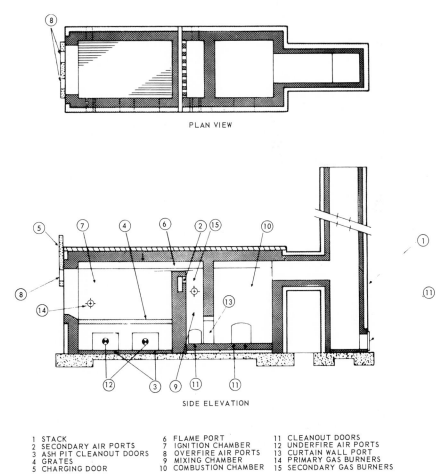

PLAN VIEW

SIDE ELEVATION

1 STACK	6 FLAME PORT	11 CLEANOUT DOORS
2 SECONDARY AIR PORTS	7 IGNITION CHAMBER	12 UNDERFIRE AIR PORTS
3 ASH PIT CLEANOUT DOORS	8 OVERFIRE AIR PORTS	13 CURTAIN WALL PORT
4 GRATES	9 MIXING CHAMBER	14 PRIMARY GAS BURNERS
5 CHARGING DOOR	10 COMBUSTION CHAMBER	15 SECONDARY GAS BURNERS

Fig. 6-4. Recommended plan for multiple-chamber in-line incinerators.

hour. A suitable flame safeguard should be used so that no gas can flow to the main burner unless satisfactory ignition is assured. On burners with inputs of from 400,000 to 1,000,000 Btu per hour, the response time of the flame safeguard to de-energize the gas shutoff device on flame failure should not exceed 180 seconds. In capacities of more than 1,000,000 Btu per hour, the response time of the aforementioned flame safeguard should not exceed 4 seconds.

The burner assembly should consist of the main burner, pilot burner, automatic valve, the necessary manual valves, and accessory equipment, plus interconnecting pipes and fittings with provision for rigid mounting. The burner should be constructed so that parts cannot be incorrectly located or incorrectly fitted together. Power burners sealed to the walls of incinerators with capacities of more than 100,000 Btu per hour must be supplied with a means of proving air supply before the main gas valve can be energized.

Electrical motors of more than $\frac{1}{12}$ horsepower on power burner equipment should be designed for continuous duty and should be provided with thermal overload protection or current-sensitive devices.

When a complete automatic pilot shutoff system is utilized, the controls should be readily accessible and arranged so that the main burner gas can be manually shut off during lighting of the pilot. When a complete automatic pilot system is not utilized, a readily accessible, manually operated, quarter-turn, lever-handle, plug-type valve should be provided to shut off or turn on the gas supply to the main burner manifold. This valve should be upstream from all controls except the pilot control valve.

Clearly defined and complete instructions for lighting and shutting down the burner should be provided in durable, weatherproof material for posting in a position where they can be read easily.

6.3.3 Sizes of Burners Recommended

Where auxiliary burners are used, their capacity range should include the values shown in Table 6-1.

Table 6-1

GAS BURNER RECOMMENDATIONS FOR GENERAL-REFUSE INCINERATORS

Capacity of incinerator, lb/hr	Size of burners, 10^3 Btu/hr		
	Primary burners		Secondary burners
	Type 1 refuse	Type 2 refuse	All refuse
50	150	250	200
100	200	550	300
150	250	650	400
250	300	750	650
500	550	1100	1000
750	750	1500	1300
1000	900	1700	1700
1500	1100	2200	2100
2000	1600	3300	2700

6.3.4 Other Fuels

If natural gas is not available, equivalent amounts of liquid fuels may be used. Fuel oils of grades higher than Number 2, however, should not be used. The National Fire Protection Association Standard No. 31, Installation of Oil Burning Equipment (1965), should be adhered to where oil burners are used.

If liquified petroleum gas is used, burners should be equipped with a device that will automatically shut off the main gas supply in the event the means of ignition becomes inoperative. The arrangement should be such as to shut off the fuel supply to the pilot burner also.

8 DESIGN RECOMMENDATIONS FOR INCINERATOR SCRUBBERS

A specific scrubber design is recommended herein, but other designs may be used if they are of an efficiency equal to that of the recommended design and are constructed of materials of equivalent resistivity to corrosion, heat, and other applicable stresses.

8.1 GENERAL

Effluents from general-refuse incinerators burning more than 200 pounds per hour should be cleaned in scrubbers to meet the particulate limit requirement. Since this will generally mean that scrubbers will be widely employed, the disadvantages associated with their use should be recognized.

When scrubbers are used, power lines may have to be installed to furnish energy to operate the induced-draft fan and water pump. Provisions must also be made to supply scrubbing water and a means of disposing of contaminated water from the scrubber. In some areas it will also be necessary to adjust the pH and process the contaminated water through a clarifier to remove fly ash and other collected solids before the water is sewered.

A scrubber may require considerable maintenance as a result of corrosion caused by the acidic water continuously flowing from it. Scrubber water is seldom recirculated because this increases its acidity and, therefore, the rate of corrosion. Even when scrubbers are lined with dense refractory material, corrosion of the steel casing may ultimately occur. In addition, there may be noticeable corrosion and erosion of the fan impeller and, to some lesser degree, of the fan housing. The continuous contact of the acidic water in the sump of the scrubber may gradually attack this surface.

8.2 SCRUBBER DESIGN PARAMETERS

Several basic factors are considered in designing scrubbers. To satisfactorily collect the fly ash, the water-gas mixture must be retained within the scrubber for 1 to 1½ seconds at gas velocities not exceeding 15 feet per second. The residence time in the scrubber should also be sufficient to vaporize all the water droplets within the effluent gas stream. Complete vaporization is important since nuisance complaints may result from the carryover of water droplets deposited on the surrounding area. From an appearance standpoint, the scrubber should not be longer or higher than the incinerator. The scrubber width should be limited to allow the scrubber to be easily located either adjacent to or at the rear of any incinerator of the retort type. The usual location for scrubbers serving the in-line type incinerator is at the rear of the combustion chamber. Placing the scrubber adjacent to the final combustion chamber is also feasible.

Air dilution of the gases from the incinerator prior to entering the scrubber is unnecessary. Water is introduced into the effluent as it enters the scrubber and flows concurrently down its first pass. By immediately introducing the water into the gas stream, the water has a longer period to mix and evaporate, which accomplishes the desired cooling. The average velocity of the gas-water mixture in the first pass ranges from 9 to 10 feet per second. The velocity of the gases in the upward pass is determined by calculating the remaining time requirement so that the gases are within the scrubber for a total time of approximately 1¼ seconds. The curtain wall port is sized to permit an air velocity range of 18 to 20 feet per second to prevent excessive pressure drop from occurring and to prevent water from the sump from being re-entrained in the effluent. The gases exist from the extreme top of the uppass so that its full length can be used for the evaporation of any remaining water in the gas stream. This location of the exit at the top also prevents water traveling up the back side of the scrubber from becoming re-entrained in the gas stream. Another feature that reduces re-entrainment of water droplets is a 4-inch channel at the bottom of the curtain wall. The channel collects the larger droplets and carries the water across the width of the scrubber, down its side walls, and into the sump below. Additional structural support for the refractory of the dividing wall is also provided by this channel.

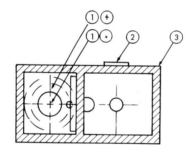

```
 1  SPRAY NOZZLES
 2  ACCESS DOOR
 3  CASTABLE REFRACTORY
 4  DOWN-PASS
 5  CHANNEL
 6  OVERFLOW
 7  WATER LEVEL
 8  INDUCED DRAFT FAN
 9  UP-PASS
10  DRAIN
```

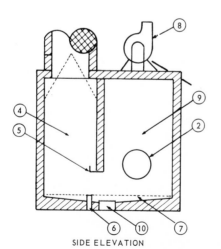

NOTES:

CASTABLE REFRACTORY - 135 lb/ft.³

EXTERIOR STEEL - 3/16 in. PLATE.

NOZZLES - STAINLESS STEEL.

FAN - 600° F RATING.

CHANNEL - 4 in.

FLOOR - 4-degree SLOPE TO DRAIN.

+FOUR NOZZLES ON '0' DIMENSION DIAMETER FOR SIZES 500 TO 1000 lb/hr.

*ONE NOZZLE FOR INCINERATOR SIZES 50 TO 250 lb/hr.

SIDE ELEVATION

Fig. 8-1. Design recommendations for retort incinerator scrubbers.

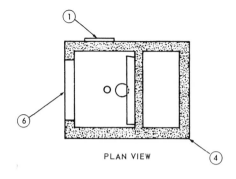

PLAN VIEW

1 ACCESS DOOR
2 PRIMARY SPRAYS
3 SECONDARY SPRAYS
4 CASTABLE REFRACTORY
5 DOWN-PASS
6 EFFLUENT INLET
7 INDUCED DRAFT FAN
8 WATER LEVEL
9 OVERFLOW
10 UP-PASS
11 CHANNEL
12 DRAIN

NOTES:

CASTABLE REFRACTORY - 135 lb/ft.^{3}

EXTERIOR STEEL - 3/16 in. PLATE.

NOZZLES - STAINLESS STEEL.

FAN - 600° F RATING.

CHANNEL - 4 in.

FLOOR - 4-degree SLOPE TO DRAIN.

*ALL SPRAY NOZZLES TO BE EQUALLY
SPACED WITHIN THE N DIMENSION

SIDE ELEVATION

Fig. 8-2. Design recommendations for in-line incinerator scrubbers.

Water in the base of the scrubber collects fly ash and other materials removed from the gas stream may be easily deposited and retained. The water depth is maintained at approximately 3 inches by extending the end of the overflow pipe 3 inches above the floor of the scrubber. Another drain pipe should be installed at floor level so that fly ash and other solids can be washed down the sloping floor of the scrubber.

Design parameters recommended are as follows:

1. The water rate to the scrubber should be 1 gallon per minute for every 100 pounds per hour of rated capacity of the incinerator. This gives a water-to-gas ratio of 1 gallon per minute for every 400 standard cubic feet of effluent stack gas.
2. Configuration of scrubbers for retort and in-line incinerators are given in Figures 8-1 and 8-2, respectively. A graph showing internal areas of the various ports in scrubbers versus incinerator size is given in Figure 8-3.

8.3 Scrubber Controls

While it is recommended that the scrubber controls described herein be

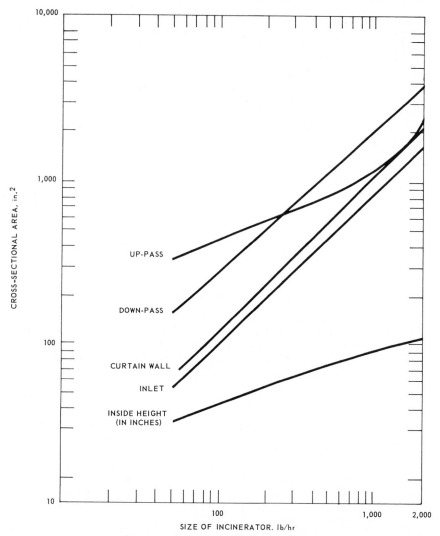

Fig. 8-3. Internal sizing of scrubbers.

installed, it should be realized that a special maintenance and testing program must be established to keep the control systems in good operating condition.

Many types of automatic controls are used to regulate the temperature of the gases leaving the scrubber. Satisfactory controls, which have proved to be both simple and economical, consist of a hand-operated control valve and two automatic solenoid valves. The hand-operated valve is installed in parallel with the solenoid valves between the water supply and the nozzles.

The solenoid valves are electrically connected so that one opens when the fan is placed in operation. The flow of water through this valve is adjusted to approximately 40 percent of the scrubber needs. The other valve is controlled by a thermocouple located at the fan inlet. When the temperature at the fan inlet reaches 220° F, the second solenoid valve opens and the remainder of the water is delivered to the nozzles. This arrangement is used to keep the temperature of the gases from exceeding 350° F. Should the automatic control system fail, the operator may open the hand valve and furnish sufficient water to the scrubber.

A back-up system also may be installed to prevent heat damage to the fan in case the automatic system just described fails. One such system frequently used consists of a thermocouple located at the fan inlets and additional solenoid-valve-controlled nozzles located in either the downpass or the uppass of the scrubber. The nozzles should be capable of supplying at least the same quantity of water as the combined volume of the primary and secondary sprays. Should the temperature at the fan inlet exceed 500° F, the back-up solenoid valve opens, and the full volume of water flows to the nozzles to cool the effluent to an acceptable level. As a final precaution, a warning alarm, actuated at 550° F, by a thermocouple at the fan inlet, may be installed to alert the operator to excessive temperature increases.

Back-up systems must be tested frequently so that they are operable when the need arises. Consequently, a safety system of this type would be of doubtful value unless a regular maintenance and testing program were established.

8.4 Scrubber Construction

The steel exterior of the scrubber should be constructed of ³⁄₁₆-inch-thick steel plate. Hangers should be mounted on the walls and top of the scrubber on 9-inch centers to hold the lining firmly to the walls. Linings of 135-pound-per-cubic-foot castable refractory should be 3 inches thick for incinerators with capacities of 750 pounds per hour or less. Units with capacities in excess of 750 pounds per hour should utilize 4-inch linings. The castable refractory floor should be sloped upward from the center of the scrubber at a 4-degree angle to facilitate the removal of collected fly ash and solids. The primary spray nozzles should be of the flat-spray type so that water droplets do not enter the connecting breeching and damage the refractory in the final combustion chamber of the incinerator. The secondary nozzles should be of the full cone type with a discharge angle of approximately 60 degrees. Nozzles mounted within the inlet duct should be provided with an access opening for cleaning or replacement. Nozzles mounted in the top of the unit should be installed out of the hot gas stream and should be removable from the exterior of the scrubber. Nozzles should be constructed of brass or stainless steel.

8.5 Induced-draft Fan

8.5.1 General

The induced-draft fan should be constructed of mild steel and be capable of withstanding 600° F. The fan should be capable of at least two-speed operation or have a variable speed drive that is adjustable from maximum delivery volume to one-third of maximum delivery volume. Controls of this type permit the operator to reduce the volume handled by the fan when the incinerator is operating at less than the rated capacity. The resultant reduction in cooling in turn will increase the operating temperature within the incinerator and reduce the possibility of water carry-over from the scrubber. The controls for such a fan should be readily accessible to the operator so that he can reduce the fan speed and thus increase the overall efficiency of the incinerator. The fan housing should have a cleanout door and a water drain.

8.5.2 *Design Parameters*

8.5.2.1 VOLUME REQUIREMENTS—The fan should be sized to deliver 700 cubic feet per minute of gas at 350° F for every 100 pounds per hour refuse capacity of the incinerator.

8.5.2.2 STATIC PRESSURE REQUIREMENTS—The fan should provide ½ inch of water static pressure, at 350°F, for a 50-pound-per-hour incinerator. Its ability to develop static pressure should increase uniformly so that it will develop 1½ inches of water, at 350° F, for a 2000-pound-per-hour incinerator. Fans operating at 350° F develop approximately two-thirds of the static pressure for which they are rated at ambient temperatures. Consequently, the induced-draft fan selected should be able to develop static pressures 50 percent higher than those desired at 350° F. For example, a fan selected for a 50-pound-per-hour incinerator should develop a static pressure of ¾ inch of water at ambient temperatures, and a fan for a 2000-pound-per-hour incinerator should develop a static pressure of 2¼ inches water at ambient temperatures.

8.5.2.3 HORSEPOWER REQUIREMENTS—The horsepower requirements of the fan should be based upon the full capacity of the fan at ambient temperature, not at 350° F.

8.5.2.4 BY-PASS ARRANGEMENTS—For inside installations, a by-pass arrangement of breechings, or flue connections with dampers, to by-pass the scrubber and induced-draft fan is recommended.

8.6 MIST ELIMINATORS

Installation of mist eliminators is not usually necessary. There are, however, occasions when water droplets may be discharged from the exhaust fan. Should this be a serious problem, the inclusion of an eliminator section near the top of the uppass is desirable. In general, eliminators need be installed only when the performance of a unit has proved to be unsatisfactory.

8.7 ALTERNATE SCRUBBER DESIGNS

The following criteria should be used in the design of alternate scrubbers or gas washers.

1. The scrubber or gas washer should contain sprays, wetted baffles, or orifices arranged singly or in combination so as not to permit the discharge of particulate matter in violation of the Code of Federal Regulations.
2. Unlined gas washers or scrubbers should have welded or gasketed seams and be corrosion resistant. Lined gas washers or scrubber casings should be made of at least 12-gauge steel and be welded or gasketed. The density of refractory lining should be no less than 120 pounds per cubic foot. The refractory should never be less than 2 inches thick and must be adequately anchored to the casing.
3. Scrubbers requiring an induced-draft fan should have a motor capable of cold startup (70°F). When the impeller of an induced-draft fan is in the gas stream, the fan must be equipped with a cleanout door and drain.
4. Where spray nozzles are employed, an optimum spray pattern must be provided to cover all the area of the gases as they pass through the gas

washer or scrubber. Nozzles and valves should be arranged for independent removal by means of unions or flanges. When water is recirculated, a pressure regulator and a strainer should be provided.

5. An access door for cleanout should be provided on all scrubbers.
6. Interlocks should be provided when induced-draft fans and sprays are used.
7. When the outside skin temperature of a gas washer or scrubber exceeds 260°F, protection should be provided.
8. For inside installations, a by-pass arrangement of breeching, or flue connections with dampers, to by-pass the scrubber and induced-draft fan is recommended.

9 RECOMMENDATIONS FOR CONSTRUCTION

This Guide sets forth minimum construction standards. When a designer feels additional strength or resistive qualities are required because of special applications, he should include them in his specifications. It is not, however, the intent of this Guide to preclude the use of specialty refractory materials for construction even though such special refractory does not have all the resistive qualities of the refractories outlined herein. Such refractory material may be used in certain areas where its special characteristics are of particular advantage, provided the materials have all the resistive qualities required for the area. For example, where weight of the structure is an important factor, insulating firebrick or insulating castable refractory may be used, but they cannot be used in any area where they will be subject to abrasion from tools, materials, or high-velocity gases.

9.1 MATERIALS OF CONSTRUCTION

Throughout this section reference is made to refractories in an abbreviated manner such as high heat duty and super duty. For exactitude, the American Society for Testing and Materials (ASTM) specifications for these materials follows.

9.1.1 *High-Temperature Block Insulation*
The high-temperature block insulation required by this Guide is in accordance with ASTM Designation C-392-63 Class 2 and has the following physical properties:

Density	14 to 20 lb/ft^3
Service temperature	up to 1800°F
Moisture absorption	nil
Fire resistance	incombustible
Linear shrinkage at 1800°F. (max.)	4.0 percent

Thermal conductivity in Btu per inch per square foot (maximum) per hour is as follows:

200°F mean temperature	0.36
600°F mean temperature	0.51
1000°F mean temperature	0.755

9.1.2 *High-Heat-Duty Firebrick*
The high-heat-duty firebrick required by this Guide is classified as spall

resistant in accordance with ASTM Designation C-106-67. It has the following physical properties:

Pyrometric cone equivalent	31½ minimum
Panel spalling loss (2910°F)	10 percent
Modulus of rupture	500 psi minimum

9.1.3 *Super-Duty Firebrick*

The super-duty firebrick required by this Guide is classified as spall resistant in accordance with ASTM Designation C-106-67. It has the following physical properties:

Pyrometic cone equivalent	33 minimum
Panel spalling loss (3000°F)	4 percent maximum
Reheat shrinkage (2910°F)	1 percent maximum
Modulus of rupture	600 psi minimum

9.1.4 *Class C Hydraulic Castable Refractory*

The hydraulic setting castable refractory required to meet the minimum standards of this Guide is in accordance with ASTM Designation C-213-66 Class C and has the following physical properties:

Service temperature	2600°F maximum
Permanent linear shrinkage	1.5 percent after heating to 2500°F for 5 hours
Modulus of rupture	300 psi after drying to 220°F

9.1.5 *Class D Hydraulic Castable Refractory*

The hydraulic setting castable refractory required to perform satisfactorily in areas of high-heat flux, such as in the arches of pathological incinerators, should meet the provisions of ASTM Designation C-213-66 Class D and have the following physical properties:

Service temperature	2800°F maximum
Permanent linear shrinkage	1.5 percent after heating to 2700°F for 5 hours
Modulus of rupture	300 psi after drying to 220°F

9.1.6 *Use of Castable Refractories*

All castable refractory walls should be installed to form a monolithic structure and should be anchored to the exterior shell of the incinerator. Suspended arches should be constructed so that their weight does not rest on the refractory walls. Alloy steel or refractory anchors should be used and spaced not more than 24 inches horizontally and vertically, and in accordance with the refractory manufacturer's recommendations.

All such castable material should be delivered to the job site in containers with the manufacturer's name and instructions stamped thereon. The manufacturer's written instructions should be followed for the preparation and application, and also for its curing.

9.1.7 *Insulation Castable Refractories*

Although other types of insulating castable refractories may be used as their resistive properties warrant, two classes, one for areas receiving direct-flame radiation, and the other for areas that do not normally receive direct-flame radiation, are recommended herein.

9.1.7.1 CLASS Q INSULATING CASTABLE—Where weight is a problem, as in an after-burner, and there is no abrasion from tools, materials, or gases, and the refractory is to receive direct-flame radiation, the minimum refractory employed must not be less resistive than that given in ASTM Designation C-401-60 for Class Q Insulating Castables. Certain physical properties of this class follow:

Permanent linear shrinkage	1.5 percent maximum when fired at 2300°F for 5 hours
Maximum bulk density	95 lb/ft³ after drying to 220°F

9.1.7.2 CLASS O INSULATING CASTABLES—Where there is no abrasion from tools, materials, or gases and the refractory will not normally receive direct-flame radiation, as in a stack, the minimum refractory employed must not be less resistive than that given in ASTM Designation C-401-60 for Class O Insulating Castables. Certain physical properties of this class follow:

Permanent linear shrinkage	1.5 percent maximum when fired at 1900°F for 5 hours
Maximum bulk density	65 lb/ft³ after drying to 220°F

9.1.8 Air-Setting Plastic Refractory

Two types of air-setting plastic refractory are specified by ASTM Designation C-176-67: high duty and super duty. The high-duty material represents the minimum type of air-setting plastic refractory recommended by this Guide. The super-duty material is recommended for use in areas of high-heat flux, such as the arches of pathological incinerators.

9.1.8.1 HIGH-DUTY PLASTIC REFRACTORY—The high-duty air-setting plastic refractory required by this Guide is in accordance with ASTM Designation C-176-67. It has the following physical properties:

Water content	15 percent maximum as received
Workability index	15-35 percent deformation
Pyrometric cone equivalent	31 minimum
Maximum reheat shrinkage	3 percent
Panel spalling loss	15 percent (2910°F)

9.1.8.2 SUPER-DUTY PLASTIC REFRACTORY—The super-duty air-setting plastic refractory recommended by this Guide is in accordance with ASTM Designation C-176-67. It has the following properties:

Water content	15 percent maximum as received
Workability index	15-35 percent deformation
Pyrometric cone equivalent	32½ minimum
Maximum reheat shrinkage	2.5 percent
Panel spalling loss	5 percent (3000°F)

9.1.9 Use of Air-Setting Plastic Refractories

All plastic refractory walls should be installed to form a monolithic structure and should be anchored to the exterior shell of the incinerator.

Suspended arches should be constructed so that their weight does not rest on the refractory walls. Alloy steel or refractory anchors should be used and spaced not more than 24 inches horizontally and vertically, and should be of flexible design, and installed according to the refractory manufacturer's instructions.

The plastic refractory should be delivered to the job site in containers with the manufacturer's name and instructions stamped thereon. The manufacturer's written instructions should be followed in preparing and applying the plastic and also in its curing and baking.

9.1.10 Air-Setting Refractory Mortar

The air-setting refractory mortar required by this Guide should meet the requirements for the high duty classification under ASTM Designation C-178-47 (1958). The mortar should have the following physical properties:

Refractoriness test temperature	2730°F
Maximum water content	25 percent
Bonding strength of joints	200 psi
Particle size	95 percent <No. 40 ASTM sieve
	0.5 percent >No. 20 ASTM sieve

If super-duty refractories are used, it is recommended that mortars meet the super-duty class of ASTM Designation C-178-47 (1958).

9.1.11 ASTM Standards

Should questions arise about specifications for any refractory or insulation construction, they may be resolved by reference to the appropriate ASTM Designation referred to above. Where ASTM Designations are modified, the latest modification should be followed.

9.2 GENERAL REFUSE INCINERATORS

There are as many methods of erecting the walls of a multiple-chamber incinerator as there are materials from which to build them. The exterior of the incinerator may be either brick or steel plate construction. Refractory lining may be firebrick, castable refractory, or plastic firebrick. Protection of exterior walls from extreme temperature conditions may be provided by either peripheral air space, air cooling passages, or insulation. Stacks, in small to medium size incinerators (less than 750 pounds per hour refuse) may be mounted directly on the incinerator, may be free standing, or may be an integral part of the building structure of the incinerator.

Incinerators with capacities of 500 pounds per hour or less, will usually be prefabricated. Larger size units, and some specially designed smaller units, are erected on the site.

The most important element of multiple-chamber incinerator construction, other than the basic design, is the proper installation and use of refractories. The manufacturer must use suitable construction materials and be experienced in high-temperature furnace fabrication and refractory installation. Service conditions should dictate the type of lining for any furnace when a choice of available materials is made.

9.2.1 Refractories for Walls and Arches

The minimum refractory specification recommended for firebrick used in walls and arches of incinerators is the classification of high-heat duty. Fire-brick should be laid in air-setting high temperature cement. Equivalent duty hydraulic-setting castable refractory and air-setting plastic refractory should be suitably anchored to the exterior wall.

Recommended minimum exterior wall thickness of incinerators is as fol-lows:

1. Up to and including 500 lb/hr refuse capacity all refractories, whether firebrick, castable, or plastic, should be a minimum of 4¼ inches thick.
2. Over 500 lb/hr of refuse capacity, all refractories should be a minimum of 9 inches thick.

The minimum thickness of interior refractory walls (i.e., those walls in-side the incinerator, the bridge wall, curtain wall, or parting wall) will generally follow the recommendations for the exterior walls. The bridge wall, with its internal secondary air distribution channels, will require greater thickness. The minimum width of refractory material between the air channel and the ignition or charging chamber, should never be less than 2½ inches in the very small size units, 4½ inches in units up to 250 pounds per hour, and 9 inches in units larger than 250 pounds per hour.

Sufficient expansion joints in the refractory construction are necessary to prevent bulging and destruction of the walls and arches. Each foot of wall made with firebrick clay refractory will expand when heated and contract when cooled from ⅟₁₆ to ³⁄₃₂ inch. Provisions for vertical expansion should be sufficient between the arch and sidewalls to allow for the vertical movement. Horizontal expansion of the various vertical walls will have to be provided for. No hard and fast rules may be laid down for the provision of expansion joints. Their proper design requires complex calculation based on the ex-perience of the contractor and engineering knowledge.

9.2.2 *Insulation Requirements*

Where the incinerator is constructed with a steel plate exterior wall, insula-tion must be used between the refractory wall and the steel plate. A high-temperature insulating block should be used. Minimum thickness for insulation is 2 inches. Units larger than 500 pounds per hour should have 2½ inches. Loose-fill insulation is not satisfactory because of its packing into the lower portion of the unit over long periods of time. When the exterior wall is of regular clay brick construction, a minimum of 1 inch air space between the exterior brick and the refractory brick, with adequate venting of the insulat-ing air space should be provided.

9.2.3 *Exterior Casing*

Minimum thickness of steel plates used for the exterior casing of multiple-chamber incinerators should be 12 gauge. The steel casing and the structural framework should be erected and set plumb before any brickwork is started. The exterior, or steel casing, should be reinforced with structural members, or if the exterior is brick, should be reinforced with structural steel to withstand interior thrusts from all arches and to support all doors, burners, and ap-purtenant assemblies. Exterior brick walls and casings must conform to mini-mum building code structural requirements, but in no instance, where clay or shale brick is used, should the exterior walls be less than 8 inches thick.

9.2.4 *Floors*

The thickness of refractory lining and insulation for the floors of multiple-chamber incinerators is dependent primarily on their physical location.

For incinerators installed on their own concrete foundations outside of build-ings, 2½ inches of firebrick lining backed by 1½ inches of high-temperature insulating material will be satisfactory. Heat transfer through this insulation will be high; but if the concrete pad cracks, only minor damage will occur. Portable incinerators mounted on 4-inch channels will have sufficient air space provided beneath the incinerator to eliminate possible damage to the pad. When incinerators are installed within buildings, provisions should be made to prevent physical damage to the building. Building damage can be eliminated by providing cooling passages beneath the incinerator, thus pre-venting excessive heat from reaching the structure. Additional insulation should be provided within the floor of the incinerator when cooling passages are not feasible. For incinerators up to 500 pounds per hour, 4½ inches of firebrick and 2½ inches of insulation should be provided on the floor of the mixing and final combustion chambers. For incinerators with capacities of 500 to 2000 pounds per hour, 4½ inches of firebrick backed by 4 inches of in-sulation should be provided.

9.2.5 Foundations

Foundation requirements for all incinerators are determined by the weight of the incinerator and the soil conditions. The prefabricated, portable units have sufficient air space between them and the foundation to prevent any problem. The on-site constructed units must provide either air insulation or a layer of insulating material.

Prefabricated incinerators should have a minimum of three heavy supports beneath their floors to provide support for their three bearing walls and to permit them to be moved safely.

When incinerators are mounted on floors, the floors should be of fire-resis-tant construction with no combustible material against the underside of the floor, or on fire-resistant slabs or arches having no combustible material against the underside thereof. Such construction should extend not less than 3 feet beyond the appliance on all sides, and it should extend not less than 8 feet at the front or side where ashes are removed.

9.2.6 Charging Doors

Guillotine charging doors used in the recommended design should be lined with refractory material with a minimum service temperature of 2600°F. Units of less than 100 pounds per hour capacity should have door linings at least 2 inches thick. In the size range of 100 to 350 pounds per hour, lining thick-ness should be increased to 3 inches. From 350 pounds per hour to 1000 pounds per hour, the doors should be lined with 4 inches of refractory. On units of 1000 pounds per hour and larger, linings should be 6 inches thick.

9.2.7 Grates

Grates should be made of cast iron and weigh at least 40 pounds per square foot. They should have at least 40 percent open area. Because the length of the ignition chamber increases as the size of the incinerator increases, especially in incinerators larger than 750 pounds per hour, the rear section of the grate is difficult to keep completely covered. The use of a solid hearth at the rear of the ignition chamber in these units is therefore good practice. Hearths at this location prevent open areas from being formed in the refuse pile that is normally thin at the rear of a long ignition chamber. The solid hearth prevents excessive underfire air from entering immediately in front of the bridge wall. Such underfire air will quench the hot gases and cause excessive carryover of ash and unburned material into the mixing chamber.

Sloping grates (grates that slant down from the front to the rear of the ignition chamber) facilitate proper charging. The sloping grate results in an increased distance between the arch and the grate at the rear of the chamber, reducing the amount of fly ash entrainment.

9.2.8 *Air Inlets*

All combustion air inlets should provide positive control. While round "spinner" controls with rotating shutters should be used for both underfire and overfire air openings in retort incinerators, they should only be used for underfire air openings in the in-line incinerator. Rectangular ports with butterfly or hinged dampers should be provided for all secondary air openings and overfire air openings of in-line incinerators. All air inlet structures should be of cast iron. Sliding rectangular dampers become inoperative and should not be used.

9.2.9 *Flues*

When flue gas temperature is not reduced, flue connections or breechings must be constructed with a Number 12 U. S. gauge steel exterior, lined with refractory, and provided with a guillotine or horizontal sliding damper. Flue connections and breechings having an internal cross-section of not more than 350 square inches should have high heat duty refractory lining 2½ inches thick, and high heat duty refractory 4½ inches thick for those having an internal cross-section of more than 350 square inches. Guillotine dampers provided for draft regulation should be properly counterbalanced, and horizontal dampers should be equipped with suitable rollers and tracks to insure easy operation. The dampers should be constructed of a steel frame with refractory lining or they may be constructed entirely of alloy steel to withstand the high temperature. All such dampers should be provided with a damper box constructed of Number 12 U. S. gauge steel to completely house the damper when in its open position. When a barometric damper is also provided, its free area should not be less than the percentage of the cross-sectional area of the flue connection, breeching, or stack in which it is located. Gas velocity in any flue connection or breeching should not exceed 30 feet per second, calculated at 1400°F.

9.2.10 *Chimneys (Stacks)*

The construction of incinerator chimneys (stacks) may vary from location to location, and local building and fire protection codes must be consulted. All chimneys exposed or partially exposed to wind load should be designed to withstand the dynamic load imposed by 100-mile-per-hour wind in addition to the dead load.

Incinerator chimneys should extend not less than 4 feet above a sloping roof measured from the highest point of penetration of the chimney through the roof and at least 8 feet above a flat roof. In no case shall the chimney (stack) be less than 2 feet above any obstruction or portion of the building within a 20-foot radius. Local codes should be consulted for regulations requiring greater heights than those given herein.

Prefabricated refractory-lined chimneys, or stacks, with the refractory providing the structural strength, may be used. The thickness of the refractory lining and the class of refractory used should be in accordance with the Underwriters Laboratory approved listing. The exterior jacket should be a minimum of 28 gauge galvanized steel or stainless steel. Adequate support, without placing any of the load on the refractory walls of the incinerator, must be provided for any stack installed on top of an incinerator.

Prefabricated steel refractory-lined chimneys, or stacks, with the steel casing providing the structural strength, may be used. The steel casing should be designed in accordance with acceptable structural design practice and the thickness of the steel should not be less than shown in Table 9-1.

Table 9-1

MINIMUM THICKNESS FOR STEEL STACK WALLS

Stock diameter, inches	Thickness
Up to 28	12 gauge
29 to 48	$\frac{3}{16}$ inch
49 to 80	$\frac{1}{4}$ inch

The refractory lining should conform to ASTM Classification C-401-60 Class Q. The thickness of the refractory lining should not be less than shown in Table 9-2.

Table 9-2

MINIMUM REFRACTORY STACK LINING THICKNESS

Stock diameter, inches	Thickness, inches
Up to 28	2
29 to 48	3
49 to 80	4

The refractory lining should be secured to the steel shell by means of stainless steel anchors or steel shelf angles. The spacing of the anchors should not be more than 24 inches on centers with a minimum of 4 anchors per perimeter.

Firebrick-lined steel chimneys or stacks should be constructed of not less then 12 gauge steel and should be designed in accordance with acceptable structural steel practices. The steel shell should have a 4½-inch firebrick lining for the full height.

Masonry chimneys or stacks may be used, but in no case should the firebrick lining be anchored to the exterior masonry shell. A clear air space must be provided between the exterior shell and the firebrick lining.

Brick masonry chimneys or stacks should be constructed with a minimum wall thickness of 8 inches of common brick with a 4½-inch-thick firebrick lining for the full height.

Concrete chimneys or stacks should be constructed with a minimum shell thickness of 6 inches of concrete and with a 4½-inch-thick firebrick lining for the full height

Stone chimneys or stacks should be constructed with a minimum wall thickness of 12 inches of stone masonry with a 4½-inch-thick firebrick lining for the full height.

Radial brick chimneys or stacks should be constructed with a minimum wall thickness of 7½ inches of radial brick with a 4½-inch-thick firebrick lining for the full height.

Unlined steel chimneys or stacks may be used only when flue gas temperatures do not exceed 600°F, and the interior is protected against corrosion from the flue gas by a suitable temperature, moisture, and acid-resistant coating. However, unlined steel chimneys or stacks are not permitted on incinerators with emergency gas washer bypass flues, where the possibility of high-temperature gases in the chimney exists. Corrosion protection of the steel chimney is required because of the presence of moisture in the flue gases carrying an appreciable degree of acidity. Condensation of water vapor with acid characteristics will cause rapid deterioration of steel chimneys, especially on outside installations.

9.2.11 *Clearances*

Incinerators should be installed to provide a clearance to combustible material of not less than 36 inches at the sides and rear, and not less than 48 inches above, and not less than 8 feet at the front of the incinerator; except in the case where an incinerator is encased in brick, then the clearance may be 36 inches at the front and 18 inches at the sides and rear. A clearance of not less than 1 inch should be provided between incinerators and walls or ceilings of noncombustible construction. Walls of the incinerator should never be used as part of the structural walls of the building.

9.2.12 *Incinerator Rooms or Compartments*

1. When the combined hearth and grate area of the combustion chamber of an indoor incinerator is 7 square feet or less, the incinerator should be enclosed within a room that is separated from other parts of the building by walls, floor, and ceiling assemblies having a fire resistance rating of not less than 1 hour, with floor of earth or other noncombustible material, and used for no other purpose other than storage of waste materials and refuse to be burned or building heating equipment. Openings to these rooms should be protected by self-closing or automatic fire doors suitable for Class B situations (metal-clad doors) as defined in National Fire Protection Association Standard 80, Fire Doors and Windows, 1967.
2. Incinerators where the combined hearth and grate area of the combustion chamber exceeds 7 square feet, should be enclosed within a room that is separated from other parts of the building by walls, floor, and ceiling assemblies which are constructed of noncombustible material that has a fire resistance rating of not less than 2 hours and have a floor of earth or other noncombustible material, and used for no other purpose except storage of waste material and refuse to be burned or building heating equipment. Openings to such rooms should be protected by self-closing or automatic fire doors suitable for Class B situations (metal-clad doors) as defined in the National Fire Protection Association Standard No. 80, Fire Doors and Windows, 1967.
3. Automatic sprinklers and a short length of hand hose connected to a suitable water supply are recommended in the incinerator room.

9.2.13 *Rubbish or Refuse Chutes*

Rubbish or refuse chutes should rest on substantial noncombustible foundations. Thickness of enclosing walls of refuse chutes should be 8 inches of shale brickwork or clay, or 6 inches of reinforced concrete. Such chutes should extend at least 4 feet above the roof and be covered by a metal skylight, glazed with thin plain glass.

9.2.14 *Chute Terminal Rooms or Bins*

1. Rubbish or refuse chutes should terminate in, or discharge directly into, a room or bin that is separated from the incinerator room and from other parts of the building, by walls, floor, and ceiling assemblies that

have a fire resistance rating equal to chute specifications. Openings to such rooms or bins should be protected by self-closing or automatic fire doors suitable for Class B situations (metal-clad doors), as defined in the National Fire Protection Association Standard No. 80, Fire Doors and Windows, 1967.

2. Properly installed automatic sprinklers provide a reliable and effective means for fire extinguishment and should be installed in all chute terminal rooms or bins, particularly where combustible waste is handled. A short length of hand hose connected to a suitable water supply should also be provided. Fires occurring at chute terminals are usually difficult to control because of the large amount of smoke evolved, causing access by the fire department to be difficult. Automatic extinguishment of such fires in the early stage is therefore of primary importance.

9.2.15 *Ventilation of Incinerator Rooms*

Rooms containing incinerators should be supplied with an adequate amount of air for combustion and ventilation. Air supply may be furnished by one of the following means:

1. A screened or louvered ventilator opening, or other suitable air intake. If communicating to other parts of the building the opening should be protected by a fire damper.
2. A duct leading from the incinerator room to the outside.
3. A duct leading to a boiler or furnace room as prescribed in Section 9.2.12 for incinerators of a given capacity, with sufficient air supply provided for both rooms.

Ducts extending from an incinerator room to other parts of a building should be constructed and protected in accordance with the National Fire Protection Association Standard No. 90A, Installation of Air Conditioning and Ventilating Systems of Other than Residence Type.

9.3 PATHOLOGICAL INCINERATORS

The general discussion for the construction, insulation, and refractory specifications of multiple-chamber incinerators given in Section 9.2, will cover most of the problems to be found in constructing pathological incinerators. The use of super-duty refractories, particularly in the arches of these units, is desirable. Refractory walls, roof, hearth, parting wall, curtain wall, and baffles should not be less than 4½ inches thick for incinerators with a capacity up to 150 pounds per hour. Incinerators with a capacity of over 150 pounds per hour should have at least 9-inch thick refractory in walls, roof, hearth, parting wall, curtain wall, or baffles.

Hearth construction must have the physical strength to sustain maximum loads of elevated temperatures. Initial charges for pathological waste incinerators could have a total weight in excess of the hourly capacity of the unit; therefore, hearths should be designed for loadings of at least twice the hourly burning rate.

10   MISCELLANEOUS RECOMMENDATIONS

10.1 STACK VIEWER

When possible, it is advisable to arrange a system of mirrors to allow an incinerator operator, who would otherwise be unable to see the top of the stack because of his location, to view the stack outlet.

10.2 Recommendations for Sampling Ports

Each new incinerator stack should have two sampling ports 3½ inches in diameter. Each port should be positioned in the stack at right angles to each other. They should be located, when possible, eight to ten stack diameters downstream from any bend or disturbance of gas flow, and two stack diameters upstream of the exit of the stack. The ports should be provided with suitable removable, replaceable caps.

11 OPERATING PROCEDURES

11.1 General-refuse Incinerators Without Scrubbers

The emission control of the multiple-chamber incinerator is built in. Even so, the discharge of smoke or solid contaminants is in large measure a function of the action of the operator, and to some degree, the type of material charged. Smoke control is attained by the proper admission of air for combustion and by proper utilization of secondary burners, where the refuse has a low heating value or a high moisture content. Use of the secondary burners is required occasionally to maintain the combustion efficiency of the secondary chamber. Proper functioning of this chamber depends upon luminous flames and a temperature adequate for gaseous-phase combustion. Use of secondary burners is readily determined by observations of the flame travel from the ignition chamber, and flame coverage at both the flameport and the curtain wall port.

Before any incinerator is placed into operation, the grate and the ash pit beneath should be cleaned and the damper properly adjusted. Incinerators with full ash pits concentrate heat on the grates, causing them to soften, bend, and even fall from their mountings.

The secondary burner, or burners, should be ignited a few minutes before the incinerator is charged in order to heat the secondary chambers. The charging and clean-out doors should be closed, and the air ports open during this preheating period. Should the flames from the secondary burners be driven upward and through the flameport when ignited, instead of downward through the mixing chamber in incinerators with natural draft, the burners should be shut off. To overcome this problem, a small piece of paper may be inserted through the clean-out door in the combustion chamber, and ignited. The door is then closed and the secondary burners are re-ignited. The burning paper in the combustion chamber will direct the movement of air up the stack and result in proper operation of the burners.

The overfire and underfire air ports should usually be approximately half-open at lightoff. They should be opened gradually to an open position, as the incinerator reaches stable operation at its rated burning capacity. Air admission is usually not critical during normal incineration.

The most important single aspect of the operation of multiple-chamber incinerators is the charging of the refuse into the ignition chamber. Proper charging is necessary to reduce the issuance of fly ash, to maintain adequate flame coverage of the burning rubbish pile and the flameport, and to prevent the fuel bed from becoming too thin at the rear of the ignition chamber in the larger units.

The initial charge should fill the ignition chamber with refuse to a depth of one-half to three-quarters the distance between the pile below the flameport opening. The initial charge should be ignited at the top rear of the pile below the flameport opening, and the charging door closed. The primary burners in the ignition chamber are used when the refuse is very moist. If use of this burner is required, care should be exercised to prevent the blocking of the primary burner by the refuse pile.

When approximately one-half of the initial refuse charge has been burned, the remaining refuse may be carefully stoked. The burning refuse should then be pushed as far as possible to the rear of the grates. This operation should be performed carefully to prevent excessive emission of fly ash. Additional refuse may now be charged to the incinerator. The new refuse should be charged at the front section of the grates but not on top of the burning pile already in the incinerator. This method of charging will prevent smothering the fire and will maintain live flames over the entire rear half of the chamber, filling the flameport and extending well into the mixing chamber. Flames will propagate evenly over the surface of the newly charged material, minimizing the possibility of smoke emissions. This method of charging also minimizes the necessity of stoking or otherwise disturbing the burning pile, so that little, if any, fly ash is emitted. After the waste material has been charged into the incinerator, the unit enters the "burn-down" phase of its operation. When the last charge has been reduced to one-half, or less, of its original size, all air port openings to the incinerator are reduced to one-half open. The secondary burners are always left on, until the issuance of smoke from any material remaining on the grates has ceased. At this time, all burners are shut off.

When incinerators are burning only paper, caution is always exercised to insure that the burning pile at the rear of the grate does not become too thin. Should this happen, excessive underfire air admitted at this point quenches the hot gases entering the flameport, reduces combustion and produces smoke with as high as 100 percent opacity. Use of adequate secondary burners will prevent the incomplete combustion resulting from the thin bed at the rear of the ignition chamber.

Smoke emissions around the charging door or ash pit door, or both, usually result from overcharging. The following steps, in sequence, have been found to successfully eliminate smoke:

1. Check damper adjustment.
2. Shut off the primary burner, if operating.
3. Observe the burning pile, and move any material blocking the flame port.
4. Make sure that the clean-out doors, or doors in any of the secondary chambers of the incinerator, are closed. Any air port on these doors should also be closed.
5. Allow the fuel bed to burn down to normal operating depth, and do not overcharge the incinerator again.

White smoke appearing at the incinerator stack is usually caused by excess air entering the incinerator. The following steps, in sequence, have been found to eliminate white smoke:

1. Check damper adjustment.
2. Ignite the secondary chamber burner, or check to see that it is still burning.
3. Close the secondary air port, or ports.
4. Close the underfire air port.
5. Reduce the overfire air port opening.
6. If all the secondary burner capacity is not being used, gradually increase the operating rate of the burner until full capacity is reached.

7. If all of these operations fail to stop the issuance of white smoke, examine the material to be charged. Possibly the white smoke is the result of finely divided mineral material present in the charge and being carried out the stack. Paper sacks that contain pigments or other metallic oxides, and minerals such as calcium chloride, cause white smoke.

Black smoke is usually caused by insufficient amounts of air for combustion, or a burning rate greatly in excess of the capacity of the incinerator. The following steps, in sequence, have been found to eliminate this black smoke:

1. Check damper adjustment.
2. Shut off the primary burner, or burners, if in operation.
3. Open the secondary air port, or ports.
4. Open the overfire air port.
5. Either ignite the secondary chamber burner, or check to see that it is still burning.
6. If the black smoke still continues, gradually open the charging door until it is approximately one-quarter open.
7. Should these steps fail to eliminate the black smoke, examine the material remaining to be charged. Highly combustible materials (i.e., rubber, plastics, etc.) that are charged in too great a proportion to the other refuse, will result in a too rapid combustion rate for the incinerator to handle. These materials may be charged in very small quantities and in relatively small pieces along with general refuse. If such materials must be burned frequently, experimentation as to the quantity that may be charged along with other materials, may be necessary. Generally, highly combustible materials must be charged at less than 10 percent by weight of the total charge.

11.2 GENERAL-REFUSE INCINERATORS WITH SCRUBBERS

11.2.1 *Incinerator Operation*
Operation of the incinerator is the same as described under Section 11.1.

11.2.2 *Scrubber Operation*
The fan should be started before either the burner or refuse is ignited. If the interlock system described in Section 8.3 has not been supplied, water should be manually turned on to the scrubber. After the fan and water have been started, burners and refuse may be ignited. If the electrical interlock system described in Section 8.3 is installed, the water will flow to the nozzles when the fan is started.

If, during the operation of the system, the alarm sounds to indicate too high a fan temperature, the primary chamber burners should be shut off, charging stopped, and the door and air ports opened to cool the incinerator. The secondary burners may also be turned off to reduce the fan temperature to the point where the alarm will cease operating.

Maintenance should be conducted on a regular basis. The scrubber basin should be drained and cleaned daily. Nozzles, pumps, and the backup system should be checked weekly.

16 BIBLIOGRAPHY

1. Code of Federal Regulations, Subchapter F, Title 42, Part 76.
2. I.I.A. Standards, Incinerator Institute of America, New York, New York, November 1968.
3. Contract Number PH27-66-B9 with the Los Angeles County Air Pollution Control District, 1966.
4. Multiple-Chamber Incinerator Design Standards for Los Angeles County, J. E. Williamson et al. Los Angeles County Air Pollution Control District, October 1960.
5. Source Testing Manual, Los Angeles County Air Pollution Control District, November 1963.
6. Air Pollution Effects of Incinerator Firing Practices and Combustion Air Distribution. A. M. Rose, Jr., et al. Journal of the Air Pollution Control Association, February 1959.
7. Cincinnati Ordinance No. 119-1965, Division J, Section 2509-8.
8. Stack Gas Sampling Improved and Simplified with New Equipment. W. S. Smith, et al. Presented at the 60th Annual Meeting of the Air Pollution Control Association, June 1967, Cleveland, Ohio.
9. Specifications for Incineration Testing at Federal Facilities. U. S. Department of Health, Education, and Welfare, Public Health Service, Bureau of Disease Prevention and Environmental Control, National Center for Air Pollution, Abatement Program, Durham, N. C., October 1967.
10. Addendum to Specifications for Incinerator Testing at Federal Facilities. U. S. Department of Health, Education, and Welfare, Public Health Service, Bureau of Disease Prevention and Environmental Control, National Center for Air Pollution Control, Durham, N. C., December 6, 1967.
11. Standard For Incinerators and Rubbish Handling No. 82, National Fire Protection Association, 60 Batterymarch Street, Boston, Massachusetts. May 1960.
12. Standard for the Installation of Air Conditioning and Ventilating Systems No. 90A, National Fire Protection Association, 60 Batterymarch Street, Boston, Massachusetts, 1967.
13. Code for the Installation of Heat Producing Appliances, Heating, Ventilating, Air Conditioning, Blower and Exhaust Systems, American Insurance Association, 85 John Street, New York, New York, 1967.
14. Standard for Fire Doors and Windows, No. 80, National Fire Protection Association, 60 Batterymarch Street, Boston, Massachusetts, 1967.
15. Standard for the Installation of Oil Burning Equipment No. 31, National Fire Protection Association, 60 Batterymarch Street, Boston, Massachusetts, 1965.
16. Standard for the Installation of Gas Appliances and Gas Piping No. 54, National Fire Protection Association, 60 Batterymarch Street, Boston, Massachusetts, 1964.
17. 1967 Book of ASTM Standards, Part 13, Refractories, Glass, and Other Ceramic Materials; Manufactured Carbon and Graphite Products, American Society for Testing and Materials, Philadelphia, Pennsylvania, April 1967.
18. 1967 Book of ASTM Standards, Part 14, Thermal Insulation; Acoustical Materials; Joint Sealants; Fire Tests; and Building Constructions, American Society for Testing and Materials, Philadelphia, Pennsylvania, August 1968.
19. Incinerator Institute of America, Bulletin T-6 Incinerator Testing, August 1968.

SELECTED BIBLIOGRAPHY

SELECTED BIBLIOGRAPHY

Adams, Robert Winthrop. *The Complete Employee: A Handbook for Personnel Appraisal.* Chicago: Public Administration Service, 1959. 72 pp., indexed, illus.

Aerojet-General Corporation. *California Waste Management Study: A Report to the California Department of Public Health.* Report No. 3056 (Final). Azusa, Calif.: The Corporation, 1965. 418 pp.

American Chemical Society, Committee on Chemistry and Public Affairs, Subcommittee on Environmental Improvement. *Cleaning Our Environment: The Chemical Basis for Action.* Washington: The Society, 1969. 249 pp.

American Public Health Association. *Economics of Composting Municipal Refuse in Europe and Israel.* New York: The Association, 1965.

American Public Works Association. "An Evaluation of Household Food Waste Disposers," *Public Works Engineers' Special Report No. 13.* Chicago: APWA, 1951. 33 pp. mimeo.

————. *Proceedings, National Conference on Solid Waste Research.* Chicago: APWA, 1963. 228 pp.

————, Committee on Refuse Collection. *Refuse Collection Practice.* 3rd ed. Chicago: Public Administration Service, 1966. 562 pp.

————, Institute for Solid Wastes. *1966 Proceedings.* Chicago: APWA, 1966. 78 pp.

————, ————. *1967 Proceedings.* Chicago: APWA, 1967. 67 pp.

————, ————. *1968 Proceedings.* Chicago: APWA, 1968. 96 pp.

————, ————. *Papers Prepared for the Fourth Annual Meeting, Criteria for Solid Waste Management.* Chicago: APWA, 1969. 65 pp.

————, Research Foundation. *High Pressure Compaction and Baling of Solid Wastes.* Prepared for the City of Chicago and the Solid Waste Management Bureau of the U.S. Public Health Service. Chicago: APWA, 1969.

————, ————. *Paper Bags for Household Refuse Handling.* A Report on Four Field Trials Employing Disposable Paper Containers. Project No. 115. Chicago: APWA, 1963. 39 pp.

————, ————, Committee on Equipment. *Public Works Equipment Management.* Project No. 116. Chicago: Public Administration Service, 1964. 238 pp.

————, ————. *Rail Transport of Solid Wastes: A Feasibility Study.* Prepared for U.S. Department of Health, Education, and Welfare, Solid Wastes Program, Environmental Control Administration. Chicago: APWA, 1968. 158 pp.

————, ————. *Resource Recovery from Incinerator Residue.* Analysis of Factors that Affect Economic Recycling of Ferrous Metals and Other Inorganic Material Contained in Municipal Incinerator Residue. A Report for the Bureau of Mines, U.S. Department of the Interior. Chicago: APWA, 1969.

509

————, ————. *Solid Wastes in Perspective: Proceedings of a Symposium on Research Needs.* Chicago: APWA, 1966. 18 pp.

————, Street Sanitation Committee. *Street Cleaning Practice.* 2nd ed. Chicago: Public Administration Service, 1959. 424 pp.

American Society of Agricultural Engineers. "Management of Farm Animal Wastes," *Proceedings, National Symposium on Animal Waste Management.* ASAE Pub. No. SP-0366. St. Joseph, Mich.: ASAE, 1966. 161 pp.

American Society of Civil Engineers, Committee on Sanitary Landfill Practice. *Sanitary Landfill.* ASCE Manual of Engineering Practice, No. 39, New York: ASCE, 1959. 62 pp.

————, Sanitary Engineering Research Committee. "Municipal Incinerator Design—A Survey of Engineering Practice," *Proceedings ASCE, Journal of the Sanitary Engineering Division,* 82:SA1:1677 (June, 1958).

————, ————, Rubbish and Garbage Section. "Investigation of Planned Refuse Collection and Disposal," *Proceedings ASCE, Journal of the Sanitary Engineering Division,* 82:SA3:1014 (June, 1956).

————, ————, ————. "Pilot Plant Composting of Municipal Garbage at San Diego, California," *Proceedings ASCE, Journal of the Sanitary Engineering Division,* 82:SA1:887 (February, 1956).

American Society of Mechanical Engineers. *Proceedings, 1966 National Incinerator Conference.* New York: ASME, 1966. 266 pp.

————. *Proceedings, 1968 National Incinerator Conference.* New York: ASME, 1968. 354 pp.

Anderson, Robert J., M.D. "The Public Health Aspects of Solid Waste Disposal," *Public Health Reports* (February, 1964).

"Army Experience with Sanitary Fills," *Engineering News-Record,* 131:829 (December, 1943).

Beckett, John L., and Oakley, Horace R. "Sewage Disposal and Refuse Composting in Leicester, England," *Compost Science,* 6:1:5 (Spring, 1965).

Bjornson, B. F., and Bogue, M.D. "Keeping a Sanitary Landfill Sanitary," *Public Works,* 92:9:112 (September, 1961).

Black, Ralph J. "Solid Wastes Handling," Vol. 2 Chapter 2 of *Environmental Aspects of the Hospital.* U.S. Public Health Service. PHS No. 930-C-16. Washington: Government Printing Office, 1967.

————. "A Review of Sanitary Landfilling Practices in the United States," *Proceedings, Third International Congress, International Research Group on Refuse Disposal.* Trento, Italy: IRGRD, 1965.

————. "Trends in Refuse Disposal Affecting the Swine Industry," *California Vector Views,* 4:1:1 (January, 1957).

————, and Barnes, A. M. "Effect of Earth Cover on Fly Emergence from Sanitary Landfills," *Public Works,* 89:2:91 (February, 1958).

————, and Weaver, Leo. "Action on the Solid Wastes Problem," *Proceedings*

ASCE, Journal of the Sanitary Engineering Division, 93:SA6 (December, 1967).

Blake, Peter. *God's Own Junkyard: The Planned Deterioration of America's Landscape.* New York: Holt, Rinehart and Winston, Inc., 1964. 143 pp.

Brennan, Thomas J. "Financing [Refuse Collection and Disposal Facilities]," *Public Works Engineers' Yearbook, 1954.* Chicago: American Public Works Association, 1954. 316 pp.

Bugher, Robert D. *Solid Wastes Research Needs.* Project No. 113. Chicago: American Public Works Association, 1962. 80 pp.

California State Department of Public Health, Bureau of Vector Control, Solid Waste Engineering Section. *Solid Wastes & Water Quality.* A Study of Solid Wastes Disposal Methods and Their Effect on Water Quality in the San Francisco-Bay-Delta Area. Sacramento: California State Printing Office, 1968.

California State Water Pollution Control Board. *Effects of Refuse Dumps on Ground Water Quality.* CSWPCB Pub. No. 24. Sacramento: California State Printing Office, 1961.

————. *In-Situ Investigation of Movements of Gases Produced from Decomposing Refuse.* CSWPCB Pub. No. 31. Sacramento: California State Printing Office, 1965.

————. *Report on the Investigation of Leaching of a Sanitary Landfill.* CSWPCB Pub. No. 10. Sacramento: State Water Pollution Control Board, 1954. 92 pp.

————. McKee, Jack Edward, and Wolf, Harold W., eds. *Water Quality Criteria.* 2nd ed. Prepared with assistance from Division of Water Supply and Pollution Control, U.S. Public Health Service, Department of Health, Education, and Welfare. Sacramento: State Water Pollution Control Board, 1963. 548 pp.

California, University of. *An Analysis of Refuse Collection and Sanitary Landfill Disposal.* Technical Bulletin No. 8, Series 37. Berkeley: University of California Press, 1952. 134 pp.

————. *A Field Study of Performance of Three Municipal Incinerators.* Technical Bulletin No. 6, I.E.R. Series 37. Berkeley: University of California Press, 1951. 66 pp.

————. *Municipal Incineration—A Study of the Factors Involved in Municipal Refuse Disposal by Incineration.* Technical Bulletin No. 5, I.E.R. Series 37. Berkeley: University of California Press, 1951. 102 pp.

————. *Reclamation of Municipal Refuse by Composting.* Technical Bulletin No. 9, I.E.R. Series 37. Berkeley: University of California Press, 1953. 90 pp.

————, Sanitary Engineering Research Laboratory, College of Engineering and School of Public Health. Prepared by C. G. Golueke and Staff. *Comprehensive Studies of Solid Wastes Management: Abstracts and Excerpts from the Literature.* SERL Report No. 68-3. Berkeley: University of California Press, 1968. 307 pp.

————, ————, ————. Golueke, C. G., and McGauhey, P. H. *Comprehensive Studies of Solid Wastes Management, Second Annual Report.* SERL Report No. 69-1. Berkeley: University of California Press, 1969. 245 pp.

"Can Engineering Cope with the Debris of Affluence?" *Product Engineering* (October 9, 1967).

Cayton, S. "Revenue from Refuse," *The Royal Society of Health Journal,* 77:4:188 (April, 1957).

Cohn, Morris M. "On Site Disposal of Solid Wastes," *Public Works Engineers' Yearbook, 1957.* Chicago: American Public Works Association, 1957. 452 pp.

Cooper, G. H., and Jackson, D. W. *Depots, Workshops and Vehicle Maintenance.* London: Institute of Public Cleansing, 1968. 121 pp.

Corey, Richard C., ed. *Principles and Practices of Incineration.* New York: Wiley-Interscience, a division of John Wiley and Sons, 1969. 297 pp.

Cosens, Kenneth W. "Household Garbage Grinders—How They Affect Sewers," *American City,* 64:9:134 (September, 1949).

Davis, Peter L., and Black, Ralph J. "Effects of Garbage Grinding on Sewage Systems and Environmental Sanitation," *The APWA Reporter* (December, 1962).

Dunn, Walter I. "Landfill Gas Burned for Odor Control," *Civil Engineering,* 27:790 (November, 1957).

Eliassen, Rolf. "Load-Bearing Characteristics of Landfills," *Engineering News-Record,* 129:369 (September 10, 1942).

————. "Sanitary Landfill: An Economic Method of Refuse Disposal," *Report No. 3, Summary of the Conference on Incineration, Rubbish Disposal and Air Pollution.* Los Angeles: Air Pollution Foundation, 1955. 52 pp.

————. "War Conditions Favor Landfill Refuse Disposal," *Engineering News-Record,* 128:912 (June 4, 1942).

"Employee Grievance Procedure," *American City,* 71:3:235 (March, 1956).

"Employee Suggestions Aid Municipal Service," *American City,* 72:10:215 (October, 1957).

Erganian, George K.; Belter, Walter G.; and Graber, Ralph C. *Effects of Community-Wide Installation of Household Garbage-Grinders on Environmental Sanitation.* U.S. Public Health Service. PHS No. 224. Washington: Government Printing Office, 1952. 42 pp.

Fenton, Richard, *An Analysis of the Problems of Sanitary Landfills in New York City.* New York: City Health Department, Bureau of Sanitary Engineering, 1947. 133 pp., mimeo.

First, Melvin W., ScD. "Environmental Hazards, Urban Solid-Waste Management," *New England Journal of Medicine,* 275:1478:1485 (December 29, 1966).

Fisher, W. Lowell. "Training and Accident Control Programs," *Public Works*

Engineers' Yearbook, 1957. Chicago: American Public Works Association, 1957. 452 pp.

Flintoff, Frank, and Millard, Ronald. *Public Cleansing, Refuse Storage, Collection, and Disposal; Street Cleansing.* London: MacLaren and Sons, 1968. 475 pp.

Foster, William S. "Sanitary Landfill Economics," *American City,* 68:3:96 (March, 1953).

Frangipane, E. de Fraja. "Present Condition, and Forecasts for the Future, of Refuse Disposal in Italy," *Proceedings, Third International Congress of International Research Group on Refuse Disposal.* Trento, Italy: IRGRD, 1965.

Gebhardt, George Frederic. *Steam Power Plant Engineering,* 6th ed. New York: John Wiley and Sons, 1925. 1,036 pp.

Golueke, C. G.; Card, B. J.; and McGauhey, P. H. "A Critical Evaluation of Inoculums in Composting," *Applied Microbiology,* 2:1:45 (January, 1954).

Gotaas, Harold B. *Composting—Sanitary Disposal and Reclamation of Organic Wastes.* Monograph Series No. 31. Geneva: World Health Organization, 1956. 205 pp.

Grim, Edgar P. "Radio Communication Systems," *Public Works Engineers' Yearbook, 1957.* Chicago: American Public Works Association, 1957. 452 pp.

Harris, Walter O. *Municipal Public Works Cost Accounting Manual.* Chicago: Public Administration Service, 1955. 108 pp.

Haseltine, T. R. "Addition of Garbage to Sewage," *Water and Sewage Works,* reference and data ed. (June, 1955).

Hering, Rudolph, and Greeley, Samuel A. *Collection and Disposal of Municipal Refuse.* New York: McGraw-Hill, 1921. 653 pp. (Out of print).

Hillenbrand, Bernard F. "Solid Wastes Problems: An Action Program for Solving Them," *The APWA Reporter* (March, 1970).

Hope, Malcolm C., and Weaver, Leo. "Characteristics of Refuse in National Parks," *Public Works,* 87:7:95 (July, 1956).

Institute of Public Cleansing, Research Sub-Committee. Prepared by R. E. Bevan. *Notes on the Science and Practice of the Controlled Tipping of Refuse.* London: The Institute, 1967. 216 pp.

Institute of Scrap Iron and Steel. *Proceedings of the National Conference on Auto Salvage and Selected Background Information.* Washington: The Institute, 1964.

International City Management Association, Institute for Training in Municipal Administration. *Municipal Public Works Administration.* 5th ed. Washington, D.C.: ICMA, 1957. 450 pp.

International Solid Wastes and Public Cleansing Association. *ISWA Information Bulletin.* No. 1. Zurich: The Association, 1969. 38 pp.

Keep America Beautiful, Inc. Prepared by A. L. Finkner. *National Study of the Composition of Roadside Litter.* A Report from the Highway Research

Board of the Division of Engineering, National Research Council. New York: Keep America Beautiful, 1969.

Klee, Albert J., and Garland, George A. "Decision Trees in Solid Wastes Planning," *Public Works Magazine* (July, 1968).

Kudlich, R. *Ringelmann Smoke Chart.* U.S. Bureau of Mines Information Circular 7718. Washington: Government Printing Office, 1955.

Kupchik, George J. "Economics of Composting Municipal Refuse," *Proceedings ASCE, Journal of the Sanitary Engineering Division,* 89:SA1:91 (January, 1963).

Leonard, George K., and Schwab, Philip A. "TVA Uses Non-Specification Fly Ash," *Civil Engineering,* 28:188 (March, 1958).

Los Angeles County Sanitation Districts, Joint Administrative Staff. *Planned Refuse Disposal.* A Report to the Directors of the County Sanitation Districts of Los Angeles County, California. Los Angeles: Los Angeles County Sanitation Districts, 1955. 118 pp.

Maier, Paul P.; Williams, Edward R.; and Mallison, George F. "Composting Municipal Refuse by the Aeration Bin Process," *Proceedings, 12th Industrial Waste Conference.* Lafayette, Ind.: Purdue University, 1957.

Mallison, George F., and Hohloch, William F. "The Composition of Residential Garbage," *Public Works,* 87:6:112 (June, 1956).

May, William F. "$C_p + D \rightleftharpoons P$," Keynote Address Before 36th National Packaging Conference sponsored by American Management Association. New York: The Association, 1967.

McDermott, Gerald N. "Pollutional Characteristics of Land-fill Drainage," *EHC Activity Report No. 3,* January-March, 1950. Cincinnati: U.S. Department of Health, Education and Welfare, 1950.

McElwee, Wendell C., M.P.H., and Wilcomb, Maxwell J., Ph.D. "Some Effects of Disposable Plastic Liners on Refuse Handling Efficiency" *Journal of Environmental Health* (March-April, 1968).

McMullin, Carleton E. "Cutting Municipal Records Costs," *Public Management,* 41:4:89 (April, 1959).

Metropolitan Engineers Council on Air Resources. Robert A. Fox, ed. *Incineration of Solid Wastes.* Papers presented at Mecar Symposium, New York, March 21, 1967. 81 pp. New York: Mecar, 1967.

Mingle, John Glenn. *Draft and Capacity of Chimneys.* New York: Van Nostrand, 1925. 339 pp.

Ministry of Housing and Local Government. *Pollution of Water by Tipped Refuse.* Report of the Technical Committee on the Experimental Disposal of House Refuse in Wet and Dry Pits. London: Her Majesty's Stationery Office, 1961. 141 pp.

"More Prosperity, More Trash," *American City,* 69:11:17 (November, 1954).

Morton, Roy J., and Struxness, Edward G. "Ground Disposal of Radioactive Wastes," *American Journal of Public Health,* 46:2:156 (February, 1956).

National Academy of Engineering, National Academy of Sciences. Prepared by Ad Hoc Committee on Solid Waste Management and Committees on Pollution Abatement and Control. *Policies for Solid Waste Management.* Washington: National Research Council, 1969. 56 pp.

National Academy of Sciences. *Waste Management and Control.* Pub. 1400. Washington: National Research Council, 1966. 257 pp.

National Association of Counties Research Foundation. *Solid Waste Management.* 10 brochures, undated. Washington: The Association.

National Sanitation Foundation. *Use and Disposal of Single-Use Items in Health Care Facilities.* Report of a National Conference. Ann Arbor, Mich.: The Foundation, 1969. 64 pp.

New York City, Works Progress Administration. *Research and Selected Problems in Sewage Treatment, Vol. 3: Annotated Bibliography on Incineration, Carbonization and Reduction of Garbage, Rubbish and Sewage Sludge.* New York: WPA, 1939.

New York University, College of Engineering. Kaiser, E. R., and Tolciss, J. *Smokeless Burning of Automobile Bodies.* Technical Report 764.2. New York: The University, 1961.

New York University, Sanitary Engineering Research Laboratory. *Survey of Landfill Characteristics, New York City.* New York: Department of Sanitation, 1941. 90 pp.

New Zealand, Interdepartmental Committee on Utilization of Organic Wastes. "The Utilization of Organic Wastes in New Zealand," *New Zealand Engineer*, First Interim Report, 3:6:563 (June, 1948); Second Interim Report, 6:11:396 and 6:12:449 (November, December, 1951).

Nordquist, A. V., and Pals, C. H. "Economic Losses from Animal Diseases and Parasites," *The Yearbook of Agriculture, 1956: Animal Diseases.* Washington: Government Printing Office, 1956. 592 pp.

Owen, Mark B. "The Future of Home Garbage Grinders," *Water and Sewage Works*, 96:5:187 (May, 1949).

President's Council on Recreation and Natural Beauty. *From Sea to Shining Sea: A Report on the American Environment—Our Natural Heritage.* Washington: Government Printing Office, 1968. 304 pp.

President's Science Advisory Committee. *Restoring the Quality of Our Environment.* Report of the Environmental Pollution Panel. Washington: Government Printing Office, 1965.

Public Administration Service and International City Management Association. *Automated Data Processing in Municipal Government: Status, Problems, and Prospects.* Chicago: PAS, 1966. 34 pp.

Quon, Jimmie E.; Charnes, A.; and Wersan, Stephen J. "Simulation and Analysis of a Refuse Collection System," *Proceedings ASCE, Journal of the Sanitary Engineering Division*, 91:SA5:17 (October, 1965).

————; Tanaka, Masaru; and Wersan, Stephen J. "Simulation Model of Refuse

Collection Policies," *Proceedings ASCE, Journal of the Sanitary Engineering Division*, 95:SA5:575 (June, 1969).

Ralph Stone and Company, Inc. *Copper Control in Vehicular Scrap, with Special Emphasis on Component Design.* Washington: U.S. Department of the Interior, Bureau of Mines, 1968. 109 pp.

"Refuse Collection and Disposal in 927 Cities," *Public Works*, 81:10:33 (October, 1950).

Rehm, F. R. "Air Pollution and the Gas Industry," *Gas Age*, 122:15 (August 7, 1958).

————. "Incinerator Testing and Test Results," *Journal, Air Pollution Control Association*, 6:2:199 (February, 1957).

Rogus, Casimir A. "Sanitary Refuse Fills in 'Wet' Areas," *Public Works*, 86:12:65 (December, 1955).

————. "Use of Completed Sanitary Landfill Sites," *Public Works Engineers' Yearbook, 1959.* Chicago: American Public Works Association, 1959. 434 pp.

Ross, William Edwin. "Digestion of Garbage with Sludge Yields Gas Worth $21,000 Per Year," *Wastes Engineering*, 29:6:300 (June, 1958).

Ruff, R. J. "Catalytic Fume Combustion of Organic Chemical and Petro-Chemical Wastes," *Industrial Wastes*, 2:3:67 (May-June, 1957).

Schwartz, Benjamin. "Parasites that Attack Animals and Man," *Yearbook of Agriculture, 1956: Animal Diseases.* Washington: Government Printing Office, 1956. 592 pp.

Singer, David E. "Municipal Uniforms," *American City*, 71:12:144 (December, 1956).

Smauder, Ellis E. "Problems of Municipal Incineration," *Proceedings of the First Technical Meeting, West Coast Section APCA.* Pittsburgh: Air Pollution Control Association, 1957. 156 pp.

Snell, John R. "Composting Around the World," *Compost Science*, 1:1:10 (Spring, 1960).

————. "Getting the Most from the Consulting Engineer," *Public Works*, 90:9:111 (September, 1959).

Solid Wastes Management. *Proceedings of the National Conference of Solid Wastes Management.* California: University of California, Davis Campus, 1966. 214 pp.

Sommers, William A. "Municipal Wage Policy for Unionized Employees," *American City*, 70:11:141 (November, 1955).

Starick, Herbert W. "How to Get Things Done Through Others," *Public Works Engineers' Yearbook, 1958.* Chicago: American Public Works Association, 1958. 436 pp.

Stone, Ralph, and Bowerman, F. R. "Incineration and Alternative Refuse Disposal Processes," *Proceedings ASCE (American Society of Civil Engineers)*, Vol. 80, Separate No. 471 (August, 1954).

U.S. Congress, Joint Committee on Atomic Energy, Special Committee on Radiation. *Industrial Radioactive Waste Disposal Hearings, 86th Congress, 1st Session.* Vols. 1-5. Washington: Government Printing Office, 1959.

U.S. Department of Health, Education, and Welfare. *A Strategy for a Livable Environment.* A Report to the Secretary of HEW by the Task Force on Environmental Health and Related Problems. Washington: Government Printing Office, 1967. 90 pp.

————, Public Health Service. *Ad Hoc Conference on Solid Waste Training.* Robert A. Taft Sanitary Engineering Center. Cincinnati: U.S. Department of Health, Education, and Welfare, 1964. 72 pp.

————, ————. Prepared by National Commission on Technology, Automation, and Economic Progress. *Applying Technology to Unmet Needs.* Washington: Government Printing Office, 1966. 12 pp.

————, ————. *Proceedings, The Third National Conference on Air Pollution.* PHS No. 1649. Washington: Government Printing Office, 1967. 667 pp.

————, ————, Bureau of Disease Prevention and Environmental Control, National Center for Urban and Industrial Health, Solid Wastes Program. Thrift G. Banks, M.D. *Solid Waste/Disease Relationships—A Literature Survey.* PHS No. 999-UIH-6. Final report of Aerojet-General Corporation, Life System Division, to the Solid Wastes Program, 1967. Washington: Government Printing Office, 1967. 179 pp.

————, ————, Communicable Disease Center, Technical Development Laboratories. Wiley, John, and Spillane, Janet T. *Methods for Examination of Raw and Composted Organic Wastes.* Chemical Memorandum No. 4 Savannah, Ga.: U.S. Public Health Service, 1956. 24 pp., mimeo.

————, ————, Consumer Protection and Environmental Health Service. *Proceedings of Symposium on Human Ecology.* PHS No. 1929, Washington: Government Printing Office, 1968. 123 pp.

————, ————, ————, Environmental Control Administration, Bureau of Solid Waste Management. Aerojet-General Corporation. *A Systems Study of Solid Waste Management in the Fresno Area.* Final Report on a Solid Waste Management Demonstration. Prepared for the California Department of Health. PHS No. 1959. Washington: Government Printing Office, 1969.

————, ————, ————, ————, ————, Combustion, Engineering, Inc. *Technical-Economic Study of Solid Waste Disposal Needs and Practices.* PHS No. 1886. Washington: Government Printing Office, 1969. 705 pp.

————, ————, ————, ————, ————. Darney, Arsen, and Franklin, William E. *The Role of Packaging in Solid Waste Management, 1966 to 1976.* PHS No. 1855. Washington: Government Printing Office, 1969. 205 pp.

————, ————, ————, ————, ————. Day and Zimmerman Associates. *Special Studies for Incinerators for the Government of the District of Columbia, Department of Sanitary Engineers.* PHS No. 1748. Washington: Government Printing Office, 1968. 80 pp.

————, ————, ————, ————, ————. Hart, Samuel A. *Solid Waste Management/ Composting: European Activity and American Potential.* PHS No. 1826. Washington: Government Printing Office, 1969. 40 pp.

————, ————, ————, ————, ————. Jensen, Michael E. *Observations of Continental European Solid Waste Management Practices.* PHS No. 1880. Washington: Government Printing Office, 1969. 46 pp.

————, ————, ————, ————, ————. Meller, Floyd H. *Conversion of Organic Solid Wastes Into Yeast; An Economic Evaluation.* PHS No. 1909. Washington: Government Printing Office, 1969. 173 pp.

————, ————, ————, ————, ————. Muhich, Anton J.; Klee, Albert J.; and Britton, Paul W. *Preliminary Data Analysis, 1968 National Survey of Community Solid Waste Practices.* PHS No. 1867. Washington: Government Printing Office, 1968. 483 pp.

————, ————, ————, ————, ————. Sorg, T. J., and Hickman, H. L., Jr. *Sanitary Landfill Facts.* PHS No. 1792. Washington: Government Printing Office, 1968. 26 pp.

————, ————, ————, ————, ————. Sponagle, C. E. *Summaries: Solid Wastes, Demonstration Grant Projects—1968.* PHS No. 1821. Washington: Government Printing Office, 1968. 90 pp.

————, ————, ————, ————, ————. *State/Interstate Solid Waste Planning Grants and Agencies—January, 1969.* Rockville, Md.: HEW, 1969. 17 pp.

————, ————, ————, ————, ————. Steiner, R. L., and Kantz, Renee. Prepared for the Drexel Institute of Technology, Philadelphia. *Sanitary Landfill—A Bibliography.* PHS No. 1819. Washington: Government Printing Office, 1968. 37 pp.

————, ————, ————, ————, ————. Ralph Stone and Company, Inc. *A Study of Solid Waste Collection Systems Comparing One-Man with Multi-Man Crews: Final Report.* PHS No. 1892. Washington: Government Printing Office, 1969. 175 pp.

————, ————, ————, ————, ————. Swavely, Donald D., and Hultgren, Lee F., compilers. *State/Interstate Solid Waste Planning Grants: Progress Abstracts.* PHS No. 1913. Washington: Government Printing Office, 1969. 94 pp.

————, ————, ————, ————, ————. *Summaries of Solid Wastes Research and Training Grants.* PHS No. 1596. Washington: Government Printing Office, 1968. 48 pp.

————, ————. Environmental Engineering and Food Protection. Prepared for the Surgeon General's Advisory Committee on Urban Health Affairs. *Solid Wastes Handling in Metropolitan Areas.* PHS No. 1554. Washington: Government Printing Office, 1966. 41 pp.

————, ————. *Environmental Health Planning Guide.* Cincinnati: National Center for Urban and Industrial Health, 1967. 100 pp.

————, ————, ————, Solid Wastes Program, Cincinnati. Bogue, M.D. *Municipal Incineration.* Cincinnati: HEW, 1968. 27 pp.

————, ————, ————, ————, ————. *Comprehensive Solid Waste Study: Johnson City, Tennessee.* Technical Services Report SW-6ts. Cincinnati: HEW, 1968. 63 pp.

————, ————, ————, ————, ————. Connolly, John A., ed. *Abstracts, Selected Patents on Refuse Handling Facilities for Buildings.* PHS No. 1793. Washington: Government Printing Office, 1968. 320 pp.

————, ————, ————, ————, ————. Cummins, Rodney L., M.P.H. *Effects of Land Dsposal of Solid Wastes on Water Quality.* Cincinnati: HEW, 1968. 29 pp.

————, ————, ————, ————, ————. DeMarco, Jack, and others, compilers. *Incinerator Guidelines, 1969.* Cincinnati: HEW, 1969. 176 pp.

————, ————, ————, ————, Hart, Samuel A. *Solid Wastes Management in Germany—Report of the U.S. Solid Wastes Study Team Visit.* PHS No. 1812. Washington: Government Printing Office, 1968. 18 pp.

————, ————, ————, ————, ————. Henningson, Durham & Richardson, Inc. *Collection and Disposal of Solid Waste for the Des Moines Metropolitan Area.* Cincinnati: HEW, 1968. 324 pp.

————, ————, ————, ————, ————. *Land Reclamation Project: An Interim Report.* Harza Engineering Company. Cincinnati: HEW, 1968. 338 pp.

————, ————, ————, ————, ————. Landon, R. A., and Farvolden, R. N. *Hydrology of Solid Waste Disposal Sites in Northeastern Illinois.* Cincinnati: HEW, 1968.

————, ————, ————, ————, ————. *Quad-City Solid Wastes Project: An Interim Report, June 1, 1966 to May 31, 1967.* Cincinnati: HEW, 1968. 181 pp.

————, ————, ————, ————. Reinhardt, John J., and Rohlich, Gerard. *Solid Waste Reduction/Salvage Plant—An Interim Report.* City of Madison Pilot Plant Demonstration Project. Cincinnati: HEW, 1968. 25 pp.

————, ————, ————, ————, ————. Ralph Stone and Company. *Solid Wastes Landfill Stabilization: An Interim Report.* Cincinnati: HEW, 1968. 145 pp.

————, ————, ————, ————, ————. Weaver, Leo, ed. *Proceedings: The Surgeon General's Conference on Solid Waste Management for Metropolitan Washington.* PHS No. 1729. Washington: Government Printing Office, 1967. 194 pp.

————, ————, Office of Solid Wastes. *Do You Need a Sanitary Landfill?* PHS No. 1012. Washington: Government Printing Office, 1963. 8 pp.

U. S. Department of Housing and Urban Development. Oak Ridge National Laboratory. *Solid Waste Management Practices: An Annotated Bibliography and Permuted-Title and Key-Word Index.* Springfield, Va.: Clearinghouse for Federal, Scientific and Technical Information, 1970. 363 pp.

U. S. Department of the Interior, Bureau of Mines. *Automobile Disposal: A National Problem.* Case Studies of Factors that Influence the Accumulation of Automobile Scrap. Washington: The Department. 569 pp.

————, ————. Kenahan, Charles B., and others. *Composition and Characteristics of Municipal Incinerator Residue.* Washington: The Department, 1968. 20 pp.

————, Bureau of Mines and IIT Research Institute. *Proceedings of the*

Symposium: Mineral Waste Utilization. Washington: The Department, 1968. 154 pp.

————, Federal Water Pollution Control Administration. *Water Pollution Aspects of Urban Runoff.* Final Report on the Causes and Remedies of Water Pollution from Surface Drainage of Urban Areas. Research Project No. 120. Chicago: American Public Works Association, 1969. 272 pp.

Waksman, Selman A. *Soil Microbiology.* New York: John Wiley and Sons, 1952. 356 pp.

Weaver, Leo. "Progress in Refuse Disposal," *Public Works Engineers' News Letter.* 23:9:1 (March, 1957).

————. "Refuse and Litter Control in Recreation Areas," *Public Works Magazine* (April, 1967).

————. "The Sanitary Landfill (A Three-Part Review)," *American City,* Part I, 71:3:122; Part II, 71:4:132; Part III, 71:5:134 (March, April, May, 1955).

————. "The U. S. Solid Wastes Burden, A Twentieth Century Challenge," *Proceedings of the Solid Waste Conference, The Conservation Council of Ontario.* Toronto: The Council, 1968. 13 pp.

————, and Keagy, Donald M. *The Sanitary Landfill Method of Refuse Disposal in Northern States.* PHS Pub. No. 226. Washington: Government Printing Office, 1952. 32 pp.

Wiley, John S. "Liquid Content of Garbage and Refuse," *Proceedings ASCE, Journal of the Sanitary Engineering Division,* 83:SA5:1411 (October, 1957).

————. "Progress Report on High-Rate Composting Studies," *Proceedings, 12th Industrial Waste Conference.* Lafayette, Ind.: Purdue University, 1957.

————. "Some Specialized Equipment Used in European Compost Systems," *Compost Science* (Spring, 1963).

————; Gartrell, F. E., and Smith, H. Gray. *Concept and Design of the Joint U.S. Public Health Service–Tennessee Valley Authority Composting Project, Johnson City, Tennessee.* Presented at the Fifth Annual Sanitary and Water Resources Engineering Conference, Nashville, Tenn. Cincinnati: U. S. Department of Health, Education, and Welfare, 1966. 14 pp.

————, and Kochtitzky, O. W. "Composting Developments in the United States," *Compost Science,* 6:2:5 (Summer, 1965).

Williams, Edward R. "Cities Report on 'Demolition' Refuse Problem," *Public Works Engineers' News Letter,* 25:11:1 (November, 1958).

————; Mallison, George; and Maier, Paul P. "Light Equipment for Small Town Sanitary Landfill Operations," *Public Works,* 89:2:89 (February, 1958).

World Health Organization. *Treatment and Disposal of Wastes.* Technical Report Series No. 367. Geneva: WHO, 1967. 30 pp.

Wright, Williard H., and Bozicevich, J. "Experiments in the Cooking of Garbage for the Destruction of Trichinae in Pork Scraps," *Public Health Reports,* 58:10:396 (March 5, 1943).

Wylie, John C. *The Wastes of Civilization.* London: Faber and Faber, Ltd., 1959. 162 pp.

Xanten, William A. "A New Development in Large Scale Odor and Dust Control Produces Nuisance-Free Refuse Handling Station," *American City*, 65:9:108 (September, 1950), *Engineering News-Record*, 65:9:35 (September, 1950).

————. "Nuisance-Free Operation for New Incinerator in Washington, D. C.," *Civil Engineering*, 26:4:50 (April, 1956).

INDEX

523